# MACLEAN'S
# CANADA

# MACLEAN'S CANADA

## Portrait
## of a
## Country

Selected and edited by LESLIE F. HANNON

ALBUMS SELECTED AND DESIGNED BY
EUGENE ALIMAN

McClelland and Stewart Limited

# EDITOR'S PREFACE

With its first century as a nation not yet quite run, Canada is to the world—and to many of her own people—already a puzzling place of curious contrasts, of mixed bloods and traditions and languages, of burgeoning and unique philosophies and ideals, of great and growing strengths, and of weaknesses—some admitted and some not. Many of the books that have attempted to take the pulse and illumine the face of Canada have lost their way somewhere between the stormy coasts, the teeming cities, the countless lakes, the fruitlands, the barrens, the mountains and the hypnotic prairies. The horizon is, simply, too wide for one pair of eyes. This is a different kind of book. It brings together the Canadas seen by dozens of distinguished men and women and reflected in a sharp contemporary light. The Canadians whose stories are told here are as diverse and diverting as the land that made them, or beckoned to them. The illustrations are usual proof of this complexity —a haunting prairie or northwoods loneliness to be sensed and interpreted above the clangor of a mighty industrial machine. It is the editor's hope that, as a tangle of tiles magically becomes a meaningful mosaic, the threads of the Canadian fabric will be woven through this book into a truthful and deeply textured tapestry, and that it might help to correct some of the regrettable misconceptions of Canada held both at home and abroad. It was my privilege to have open sesame to the files of *Maclean's*, for more than fifty years Canada's national magazine. Every page here first appeared, sometimes in slightly different form, in *Maclean's*. The book as a whole is testimony to the steadfast way, in a time of shifting values, that the magazine under distinguished editors and responsible proprietors has followed its course of holding an unwavering mirror up to Canada. To those persons who appear in this book, and to many who do not, I offer grateful thanks.

*Leslie F. Hannon*

# CONTENTS

# ILLUSTRATIONS

ERIC HUTTON

# Ordeal on Mount Howson

Major Rex Gibson braced himself against a rock pinnacle seven thousand feet up Mount Howson to change places on the safety rope. His two companions wanted him in the lead for the final climb to the summit, partly because he was the most experienced snow climber and partly because they knew he had a personal account to settle with this mountain. They had reached this height to discover that the only way up was a snow-filled cleft that rose steeply to the peak. Downward, the narrow snowfield disappeared abruptly over a cliff five hundred feet below.

Gibson and his companion, Dr. Sterling Hendricks and Dr. Donald Hubbard, knew the climb would become somewhat more dangerous when they stepped out on the snow crust. What they did not know was that they stood literally on the verge of one of the most remarkable episodes—an episode at once tragic and triumphant—in all the eventful annals of the supremely dangerous sport of mountain climbing.

The idea of turning back did not occur to any of them. Gibson, particularly, was in a mood of rare elation. As he knotted the nylon line about him with practiced fingers he nodded toward the panorama of forest and mountain that started at timberline far beneath their feet and spread to the horizon. "When people ask me why I climb mountains I can't find words to tell them," he said. "But here is the answer—getting up where nobody ever stood before, then looking down at a thousand square miles with not a soul in it."

Hendricks and Hubbard, in a hundred climbs with him, had seldom heard the trenchant, matter-of-fact Gibson speak in such terms. On the contrary, they had seen him cringe at being referred to as "Mr. Mountaineer of Canada" and knew he took no collector's pride in having made more first ascents of peaks in the Canadian Rockies than any other man. But this was no ordinary occasion. During the three years he had been president of the Alpine Club of Canada, Rex Gibson's goal had been the conquest of Howson. Three times in the short climbing seasons of northern British Columbia he had come to this lonely mountain fifty miles beyond Kitimat, accessible only if one could persuade a chartered pilot to risk setting down a float plane amid the unmapped shoals of Burnie Lake in the foothills. Each year it seemed as if Mount Howson reserved its worst storm of the summer to hurl at Gibson. Torrential rain on the lower slopes and blizzards above the snowline had blockaded him. Each year the weather cleared only long enough for him to scout the glacier that guards the approach to the main peak and to catch glimpses of forbidding heights lost in clouds of snow.

Gibson determinedly renewed his attack on Howson. He felt fit as ever, but at sixty-five he was past the age when most alpinists have climbed their last mountain. This time he came with Dr. Alexander Fabergé, of the University of Texas, who had, in vain, tackled Howson with him twice before, and three other United States members of the Alpine Club, all experienced climbers but of age and eminence that made them a little incongruous as athletes in this most strenuous of sports. Fabergé, at forty-five the youngest of the party, and fifty-five-year-old Sterling Hendricks are among the world's top agronomists. Fabergé, called by associates "a genius in genetics," was born in Russia of French parents. Hubbard, fifty-seven, is a research physicist with the United States Bureau of Standards. The fifth man, Alvin Peterson, fifty-two, is an experimental

1

engineer with the United States ordnance laboratory in Washington.

This party landed in Burnie Lake on August 8. The members had agreed to devote twelve days to the attack on Mount Howson, and the chartered plane was to return from its base at Terrace, on the Skeena River forty miles westward, on Monday, August 19. No sooner had they pitched their base camp in the foothills three miles upslope from the lake than what they came to call "Gibson's weather" started. For a solid week it rained on the camp and snowed on the mountain. Then, with only four days remaining before the plane's return, the skies cleared. The five men hurried to reconnoitre the mountain.

In the sunlight Howson was a grimly beautiful study in black rock and white snow, towering more than nine thousand feet, its flanks guarded by four stark ridges. Those formidable buttresses, though, offered the best hope of climbing Howson safely. "Scale the ridges," warns unwritten mountaineering law, "and avalanches or rock slides can't come down on you." For two days Gibson and his party circled the base of the mountain, sizing up the ridges. In turn they wrote off the north, east and south ridges as impossible. That left only the west ridge. Gibson's face showed mingled hope and anxiety as this last route came into view. The five men stood amid the vast untidiness of boulders in a moraine at the foot of a thousand-foot glacier under the west ridge and studied yard by yard the cliffs and the outcrops and the ravines that marked the upward climb of the ridge as far as the eye could distinguish perspective.

"Rugged, but not impossible," pronounced Gibson.

Fabergé, his companion on many a hazardous climb, disagreed. "Impossible—unclimbable," he said.

Hendricks and Hubbard agreed to try the west ridge with Gibson. Amicably, Fabergé and Peterson decided to tackle another peak of the Howson range some miles to the south. The Gibson party spent the rest of the day establishing an advanced camp near the foot of the west-ridge glacier, three miles from base camp and a thousand feet higher.

At dawn of a bright day, Sunday, August 18, they started upward. Five hours of hard climbing confirmed Gibson's estimate of the west ridge: "Rugged—but not impossible." But now, seven thousand feet up, the ridge sharpened into a pinnacle that barred further progress. On the south shoulder of the ridge, though, ran a narrow cleft filled with snow. It was no more than fifteen feet wide and en-

closed in rock walls, so that the sun scarcely touched it and the snow's crust was hard and slippery as glass. Down the middle of the narrow snowfield ran an even harder gutter of ice, three feet wide, formed by the periodic avalanching of snow from above. The climbers could trace this gutter's path downward in a series of hummocks and fall-offs to the lip of the cliff where it ended.

Gibson, in the lead, had to chop steps in the snow with his ice axe for himself and his companions. Hubbard was ten feet behind his leader. Every few steps he would thrust the steel-tipped handle of his ice axe into the snow ahead, ready to hitch the rope, which joined the three men, around the handle if the lead man should fall. Hendricks followed twenty feet behind Hubbard, also climbing between thrusts of his axe handle, in the role of anchor man.

Then with frightful suddenness the unexpected, the unexplained, happened. Hendricks, looking directly up at Gibson, saw him half turn in his tracks, utter a soft exclamation and lose his foothold. Gibson slid into Hubbard who, by great ill chance, had at that instant of time raised his axe to thrust it in for a new hold. The tangle of two men skidded down on Hendricks and accelerated past him on the steep, glassy crust.

Instinctively, Hendricks braced himself for the shock that would come in an instant. He had been twenty feet behind Hubbard, and since they were tied at fifty-foot intervals, the rope Hendricks clutched had thirty feet of slack before the weight of two falling men jerked at the knotted rope firmly tied to his own waist. If he could only brake the rope with his hands before the thirty feet ran out . . . Now the slack ran out and the weight was on the rope. He closed his hands on it tighter and tighter until he was holding it with all his desperate strength. Pain seared his palms as the rope cut through gloves and burned through flesh. But it was elation Hendricks felt instead of pain. The headlong flight of Gibson and Hubbard was slowing. If Hubbard could make a lucky thrust with the ice axe he still held in his flailing right hand, this nightmare might end in just another incident to be added to their mountaineering "close ones."

In a sort of agonizing slow motion, Hendricks felt the rope come almost to a stop in his hands. At just the right moment, Hubbard drove his axe head into the ice crust. But in the same instant safety was snatched away. The two men, still tangled, reached the brink of a short drop in the snowslide before they could come to a total stop. It was an inconsequential fall-off, not more than three feet deep. But it was enough to jerk Hubbard's hand off his axe, coming at the point where Hendricks ran out of slack in his rope, to snap him off his feet.

Instantly the three men pitched down the slope, not sliding but in sickening bounds of ten or twenty feet at a time, a tangle of arms and legs, rope and flailing axes and rucksacks heavy with equipment, ricocheting toward the cliff they had seen five hundred feet below.

A man's thoughts during a moment like this have seldom been described because few have survived such an experience to tell their thoughts. Both Hendricks and Hubbard remember clearly what flashed through their minds during the seconds they were falling off Mount Howson. There was no passing of life's incidents before the eyes, no philosophizing at death's imminence. Hendricks, indeed, thought as he fell that his own death was certain. He gained some comfort from the thought that the unbearable shock of pain that came with each crash landing could not continue, that one more must knock him into merciful unconsciousness. One more . . . two more . . . three more. His brain kept on counting the rhythm of his awful plunge. Hubbard thought with angry resentment at himself of having "missed his catch" when Gibson first lost his footing. This was followed by desperate exhortations to himself to "get that axe in"—which had so nearly succeeded. And in the last part of the fall humiliation at total failure flooded his mind.

Hendrick's count had reached ten when the falling men were jarred by the heaviest blow yet. But when its shock was over they realized that they had stopped falling. They had broken through the ice crust, adding extensive cuts and bruises to their other injuries, but halting their descent just short of the final cliff that would certainly have been fatal to all. In fact, Hubbard, who fell farthest, found himself so near the brink when he pulled himself out of the snow that he shouted a repeated warning to the others, "Don't move! Don't move! Don't move!"

The warning was not necessary. Gibson was unconscious, bleeding from a severe head wound. Hendricks was under Gibson, deep in the snow and doubled up with intense pain. Hubbard tried to stand up to go to their aid but his right leg collapsed under him and a wave of nausea resulted from the sudden agony of putting all his weight on a broken leg.

Hendricks worked his way out from under Gibson, dazed and weak. The two conscious men took a quick inventory of their injuries. Hendricks could stand up but his left shoulder was broken and his arm useless; one rib at least was fractured and his back hurt. Hubbard could not stand, but he had the use of his arms. Gibson, still unconscious, seemed obviously the most seriously injured. The wound on his head was the only visible damage.

Hubbard, propelling himself cautiously with his hands while sitting on the ice crust, tried to move Gibson but found he was solidly frozen in. Under the insulation of the crust the snow was intensely cold, even though the air temperature was above fifty degrees. This meant that the three men could not long survive where they had fallen. Atop the crust they were in constant danger of sliding into the abyss; under the ice lurked fatal frostbite. So the discovery of a narrow shelf in the sheer wall of the gully was scarcely less providential than the interruption of their fall.

Gibson regained partial consciousness while Hubbard was chopping him out of his ice prison and was able to help propel himself as Hubbard dragged him to the shelf. Hubbard drove a piton—the mountaineers' indispensable ringed iron stake—into a crevice above the shelf and roped Gibson securely in a half-reclining position. Gibson spoke for the first time, to ask a pertinent question: "What stopped us?"

The answer, Hendricks and Hubbard had discovered, was that at this point a trickle of water flowed under the ice field, too small to be called a stream or even a rill but enough to weaken the ice crust so that it collapsed under the weight of three tumbling bodies.

Hendricks and Hubbard knew, without discussion, what had to be attempted. Hendricks, with a broken shoulder, useless arm, broken ribs and—although he did not know it at that moment—a fractured spine, must try the almost impossible task of descending the mountain for help because he alone could walk. Fabergé and Peterson, if they had returned from their own climb, would not begin to worry about the three men unless they did not return in time for the rendezvous with the plane on Monday afternoon; a search of Mount Howson's wildernesses of rock and snow might take a week—which would be the same as an eternity as far as the fate of the waiting men was concerned.

Hendricks had to work on an agonizing timetable: he must descend the mountain fast enough to bring help before Gibson and Hubbard had spent more than two nights on the ledge. The air temperature would drop below freezing at sundown; exposure would endanger an injured man's life even on the first night, more gravely the second, and a third night would almost certainly be fatal. Yet Hendricks must climb down with utmost caution so as not to injure himself further. Even a slight aggravation of any of his injuries might, he knew, leave him unable to move and death for all three would be certain instead of probable.

Hendricks refused any share of the party's food supply and shed his waterproof coat and spare socks. At eleven o'clock on a bright Sunday morning, he bade a brief farewell to his companions. Gibson seemed semiconscious but he whispered: "Tell them to bring in a helicopter. That's our best chance for getting out."

Hendricks nodded and silently started the climb back to where the fall had begun. He carried with him eighty feet of nylon rope, his indispensable ice axe, and a supply of pitons he would need to lower himself over half a dozen sheer drops on the way down. He and Hubbard had debated briefly whether he should try to find a way down from the point at which their fall had stopped, or undertake the ascent that would be both tedious and perilous. Hendricks decided that since he knew the way down from the top, it would be safer to start from there, climb and all, than to venture into the unknown terrain beside the cliff that yawned so close to their feet. Hubbard paid out rope behind Hendricks as he climbed, but so slowly did the latter move that the rope scarcely ran. Gibson opened his eyes and peered after the laboriously retreating figure.

"He's a tough boy, Sterling Hendricks," he said. "He can make it if anybody can."

Hubbard nodded an agreement he was far from feeling. And, he later admitted ruefully, he might have given up hope altogether if he had known then that the injury that reduced Hendricks' step to a painful shuffle was a fractured spine.

An hour later Hendricks was still in sight, and Hubbard became so discouraged that he stopped looking up. Half an hour later when he allowed himself another glance the climber had merged with the rocks. He had made the first lap.

To Hendricks that climb was an unforgettable nightmare of frustration. Normally a mountain climber leaps lightly down a drop as much as five feet deep, but Hendricks had to crawl down even the smallest declivity because of his back injury. He could not turn on his stomach and use his chest for leverage because of his fractured rib. One good arm and a pair of moderately operative legs proved to be surprisingly poor equipment for climbing down a mountain. The first crucial test came when he encountered a fifteen-foot sheer drop. He drove a piton into a rock cleft at the brink, snapped a ring to the stake, passed his rope through the ring and began to experiment with the rope wrapped around his body and legs in various ways that might permit him to lower himself safely. Two-handed, it was a five-minute routine operation. One-handed, it became a perilous experiment in an unknown technique. It was an hour before Hendricks felt he had worked out a procedure safe enough to trust.

When he reached the bottom of that first drop, he sat exhausted with his back to rock wall for a long time before he could continue. Nearby was a small pool of melted snow. Hendricks leaned over for a drink but the agony of his back prevented his reaching the water. He chewed a mouthful of snow instead.

There were steeper, deeper cliffs to be scaled yet, Hendricks knew. When he had picked his way to the next, the trial-and-error process started again. This time he must be sure beyond question that he had the rope rigged for a controlled descent. He might survive a fifteen-foot drop, but not a plunge of thirty feet. It was another hour before Hendricks touched rock at the bottom. With his good arm he tugged at the precious rope, to free it from the piton ring and coil it for the next *rappel*, or rope descent. The rope stuck. Hendricks pulled harder, but the rope did not give. It was a desperate situation. Unless he could retrieve the rope he would be unable to negotiate later drops. He would be marooned alone on Mount Howson's west ridge, as far from aid as Gibson and Hubbard back there on the ledge. He tried again, this time taking the rope in his teeth and pulling with his neck muscles in unison with his arm. The added force freed the rope and it snaked down upon him.

When he had roped himself down the last of the sheer drops, Hendricks could see far below the rim of the glacier above the advanced camp. Mentally, he worked out a rough timetable for survival: if he could reach the glacier's final snow slope, six hundred feet above where it debouched into the rocky moraine near the forward camp, before darkness descended, his own chances and that of the injured men behind him would be doubled. The surface of the glacier, with the sun still shining on it, would be soft enough to be kicked into footholds; and only with light to see could the glacier be negotiated. He could rest in the advanced camp and gather strength to make the three-mile journey down to the base camp in time for Fabergé and Peterson to meet the plane, which they had arranged to return for them on the next day, Monday, and send it back for a helicopter. Meanwhile, Fabergé and Peterson could try to get a tent, sleeping bags and first-aid supplies up the mountain to Gibson and Hubbard after only one night of exposure. Hendricks also made an estimate of his own chances of survival: good, if he could get down the glacier before dark; zero if he tried the descent after sundown; fifty-fifty if he had to spend a night in the open at below-freezing temperature. The clothes he was wearing were pitifully inadequate—medium-weight underwear and a Dacron-lined jacket were his principal protection against cold.

So Hendricks increased his ratio of speed to safety. The ground above the glacier was rough and broken, but it was the least difficult going he would encounter in the whole descent. Sometimes sliding painfully on the seat of his pants, sometimes shambling from rock to rock, steadying himself with his good hand, he made his best time yet. Whenever possible he traveled so that a patch of snow was behind him, in the hope that the westering sun might silhouette him against the white and be visible to the men in the base camp more than three miles away. There were two hours of daylight remaining when he reached the glacier. The upper part of it was an unpleasant mixture of short, sharp rock drop-offs and steep snow slides, almost beyond the powers of an injured man traveling alone to cross. One careless step could mean a fatal tumble. Even though he kept his pace of descent at the danger point, Hendricks' progress was maddeningly slow. In two hours the sun was on the horizon's rim and he was still two hundred feet short of the final snowfield.

Hendricks now had to accept defeat, to face the ordeal of spending the night on the glacier, within sight of the unattainable camp with its tent, food, gasoline stove and sleeping bag. He knew that this night must be devoted to one objective: survival. He must not sleep, therefore he must not try even to make himself comfortable. He sat in a crouch through nine hours of darkness. At intervals he opened his jacket and shirt and breathed into the space between his clothing and his body, using the warmth of his lungs, retained by the Dacron lining of his jacket, to keep the temperature of his body above the danger point. That lining saved his life, he says now. His arms and legs were numb with cold, but his body kept thawed out. Dawn found him cramped and with energy at a low ebb.

The coming of the sun revealed a dull overcast day. The glacier's final snow slope would remain frozen and impossibly dangerous to descend. A bright sun would have softened the surface and made it possible for him to kick steps for his downward passage. Hendricks also needed the sun badly to put his own battered body into a semblance of working order. In the chill early light he was slowed down even more than the day before. It took him a painful hour to travel the two hundred feet from his night's resting place to the top of the snow slope. There he sat and watched the surface impatiently for signs of softening. Three hours, and the snow crust remained glasslike. Another hour brought slight signs of softening.

Hendricks would wait no longer. He wrapped his eighty feet of rope around his body, hoping it might have some braking effect on the snow crust. He drove his axe into the snow with his good arm, swung his legs over the rim of snow, kicked two shallow heel holds in the resistant crust, and launched himself onto the giant slide, six hundred feet above where its tail fanned out in an ambush of waiting rocks. The rope and the axe and the heel holds combined to hold his descent. He kicked more holds and lowered himself cautiously. Then more and more. In two hours he was 150 feet beneath the rim. The time was noon.

Hendricks knew he was not moving fast enough. At this rate he might not be able to reach the base camp before dark. It would mean another night in the open, with the odds against him higher. Worse, it would mean that the plane, due this afternoon, would be sent back by Fabergé and Peterson when Gibson and his party didn't show up, with instructions to return in a day or two—but without the summons for a helicopter. Hendricks tried to kick his heel holds faster, but succeeded only in kicking them shallower—too shallow to hold his weight. He lost control of his descent and started sliding freely on his back toward the black rocks below.

His first thought was annoyance at all the ordeal of yesterday and last night being in vain, at his failure to survive on this last traverse. He abandoned himself to the grim exhilaration of riding a glacier to doom. Somehow, the uncontrolled acceleration of such a fall did not come. In fact Hendricks realized that he was descending at a brisk but reasonable speed, braked by the friction of his roped body against the softening snow. Tentatively, he dug his axe head in—and his slide slowed, then stopped. He felt pleased with himself. He had finally evolved a way of traveling fast. Now he could survey the next section of the slide for hazards and calculate how far he could ride freely to the next rough part or other obstacle. He tried to sit up. Nothing happened.

For the first time since he had extricated himself from under the crust after he and Gibson and Hubbard had fallen down the mountain, Hendricks' injuries had taken over. He lay paralysed on his back on the snow crust. He flailed with his good arm; he kicked at the snow with his legs, but these struggles only brought pain. It required half an hour of concentrated desperate effort for Hendricks to sit up. From what he could see of the snow-field below he calculated that he could slide another 150 feet safely. This time he traveled on his stomach, hoping that it would be easier to sit up from that position when he came to a stop. But he had to keep his broken rib from scraping on the ice, and his posture was so awkward that he had to use both hands on his axe to bring himself to a stop. The pain of using his broken shoulder was so great that he had to lie still and muster strength for another half hour before he could sit up.

Somehow Hendricks summoned the patience to descend the last part of the snowfield with caution, and finally he stood on solid ground below the snowfield—past danger. A few steps away was the tent of the advanced camp, and in it food and warmth and safety for blessed sleep. But that would be defeat. He turned doggedly toward the base camp. He stumbled the three miles in five hours. Near the camp Peterson saw him coming and ran to help the dazed man.

Hendricks was almost incoherent, but he made Peterson understand what had happened. Peterson told him that Fabergé had gone to Burnie Lake to meet the plane. Since the Howson party had not returned, Fabergé intended to send the pilot back to his base at Terrace, forty miles westward, with instructions to wire Mrs. Gibson there had been a delay, and to return in three days.

"Stop the plane," Hendricks demanded. "Get there before it takes off."

Peterson ran. From the base camp to the lake was three miles, half of it through scrub woods just below timberline, none of it friendly to a runner. He was deep in the woods, with the lake almost in sight, when he heard the roar of the plane's motor. Peterson's shouts were drowned in the plane's take-off.

Fabergé and Peterson returned to the base camp. There was never any doubt what they would do—go up the mountain after the two injured men. But first they must attend to Hendricks' injuries. He refused their attention.

"I've survived to this point," he said testily. "Put me in a sleeping bag, leave some food within reach, and I'll manage." He gave the two men directions as best he could for reaching the ledge at the foot of the snow-filled cleft. From what he had observed on his descent he believed they could climb directly from beneath instead of taking his route.

Fabergé and Peterson left immediately for the advanced camp, although it was by then nearly dark and the last mile would be perilous. They spent the night at the camp and at dawn on Tuesday, August 20, they packed up most of the camp into two shoulder packs of fifty pounds each—tent, sleeping bags, food, medicines, primus stove, cooking gear and half a gallon of gasoline. They had to be prepared to set up some semblance of a field hospital for two men with severe but unknown injuries. Under the heavy burden Fabergé and Peterson climbed slowly. By late morning they could see the incredibly steep snow-filled gash in Howson's southwest face described by Hendricks. Somewhere up there were the men they sought. From time to time they paused, to shout and to listen for a sign of life, for an answering call from Donald Hubbard.

Hubbard, crouched on the narrow ledge with his back against the wall, supporting Rex Gibson's head in his arms, had indeed been shouting periodically that morning; not long-odds cries for help, but signals to guide possible searchers.

He had survived the two most unearthly days of his life there on the ledge, sweating out two mathematical formulas that would decide their fate. First, the certainty that they could outlast only a limited number of nights' exposure. Even if Hendricks got down safely, Hubbard did not believe Fabergé and Peterson could rescue Gibson and himself. He did not think they would try, but would consider it wiser to fly out for help, either for a helicopter or an experienced rescue party. Hubbard drew considerable comfort from the thought that he shared the ledge with Canada's foremost mountain climber, and that the thousand-member Alpine Club would rush into action as soon at it heard of its president's predicament. Nevertheless, Hubbard had to draw up a grim balance sheet: help could not come before Thursday at the earliest—and he could not live beyond Thursday night at the latest. Gibson probably could not last as long.

On the other hand there was a wildly unpredictable danger that a rock fall or an avalanche would snuff out their lives at any instant. The first rock fall had crashed and ricocheted past their ledge a few minutes after

6

Hendricks disappeared over the rim of the rock face above. It seemed to Hubbard that the shrapnel of rocks had come from the height where he had last seen Hendricks. This lent a chilling thought: the climb had been too much for Hendricks; he had collapsed of his injuries just beyond sight and his struggles to arise had started the rock fall. For two days now he had lived with that fear, that Hendricks lay helpless on the mountain and he was patiently waiting for help that would not be summoned.

Their bombardment by the mountain punctuated the monotony of that waiting. Mostly the rocks, like flocks of nightmarish black birds, whistled past the shelf and on down the gully. But one fall came from directly overhead and the biggest boulder shattered itself just above them and leaped over them. Gibson opened his eyes and said evenly, "That was close." As the sun softened the snow the avalanches started. Most of the falls followed the "avalance gutter" in the middle of the gully down which he and his companion had fallen, but some piled their ten-foot drifts too close to the ledge for comfort. One spent itself so near that the boots of the two men were buried in its side.

Hubbard fought the sleepless hours of ever-present danger by instituting a system, a routine, for life on the shelf. First he made an inventory of the food supply. They had started out with enough for two meals for three people, and had eaten nothing. In the food pack was half a pound of cheese, a can of corned beef, a can of sardines, a loaf of bread, a quarter pound of butter, dried apples, dates and shelled pecans.

Hubbard opened the corned beef and gave some to Gibson. He became violently nauseated, which caused Hubbard to fear severe internal injuries. Gibson asked for water. Their only cup was the corned-beef can. To reach the water—the same trickle that had saved their lives by weakening the snow crust—Hubbard had to edge his way past Gibson, who was tied to the widest part of the ledge for safety, and reach out to the extreme limit of his balance until the trickling water filled the can. The procurement of water became Hubbard's major project. He counted twenty trips.

Hubbard also experimented with his broken leg. In the event that Hendricks *was* on the rocks above, his own ability to descend the mountain somehow depended solely on that numb useless limb. Hubbard tried holding the broken bone in various positions. Suddenly he found one in which, when some weight was

put on the leg, nauseating pain did not ensue. He padded and bound the leg in that position, and ensuing trips for water became exercises in how to walk with a broken leg.

Hubbard could do little for Gibson, and it saddened him that Gibson was so deeply grateful for what little he could do. Gibson refused food, so Hubbard plied him with water; Gibson sometimes showed discomfort and Hubbard would shift him to a new position; sometimes he seemed cold, and Hubbard lined his torn clothes with the socks and jacket Hendricks left behind.

"Ah, splendid of you . . . that's just right now," Gibson would say gently, and Hubbard would almost weep at his own impotence to do anything worthy of thanks.

On Monday, Gibson seemed semiconscious and had scarcely stirred. Then, in the afternoon, came a strange and pitiful change. In a clear forceful voice, without stirring his body, Gibson enacted his own rescue. In his imagination, the helicopter landed on the glacier below the cliff at their ledge. Gibson took charge of the operation from there. He had praise for this one, a word of advice for that one, as the rescuers reached the shelf. He directed them how to place him on the stretcher and carefully lower him down the rough slopes to the waiting helicopter. Then he was in hospital, battered but quite comfortable and inclined to treat the whole incident as a bit of the price a man must pay for good mountain climbing.

Presently Gibson said to Hubbard, "Have they got you down yet?"

"Not yet," said Hubbard.

"Don't worry," Gibson told him. "I've been through it and it's all right."

On Tuesday morning Gibson seemed weaker. He refused a drink for the first time, by shaking his head. He did not speak. Later Hubbard saw him smile. "Getting rescued," he said, "was a wonderful dream." Those were his last words.

Toward noon Hubbard knew that Gibson's end was near. He was holding Gibson's head on his knees and rubbing his head and chest, which seemed to ease his discomfort, when he noticed his breathing had become almost inaudible. Hubbard thought: "I cannot let a friend die like this, without some sort of religious rite." Holding Gibson, Hubbard raised his head and pealed the words of the hymn "Lead Kindly Light" into the echoing mountains. After a long silence he knew that Gibson was dead.

An hour later he heard a noise that came to him from up the slope. It was unmistakably a human voice calling. Hubbard thought it was

Hendricks, thought that this confirmed his fear that Hendricks had never got down. He shouted in answer. Then he saw two heads appear over the rim of the cliff *below* him. It was Fabergé and Peterson. Their calls had echoed above from a trick of mountain acoustics.

Little was said. Hubbard set about the melancholy task of securing Gibson's body with extra ropes to the shelf. Peterson spoke a silent Quaker prayer, and the three men started downward. There was no question of trying to bring back the body then. To get Hubbard down was in itself a task of incredible patience and fortitude that lasted three days. Each stage of the descent required elaborate roping procedures by Fabergé and Peterson to lower Hubbard and his almost useless leg. Hubbard had to rest every half hour, and this added to the delays because after two sleepless nights he fell asleep repeatedly at rest stops. On the last day of the climb down an airplane suddenly appeared around the mountain, flying as low and as slowly as it dared.

It had been sent by Mrs. Gibson to reconnoitre, after she had learned that her husband's party had been delayed. Fabergé signaled it with a mirror. The pilot blinked his landing lights three times, as if confirming that three men were coming safely down the mountainside. Unfortunately, the pilot's optimistic report raised Mrs. Gibson's hope that her husband was safe—hope that was dashed when the four survivors reached Terrace in their own chartered plane.

Immediately, members of the Alpine Club of Canada organized a party to go to Mount Howson to attempt to recover Major Gibson's body. Provincial government officials discussed a similar operation. But Mrs. Gibson requested that nobody climb the slope that had killed her husband. She said he had left this request with her: should he die in the mountains, no life must under any condition be risked to bring his body out. She asked that his wish be respected. Both the Alpine Club and the government have acquiesced.

BLAIR FRASER

# The Saintly Failure Who Changed Canada

When a CBC Citizen's Forum panel was asked to name the ten greatest Canadians of this century, only two were chosen unanimously: Mackenzie King and James Shaver Woodsworth. They made an odd contrast. By any material standard Mackenzie King's life was a triumphant success, Woodsworth's a failure.

A Methodist minister whose doubts of his own creed began even before he was ordained, Woodsworth left the church at forty-two to become, for a time, a day laborer. He founded a political movement, the Co-operative Commonwealth Federation, which gives no sign of ever attaining federal power. Of all his ideals and convictions, pacifism was the one for which he made the greatest sacrifices; to that ideal he never converted his own party or even his own children. Why should this crusader for lost causes be ranked among the great men of his generation?

One Forum speaker gave an answer which the others accepted: "Woodsworth was a saint." It's a queer word to apply to a professional politician, but that is what he was. And that was the secret of his astonishing political power. Physically he was not impressive—he was a handsome figure with his neat white beard and fine features, but so small and frail as to give no hint of the strength he was able to summon. He was a competent experienced speaker but no orator, no rabble-rouser. Yet for more than twenty years, and for half of that time alone, this little man influenced Parliament as no lone individual has done within living memory.

Woodsworth was the father of the welfare state in Canada—of what we have now, and of what we may have in store. He and one supporter, A. A. Heaps of Winnipeg, forced the Liberal government into a firm undertaking to bring in old-age pensions in 1925. He spoke for family allowances fifteen years before they became a fact; for unemployment insurance nearly twenty years ahead; for national health insurance in the mid-twenties. Things that are commonplace today were Utopian dreams when Woodsworth began to fight for them—more than Utopian, they were radical, dangerous, subversive. Yet Woodsworth, even in those days, was seldom attacked personally for the things he advocated. Even in those days he had proven, to friend and foe alike, his sincerity and his character.

He was a rising young pastor at one of Winnipeg's more fashionable churches when, in 1907, his misgivings about the Methodist creed impelled him to resign from the church. A special committee examined him on doctrine and gave him a clean bill of health: "We find there is nothing in Bro. Woodsworth's doctrinal beliefs or adhesion to our discipline to warrant his separation from the ministry." So Woodsworth agreed to remain a clergyman, but he left his comfortable pastorate to open All People's Mission in the slums. Ten years later he was established in another career, that of practical social work. As director of a bureau of social research supported by all three prairie governments he was becoming known across Canada. He was in demand as a lecturer from Montreal to Vancouver; he basked in the approval of rich and poor alike.

The conscription issue came along. Woodsworth, the Christian pacifist, felt that he could not remain silent. He sent a letter to the Manitoba *Free Press* denouncing the new national service registration scheme of the Borden government. Immediately he lost not only his job but also his status and his friends. When he and his wife and six children (the youngest an infant in arms) left Winnipeg on a bitter January night in 1917, not a soul was at the station to see them off. A year later, after a short and stormy term at a mission station on the British Columbia coast, Woodsworth again offered his resignation from the Methodist Church; this time it was accepted without comment. He went to work as a longshoreman on the Vancouver docks.

After that harsh experience it was easy, even exhilarating, for him to go to jail in the Winnipeg general strike of 1919. (He was charged with sedition for printing, among other things, a quotation from Isaiah: "Woe unto them that decree unrighteous decrees, to turn aside the needy from judgment.") Woodsworth was rather disappointed when the charges against him were dropped—he was in jail only five days whereas other strike leaders were convicted and served terms in prison. As a young pastor on probation in a Manitoba mission field he had written in his diary: "I do not pray to be an eloquent or popular preacher or a profound scholar, but Oh that God would use me as an instrument through which the Holy Spirit may speak to the people."

Woodsworth never lost that sense of mission. In 1936, when the CCF decided to hire young David Lewis as its first (and for a long time its only) salaried official, founder Woodsworth was opposed to the idea. He liked Lewis, he knew there was plenty for a national secretary to do, but he disliked the thought of anyone working for the CCF for pay. "It makes us too much like a political party," he said. To J. S. Woodsworth the CCF was never a party, it was a national crusade. Speaking of him, old associates and disciples often use the same words: "J. S. would have gone to the stake for his principles without a moment's hesitation." It would not have occurred to him that any other course was open. And he expected the same strength of character in other people.

In his old Room 616 of the House of Commons, for twenty years the headquarters of the democratic Left in Canada, Woodsworth used to keep portraits of people he admired. On his desk was a bust of Savonarola, the monk who was burned for heresy in Renaissance Italy. On the wall, among others, was Ramsay MacDonald, the first Labour prime minister of Britain. On the day in 1931 when MacDonald deserted the Labour Party to join Baldwin in a "national" government, Woodsworth took down his picture.

Agnes MacPhail, then halfway through her long career as Progressive MP for Southeast Grey, dropped into Room 616 that morning and noticed the change in the portrait gallery. "Oh, J. S., if you ever take my picture down it'll break my heart," she said.

Woodsworth twinkled at her: "Better watch your step, young lady." It was said in fun, but she knew he meant it.

Rectitude came naturally to J. S. Woodsworth. His grandfather, a lay preacher, was a prosperous builder in Toronto until he endorsed a note for a friend. The friend defaulted. Grandfather Woodsworth paid off every cent, though it left him nearly bankrupt. As a result his three sons were unable to go to college, but J. S. Woodsworth's father went into the ministry anyway. Young James was born in 1874 on the farm at Islington, Ontario, where his mother Esther Shaver had grown up. He was still a small boy when his father moved to the western mission fields and settled the family in Brandon. His childhood recollections were of the old, still unopened west—field trips with his father by buckboard or horseback; the open table his mother kept for wayfarers, white and Indian; the hard, healthy, satisfying life of the prairie. He was the eldest of six; with his father away so much, young James took charge of the family.

He was a sterner disciplinarian than either his father or his mother. Fifty years later his own children observed with amusement their middle-aged aunts and uncles still in evident fear of James's indignation. As a student at Winnipeg's Wesley College he didn't smoke, dance, play cards or go to parties, and he had a very low opinion of those who did. In the mission field in 1896, the year he graduated from Wesley, the 22-year-old preacher noted in his diary: "Had a long talk today with a man of twenty-five or thirty. He knows he is not living as he ought. Tobacco is what keeps him from Christ."

That aspect of Methodism survived in him when the creed itself had died. His children remember Sunday at home as a rather grimly devotional day. The young Woodsworths suffered also for Father's own personal beliefs. His son Charles, later editor of the Ottawa *Citizen*, never forgot the humiliation of sitting alone in a Vancouver classroom while the other boys (whose parents were not pacifist) went out to cadet drill.

To the children he was Father, not Daddy. His wife called him James; some of the CCF "old guard" used to call him J. S. to his face, but to M. J. Coldwell, his successor in the leadership, he was never anything but Mr. Woodsworth. The only people who called him Jim were the friends he made as a laborer on the Vancouver waterfront. His wife once remarked to a friend: "If James had more sense of humor he'd never have amounted to anything. He could never see how funny he looked, one little man struggling against the whole world."

But he never really did look funny (least of all to his wife, who shared all his troubles and trials without even a thought of complaint). Even a sympathetic observer finds himself wondering why this rather officiously virtuous young man wasn't written off as a prig.

He wasn't, as a matter of fact. He played football all through college (in spite of his small size he was a fast three-quarter at English rugby) and took an active part in college life. In his last year at Wesley he won the Senior Stick, a gold-headed cane which was a token of all-round excellence, the highest honor a student could win. Except for the brief period when his pacifism made him an outcast he was always popular. One reason may have been his utter sincerity and his respect for sincerity in others. Woodsworth admired a man who fought for his principles, whether he personally agreed with the principles or not. One of his proud possessions, which hung on the living room wall in Winnipeg was the sword his grandfather Woodsworth had carried in the Rebellion of 1837.

Another endearing thing about Woodsworth was that he always paid the full price of his own beliefs. Unlike the average do-gooder, he had only one standard of conduct. To take one minor example: As CCF leader in the thirties he did an exhausting amount of traveling, but he never took any other accommodation than a day coach or a tourist-class berth. This was a matter of embarrassment to other CCFers, who like their creature comforts as well as anyone else. Also they worried, with good reason, about the old man's health. But Woodsworth used to say, "It's poor people's money we're spending."

In the campaign of 1940, three months before the paralytic stroke that finally killed him, the party took stern measures. They bought him a first-class compartment for every journey, and put him on every train. Woodsworth made no protest. At the end of the campaign he handed the compartment tickets back to the CCF national office, all properly canceled, and told them to collect the refunds. He had given his chaperons the slip and traveled by day coach and tourist sleeper as usual.

The sincerity he inherited; the keen awareness of poverty and the passionate sympathy for the poor developed more slowly. When he went to Oxford for a postgraduate year in 1899, he spent his vacations in settlement houses in the east end of London and saw at close range a kind and quantity of poverty for which the prairies had not prepared him. Memories of it dogged him when he came back as assistant minister to Grace Church, Winnipeg. He began to wonder if the church were doing enough to relieve human misery on this earth, and if not why not. One of the things that bothered him was the funeral service for children. He told a friend years later: "I couldn't go on saying these babies had been taken by God's will, when I knew what had killed them was dirty milk." Another thing was the flood of immigrants then pouring into the west and the inhuman indifference that greeted them. Doubts of the church as an institution, as well as doubts about dogma, underlay that letter of resignation from the ministry in 1907.

He married Lucy Staples, a fellow-student during the year he spent in Victoria College, Toronto, and she was a pillar of strength to him for the rest of his life. She had more warmth than he and a greater sense of fun, but no smaller sense of duty. When he decided to give up comfort and go to work among the poor, she took it as a matter of course. At that time they had two small children, whose earliest memories now are of those strenuous happy years in the Winnipeg slums. Mrs. Woodsworth started a kindergarten which her own children attended along with those of the immigrant families. Woodsworth started classes in English—he spoke no other language himself, but he taught by demonstration. His daughter Grace, then a child of five or six, has a clear memory of her father saying, very slowly, to a shy and awkward foreigner: "I get out of bed . . . I put on my pants . . . I put on my socks . . . I put on my shoes . . ."

Through the mission Woodsworth first came into contact with the labor movement. He was appointed delegate of the Ministerial Association to the Winnipeg Trades and Labor Council and he began to contribute weekly essays by "Pastor Newbottle" to the local labor paper. They sounded increasingly "radical" as he learned more about workers' problems. They also show a revival of his doubts about the church's effectiveness as a force for reform, doubts by no means diminished by the anger he aroused among many of Winnipeg's respectable parishioners.

That was one reason he left the mission in 1913 to head the Canadian Welfare League and, later, the prairie Bureau of Social Service. It was this latter job which the governments abolished after Woodworth's anticonscription outburst in December 1916. He spent only one more year as minister then, at Gibson's Landing, a tiny hamlet twenty miles up the coast from Vancouver. His parish consisted of a handful of English-speaking families, but there was also a settlement of Finns up the Hill. They were foreigners and many of them were communists. On both counts the older

parishioners took a dark view of the new minister's immediate attempts to include these lesser breeds in the congregation. Solid citizens also resented his active support of the local co-operative.

But the worst bone of contention, again, was his opposition to war. Use of the pulpit as a recruiting agency had revolted Woodsworth for years. His attitude went back to the Boer War when he had been in England, but it became acute after 1914. He found himself at a recruiting meeting in St. James Methodist Church, Montreal, one evening in October 1915. "Really, Lucy," he wrote to his wife, "if I weren't on principle opposed to spectacular methods, I would have got up and denounced the whole performance as a perversion—a damnable perversion, if you like—of the teachings of Jesus and a profanation of the day and the house set apart for Divine Worship . . . I felt like doing something desperate—forswearing church attendance, repudiating any connection with the church . . . I walked the streets all night."

Even at Gibson's Landing he ran into the same kind of pressure. He refused to read war bulletins from the pulpit, he continued to preach in a pacifist strain, and he incurred the bitter enmity of several leading parishioners, notably a superpatriotic storekeeper. (It turned out later that this particular patriot was the chief supplier, in the last year of war, of a large camp of draft-dodgers just over the hill from Gibson's Landing.)

Finally, in June 1918, Woodsworth sent his second letter of resignation from the Methodist clergy. By an odd irony the man who accepted it was the Reverend A. E. Smith, then president of the Manitoba Conference of the Methodist Church but later a leading figure in the Canadian Communist Party.

Woodsworth went to Vancouver to look for work. His wife stayed on at Gibson's Landing with the children; she had been a teacher before their marriage and she got a job teaching in the local school. (The same patriots tried hard to have her fired for her husband's opinions but they failed.)

Woodsworth wasn't a union member but the secretary of the longshoremen's union knew of his support of the labor movement in Winnipeg, and gave the ex-minister a job. Woodsworth weighed a hundred and thirty pounds and had done no manual work since he had left high school; he was hired at sixty-five cents an hour to unload raw rubber in 150-pound boxes.

"For the first time in my life I've done a day's work and earned a day's wages," he wrote to Lucy. "There's no doubt about this being the way to get an insight into labor conditions. But think of you as the wife of a common laborer—a casual laborer at that, a docker!"

That was the last time in Woodsworth's life he ever expressed anything but pride in the status of a common laborer. (Lucy, of course, wrote back: "I am proud to be your wife and the mother of the children of a docker.") He still wrote articles for labor and leftist papers; one of them was entitled, "Come On In, The Water's Fine," and it describes the "strange thrill in being, for better or worse, 'one of us' —one of the common people." He sealed that union a year later by taking an active part in the Winnipeg general strike and going to jail for it.

For Woodsworth, as for all the strike leaders, being imprisoned by the Meighen government was an open sesame to elected office. He ran for the Independent Labor Party in Winnipeg North Centre and was elected to Parliament in 1921. Thereafter he was undefeated until his death twenty-one years later. He had an astonishing influence: probably no private member since Confederation has had as much influence on legislation. When he came to Parliament the subject of old-age pensions had been discussed for ten years and had been in the Liberal Party platform for two years. Nothing was done about it until 1925 when the balance between the two old parties was so delicate that even a couple of backbenchers could upset it. Woodsworth and his Labor colleague A. A. Heaps sent identical letters to Prime Minister King and Opposition Leader Meighen, asking what they intended to do about pensions. King wrote back immediately, undertaking to bring in a pension law.

One day in 1931, when Mackenzie King was telling Parliament how the Liberals had brought in pensions, Prime Minister Bennett answered: "What would the honourable member from Winnipeg North Centre have said if, when the bill was introduced, he had listened to the speech he has listened to this afternoon? He was the man who forced this upon a reluctant (Liberal) administration."

Woodsworth's exploit in forcing the creation of an Ontario divorce court was even more spectacular, for this time no balance-of-power situation existed. Woodsworth was literally one man alone against a Parliament half-hostile and half-indifferent, yet he won. His technique was part stubbornness, part mere application of parliamentary principles. Divorces then (as they still are for Quebec) were sent through the House of Commons in bales of private bills. They are examined by a Senate

Committee, but they are not debated in either House. Woodsworth stalled the whole machinery of the parliamentary divorce mill by asking a simple pertinent question on each bill: "Is there any provision for the children?" The sponsor of the bills didn't know. On enquiry he often found there was not, in fact, any adequate provision for the children. By the time the government gave in before Woodsworth's one-man blockade, a very large number of MP's had come to realize how silly the Canadian divorce system is.

In those two cases Woodsworth's influence was obvious and decisive. No one can measure how much he did for other welfare legislation, he was so far ahead of his time. He was the only supporting speaker when, in 1929, a Quebec MP introduced a motion for family allowances. He argued for unemployment insurance constantly throughout the twenty-one years between its appearance as a plank in the Liberal platform and its enactment by a Liberal government. He began agitating in the twenties for health insurance.

Indeed it could be argued that he was just as effective alone as when, after 1932, he led a political party. The Co-operative Commonwealth Federation comes honestly by its cumbersome title. It was indeed a federation, born with much travail of the Canadian Labor Party and a group of provincial farm organizations. They had no trouble agreeing that J. S. Woodsworth should be their leader, but they did have trouble agreeing on almost everything else.

Woodsworth was more than the founder, he was the heart and soul of the new party. Never in his lifetime did the CCF attain political victory (he had been dead two years when Tommy Douglas came to power in Saskatchewan), but he laid the ground work for any success the party has had or will have. Yet, by a final bitter irony, the most memorable of all his experiences with the CCF was another parting of the ways. Another war raised the old issue. Woodsworth had not changed his views. Even his own party did not share them. The CCF voted for the war, with some reservations and stipulations which were quickly voted down in Parliament, but with a straight "yes" in the end. Woodsworth was uncompromisingly against it.

Hansard shows no recorded vote on the issue of declaring war, and many people think the decision was unanimous. It was not. By House rules at least five Members must rise to demand a recorded vote before Mr. Speaker may grant it. Woodsworth stood up, but he stood alone. His speech on the eighth of September was vigorous, even violent. He said again what

12

he had been so bitterly attacked for saying: "I have boys of my own, and I hope they are not cowards, but if any one of those boys, not from cowardice but really through belief, is willing to take his stand on this matter and if necessary to face a concentration camp or a firing squad, I shall be more proud of that boy than if he enlisted for the war." It was the kind of statement for which, in 1917 and 1918, he had been execrated and hounded out of employment. This time only a lone backbench Tory cried "Shame!"

This time the old man escaped any public ordeal. His opinions had been known for years, and his sincerity respected. If any Liberals had intended to heckle him when he rose to state them again, they were silenced by their own Prime Minister, W. L. Mackenzie King. Speaking that afternoon, King had turned round to face his own followers, as he said: "There are few men in this Parliament for whom I have greater respect than the leader of the Co-operative Commonwealth Federation. I admire him in my heart because time and again he has had the courage to say what lay on his conscience, regardless of what the world might think of him. A man of that calibre is an ornament to any Parliament."

Until the last moment his lieutenants in the CCF thought they had worked out a compromise Woodsworth would accept. He had made no attempt to dominate the discussion, uttered no threats of resignation. But when the talk was all done and the party's position defined, he rose to say quietly: "This is how democracy should work—this is a party statement worked out by discussion. But I myself, I'm afraid, cannot accept it; I shall have to resign." They talked him out of that, but the effect was the same. He remained as a kind of leader emeritus, a "chairman of the board." M. J. Coldwell became party leader in everything but name. Woodsworth felt no resentment but he must have felt very much alone.

However, he was used to that. He'd spent most of his life alone, as a man must who follows his conscience without ever drawing back or turning aside. He never let loneliness discourage him. He believed that he was right; he believed right would triumph in the end; therefore he could never feel defeat.

BRUCE HUTCHISON

# Oh, How I Hate the Country

Ninety per cent of the middle-aged men in North America dream and drool over an imaginary dozen acres of land where they will retire some day and lead the easy life. Happily they never get past the dream-and-drool stage.

Ten per cent, more daring and insane, retreat to the country, sink into the earth, are swallowed up and forgotten. They never have a day of ease thereafter. This I know for I am one of them. And just look at me. No, better not. It would only embarrass both of us.

For the unknown victims of the great North American Dream I propose to speak out here as no one has ever dared to speak before. I am doubly equipped for this harrowing personal confession, by experience and perfidy. First, after a quarter of a century of the dream life, I am broke, friendless, ignorant, insular, prejudiced, calloused, cantankerous, prematurely aged, and my feet hurt. I have mildew, rust, root rot, black spot, wireworm, cutworm, aphis, weevil, earwig and a cardiac condition. And I hate my fellow man. Second I am personally responsible for dragging down countless others with me, breaking up marriages and blighting the lives of little children. This I have done by writing and selling for sordid profit innumerable sweet and soggy articles on the joys of the country. Hundreds, perhaps thousands of contented city folk have read and believed me and moved to the country and lived to curse my name.

At the start I wrote in all innocence, before the country had clutched me in its long green tentacles and squeezed out my last drop of humanity. Then I wrote to support my farm and thus earn the privilege of laboring, without wages, some twelve hours a day. Finally I wrote out of sheer malice (and, I will say, with a horrid craftiness and a fine lyrical swing) because by now I drew a cold, sardonic pleasure from the sight of my companions in exile.

That, briefly, is how I became the tired monster you now behold.

It was great fun the first year or so—nature baits her trap with devilish ingenuity before the kill. The first thing a city man does in the country is to plant trees as if they were a new invention. They are quite old really and any fool can plant them. Any fool does. Like all people who had seen them only through a car window I used to wax very sentimental and sloppy about trees. I used to write purple and gooey pieces pointing out the fairly obvious fact that only God can make a tree. But when I found myself writhing in a tropical jungle which I had planted, slashing out blindly in all directions with an axe, the sap of slaughter dripping from my hands, then I began to take a more practical view of trees. I stopped writing about God.

It sobers a man, I can tell you, when he is drenched three times a year in lime and sulphur spray, his skin breaks out in azalea-colored blisters, he smells like an over-aged egg, he is not allowed in his own kitchen and the dog walks away with his tail between his legs.

Please don't tell me that only God can make a tree. It only turns me to blasphemy when every winter, hanging like an ill-made spider above the earth, I have to prune five tons of branches and pile them and burn them, with inflamed cheeks and singed eyebrows, wasting enough heat to warm the winter population of Toronto and enough energy to make an honest living. Don't start me talking about God and trees or I'll forget that I was raised in a good Christian home.

And then the precious little acorns that grow into mighty oaks, the fluttering, long-distance propellers of maple seeds and the wild, tasteless, caterpillar-infested apples that spring up on the fence lines. I wrote a lot of sickly, oozing stuff about the breeding habits of vegetable life, and more of my city friends itched for the feel of a shovel, resigned their jobs and drove their wives into the wilderness. I wrote thus, for I needed the money, but I knew by now that the acorn was my deadly enemy. A seed of any sort aroused the beast in me. They grow, that is the trouble with seeds, they grow. Everything grows except me and I have shrunk two full inches in my twenty-five years of the easy country life.

There were touches of rough humor in those early days, when one could still laugh, and in my poverty I exploited them in the newspapers until people thought I was having a hell of a time.

There was our first crop when I carefully stored my choice tulip bulbs in the root cellar and my wife cooked them, being a city girl who took them for onions, and fed them to our infant daughter and came screaming down the road to ask the neighbors if tulips were poisonous; whereat Miss Snape suggested bread poultices, Mrs. Noggins urged a stomach pump as used on her Uncle Herbert (an alcoholic), Mrs. Shipley said it would certainly prove fatal and began to cry, and George Pudbury laughed so hard he fell off his manure spreader.

They weren't poisonous, as it turned out, but they cost nearly a dollar each. I wrote that story in several papers, but I couldn't afford new tulip bulbs. By then I was bankrupt paying for fence posts, shovels, hoes, saws, fertilizers, liniment and painkiller which the real-estate advertisements never mention. After that we had to eat onions.

It was fun, too, before the illusion wore off, and it gave us a quaint sense of peasantry to join in the frolics of the countryside. Especially to drink Pudbury's homemade beer which he had to open over the sink because of its explosive qualities—the secret origin of the atom bomb. Most of it escaped into the sink but a fraction escaped into Pudbury who, after a few good explosions, would sometimes give an imitation of a one-armed Frenchman reciting "The Charge of the Light Brigade." But you grow tired of explosions and "The Light Brigade" after a while. There is much to be said for a sanitary liquor store, nonexplosive, where the bottles are reliably labeled.

I made a few dishonest dollars—though seldom enough to afford a bottle of good stuff—writing about Pudbury's beer and Mrs. Noggins' parsnip wine. The latter was very good for lubricating a wheelbarrow, but in the papers I always presented it as a shimmering amber essence, compounded of sunshine, wind and autumn frost, which made my city friends' tongues hang out. Mine did, too, after one gulp.

I once earned enough to buy a secondhand cultivator by recounting the literary adventures of Alfred Beake, who bought an encyclopedia on the instalment plan from a traveling salesman because his thirst for learning had been aroused by pictures of a Turkish harem, but was compelled to return the books and lost his deposit because his wife thought his morals were being undermined, and anyway she wanted money to buy a load of natural fertilizer for her asparagus bed. She was a practical woman who didn't go along with fertilizing the mind. You could eat asparagus, she pointed out, but what could you do with a Turkish harem? Beake could have answered that but thought it wise not to.

It all seemed funny at the time before the country soured us. It doesn't seem funny any more. Nothing seems funny any more. It takes more than a glass of parsnip or an explosion at the sink to arouse me these days.

Besides, my neighbors didn't like to be made fools of in print. Country people are odd that way. City people are willingly made fools of by every radio program, movie and parliamentary debate, but country people don't like it. They began to slink up side roads and hide in the barn at my approach. I became a rustic pariah. I haven't the heart to write about my neighbors any more. I am a reformed character and tell the truth and no editor will buy it.

All editors love the country as long as they can observe it in colored photographs and they publish expert hints on horticulture written by a half-witted old maid inhabiting a garret on Third Avenue, New York. Any editor will fall for you if you come into his office with shabby clothes, the aroma of horses and a proper look of shyness. The sight of you makes him apologetic for his own wealth, makes him feel like a parasite. Murmuring about his wasted life he will take you out to lunch and exhibit you to his friends as an unspoiled child of nature, and all their eyes will light up with The Old Dream. The lights go out, though, when they see your cracked hands and haggard cheeks and remember when you were a prosperous, well-fed citizen.

While I was new to the country and still retained a few decent instincts it was a pleasure to give my produce to visitors from the city. This charity with my crops got to be a bore. Presently my friends stopped coming for my handouts. They now expect me to pick the vegetables and fruit, grade them according to government regulations, package them in new boxes and deliver them to the door, for nothing, of course. They resent it bitterly if the delivery is a little late and sometimes they compare my stuff unfavorably with the expensive goods of the chain store.

I kept a strict accounting one year and found that, reckoning my wages at five dollars a day —and even I ought to be worth that much, though I grow weaker every season—each squash I gave away cost me $150.75. No squash is really worth that. No city friend is worth that. Nowadays I don't raise many squashes and I have no friends. That way I save a lot of money and adrenalin.

So don't talk to me about vegetables. It only irritates my cardiac condition. And most especially don't come driving gaily by here in your new car, with the trunk cleared out to take home your loot, and tell me how wonderful I am to be able to grow such luscious produce when you try so hard and never get a crop. Don't tell me for I know you were lying on the beach all summer while I was slaving with a hoe under the merciless country sun. I know you were lolling beside your steam radiator in the bitter days of March when I was turning the soil with my shovel and praying for the time when somebody will dig me under.

Don't talk to me about vegetables when I am strangling in blackberry vines, a slave carrying water to a cucumber, a valet to a marrow, a prisoner locked behind the bars of a corn patch. I know vegetables because I have become one. Please just stay away from here, let me decay in peace, and buy your goods at the chain store. I wish I could.

What drove me from the city was its nervous strain, the hour-by-hour schedule starting at 9:30 a.m., coffee at 11, lunch from 12 to 2, tea at 4 and dinner at 6—never a moment of relaxation. The human animal, I said, was never built for such a load. In the country, I said, a man can take his time.

The first thing I bought in the country was an alarm clock to rouse me at 5:50 and from that hour to darkness every moment was scheduled like a radio program, with fifteen minutes for meals, with hardly a word to my family, because I didn't trust myself to speak, and a curt nod to any passerby lest he lean over the fence and interrupt the schedule by passing the time of day.

I have found no peace but I have found isolation all right. I have become a better isolationist than Senator Borah. I can read nothing except seed catalogues and cures for hog cholera and advertisements for the latest garden poisons, over which I pore with the gibbering delight of a ghoul. I read nothing and I know nothing, and just outside a sizable city I might as well be in the middle of the Gobi Desert swinging a prayer wheel. Would that I were.

When my wife shouted from the back steps that the Japs had bombed Pearl Harbor I was pruning an apple tree but I didn't stop pruning, not for a second, because I had a whole overgrown orchard ahead of me and, Japs or no Japs, it will keep growing. I shall still be pruning on the same tree, no doubt, when the explosion of atom bombs at last brings me happy release.

The advertisements for real estate and annuities always show the country cottage heaped with fruit, blossoms, vegetables and honey, but the only product I ever traded profitably was manure. In exchange for my hay Pudbury gives me a big load of manure and if you know how to use manure you can make money on it. I guess I wrote ten pieces a year about manure and, in the abstract, so long as I handled it in the concrete, the city readers loved it. There's something wonderfully wistful and nostalgic about manure that moves the urban heart and sets tycoons sniveling about their grandfather's farm in Bruce County. You can always set a whole city dreaming with a column of good barnyard stuff. There's big money in manure if you dress it up right.

In the same fashion I used to write an annual ode to the falling leaves every autumn. Many hardened captains of industry, reading it in their club, would break down over their highballs and cry for their lost childhood, and sometimes I felt a little tearful myself. Not for long. When you have to rake, lift, carry and dump seventy cartloads of oak leaves you can't afford to break down, which is a luxury reserved for the rich.

I used to describe in print the leaves rustling under your feet with the sound of waves on a sandy beach; I used to paint such vivid pictures of my compost pile slowly decomposing into the rich black stuff of fertility, the ultimate substance of growth, the true elixir of life that you would think it edible. Just dirt, that's all, just dirt. You might as well know that now.

And it was a sure-fire tear jerker when I told how, digging down into the compost after five years of the maturing process, digging down through the vintage years as through a wine cellar, I would exhume, layer on layer, each year telling its separate story, the lost and broken toys of my children's vanished childhood. The only things I ever found, in point of fact, were a pair of false teeth and an old rubber girdle.

Even my defenseless children could not escape the fury of my battle with the land. To support my farm—twelve acres being more expensive than the twelve wives of Mr. Beake's harem and much less productive—I had to write all night as I toiled outside all day, and the children, so long as they were too young to read, offered abundant copy of a whimsy-whamsy sort. It was a kind of legal method of eating your young. No family can survive the carefree country life. When my son and daughter could read what I had written about them they began to regard themselves as freaks, to quail before visitors and to consider their father a cockatrice. As soon as they were old enough they fled from the country. There are two young Canadians who will never fall for The Dream.

MARJORIE WILKINS CAMPBELL

# The Mysterious Kingdom of the Saguenay

The Saguenay is one of the world's faraway places. It exists, it has always existed, as much in the mind as in fact. It is a land of fabulous wealth and beauty; the very word fabulous is dwarfed by its towering industrial potential and its equally towering scenery. It is the legendary *Kingdom* of the history books and a modern tourists' mecca, the scene of the *habitant* classic, *Maria Chapdelaine*, and a key centre of the world's aluminum and newsprint production.

Strange, romantic names spice its story—Cartier and Donnacona, Champlain and Father Albanel. Kenogami and Chicoutimi and Arvida are among its principal towns. Shipshaw, its vast hydro-electric plant, is the twentieth-century equivalent of Aladdin's lamp.

Nothing about the Saguenay is what you expect it to be. Offhand, you expect it to flow into the St. Lawrence from the north. Actually it flows in from the west-northwest, about one hundred and thirty-five miles below Quebec City. Tadoussac on its north bank was an ancient summer rendezvous for Indians from Hudson Bay to the Gulf of Mexico, before it became a fur-trading post and eventually site of one of the continent's finest summer hotels.

As you travel up the sombre stream you cannot realize that the ramparts towering on either shore are two thousand feet above the water, because the stream is so wide. Nor can you understand that the river beneath the deck on which you stand is nine hundred feet deep in places. For forty miles, only an occasional lonely hamlet gives a hint that anyone ever lived along those forbidding shores. Yet each year hundreds of ships from all over the world snuggle up to the huge modern wharves at Port Alfred, the Saguenay's great inland dock at the head of Ha! Ha! Bay.

It is more than a river. It is a valley and a region of some thirty thousand square miles —a fiord that is both river and tide flowing against each other between a fault in the Laurentian rock, in places two miles wide. It is also Lake Saint John, a natural saucer of a reservoir scooped out by Ice Age glaciers and fed by a dozen rushing brown tributaries. The largest of these tributaries, the Mistassini and Peribonca Rivers are a good mile wide. And at almost every scenic site where a tributary flows into the Saguenay or its lake there is a town or village, built by pulp or agriculture.

Before I visited the region I thought the Saguenay had a truly great history. Most of its history is based on legend, and for three centuries almost all who knew of it shunned it. I understood it had tremendous wealth— and its wealth consists of timber and water, about 350,000 acres of good clay farming land, a two-million-dollar annual blueberry crop and a tourists' and sportsmen's paradise in big game and *ouananiche*, the valley's famous landlocked salmon. I expected to see several hundred native Montagnais and Mistassini Indians, but was told that few remain. I had prepared myself to find the fabulous Saguenay Valley scenery violated by a Ruhr Valley or a Pittsburgh and, instead, there was a clean-lined plant a mile and a half long and Arvida, an utterly modern town.

But the legends haven't prepared visitors for Port Alfred, Canada's third largest port in ocean-going tonnage; the modern city of Chicoutimi whose hills and churches are an echo of Rome; nor for all the pulp-and-paper towns from which comes one-tenth of the world's newsprint. I had expected the Saguenay to have the frontier feel of the Peace River. But half of today's 200,000 population, the *habitants* immortalized by Louis Hémon in his Peribonca River romance, *Maria Chapdelaine*,

17

are related to the handful of hardy Canadien settlers who came to the valley a hundred years ago. They have accepted the new industries, but they are not newcomers.

Only two factors suggest the frontier in the Saguenay Valley: the friendliness typical of people in sparsely populated areas and the trip into it. For whether you come by the river's SS "Richelieu," over the new Talbot Highway through Laurentides Park north of Quebec City, or by plane to Bagotville, the northern Quebec geography insists that you have left civilization behind you.

For more than half a century wealthy tourists, honeymoon couples and teachers on vacation have been taking the Saguenay cruise. Even from the deck of a modern vessel you sense the awe which sobered the first white men who ventured upstream in their tiny bark canoes, bending back their heads till their necks ached to see up to the top of the mighty chasm. Some forty miles above its mouth the river branches into Ha! Ha! Bay, named not from the hollow laughter of early explorers who mistook it for the Northwest Passage but from the old French word used by Joan of Arc meaning an obstacle suddenly encountered.

Two capes—Eternity and Trinity—guard the entrance to Ha! Ha! Bay, vast brooding sentinels dwarfing the cruise ships and the hundreds of cargo ships that link Port Alfred at the end of the bay with the world's ports. And high up on Cape Trinity stands the benign white statue of the Virgin, erected in thanksgiving by a nineteenth-century French traveler who escaped after breaking through the ice on a winter trip. Ha! Ha! Bay is large enough and deep enough to float a wartime Royal Navy. Until the end of World War I when Port Alfred was developed as a great inland dock, nearby Bagotville served the needs of the community. Now Bagotville gives its name to the RCAF jet station. Here the populated Saguenay commences.

Thirteen miles farther on by highway is Chicoutimi, until recent years the farthest point up the hundred-mile-long Saguenay familiar to tourists. It is the county town, site of the *seminaire* and museum where Canon Victor Tremblay, lecturer in history and president of the Saguenay Historical Society, lovingly collected the lore and mementos of the land of his birth. Right in the centre of the city the Chicoutimi River hurtles into the Saguenay, a vast roaring torrent of brown water generating power on the spot.

Across the river from Chicoutimi a great cross on the rocky height of Ste. Anne de Chicoutimi, one of many throughout the valley lit by Saguenay power, nightly outwinks the stars above a twelve-foot tide. This is the end of navigation, the place where the brackish tide meets the swift flow of the Saguenay's rapids. The river is more than a mile wide and very, very deep; the word Chicoutimi means "Here the river is still deep." Certain strong swimmers among local sportsmen like to time the brackish tide carefully, and in the twenty minutes calm between tide and swift water swim the Saguenay.

Immediately upstream are the rapids which produce the region's real wealth. In thirty miles the river drops over three hundred feet from Lake Saint John, roaring over the rocks at the rate of 35,000 cubic feet a second. The rapids built the vast plant of the Aluminum Company of Canada and Arvida, the model town named after the first two letters in each name of Arthur Vining Davis, president of the Aluminum Company of America in 1925, the year Alcoa acquired rights to the enormous potential of cheap power needed to process bauxite into aluminum. West from Arvida lie the two Shipshaw power developments whose turbines harness one and a half million horsepower of the Saguenay's invisible might.

Even then you've only begun to see the Saguenay. Five miles beyond Arvida the two pulp-and-paper towns of Kenogami and Jonquière overlook the Au Sable River and the eleven-mile-long flume which floats logs overland from Lake Kenogami to the Price Brothers' mills. The logs are the Saguenay's other natural resource, carpeting the river-veined hinterland of Quebec Province, employing thousands of loggers in winter, choking the streams when melting snows swell them to flood level.

It's a strange and exciting country. Wayside shrines flank modern filling stations. Every neatly painted house has its long veranda and its rocking chair and often its outside stair. The farms are tidy, with neat woodpiles and rakish split-rail fences. The Trappist monastery at Notre Dame de Mistassini lies hard by the modern Saint John pulp-and-paper mill, a curious mingling of the contemporary and the medieval—the shrill whistle of the mill and the monastery bell calling to worship a little band of men vowed to eternal silence. Brown-robed, sandal-shod, they shuffle into their exquisite chapel where women visitors are courteously requested to remain at the vestibule but where a beautiful eight-foot statue of the Virgin is enthroned above the altar, where they keep constant vigil and know the torment of prolonged fasting.

Motoring around Lake St. John, you are in a mood for the shrine of Louis Hémon and his fictional Maria Chapdelaine. At the Peribonca River, she could have been any one of several women I met. I could see her in the mother of ten, quick and yet placid, with eyes so unlike those of the silent monks, and with whom I talked about education for women.

"But of what use is higher education for girls, madame?" I was asked. "It does not help to bring up the family. For boys, yes; for girls the home is the career."

I had to agree. She was gay. Her life was full. She had comfort in her church, an air of chic in her clean apron, and the knowledge that there was good pay in the mills.

Jacques Cartier visited the mouth of the Saguenay in 1534 and, eager to inform his monarch of the country, carried to France one of the native chiefs, Donnacona. Desperately unhappy and homesick, Donnacona sought some means of securing a return to his beloved woods and streams and with Indian cunning told the king of the great riches of the Saguenay Country. Naturally he translated his story in terms familiar to the king, and the riches became rubies and gold and silver. Seeking to snare the king's interest, Donnacona told a tale of strange people who "never eat, have no bottoms and do not digest food." He died in France, but he had started something. Soon the French were seeking the rubies and the gold. When they failed to find either they turned to the whales playing at the mouth of the Saguenay. Soon ships were anchoring at Tadoussac, countless barrels of whale oil were being boiled and, in the sixteenth century, the Saguenay was providing light for Europe's capitals.

Champlain came later, sailed a few miles upstream, then passed on up the St. Lawrence. Champlain named the Saguenay the Domaine du Roi on his map, the French king having chosen the region as his personal fur monopoly.

When Wolfe had climbed the heights at Quebec the Saguenay Lands passed to the North West Company. Then Napoleon forced the Royal Navy to search elsewhere than the Baltic ports for spars and masts for its ships. The admiralty's agent, one William Price, found the much-needed tall straight timbers growing along the Saguenay.

Price saved the day for the Navy and then decided to settle in the land of pine. With James McGill, founder of McGill University, he went into the lumber business on the Ottawa and St. Maurice rivers. But no river was large enough for both of those Paul Bunyan pioneer

industrialists and Price hadn't forgotten the timber on the Saguenay. He opened stores, brought in cattle, operated a grist mill and circulated his own paper money. The Compagnie Price acquired more and more timber limits, either by purchase or lease, until it controlled much of the Saguenay country. And the regime turned out to be just according to the standards of the time. When William Price died in 1867 local residents demanded a continuance of the familiar Price notes, refusing to accept the new Dominion of Canada paper money.

William Price's three sons carried on the business until the death of the last in 1899 when control went to a nephew and namesake, William Price, born of a Chilean branch of the family, educated in England and in the Compagnie Price. By that time the tall white pine had gone and forestry conservation was husbanding the vast stands of spruce and balsam. A new era had come to the Saguenay, and the twentieth-century William Price in 1902 purchased a Jonquière paper mill which had failed. Newsprint had proved its Canadian promise at St. Maurice, and Price Brothers controlled a fortune in spruce and balsam. They had water to float their logs and process them, and the habitant families, content with their church and a little beer and some music, to provide labor. The railway had linked up Chicoutimi with Montreal and ocean-going vessels could haul newsprint and pulp right from the mills to the world's markets. The next step was hydro-electric power.

By World War I William Price had power plants at Jonquière, Kenogami, Chute Murdock and Chute aux Galets. He had built a modern newsprint mill at Kenogami. When he was knighted during the war he was virtually the uncrowned king of the Saguenay. Down in the United States the American tobacco tycoon, J. B. Duke, also interested in hydro-electric power, heard about the Saguenay, came up in his private car, looked it over and announced characteristically: "I'm going to buy this."

The Duke-Price partnership was formed in 1922 and plans drawn for Isle Maligne's giant turbines. Those first half-million horsepower harnessed from the Saguenay's wasting water gave Chief Donnacona's legend a prophetic twist. And there was Chute à Caron, near the mouth of the Shipshaw River, closer to tidewater than Isle Maligne and potentially an even greater development. Among the bluets (in the Saguenay and Lake St. John country they call old-timers "blueberries" after the lush wild crops) they say that Sir William Price had paid two thousand dollars for Chute à Caron rights which sold to J. B. Duke for six millions.

Sir William liked to be familiar with every operation in his empire. He was inspecting one of the 170-feet-high stockpiles, huge beehives of pulp logs, overlooking the Au Sable River at Kenogami when the bank slipped. Down, down to the river tumbled the logs and the president of the *Compagnie Price*. When they found his body, it was as though the king had died. At each of the plants, in the towns and villages where his men worked, they mourned him. His business associates set aside a park in his honor, and high on a foreland overlooking the Au Sable, the Saguenay and Shipshaw rivers they laid him to rest in sight of the twin pulp towns of Kenogami and Jonquière and with the majestic Laurentians to stand guard.

Newsprint is a comparatively economical user of electrical power. It is the manufacture of aluminum into ingots, sheets and wire that consumes most of the two and a quarter million horsepower generated on the Saguenay. Back in 1925 J. B. Duke traded his Duke-Price interests with Andrew Mellon, then looking for cheap, abundant power for processing his vast bauxite holdings into aluminum. For his Chute à Caron rights, Duke received a one-twelfth interest in the projected $250,000,000 Aluminum Company of Canada, thereby providing an often overlooked Canadian slant to heiress Doris Duke's colorful career.

Nowhere near the source of this cheap Saguenay power was there living accommodation for thousands of engineers and other imported workers. So Arvida came into being along with another legend. In a single summer four farms between Chicoutimi and Chute à Caron became a town. Model houses were built at the rate of 270 in 165 days, with curving streets, a marketeria that looks like a suburban library, churches, schools, recreation centres. In no time streets named appropriately Mellon and Davis were nicknamed, also appropriately, Maternity Row and Pregnancy Boulevard—and in English as well as French.

The first ingot was poured in 1926. Present capacity is two million pounds a day, a big fraction of the world's aluminum for planes and barn roofs, frying pans and insulating foil and patent medicines to ease the curse of stomach ulcers. For each ton of aluminum shipped by Saguenay Terminals from Port Alfred, four tons of mealy, pink bauxite is shipped in from British Guiana—through Port Alfred, together with cryolite from Greenland, petroleum coke from the United States and several other minor ingredients. They say in Arvida that you can find someone there who can speak every known language. At Port Alfred, and even in Chicoutimi, sailors hungry for dates and speaking Norwegian, Italian, Portuguese, English and even Chinese, are teaching the local girls not only the languages heard at United Nations headquarters but many customs utterly unknown to the region a generation ago.

What of the Saguenay's future? I thought about that as I sat on the terrace at Saguenay Inn and watched the evening mists rise above the shining surface of Shipsaw but still far below the purpling heights of the majestic Laurentians. And I thought of the simple, gay French folk to whom the Saguenay was home long before the river's invisible power changed the countryside from a pastoral farming community to an industrial centre.

Was I mistaken in sensing a leashed resentment against the powerful interests which had accomplished what native sons had lacked both the vision and the capital to attempt? Could it be that the Prices, hinted in more than one local yarn to have founded their fortunes on the hard-fisted business methods of pioneering days, were more loved than the great aluminum trust because they were a little less benevolent and so a little better understood? But Saguenayans are shrewd and sensible. Enough among them know that their Laurentian Valley is only at the threshold of its history and its wealth, that whatever you say about its future is likely to be understatement.

I even find myself wondering when someone with vision and capital will divert the flow from enormous Lake Mistassini from Hudson Bay to the St. Lawrence by way of the Saguenay, and thereby greatly increase Saguenay power and future Saguenay industry.

Whoever it may be, Saguenayans are likely to give more credit to the genii in their river than to the men who harness it for them. Perhaps it is best that way. Whatever man attempts or achieves, the Saguenay will flow on. That is the great fact.

MAZO DE LA ROCHE

# A Writer's Memories

## I

Remembering the quiet country roads of my childhood, the exhilarating sights in the city, I feel pity for the child of today with nothing to see but the hideous mechanized traffic making its stinking way, bumper to bumper, through the gloomy streets; nothing better to do than to learn at sight the makes of different motorcars. How different were the streets in those days!

A dray would pass, drawn by a team of powerful draught horses—a butcher's cart, the butcher wearing his light-blue apron—a splendid equipage, with coachman in fur cap—horses, horses, everywhere! Women, holding up their long flounced skirts—men who looked like gentlemen. In summer, fruit vendors, with their cry of, "Strawberry, strawberry ripe! Two boxes for a quarter!" And they were quart boxes, not the miserable little pint boxes we buy today. There was an Italian boy I well remember who pushed his barrow of bananas twice a week to our door, with his musical call of, "Banana ripe, fifteen cents a dozen!" I even remember his name—it was Salvator Polito—and the big red bananas.

In those days everyone who had the use of his legs went for walks. Today nobody walks for pleasure. You may walk for miles and meet nobody but yourself. In the morning and afternoon people walked. In the evening they sat on their verandas behind the shelter of syringas in flower, the white skirts of girls billowing over the steps. From indoors might come the sound of a piano. Now and again one heard the clip-clop of horses' hooves. Children went to bed, tired out by their play. Whenever they were free to play they were absorbed in their games.

What has happened to the play spirit in the child of the present? Not long ago I had lunch at the Toronto Skating Club and, looking down on the ice, saw a dozen earnest children practicing figure skating. Over and over the little perfectionists, in their faultless skating gear, repeated the monotonous figures. Nobody was forcing them, nobody was urging them. They wanted to do just what they were doing, each doubtless picturing herself as a champion of organized sport. I thought of our childhood's helter-skelter skating—hand in mittened hand doing a crack-the-whip across the rink—skates never quite fitting—skirts, flannel petticoats, getting in our way. I thought of the admiring group that would gather to see my father execute the grapevine or perhaps the figure eight —he loftily ignoring them, pretending it was easy!

And the games of summer on the green, green grass!

London Bridge is Falling Down—Here we Come Gathering Nuts in May—The Farmer Views His Lands—Hide and Seek—Old Witch, this last throwing one into a madness of chase and pretended fear. Afterward the throwing of oneself exhausted on the grass, staring up at the blue sky or investigating the doings in a tiny anthill . . . The winds in which one ran, all by oneself, swifter it seemed than the wind, wilder than the tempest.

## II

When I was nine someone gave me copies of a young people's paper. It was, I think, *The Youth's Companion*. In it was announced a short-story competition for children of sixteen and under. Unconcerned by my youngness I set out at once to enter the competition. Optimistic, though easily downcast, I saw no reason why I should not be the winner.

With foolscap paper, pen and ink I began to write, and so on and on till a total of eight pages were filled.

The story was about a lost child named Nancy. Terrible times she went through but at last was restored to her mother's arms—my own heart ready to burst with emotion as I finished the story with a text from the Prodigal Son.

"But, darling," said my mother, "do you think a child would ever be so hungry she would eat potato parings?"

"Nancy was," I said firmly.

"And do you think her mother would quote a text the moment her child was given back to her? It sounds so pompous."

This was my first experience of criticism and how it hurt!

My father standing by exclaimed, "I'm dead sure I'd eat potato peelings if I were hungry enough and, as for the text—it was the proper thing for the mother to quote. Don't change a word of it. It will probably get the prize."

Off he went to the letter box to post the manuscript.

No stamps for its return were enclosed but a few weeks later, when I had ceased to think of it, a long envelope was put into my hand. Tremblingly I opened it, and there was my manuscript returned! With it was enclosed a letter from the editor saying, "You are very young to have entered the competition but, if the promise shown by this story is fulfilled, you will make a good writer yet."

"Isn't that splendid!" exclaimed my mother, her pitying eyes on me.

I sat down on a low stool in a corner and covered my face with my hands. Sobs shook me.

Nobody came near me. The family stood about me, realizing that for the moment it was best to leave me to my grief. It was ridiculous, of course, but how well I remember it.

### III

Something new was stirring in me. I discovered that I wanted to write a story—one that I might send to a magazine. It must be done in secret, so that if I were not successful no one need know and, if I were, it would be a lovely surprise for the family.

For some reason I chose to write about French Canadians. I was not a French Canadian—my connection was with Old France—yet something in me drove me to place the scene of this story in Quebec. I shut myself in the dim end of our huge sparsely furnished drawing room in Toronto. I wrote the story in lead pencil (as I have written all since) and then copied it painstakingly in pen and ink. The thought that it should be typed never entered my head.

I have little patience with writers who declare that all their works are composed in agony of spirit. This agonized creation seems to me affected for, in truth, imaginative writing is one of the most delightful of occupations. It is exacting, it often is exhausting. It demands everything the writer has in him to give. He must believe in the characters if he is to persuade the public to believe in them. What the writer of fiction needs—first, last, and all the time—is the public. Its interest is the steady wind that fans the fire of his creative ability. All his "agonizing" will not create a public for him.

My first stories, however, were written in a kind of calculated agony. I had the idea that I must work myself up into a state of excitement before I could write of what was in my mind. I would lie on the sofa in the dim room, my body rigid, my mind hallucinated by the pictures that passed before it. Then I would rise, take up paper and pencil and write. Again I would stretch myself on the sofa. Again I would write. I remember my reflection in the old gilt-framed mirror that hung above the sofa, the glitter in my eyes, the flushed cheeks, as of one in a fever. And so in this way the story was completed.

Related long afterward, in cold blood, it sounds rather ridiculous. But I think it is rather touching, too, because I was so very young, so ignorant. I am sure that most twelve-year-olds of today are more knowledgeable than I was at that time.

In secrecy then, the story was finished. In secrecy it was posted to *Munsey's Magazine*. I did not know that I should enclose return postage.

At the hour for the postman's call I was on hand to be the first to get the mail. From an upstairs window I would see him coming. I would tear down the stairs, my heart hastening its beat. Weeks passed. Then came a small envelope from Munsey's—not the dreaded long envelope containing my manuscript—and in it a note from the editor saying that he had much pleasure in accepting my story. I flew to where my mother and cousin Caroline Clement were sewing.

"I've written a story," I said, "and it's accepted and I'm to be paid fifty dollars for it."

My mother began to cry. "How lovely!" she said through her tears.

"So that's what you were up to," said Caroline. "We've been wondering."

I had had little money in my young life. To

me it seemed something of which there was a perpetual shortage in our family. I made up my mind that the cheque for this story was to be spent on a present for my mother, something she could keep always.

Caroline and I went to Junor's store and there we discovered an ornate lamp, the base of wrought iron, the bowl of bronze, the shade of beautiful amber glass, like a full moon, and on the side of the shade a golden dragon. How much was it? Fifty dollars—the very price!

My mother was delighted. A few years later she broke the shade and one would have thought the end of the world had come, so devastated was she.

When the magazine containing my story appeared I was strolling along Yonge Street. In the window of a stationer's shop I saw the latest number, I went in and asked if I might look at the index page. I was allowed to see it, and there, in print, was my name! I had no money with me and ran along Maitland Street home for the price of *Munsey's*.

At that time my paternal grandmother was visiting us. My father was determined that his mother should appreciate what I had achieved. He was going to read aloud my story to her. I never knew her to read anything but the Psalms of David and of these she knew quite a number by heart. He had placed two chairs side by side in the dining room. He took her hand and led her with ceremony to one of them.

"Do you think there will be time before lunch?" she asked, with a yearning look toward the table upon which the maid had already laid a white cloth.

"A full half hour," beamed my father. "So sit down and prepare to enjoy yourself."

"Is this story true?" asked Grandmother.

"No, no, it is purely imaginative." Dramatically he began to read aloud, and she to endure.

Never could I forget the picture of them sitting there, he with a small dog on his knee, another between his feet; she a stately figure in her black silk dress, with ruchings of white at neck and wrists, and a long gold chain. Her cap, of white lace and ribbon rosettes, was on a foundation of wire. She herself made her caps and, during all the years I knew her, I never saw her do anything more arduous than this and the making of patchwork quilts. Those quilts were quite handsome, being of silk and satin with wide borders of black velvet. She scorned any material but what was absolutely new. One she made for each member of the family and, when at work on the one destined for me, she met a young man who came to the house frequently as my friend. She was favor-ably impressed, especially by the young man's height, and at once set about making the quilt six inches longer.

Now, with a resigned "heigh-ho" and a lifting and a dropping of her shapely white hands on the arms of her chair, she listened to the reading of the first published story of her loved granddaughter—the only grandchild of hers ever to be produced. And she listened with every evidence of boredom.

Yet she was not to escape. My father was determined that she was to hear that story. After a few miserable moments I slunk from the room.

When I returned the lunch was being brought to the table. My father, looking somewhat subdued, was heaving my grandmother to her feet and she, gratefully, was approaching the table. Her ordeal was over. The little Yorkshire terrier was dragging *Munsey's Magazine* under the sofa.

## IV

I have reason to remember my first visit to a publisher's office. Hugh Eayrs, of Macmillan's, had invited me to have tea with him. It was winter and before I left the house I went down to the basement to have a look at the coal furnace, to make sure that all was well there.

Before I went down I drew a grey sweater over my pretty dress, for its protection. The sad thing was that I forgot, in my excitement, to take the sweater off. On top of it I put my muskrat coat and set out. Hugh Eayrs made me welcome in his private office. A typist brought in the tea things and left us.

Hugh was about to help me off with my coat when he was suddenly called from the room. "I shall be back in a moment," he said and hurried away. I was left alone and thought I would myself take off my coat. What was my shock to discover that I still wore the sweater, old, shabby, with a hole in one elbow! I decided that I must refuse to part with my coat. I would say I had had a chill. But the room was hot. I should surely faint in a fur coat. I was in a panic. Then I discovered that a window was open on to the street. I did not hesitate. I threw off my coat, I tore off the sweater, rolled it up and cast it out of the window.

Hugh briskly returned. "What a pretty dress!" he exlaimed. Then, "Will you pour tea?" But I could not forget the sweater, lying in the street. I expected, at any moment, that it would be returned to me but never did I see it again.

V

In the summer of 1925 I began a new novel. Two of the characters in this had been half-formed some years earlier and were to have been characters in a play that never was written. They had no names but later they were to emerge as Meg and Renny Whiteoak in the novel *Jalna*.

*Jalna* was inspired by the traditions of that part of southern Ontario that lies a few miles west of Toronto. The descendants of the retired military and naval officers who had settled there stoutly clung to British traditions. No house in particular was pictured; no family portrayed.

From the very first the characters created themselves. They leaped from my imagination and from the memories of my own family. The grandmother, Adeline Whiteoak, refused to remain a minor character but arrogantly, supported on either side by a son, marched to the centre of the stage.

The name "Jalna" was suggested to me in this way: a member of the Civil Service, who worked in the same department as my lifelong friend Caroline, had spent many years in India. When she told him that I was in search of names of military stations there he sent me a list of quite a number. I pored over them and chose Jalna because it was the shortest; it was easy to remember and looked well in print. When I wrote it at the top of my first page of manuscript, it never entered my head that one day it would become well-known to quite a number of people.

That summer I lived with the Whiteoaks, completely absorbed by them. In fancy I opened the door of Jalna, passed inside, listened to what was going on. Except for my beloved dog Bunty I was isolated in my woodland cottage till Caroline's return in the evening. As the chapters were finished she read them aloud.

In time, *Jalna* was finished and the typed manuscript sent to Macmillan's of New York; Hugh Eayrs had already expressed great hopes for it. The New York house agreed and were to publish it in a few months. Then, in a chance copy of the *Atlantic Monthly* I came upon the notice of a competition the editors were holding for "the most interesting novel" by any author from any part of the world. The prize was large. Very much I should have liked to enter *Jalna* in this competition, but there it was—bound by contract to the New York Macmillan's!

The more I thought of it, the more I wanted to enter that competition. "I don't see how you possibly can," said Caroline. Neither could I see how I could but still I mused on the possibility.

Then brightly came the thought that as my chances of winning were slight it would do no harm to anyone and would be a satisfaction to me just to send *Jalna* to the Atlantic and discover if it made any impression. I could not resist the temptation. The bulky manuscript (a carbon copy) was posted and when Caroline returned that evening I confessed what I had done.

"Now," she said, "you may be in for trouble."

Weeks passed and more weeks. Between the Atlantic on the one hand and New York Macmillan's on the other I began to get really nervous. Then came a letter from Harold Latham, fiction editor of Macmillan's, setting the time of publication and speaking of proofs to be corrected. This sort of double life could not go on. I decided that I must retrieve my manuscript from the competition. How terrible it would be, I thought, if I should win the competition during the full tide of preparation for publication by Macmillan's. Why, I might end in prison!

I wrote to the editor of the Atlantic, asking them to return *Jalna* to me, as I had a publisher for it. They replied that my manuscript was being held, with two others, for further consideration. I should hear from them soon.

A flood of excitement shook me, but I was not submerged. I had promised myself that I would be henceforth honorable and above board with publishers, and so must I be. I wrote to Mr. Latham telling him that I had entered a second copy of *Jalna* in the Atlantic competition. I asked him if, in the event of my winning, Macmillan's would release me from my contract with them. He replied (I suppose that in his wildest imaginings he did not consider this a possibility) that they would release me. There was kindness indeed. I settled down to wait.

Oh, the cruel suspense of that waiting! Each morning after breakfast I perched on the window seat to watch for the postman. Each morning I flew down the stairs to get the mail. There was nothing from the Atlantic. I made up my mind that one of the other manuscripts had been chosen, *Jalna* had been thrust aside and forgotten . . . Again I wrote demanding the return of the manuscript. "How I wish you never had gone into that dreadful competition," exclaimed Caroline. "You grow paler every day. It is killing you."

It turned out that Ellery Sedgwick, editor of the Atlantic, was ill in bed at the time—

and wanted no one but himself to give me the good news. He and I had had some very friendly correspondence—confidential on my part, warmly sympathetic on his. He had remarked of me to a visitor from Toronto, "She has a far better friend in me than she guesses." It was he then who wrote to me of the judges' final decision.

When Caroline came home from the office I told her that *Jalna* had won the Atlantic competition, but she was past rejoicing. Too long had she suffered suspense. She simply said, "Oh," and sat down and looked at me. The fount of our enthusiasm had dried. We sat silent, unable to rejoice.

After a little I said, "It is a large prize I have won."

"Yes, it is large," she agreed.

"Now we can travel."

What emotion we felt was dammed within us, for the editors had begged me to preserve complete silence on the subject of my triumph till they had sent proper notice to the press. It was not easy to mingle with one's friends—to appear nonchalant when they asked me if I had had any news of the competition, to look subdued when they implied that I had better give up hoping.

The Atlantic was to publish *Jalna* in collaboration with Little, Brown of Boston, and in Canada by the firm with which they were affiliated, of whom a Mr. Gundy was head. Nothing appeared impossible to Hugh Eayrs. When I told him that I had entered the *Atlantic Monthly* competition he at once wrote to Mr. Gundy (word of mouth would not suffice) and asked him if, in the event of my being successful, he would agree to the book's being published in Canada by Macmillan's. Mr. Gundy cheerfully agreed, in writing. Therefore when the headlines filled those in his office with joy, he could only ruefully admit that he had promised the rights of *Jalna* to a rival house.

The warmth, the feeling of good will toward me was, as I remember, universal. Even critics who had not been very kind to my earlier books joined in the praise. The general feeling seemed to be that of rejoicing that a Canadian (not this Canadian in particular) had achieved distinction in the United States, a country that heretofore could scarcely have shown less interest in Canadian letters. Thomas Raddall, the Nova Scotian novelist, has written to me: "You cannot imagine what your winning of the *Atlantic Monthly* prize meant to us other Canadian writers. It was as though you opened a door that had been inexorably shut against us."

A really splendid dinner was given for me by combined literary societies. Speeches by the lieutenant-governor and other dignitaries—a handsome silver tea service presented to me by the City of Toronto—I making a small, rather tremulous speech of thanks, and wearing a French evening gown, long-waisted, short-skirted in the extraordinary fashion of the day. This dinner was held in the Queen's Hotel, a house of dignity and fine tradition, quite unlike the seething anthills of business conventions and heartless high-pressure traffic which the hotels of today have become.

## VI

The *Master of Jalna* had been published, and I began a new novel of the Whiteoaks which I called "Cousin Malahide" but later changed the title to "Young Renny." I could not deny the demands of readers who wanted to know more of that family. Still less could I deny the urge within myself to write of them.

Sometimes I see reviews in which the critic commends a novelist for not attempting to repeat former successes, and goes on to say what an inferior thing his new novel is. If a novelist is prolific he is criticized for that, yet in all other creative forms—music, sculpture, painting—the artist may pour out his creations without blame. But the novelist, like the actor, must remember his audience. Without an audience, where is he? Like the actor, an audience is what he requires—first, last and all the time. But, unlike the actor, he can work when he is more than half ill and may even do his best work then . . .

My public was steady and warmhearted. They understood me and I understood them; that is to say, I offered them lucidity and living characters and, in return, they gave me a belief in those characters which was equal to my own. In truth, considering the letters I continue to receive through the years, it seems to me that their acceptance of them exceeds mine.

This applies only to the Whiteoak Chronicles, because to them I have given the sustained work of a lifetime, and my other books and my short stories are diversions, distractions. I make four exceptions—my novel *Growth of a Man*, my history of the Port of Quebec, and my first two novels, *Possession* and *Delight*. These four, so different, represent living experience, and, in a way, failure, because they have been so overshadowed by the Whiteoaks.

Looking back, it seems to me that the life of the novelist is the best of all and I would never choose any other.

FARLEY MOWAT

# The Riddle of the Viking Bow

I sat in the doorway of my tent watching Haluk at work and for the hundreth time I looked into the old Eskimo's lined face and tried to penetrate its mystery. His high straight brow shadowed his eyes so it was difficult to see that they were not the sombre black of all his people, but a deep and piercing blue. The key to the mystery lay in those eyes, but lurking far back in time—too far to let me glimpse its meaning, though as an archaeologist it has long been my work to pry into the ancient secrets of man.

Idly I watched him work. Those strange eyes dreamed over his task so that he neither saw nor heard the world around him; for Haluk was intent on giving new life to an almost forgotten memory from another age. I waited silently until his task was done.

When the long Arctic sun was lying gently on the west horizon of the northern plains Haluk came to my tent bearing the completed product of his memory and of his hands. It was a thing of antler bone and black spruce wood; a crude mockery of the crossbows that won a thousand victories upon the battlefields of Europe seven hundred years or more ago. But it was much more than that to me, for the crossbow's existence in these Arctic plains was a baffling riddle.

Only a few days earlier Haluk had been telling me stories of his childhood and of the hunts made after the musk ox, and he had spoken casually of a weapon that I knew did not exist in the culture of the Eskimos. Thinking that I must have misunderstood his words, I questioned him until at last he drew a picture of a crossbow in the sand to show me what he meant. Still I could not believe it, for it was impossible that his isolated inland race, cut off for centuries from the outside world, should have known and used a weapon that no other native men in the Americas had ever seen.

It seemed impossible, and yet I asked Haluk if he could make one of the weapons that he had described. And now the crossbow was reality. I could no longer doubt.

A slow smile drew the weathered skin taut over his sharp cheekbones as Haluk watched me struggling with my disbelief. He did not speak but, laying an arrow on the grooved shoulder piece, he drew back the sinew string. On the dark and shadowed river near at hand an Arctic loon dipped and swam quietly. There was a sudden resonant vibration on the still air. Something whispered furtively over the river, and at once the great loon half rose, flashing its wings in dying agony before it floated down the stream, an inert dark patch upon the sullen waters.

Haluk lowered his bow and, placing it beside him, squatted down to light his stained stone pipe. He did not wait for the outburst of my eager questions but, turning to watch the river, he began his tale, a tale called into words across uncounted centuries by the vibrant song of the crossbow:

Ah, Haluk began, but this was a weapon for a man! It was the strength that gave us life for many generations; and it was the tool we laid aside to rot when you white men brought rifles to our land. That was a wrong thing we did, for men should not discard the gifts that make them great.

It came to us in times almost out of memory, but I hold the fragments of that memory, for my fathers and their fathers' fathers were *shamen* and workers of magic, and to such men it is given to know the ancient stories of our race. So I can tell you of the *Inohowik*— the Men of Iron—and I speak not from old tales alone but also from what my own eyes have seen. I am a *shaman* too, and in my trances have had visions of the *Inohowik*, and have even heard their voices. They were mighty beings; more than human, and yet not quite gods, for death felled them with the same evil hand he lays on us. They were pale-skinned and bearded, but their beards were flaming brands as bright as newly hammered copper. Their eyes were blue, but with the depths of lakes in winter when the cold grows so terrible that the frozen waters boom and rumble in their torment. So also were the voices of the *Inohowik*—deep voices that rumbled strangely and spoke no words my people understood.

As for the place from which they came; who knows their lands? We only knew that it lay eastward beyond the salt sea. They traveled over it in boats ten times the length of a *kyak*, and open to the seas and winds. In my visions I have seen those high-prowed ships driven on before the gales by great square sails that carried images of fantastic beasts such as we do not know. I have even seen, and marveled at, the rows of paddles that thrust out from the flanks of those long ships like rib bones thrusting from the skeleton of a gigantic fish.

But in those times, even as now, we lived far inland from the coast and so we did not see the *Inohowik* come out of the eastern mists. We heard nothing of their arrival until a day when the strangers came to us. Midsummer lay over the plains; the lichens were grown brown and the leaves of the dwarf willows were darkening under the hot suns, when that day dawned. By Innuit Ku—the River of Men— there were many tents of my ancestors, and these stretched southward almost to within sight of the forest's edge. They went no farther, for the forests were the homes of the *Itkilit*— the Indians as you call them. Much spilled blood lay between us and those savages, for it was their custom to fall upon our isolated camps and slaughter all within, before they slipped away into the forest's sanctuary where we dared not follow. We hated them and yet the plains were ours by right and so our tents stood only a few hours' journey from the concealing trees.

On the day I tell about, a young boy lay on the hill crest within sight of the forest's edge, for it was his duty to bring us quick warning if the long canoes of the *Itkilit* appeared. This youth was quick of eye and when he saw a moving thing upon the distant river he did not stay to watch but fled toward the camp. He came running over the high plains and his gasping cry brought the alarm to the southernmost camp where a dozen tents stood near the river's shore.

It was hot noon then and the men lay in the dark tents resting; but as the boy's voice came to them they sprang up, seizing their deer spears, and ran out into the blazing light. Women quickly clutched their children and carried them back into the broken hills beyond the river. Even the dogs sensed the sudden wave of fear that filled the place and they too slunk from the camp to vanish among the grey rocks.

But that camp had been chosen with care, and with a plan. A few hundred yards to the south of it the river passed through a narrow gorge, and here the angry current tossed great plumes of spray along the centre channel. Neither canoes nor *kyaks* could pass by unless they hugged the looming cliffs beside the shores, but from the abrupt edges of these cliffs men could look directly down on all who passed below. It was along the gorge that the *Innuit* men gathered to await the arrival of their forest enemies. Beside each man there was a pile of boulders, riven by the frosts and jagged edged. These were the weapons of defense, for in those times my people used only spears for hunting, and had no weapon that could match the long bows and feathered arrows of the Indians.

It was a long tense wait before a dark shape came into view far up the river. But as it hurtled down the current the watching Eskimos stared at it with puzzled eyes, and frightened murmurs rose among them. It was a boat, but such a one as no *Innuit* man had ever seen before; no longer than an Indian canoe, but very broad and heavy, and built of mighty planks.

The men it carried were even stranger than the boat. All save one sat with their backs toward the approaching gorge and they pulled on long paddles set between pins, along the thwarts. They sat in pairs, and there were ten of them, but one more faced them from the stern, standing erect and looking like a god in human form. He wore a shining cap of iron on his head and under it his beard was brilliant as the setting sun at summer's end. Iron sheets upon his breast caught the reflections from the swift waters and sent dazzling shafts of light into the eyes of the watching Eskimos who were now trembling with a great unease, and with a fear that even the *Itkilit* could not have brought into their hearts.

These strangers—towering giants clad in iron—were not *Itkilit*, that was certain. But were they men at all? My ancestors could not tell, and so not a hand was raised against them as the strange craft swept through the gorge, clinging to the shore line where the waters were swift but deep. They were allowed to pass on down the river, to the deep music of their leader's voice that rolled even above the thunder of the rapids.

There was no time for the *Innuit* to gather and to speak of this uncanny sight, for hardly had the strange boat passed when seven long canoes leaped into view above the gorge. There was no doubt who came in them. Half-naked men whose faces were the faces of death knelt in the canoes and drove them over the river with the hungry power of many paddles. But this time it was not *Innuit* blood they sought. It was the blood of the giants who had already passed. The Indian canoes raced down the river in wild pursuit, and such was their frenzy that they forgot about the men who owned that river.

They forgot until the seven war canoes were flying through the gorge, and until the boulders fell upon them. Ah, but that was a sight I would have given much to see; for then there was a slaughter that spelled revenge for many of my people who have died under the long arrows of the *Itkilit* bands. Six of the canoes shattered like leaves under that rain of stone, and those *Itkilit* who survived the rocks were at the mercy of the river's rage. Those who survived its fury and gained the shallows were few indeed, but there were none who reached dry land, for the deer spears met them, and had no mercy.

Red was the river then; but from the stained plumes of spray one canoe emerged unscathed and fled downstream with the frantic agony of those who have escaped a massacre. The surviving Indians were instantly pursued. A dozen *kyaks* were launched behind them, and the pursuers were men filled with the madness of a victory.

It was on that day the Killing Falls received its name. A roaring cataract, it blocked the river a few miles below the gorge, and it was toward the falls that the last Indian canoe was driven as deer are driven by the winter wolves. When the funneling current above the falls was reached the Indians saw death ahead but they were trapped inexorably, for the current had them. The pursuing *kyaks*, lighter than birds, skimmed free of that deadly funnel of roaring water and paused in quiet backwaters near the shore to watch as the canoe poised for an instant on the brink of the falls, then vanished into the white spume below.

My people watched that sight with glowing eyes, but they did not watch alone. The iron-clad strangers, forgotten for the moment by the *Innuit*, had also met the falls but they had been warned in time by the sullen roar of

water, and had made shore. Knowing that the *Itkilit* were close behind, they had hauled out their boat and hidden it, and then had made a circle on a rocky ridge prepared to fight what they believed must be their final battle against the Indians. With incredulous eyes they too had watched the violent destruction of that one last canoe, and they understood that the little men in the slim *kyaks* had done this thing. We had indeed struck the blow in their defense, but the Iron Men could not be sure we would not turn on them as well, for we must have seemed as terrifying to their eyes as they had seemed to ours. But they were brave.

One of them came slowly down the river slope to where the *kyaks* were, and when my people saw the stranger coming they pulled quickly out of the backwaters and hovered on the current in tense expectancy. At other times the *Innuit* would have fled, but having just destroyed ten times their own number of the enemy they were no longer prone to fear. They waited while the red-bearded leader of the strangers came to the water's edge. He stood there, towering twice as high as any one of us, and then he took a short knife from his belt and held it out toward us, handle first.

The legends say it was Kiliktuk who paddled his *kyak* cautiously toward the spot and, reaching out his long double-bladed paddle, touched the handle of the extended knife. The strange giant smiled and laid his knife upon the paddle blade so Kiliktuk could draw it to him without touching shore.

Now you well know the friendliness we feel for strangers who come to us without evil in their hearts; so you will understand how it was that all the *kyaks* came to shore and soon the short fur-clad figures of my forefathers were crowding about the Iron Men, fingering their tools and ornaments and laughing as loudly and as freely as if all memory of the *Itkilit* killing had already vanished. For whether these strangers were men or spirits it was clear that they were not evil, and so we took them home with us as friends.

Far into that night the song-drums sounded and my people sat with the strangers about the fire and feasted on caribou. The strangers ate like men—like hungry men—although they looked like gods. And I think they were more men than gods for they looked upon our women with keen eyes. It was a night of nights for us when the *Inohowik* came into our camps. It was the beginning of our greatness.

As to what happened afterward, the legends speak of many things. They tell of the strength of the strangers and of the tools and weapons they possessed. Fine tools of iron that had never before been seen in the wide plains where the only metal was the rare scraps of copper that we traded from the people in the north.

When the Men of Iron had been at the river camp for a few days they began to ask questions by means of signs and by drawings on the ground. They wished to know if Innuit Ku led to the salt sea. After they had been made to understand that it did not, but led instead only to the far northern ice seas that never thaw, then they became bitterly unhappy for a while. They talked much with one another and at last made it known that they would linger in our camps till winter came. In truth they could do little else for their awkward boat could not ascend the river, even if they had cared to go again into the *Itkilit* lands to retrace their path.

Through the remaining summer months the strangers lived with us and learned to hunt the caribou upon the river crossings. They gradually gave up their own clothing of thick hides and cloth, and wore the soft skin garments that our women made for them. When the snow came they even laid aside their iron caps, for these round hats with their metal horns that made the wearers look like musk ox bulls soon grew too cold to bear.

That was a good time for the *Innuit* of the plains. The *Inohowik* knew many secret things that they shared with us. They could strike fire from iron and rock; they knew the stars and could tell their way by them as easily as we could find our way in daylight. And yet for all their wisdom they were as children in our land. They taught us much, but we in turn taught them the things they had to know—and for the moment it was they who learned the most.

Their leader was a giant even among his own. His name was Koonar and that name still lives, for he was a mighty man above all other men. He could carry whole carcasses of caribou back to the camps after a hunt. His arm, wielding a long iron blade, could split a caribou as easily as we might split a hare. But not all his strength was in his body, for his mind was very quick and in a little while he could understand and speak our tongue. From his lips my people heard a little about the Iron Men in their voyage to our river—though it was very little.

It was told how, when their long ships reached the west shores of the salt sea, some of the *Inohowik* went on up the rivers in small boats, in search of what we do not know. But it is told that they found death. Koonar's small boat went south into unknown lands and traveled many days. Then, as the *Inohowik* slept one night, they were set upon by Indians and many perished. Those who survived turned north again but found their return route barred by Indians. In desperation they journeyed west then north, hoping to swing back eastward to the shores where the long ships waited. That was how it happened that they came to Innuit Ku, and on its headwaters met the *Itkilit* who drove them out into our plains.

Koonar lived in Kiliktuk's tent and also in that tent there was Airut, Kiliktuk's daughter. She was young, with full round cheeks and with the promise of love in her black eyes; and it was the secret hope of Kiliktuk that she would seem fair in the sight of the leader of the strangers. Kiliktuk hoped that Koonar might become his son, so that all the *Inohowik's* strange knowledge, and body's strength, might come to be a part of the inland people. But in those early days Koonar did not look on any woman. He was a leader, and perhaps he knew what women may do to the hearts of those who must lead other men.

Then, on a day when summer was almost at an end, Koonar went alone to the crossing place to hunt caribou. He made a good kill, but as he was returning to the camp with the weight of two whole carcasses upon his shoulders, he slipped and fell among the rocks with such force that one of his thigh bones was shattered. He was carried to Kiliktuk's tent but for a long time even his own men despaired to see him alive. His wound was terrible to see; the broken bones stood out from the torn flesh. He lived only because the girl Airut nursed him with all her skill and patience, and because Kiliktuk, who was a mighty *shaman*, used all his sorcery to heal the wound. So Koonar lived, but he never walked again nor did he recover his great strength, for the injury he suffered ate into his heart and body both. But now the wishes of Kiliktuk bore their fruit. During the long weeks of agony it came about that Koonar gave in to love, and after a time he took Airut to wife. Nor was he alone, for others of his men had taken wives, and the *Innuit* believed that now the strangers would stay forever in my people's camps.

But that was not to be. When the big snows came and when the rivers froze, the *Inohowik* gathered in their leader's igloo and talked for many hours. When all the talk came to an end the strangers made ready to forsake their women and our land. They had made up their minds to strike eastward across the barren plains as soon as dogs could pull the winter sleds. It was said of them, by the angry Eskimos, that evil spirits possessed their hearts and would not let them rest.

The *Innuit* were very bitter when they heard the plans and knew their sisters were to be deserted. It is even possible that blood might have been shed had not Koonar made a peace with the *Innuit* men. Then, as the price of their release, he told the people that he would remain behind and all the gifts of the *Inohowik* would be ours through his great giving. Perhaps he thought his injuries would be a burden to his fellows in their trek across the frozen plains. But I believe it was because the woman Airut, whom he loved, was growing big with child.

In the worst time of winter, when the blizzards ruled, ten of the *Inohowik* left the camp, and left their women, to drive eastward with dog teams in search of the salt sea and their lost ships. They vanished into the lifting snows and were never seen again. Somewhere in the dark depths of winter they met the full fury of our land and perished as we had known they must.

And so the tale of *Inohowik* becomes the story of Koonar, of Airut and of the children that she bore. First was the son Haluk, born in the spring of the year. In the next year there was a daughter born to them whose name is not remembered; and this was Koonar's family. Though he could not leave his sleeping ledge to hunt, and other men had to procure the meat that fed his wife and children, yet Koonar was much loved among my people. He kept his promise and he gave us his great wisdom freely, in all things but one, so that the *Innuit* prospered.

Kiliktuk, who was his father-in-law, was also Koonar's greatest friend, and sometimes they would talk of the things Koonar had known in far-distant lands. Many of the stories Koonar told seemed terrible beyond belief for he sometimes spoke of great battles fought on land and on the sea and with such weapons that men's blood flowed like spring rain.

One day, after such a tale was finished, Kiliktuk asked Koonar to show the *Innuit* how to make weapons such as these, but Koonar refused, saying that he would not give us the means to destroy other men, and then ourselves. In our lands he had found peace after a lifetime spent in battle.

Things were well in the *Innuit* camps until the child Haluk had seen six winters and was looking on his seventh. That year, after the snows had come, Kiliktuk announced that a journey must be made southward to the edge of forests to gather wood for the making of sled runners and other needed things. Before the coming of the *Inohowik* this had always been a dangerous journey and rarely under-

taken, for the forests belong to the *Itkilit*, as the plains belong to us. But because the Indians had suffered so heavily at our hands, the danger was no longer thought to be very great, and on this expedition it was planned to take some women so that good camps might be established for the men who felled the trees.

Now because Koonar could not leave his place to teach Haluk, his son, the ways of men and hunters, Kiliktuk suggested that the boy should be permitted to accompany the timber-gathering party so that he might begin to know the land and the duties of the men who lived in it. Koonar did not oppose this suggestion, though he was ill at ease at the thought of a separation from Haluk, even for a week. He agreed that the boy might go, but he insisted that Airut should also go so that she might see to it that the child came to no great harm.

It is told that they came to the place where the forest meets the plains and here a camp was made. For five days the men went out each morning and, choosing the best trees they could find, felled them and roughed them into timbers. At dark they came wearily back to the travel camp and the women greeted them with hot soup and mounded piles of boiled deer meat. Then, on the sixth day, while the men were far away, a band of *Itkilit* came swiftly out of the shadowed woods and fell upon the camp. Their work was swift and silent. The *Innuit* men knew nothing of it until they returned at evening to find their women and their children dead upon the snows, their bodies torn and mutilated by the fury of the killers.

Kiliktuk and his followers did not pursue the *Itkilit* for they dared not venture inside the forests. They could do nothing but return to the river camp carrying the bodies on their sleds and lamenting so that the sound was heard long before they themselves were seen. It is remembered that when Kiliktuk came into Koonar's igloo he thrust his own knife deep into his arm so that the blood spurted freely as he fell to the floor and wept at Koonar's feet, telling the *Inohowik* that his wife and son were dead.

Then Koonar swore terrible oaths in his own tongue, and so frightful was his rage that the *Innuit* shuddered and were afraid of him.

After a time Koonar's anguish calmed and he called all men before him. He took the antlers of a deer and a piece of fine spruce wood and he set to work to fashion a thing such as no Eskimo had seen before. His task took him many hours but he would not rest nor yet allow the watching men to rest. He knew many failures, but in the end the thing was done. Still without pause even for sleep, he showed the *Innuit* how to make weapons such as the one that he had built from bone and wood, and he ordered each man to make one for himself.

At first the *Innuit* believed that this was only the work of a man crazed by grief, and yet they were so afraid of the deep anger that burned in Koonar's eyes that they obeyed his bidding. When each man owned one of the new weapons, Koonar showed them how to shoot—and then they saw he was not mad. This new weapon was a fearsome thing that could strike down a caribou in full flight at three hundred paces!

For a whole month Koonar ordered every minute of the men's lives. Lying on snow blocks outside the igloo he drove the men to practice shooting until they cried with cold and tiredness—but he would not let them rest. It is not my people's way to give themselves entirely to any task; but Koonar made this a way with them. He drove them, but he also drove himself until his old wound opened and dark blood soaked his deerskin clothes.

The month ended with the coming of the blizzards and the long night that is the heart of winter. Then Kiliktuk, who had become the body's strength for Koonar, chose the ten best marksmen from among the *Innuit* men and ordered them to feed their dogs for a long journey. When this was done, ten teams were hitched to ten great sleds and the chosen men left the camp and headed south along the frozen river. Kiliktuk, who alone of all the *Innuit* understood the work in hand, was in the lead, and on his sled lay Koonar, sick almost to death, and wrapped in heavy furs against the brittle cold.

It is told how these men traveled to the forests and boldly entered them, for Koonar had banished fear out of all hearts. For five days they drove south into the forests, and on the fifth day they came in sight of the smoking tents of a great Indian camp. The few hours of feeble daylight were almost at an end and the *Innuit* would have preferred to draw away and lay in ambush, but Koonar would allow no pause.

Under his orders the ten sleds drove at full speed straight into the heart of the sprawling camp and they were among the tall tents almost before the Indian dogs could howl their hysterical alarm. Now the sleds halted in a tight line and the *Innuit* men leaped off and knelt in the snows with their bows raised, and arrows poised. There was a terrible confusion then, for the *Itkilit* came spilling out of their tents without caution, and many of them did

not even pause to seize their weapons, for they were taken unawares. As they came from the tents they were met by short, unfeathered arrows driven from the taut strings of the *Innuit* bows. The whine and murmur of the arrows could be heard above the wild screams of people and of dogs; and the sodden thud of arrows striking home was like a drum beat under all other sounds. It was a killing beyond all others we have known. More than a hundred died with the crossbow arrows lodged in their lean bodies. There was no mercy for the women and children.

So sudden was that onslaught, and so ruthless the new weapon, that the *Itkilit* did not fight. Hardly an arrow was fired by them. Those Indians who passed their own doors and lived, fled into the darkness carrying with them no more than their frightened lives. And when no living thing remained about the camp, the *Innuit* left their sleds and laid a torch to every tent.

Then Koonar's voice was raised. It boomed into the silence that was now broken only by the whimpering of dogs and crackling flames, and the *Itkilit* who heard it as they fled believed it to be the voice of a devil-spirit and they fled faster still.

"Men of the River!" Koonar cried, "because revenge burned in my heart and blinded me I have given the powers of death into your hands. But hear me now! If you should ever use those powers, unprovoked by direst need, then be sure I will come back from the farthest places of the sky, and my anger shall be more terrible than all the devils of this land!"

Silence returned, and in that silence the sleds were turned into the north again, and they drove on until forests ended and the plains lay stretched in sombre silence under the endless night. They traveled onward until they were almost in sight of the home camps, and then Kiliktuk's sled suddenly turned from the trail. The others would have followed but he waved them on, bidding them carry the news of victory into the camp. And so a single sled turned off and vanished into darkness, and on that sled Koonar was dying.

Late that night a strange tongue of fire was seen on the river to the north. All those who had gathered to sing of the victory stared as a great flame licked upward from the distant ridge by Killing Falls, so that the long roll of snowy hills glowed briefly with the tint of blood. They were still watching in fear and wonderment when a sled came swiftly down the river and drew up in a flurry of fine snow. On it was Kiliktuk and he was alone.

The people deafened him with questions but

there was a look upon his face that silenced them. Neither then nor later did he tell them what had come about. Only to his grandson, the child of Koonar's daughter, did he tell the tale before he died. That child was called Haluk and he was the father of my father's fathers: and through them I too have heard how Kiliktuk drove Koonar up the river to the place where the old boat of the *Inohowik* was cached among the rocks. I have heard how Kiliktuk tenderly placed the dying giant in that boat and, at his orders, laid piles of dwarf willow scrub about him. Then Kiliktuk wept and parted from the stranger who was a son, and more, to him.

Kiliktuk drove away as he was told to do, and when he looked back red flames were lifting above the dark shadows of the boat, against the crimson snow. The boat flamed into ash at last and with it Koonar, the last of the *Inohowik*, vanished from our lands.

Koonar was gone, and yet the wishes of Kiliktuk had come true for Koonar gave us the greatest gift we ever had—this crossbow that was our strength for more generations than my hands can count. We used it as Koonar had said we must, and so we prospered until we were as many as flies over this land that now knows only half a score of men. And Koonar's blood stayed with us too, for it has happened that each generation has seen a child who bears that blood and who must take the name Haluk.

Now I, Haluk, am the last of these, for I am not quite as others of my people are. There is a difference in my spirit, for I have visions that are beyond reality, and in them I have seen and known the men who were the *Inohowik* and I have understood they were my fathers too.

And so it ends. You are the first outside my race to hear the tale, and I have told you because very soon there will be no more *Innuit* ears to hear. I too will go, and soon. And yet I have one all-devouring wish that I would realize before death comes for me.

I wish that I might journey to the salt seas where I have never been, and I wish that I might look out into the east where the long ships drift with their great sails catching the setting sun, as I have dreamed of them. And I would have it that this ancient body might be laid upon the deck of a long ship, that it might be carried eastward, ever eastward through the mists; to vanish, as did Koonar, in flames.

# THOMAS   B.   COSTAIN

# The Great Intendant

Today Jean Talon would be called a civil servant. In his own time he might have been called Canada's first big businessman. For Talon, unlike the other figures who bulk heroically in the early years of our country, was not a soldier, a missionary or an explorer. He did none of the spectacular things which remain on the pages of history while services of much greater importance are dismissed with a paragraph. He was, instead, an administrator, a man of far vision who realized that the mere act of sending settlers out to New France would not bring growth and prosperity to the colony.

It was Talon's great contribution that he saw the need of making the colony a small replica of the mother country, a place where employment could be found and opportunities for small businesses. There had to be prosperous little shops and small but busy factories and inns where the food was good. Talon provided the colony with what it had always lacked, a solid background of sound money and honest barter, where a man and his wife could strive together for a secure future.

The need for these things had become urgent almost overnight. In 1664, Louis XIV's chief adviser in France, the able Colbert, had inaugurated a new policy by creating a Company of the West which was to have control of all French dominions beyond the seas—New France, West Africa, South America or the parts of it which Spain had not pre-empted, Cayenne, the Antilles.

Colbert was filled with visions of a huge trade empire such as the world had never seen before. It became necessary almost at once, however, to adjust the vision as far as New France was concerned. The new company showed immediate signs of operating in the old ways which had been so disastrous. The directors wanted to collect all the revenue and forget the obligations. A compromise was soon made so far as Canada was concerned: the company would pay the cost of administration, with no control over the conduct of the main officers, and find reimbursement out of taxes levied on beaver skins, *le droit du quart*, and on moose skins, *le droit du dixième*.

The sums expended each year in the direction and control of the colony amounted to something just under 50,000 livres. To carry the cost of his Grand Plan for New France the King had created what was called an Extraordinary Fund, the inroads on which were to prove quite as extraordinary as the fund itself. In the year 1665 alone the sum of 358,000 livres had been expended. This, of course, had been the year of greatest effort, which had seen the arrival of the Carignan regiment and of a thousand other people. This would never have to be repeated (or so it was hoped), but the carrying out of the royal designs would continue to cost the ambitious monarch staggering sums year after year.

An operation of this scale demanded careful supervision at both ends of the horn of plenty. No longer could the control of the colony be left to the proud and generally futile aristocrats who had been serving as governors, nor to zealous churchmen whose concern was the saving of souls. France now had in Colbert a remarkable administrator. New France must have the same; and so the post of Intendant was created. The first man selected for the office was one Sieur Robert, about whom nothing much is known save that for some reason he never assumed the duties of his office. Colbert looked about him for a replacement and he recognized in the brilliant controller of Hainault a kindred spirit. He dismissed all other possibilities from his mind; Talon, obviously, was the man.

Jean Talon was born at Châlons-sur-Marne about the year 1625 and as a young man secured employment in the commissariat of the French Army. His ability was so remarkable that he soared rapidly in the service and soon became chief commissary under the great Turenne. In less than a year he was made controller of the province of Hainault, a post of major importance.

His looks, if he can be judged by the one portrait which is granted authenticity, belied his character. He is shown as a stocky man, with a full and rather round face peering out with amiability from the background of an elaborately curled wig, a hook nose, lips which curled up at the corners with a promise of joviality (which on occasions proved highly misleading), a pleasant enough eye under an arched brow. There was more than a hint of the dandy in him. He might have been a minor aristocrat, the owner of a small estate in the provinces, an opulent attorney. There was nothing of the ruffler about him; he wore a sword, of course, but it did not clank against his plump calves as though conscious of pride and privilege.

Talon was a fair imitation of the resourceful Colbert—cool, able, hard-working and blessed with that greatest of gifts which is known as sound judgment. He was absolutely honest and fearless and he had a sense of the future which the soldier governors of New France had lacked. His coming was to prove the turning of an important leaf in the history of New France.

Talon's first activities were in connection with the need for a steady increase in the population. He was full of schemes, some of of them as bold as anything which had ever entered the soaring brain of Richelieu. He conceived a plan to have the holdings of the Dutch, which had been taken over by the British, transferred to France instead. It was a decidedly Machiavellian idea, which he outlined in letters to Colbert. When the time came for the three nations to make permanent peace settlements France should insist on the return of the New Netherlands colonies to Holland. In the meantime a secret understanding would be reached with the Dutch government by which the colonies would then be ceded to France. Once this had been accomplished, the Intendant pointed out in his communications with Colbert on the subject, the English would be hopelessly hemmed in and France would have a stranglehold on the Atlantic seaboard. As a corollary of this devious plan, he suggested that five hundred settlers be sent out each year without fail, an addition which would soon assure Canada of a thriving population.

Colbert reached the conclusion that this appointee of his was going a little too fast. He cautioned the new Intendant not to expect too much, to be content with less ambitious strides. Sending out five hundred settlers a year would in time "unpeople France." Colbert, it may be taken for granted, was too shrewd to believe anything as untenable as this. Obviously he was using the argument as a means of meeting the importunings of the overbrisk Talon.

Failure in this direction did not quench the enthusiasm of the Intendant. He began to work out plans himself, the most ambitious being the establishment of new settlements around Quebec, selecting the neighborhood of Charlesbourg for the purpose. Forty houses were erected in three separate communities called Bourg-Royal, Bourg-la-Reine and Bourg-Talon. With Quebec still hopelessly crowded, there was an immediate demand for all of the houses. To show his faith in the plan, Talon bought a tract of the land himself. He had it cleared and erected thereon a large house, a barn and other farm structures.

A shrewd plan had suggested itself to Talon to make these new villages easy of defense. The tracts of land for individual use were cut in triangular shape like wedges of cheese. The houses were built at the narrow angle where the tips of all the tracts came together, which provided a solid core of settlement at the centre with the shares of land widening as they progressed outward. Security was what prospective settlers demanded first of all, and so this unique idea took hold at once. This was putting in concrete form a plan which was being tried out elsewhere; and it established a pattern which persists to the present day, the very long and thin type of farm, with the farmhouse itself in close proximity to neighbors.

The settlers who swarmed to the Charlesbourg developments, to borrow a modern term, were given a supply of food to keep them going while clearing the stipulated two acres of land. They were paid something for their time as well, and the necessary tools were supplied to them. In other words, a man could start with nothing save the will to make himself a landholder. The money to pay for all this came out of the King's Extraordinary Fund. One obligation was assumed by the new settlers: each must clear two acres of land on other tracts, to ease the strain on those who came later. On these terms the Talon villages began to fill up rapidly.

The King viewed these steps with paternal approval. As Colbert phrased it in one of his letters, "The King regards his Canadian subjects, from the highest to the lowest, as his own children." He wanted them to enjoy "the mildness and happiness of his reign." The Intendant was directed, in order to make sure that this beneficent design was being observed, to visit the people in all parts of the colony, "to perform the duties of a good head of the family" and so put the people in the way of "making some profit." It was a generous thought and the young monarch was to be commended for his intentions. Carried to an extreme later, however, the paternalistic design was to prove the basis of a cramping and irksome tyranny.

The resourceful Talon proceeded then to attack a problem created by the increase in population. An industrial background was needed to supply some of the necessities of life and at the same time to provide employment. He started the farmers growing hemp and then created demands for the crop. This was done by an arbitrary method which, fortunately for all concerned, worked out very well. The hemp seed was distributed to landholders on the understanding that they must plant it at once and replace the seed next year from their own crops. In the meantime Talon went to all the shops and seized the supplies of thread. It was given out that thread could be secured only in exchange for hemp. As the mothers of growing families had to make clothes for their children, they either saw to it that their husbands raised hemp or went into the market and bought it. This highhanded procedure was maintained for a brief period only, as it resulted in starting a steady crop of hemp and provided the demand for it at the same time.

It was very clear in the practical mind of the Intendant that the colony should reap some of the profits that fishermen from European ports were still sharing every season. Codfishing stations were established along the lower St. Lawrence and the "take" was good from the very beginning. Settlers were encouraged to go out to the sea where the seal and the white porpoise could be caught. The oil extracted was a valuable commodity and could be sold readily on home markets, thus creating a balance for the purchase of needed goods in France.

One of his most ambitious moves was the creation of a shipbuilding plant at Quebec.

New France, he contended, must no longer be entirely dependent for supplies on the ships which plied to and from French ports. The men of the colony must be in a position to venture out under their own sails and to establish trading connections with the French colonies in the West Indies. The first ship completed was at Talon's own expense. The cost of the second, a much more ambitious attempt, was borne by the King. The venture had provided the colony with an excellent vessel and had at the same time given employment to 350 men. It is recorded that in 1667 six vessels of various sizes and kinds were finished and put into use.

Having thus provided the colony with a thriving industry, the creative mind of the Intendant turned in another direction. The brandy trade was still a bitter bone of contention in the colony. There seemed no way of preventing independent traders from using it as their main item of barter, and the colonists themselves liked it almost as well as the Indians. Talon conceived the idea that there would be less demand for brandy if fresh beer were available. He decided to build a brewery and, having every confidence that the plan would prove profitable, supplied the funds from his own purse. The idea found instant favor. In commenting on it, a correspondent in the Jesuit *Relations* spoke of the beer as "this other drink which is very wholesome and not injurious." The brewery had been erected in the St. Charles section of the town. This was in 1668, and three years later the Intendant reported the plant capable of producing 4,000 hogsheads of beer annually, although there is no indication this high level had been reached.

In many of his letters to Colbert the Intendant stressed the need of livestock as a means of putting agriculture on a broader base. His demands fell on attentive ears. Increasing supplies of cattle, sheep and hogs were sent out. A few horses were supplied also. This led to the establishment of tanneries. To make use of the wool the housewives were given looms, and this was the beginning of the carpet weaving which has been a characteristic activity in Quebec ever since. Potash was extracted from wood ash. Tar from the trees was collected and sent to France for sale.

The world still watched enviously as Spain grew ever richer on the easy gold of Mexico and Peru. North America had beaver skins and an abundance of sea fish but there was no easy profit in either field; hard work and not luck was the key to financial returns there. The hope was never abandoned in France that ultimately Canada would provide natural re-sources from which wealth would flow eastward. This had always been behind the formation of the commercial companies to whom colonization had been entrusted.

Knowing this, Talon was always alert to any rumors of the discovery of mines. When it was reported that lead had been found on the Gaspé peninsula, he had investigations made at once. The search proved unsuccessful. It was found that iron ore existed at Baie St. Paul which was sufficiently high grade to be profitable, and immediate steps were taken to begin mining operations.

A thrill of excitement ran through the colony when it was rumored that coal had been found—and, of all places, in the Rock itself! The first trace of it had been stumbled on in the cellar of a house in Lower Town. Talon was swept along by the enthusiasm which had gripped the place and wrote to Colbert: "The coal is good enough for the forge. If the test is satisfactory, I shall see to it that our vessels take out loads of it." He was seeing rosy visions: the colony well supplied with coal for the heating of homes, the shipbuilding industry receiving impetus on being freed of the necessity of buying coal from England. There was one drawback: if the shafts were carried into the heart of the Rock, the security of Upper Town would be imperiled. Talon began to experiment with the possibility that the shafts could be extended in other directions. His last letters to France indicated that he was convinced the grade of coal being found burned well enough to be used, at any rate, for industrial purposes.

If there actually was coal in the Rock, it is still there. After the initial excitement subsided Talon wrote no more reports, favorable or otherwise. Any attempts at mining were abandoned. Even the location of the cellar where the initial discovery had been made was forgotten. It can be taken for granted that later tests had not been as encouraging as the first. It is even possible that the whole thing was a hoax.

Jesuit priests returned from the missionary fields with persistent stories of great copper mines and sometimes they brought specimens of the metal with them. These stories tantalized the Intendant with dreams of great wealth to please the King as well as the merchants of France who had never yet given wholehearted support to the colony.

The most exciting reports came from the islands formed by channels between Lake Huron and Lake Superior. Father Claude Dablon, who had been assigned to the Upper Algonquin missions, wrote a letter for the

*Relations* which created an immense amount of excitement. Copper was to be found in great quantity, in particular on the Island of Michipicoten. This fabulous isle had one drawback: it was a floating hill of ore and shallow vegetation, never to be found in the same location because it shifted its position with the winds. The Indians seldom went there because they regarded it as the home of evil spirits. On one occasion some hardy natives ventured to pay it a visit and came back with large pieces of reddish metal which was found most useful in cooking food. The squaws would heat it to a ruddy glow and then throw it into the kettles where it would set the water to boiling. But they never went back for more. As they paddled away from the shore on their one visit, they heard a wrathful voice as loud as a thunderclap speak to them from the sky. "Who," demanded this dread voice, "are these robbers carrying off from me my children's cradles and playthings?" They knew it was the voice of Missibizi, the evil god of the north winds, who thus complained that they were removing the slabs of bright metal which children liked to collect and which were sometimes used as the base of cradles. The natives were careful not to arouse the wrath of the god again.

More reliable reports about the abundance of copper began to come back as the missionaries pushed on farther west. They found an island which did not shift with the winds and which Missibizi did not haunt but which had enormous stores of the metal. It was called Minong (later named Ile Royale by the French) and the engineers who inspected it on Talon's orders found that its clay hills had large deposits of copper. Father Dablon reported the existence there of a copper rock which he had seen with his own eyes and which weighed seven or eight hundred pounds.

In the spare little office he used (there was not yet in Quebec enough space to go around) Talon kept specimens of the copper on his plain oak desk, using them as paperweights for the piles of letters and documents, with official seals dangling from them, which always lay in front of him. They were both a challenge to him and a puzzle. Here was the wealth which had so long been sought. But how could it be mined and smelted and brought from these far-distant islands? Talon had plenty of plans for solving the difficulties. He saw visions, no doubt, of the copper islands so black with the smoke from smelters that even the wrathful eye of Missibizi would not be able to see what was going on. He pictured fleets of

flat-bottomed barges being towed all the way to Quebec through the Great Lakes. He saw mills in the colony where the muzzles of great cannon would be cast for King Louis to use in his European wars.

If this resourceful man had lived a hundred years later he would have been able to solve the difficulties and to turn his dreams into actualities. He might have converted French Canada into a busy industrial country. As it was, he made the colony a going concern and created a background of prosperity and content. But New France, still no more than a precarious toe hold on the edge of a continent, was not ready for a Talon.

What was Governor Courcelle doing while this energetic man of business turned the colony upside down and gathered the control of things into his own hands? Courcelle grew more antagonistic all the time and more ready to display his disgruntlement. He sat in the citadel behind the handsome rosewood desk which had been brought out from France, unhappily aware that it was more likely to have on its polished surface a set of chess men or a *trictrac* board than communications from France. The candles burning in the crystal chandelier above his head reflected the marks of chagrin which had become habitual on his features. Sometimes he lashed out furiously at the Intendant when they met to discuss business and often he allowed his resentment to show in his letters to France.

The reason for Talon's increase in official stature and the shrinkage in Courcelle's was easy to understand. The governor never lived down the failure of his invasion of the Mohawk country and the heavy losses which had resulted from his rashness. It soon became apparent to Colbert also that when he referred matters to Talon they were attended to promptly and satisfactorily while in Courcelle's hands they dragged along interminably. The notes which the King scribbled on the margins of the reports from New France (the busy monarch read them all carefully) and the decisions which were arrived at in the morning meetings of the royal council were referred, therefore, to the Intendant and not to the governor.

Talon always knew what was going on in France and the latest ideas which had sprouted in the mind of the monarch. Courcelle was frequently in the dark. The governor often went to Talon for information, even for instructions. It was inevitable that Courcelle would complain to Colbert of the way he was being pushed aside. Talon found it necessary at times to complain also of the jealousy of the governor and to the obstructive attitude he was adopting.

It must seem that the progress recorded in Talon's period of administration was the work of many years. In point of fact he was in Canada for two terms, each of no more than three years. It is no exaggeration to say that he had accomplished more in these brief years than all the officials, glittering with jeweled orders and resplendent with lace and velvet, who had preceded him; with one exception, of course —Champlain.

It was partly due to his frequent disagreements with Courcelle that Talon asked in 1668 to be recalled, partly also to ill-health and the need to attend to personal affairs in France. Reluctantly the King agreed, and in November of that year Talon sailed for home.

A new Intendant sat after that in the small office with the plain furniture which had been made for Talon but, in actuality, the reins were never out of Talon's hands. The King and Colbert saw to that. Instead of engaging himself immediately in the straightening out of his properties in France or in bolstering his health in the balmy airs of the south (he had always disliked cold weather), Talon was kept in constant attendance on his royal master. The King's interest in Canada had been growing all the time and now he had available the one man who understood the problems of the colony intimately and could give advice out of this practical knowledge. Day after day, week after week, the conferences went on among the trio, the aggressive and lordly King, his ubiquitous minister and the ex-official who was supposed to be recuperating.

During these protracted talks Talon succeeded in committing the King to a remarkable program. In the first place Canada was removed from the control of the Company of the West. Colbert may have jibed at this, having been responsible for the company in the first place, but Talon fought the issue vigorously, making it clear that the moneygrubbing merchants who composed the company had no concern for the welfare or the future of the colony.

It was decided to reinforce the remnants of the Carignan regiment, who remained under arms in New France, with six companies of fifty men each and thirty officers, all of whom were expected to settle down in the country after their terms of enlistment were over.

In addition, the King agreed to send two hundred more settlers and a great list of supplies. A steady program was laid out for the sending of "King's Girls" to provide the un-married men of the colony with wives, an initial shipment of 150 being arranged.

One outcome of these extended deliberations was inevitable. Talon had been a bare three months at home when he was reappointed to the post of Intendant. He accepted the responsibility for the second time without any outward show of reluctance. On July 15, with his new commission signed, his brief instructions in his pocket, he set sail from La Rochelle.

But he did not reach Canada that year. The ship was buffeted about by a succession of heavy storms and finally had to put back to the port of Lisbon to be refitted and revictualed. Starting out again, they were wrecked in shoal water no more than three leagues out from port and those on board were rescued with great difficulty. It was not until August 18 of the following year, 1670, that the Intendant arrived at Quebec for the second time.

His mind was filled with plans of magnificent proportions, for he was confident now that he would have the backing of the King in anything he undertook. Above everything else he wanted to stimulate exploration. His immediate task was to see that the steps already discussed with the King and duly ratified were properly carried out. The work involved was heavy and seemingly never-ending. The health of the Intendant was not good, and it was clear from the start that the burden of so much detail weighed heavily upon him.

It is easy to picture him at this important stage of work: seated at his desk, his luxuriant and heavy wig removed and his hands clutching at times of stress at his lank and not too abundant hair, his face grey and showing a multitude of lines. He felt it wise to look after everything himself, leaving practically nothing to the initiative, or lack of it, of his subordinates. The division of the land was to be attended to as well as the wholesale bestowal of seigneurial rights which Talon took upon himself in the last few months of his second term. There was, finally, the matter of creating a proper system of education.

For three years Jean Talon worked incessantly to accomplish all the things which had been discussed and agreed upon during the many conferences with the King. By the fall of 1672 he had done as much as was humanly possible; and again he sought his recall. He was rewarded on his return to France with the title of Comte d'Orsainville and given an easy post as captain of Mariemont Castle. He died twenty-two years later, on March 24, 1694.

# FRANKLIN RUSSELL

# The Secret Life of a Pond

To most people a pond is merely a mosquito-ridden patch of stagnant water that smells of rotting weeds, can't be used for swimming or drinking, and gets in the way of road builders and real-estate developers. But to a naturalist it is a battleground for a host of weird creatures: the scene of a silent, relentless, invisible struggle for life by billions of fighting organisms.

In every type of pond—in swampy forest pools, in western sloughs and potholes, in farm ponds created with bulldozers, even in puddles —the struggle goes on endlessly. Perhaps nowhere in Canada has this everlasting aquatic fight for survival been studied by scientists as closely as in an oversized pond two miles from the downtown section of Hamilton, Ontario. Although this pond is crossed by a bridge that carries a heavy stream of traffic it has no name, few visitors and fewer admirers.

Behind its serene and disregarded beauty lies a gripping story of birth and death, of the hunter and the hunted, of charm and horror, that is typical of ponds everywhere in the world. It is almost a lake, its elongated shallow basin covering about six acres. It is surrounded by steep slopes covered with trees and is flanked by a rock garden maintained by the Royal Botanical Gardens of Hamilton. The gardens maintain the Dundas Marsh (also called Cootes Paradise) south of the pond.

The location of the pond close to Dundas Marsh's six hundred acres of aquatic plants, insects, fishes and wild fowl is important. The area is one of Canada's largest field laboratories for scientists. It is particularly convenient for scientists at McMaster University, and the dramas of life in marsh and pond are exhaustively chronicled in their notebooks. But the pond remains mysterious. All its secrets aren't known. It may contain the answer to how life began on earth.

While we are still only at the surface of the deep mystery of life in the pond, we do know that at the beginning of any year there are billions of ruthless enemies in the pond lying asleep side by side waiting for their chance to stalk, chase, ambush and kill one another. We know that this one pond's inhabitants outnumber the earth's human beings many billions of times.

We know as the motorists slither and skid on the bridge in midwinter January, the creatures of the pond below are sinking toward their lowest ebb of life. Beneath the thick ice there is a repelling silence of seeming death. The ice above looks like an imperfectly translucent roof. The winter sun comes through in a pale and sickly glow. The wreckage of last summer's water plants straggles down from the clutch of the ice. The only signs of underwater life are some slow-moving sunfish, carp, pike, bass, perch, suckers, and perhaps some oversize goldfish which have been washed into the pond from the nearby rock garden. An occasional muskrat swims underwater toward its ice-bound home in the shallows, and there are vague, mysterious flickerings of life in the shadow-filled recesses in the basin of the pond.

In the clear, cold water plains and hills and valleys can be seen on the pond bed. The piles of a long disused canal jut from the bottom, relics of the days when the pond was a river draining the Dundas Marsh before it was sealed off by two railroad embankments. Above, heavy snow blankets the ice and the gloom of the pond grows. The oxygen is diminishing fast and the lives of many creatures depend on an early thaw. Some of the fish begin to die of starvation and suffocation.

It is only when the equinoxial gales begin to blow in March, melting the snow and sending warmer water tumbling beneath the ice into the pond, that the organisms there begin to feel the first stimulus of spring. Tiny primitive plants wake and reproduce. These are the algae and they are the pond's food. They are among the smallest organisms in the world, each one a single tiny cell of living matter. Forty million of them would fill one cubic inch. Individually they are insignificant. Collectively, they are one of the most important organisms of the pond and of the world.

The algae stock rivers, lakes, oceans, in countless billions. Though plants, many of them can swim, lashing the water with tiny hairy propellers. They color lake waters green and, in some instances, blue. They make the Red Sea red. They are the green slime on stones, the soft green clouds in still water. They can reproduce at fantastic speed and at short notice and are eaten by many animals and plants.

The increase of the algae as the water warms seems to be a catalyst to other forms of microscopic life. The peculiar rhizopods, which include amoebae and are the lowest animals on the scale of life, protrude long threadlike arms from their protoplasmic bodies to seize passing algae in millions. The arms swiftly withdraw and the algae disappear into the jelly mass where they are visible as they are being digested.

As the days lengthen through spring an underwater observer with microscopic eyes would see life begin to teem. The single-celled animals—called the protozoans—are dividing and redividing constantly. The algae grow children within their bodies, then burst to release them. If protozoans and algae were left unchecked all over the world for one year, they would grow to a mass as large as the earth itself.

The observer's eyes would be caught by a profusion of rich color spreading in every quarter of the pond. There would be greens, crimsons, indigo blues, purples, oranges and glistening silver filaments branching through the water. In one species of tiny animal or plant there might be a dozen different colors in a hundred different physical forms. These brilliant underwater colors, this swarming of life, are invisible to an observer on the shore. But each spring John Lamoureux, the gardens' conservationist, notices the surface of the pond slowly turning red at this time of the year. The sluggish carp, roused from their winter sloth, are busy at a silty inflow to the pond at the western end, digging for food, fanning the silt so that it rises in fine red clouds and spreads throughout the pond.

The shapes of the microscopic animals would be astounding to Lamoureux's eyes if he could see them as they spread through the reddening water. Some would look like ducks floating on a lake, some like a rising atomic cloud, some like the barrel of a gun exploding; others would look like miniature whales, like harps, like bears, like swans with long graceful necks. Some would look like sea serpents, others like design work on an Indian rug. Just as surprisingly the animals and plants, visible and invisible, would have legs, wings, arms, paddles, oars, wheels, snorkel tubes and even jet propulsion.

There would be strange sounds echoing through the water world. The underwater observer might be surprised to hear the sound of propellers approaching. He would see a tiny transparent animal, called a rotifer, bearing down on him with two small rapidly rotating wheels mounted along the front border of its body. Situated between the wheels would be a primitive mouth scooping in algae and other single-celled organisms. The "wheels" are actually two discs bearing marginal wreaths of tiny hairs which vibrate so rapidly that they look as though they are revolving.

The rotifer passes on but in a second is seized and eaten by what seems in comparison to be a gigantic ten-legged flea. While one hundred times the size of the rotifer, this creature is one of the smallest visible to the naked eye. It's one of the crustacean family and is a fully developed cousin of the lobster although it's less than one twelfth of an inch long. Its simple coiled gut is visible and its heart, a very thin transparent disc near the stomach, pumps discernibly at one hundred and fifty beats a minute. Even the blood cells are visible as they course round the body.

As early summer blooms the water is warm and the life in it is increasing a million times a day, or a minute, or even a second, for all the scientists know. Lamoureux, making a casual inspection tour, notices the water becoming darker with masses of newly created creatures—insects, animals, plants. A thousand frogs have crawled from their winter hiding places under logs, under mats of leaves, from under the slime and mud at the bottom of the pond. The brightly colored salamanders —lizard-like amphibians—have slid out of their hibernating holes under logs among the trees and have gone down to the pond to breed. The water beetle larvae have pupated into winged creatures, dug themselves out of shallow winter cells in the earth and, paradoxically, have gone flying down into the pond to lead a life that will be spent largely underwater.

Even the plants have become part of the desperate fight for life which is now beginning. They fight for oxygen, sunlight and breathing space. All through the shallows of the pond countless plants are jostling and struggling to reach the surface. Under the bridge the water lilies spread their broad flat leaves as widely as possible; if they shade a competing plant they will kill it. The duckweeds come hastening after them and surround the lily pads in a thick scummy mass and smother competing seedlings. Bulrushes are springing up around the pond. Sago pondweeds and smartweeds float on or under the surface; the whorled leaves of coontail crowd together underwater. The carnivorous bladderworts, branching out underwater, extend tiny hinged traps which, on one plant, may catch half a million tiny animals an hour.

For the scientists this is a fascinating time. Dr. Norman W. Radforth, McMaster's professor of biology and one of the world's great authorities on muskeg, studies in the marsh the ecology of water plants—how billions of tiny plants can eventually fill in a pond. John Lamoureux checks the new species of plants he has established in the marsh as part of a project financed by the Toronto Anglers' and Hunters' Association to find the best conditions to attract waterfowl. McMaster students use the marsh and the pond to win master's degrees and Ph.D.'s by studying the complicated biology of the plants, animals and insects there.

As the vegetation spreads like some wild green fire across the surface, the reddish water itself is being tinged green with the growth of billions of algae. But they aren't the most numerous organisms. In every drop of the warming water of the pond there are several million bacteria, ever present and all-powerful, so tiny that powerful microscopes can barely reveal the details of their bodies. As we watch, some of them are attacking the proteins in the water and are producing ammonia. Others are attacking the ammonia—which feeds plants—and are changing it to simpler compounds like nitrites. Others are transforming these nitrites into nitrates—which feed the algae. The pond's store of nitrogen, normally locked up in the living bodies of plants and animals, is thus released for further use.

One science student, E. A. Botan, earned his Ph.D. in the marsh with years of study of how bacteria decompose nitrogenous organic matter. When, in 1957, five hundred fish were found dead in the pond after the thaw, he theorized that the decomposing bodies of billions of algae had exhausted the oxygen and had actually suffocated the fish. A mortally injured robin, shot by a youngster's air rifle, splashes into the water and drowns. In their efforts to eat the dead bird the bacteria begin its putrefaction, a process which maintains the undiminished growth of life in the pond and in the world.

Now it is midsummer. The pond life, as well as fighting desperately for survival, is reaching its breeding peak. The frogs and salamanders are laying strings of gelatinous eggs in the shallows. Dragonflies bomb the surface with eggs. Midges settle on the water in millions and let clusters of eggs into the water attached to floating rafts. A black wasp, using a homemade tow-rope, buzzes over the pond dragging a paralysed spider which will be a meal for her young. Young birds fall from their nests overhanging the water and are eaten by pike and bass. The creatures of the pond are laying eggs, giving birth to live young, pupating into adults, dividing their cells, eating one another with a fantastic urgency which foreshadows the approach of fall even though summer is still at its highest peak.

In the swarming surface waters the hideous hydra, a creature straight from science fiction, is breeding by an unearthly process of budding. Its body is a narrow quarter-inch-long cylindrical bag with tentacles and stingers at one end; its other end is fastened to the surface skin of the water or to a plant. The young hydras are growing like the buds of a plant on their parents' bodies and they will fight their parents for food, even though they do not yet have stomachs of their own and depend on their parents to do their digesting for them. Two hundred years ago a Dutch scientist, Trembley, wrote with some surprise, "If one of them [the hydra] be cut in two, the fore part which contains the head, mouth and arms, lengthens itself, creeps, and eats on the same day."

Frequently a hydra scores a near miss in its clutch for passing worms or larvae. Its prey slips through its tentacles but its body is riven by the deadly stings. Slowly the shaft-impaled body falls to the bottom. It has fallen from one way of life—the swarming life of the July-warmed suface—to another way of life which is quite different. Near the body is a bear. It stands stiffly erect and its short legs have sharp claws at the ends. It is a water bear, a rare microscopic animal, and it will soon be dead.

THE PROVINCES OF CANADA


THE INTERPRETATIVE EYE
OF THE CAMERA
LOOKS AT THE NATION


BRITISH COLUMBIA

DAMP MOMENT ON VANCOUVER'S HASTINGS STREET

A WHINING SAW BUCKS IN BRITISH COLUMBIA'S WOODS

A FOOTHILLS CATTLE RANCH QUIETLY AWAITS THE SPRING

**ALBERTA**

CALGARY STENOGRAPHERS CATCH A TAN IN THEIR LUNCH HOUR

AN OLD BUGGY TELLS A SIMPLE STORY OF AN ERA PAST

## SASKATCHEWAN

A SCHOOLHOUSE BRINGS LIFE TO THE PRAIRIE VASTNESS

A COMPLEXITY OF SIGNS ON WINNIPEG'S MAIN STREET

**MANITOBA**

FORTUNE FLUTTERS ON THE FLOOR OF THE GRAIN EXCHANGE

A FARMHOUSE SNUGGLES CLOSE TO THE LONG-SETTLED LAND

# ONTARIO

NEW BLOOD, NEW FACES, NEW PROBLEMS TYPIFY TORONTO

BEYOND FRONTENAC'S SPIRES LIE THE PLAINS OF ABRAHAM

QUEBEC

MONTREAL'S SHERBROOKE STREET IN A GENTLE SUMMER MOOD

## PRINCE EDWARD ISLAND

THE LOYALISTS PLANTED THIS "GARDEN OF THE GULF"

## NEW BRUNSWICK

THE CHURCH, THE STORE—HUB OF AN ACADIAN VILLAGE

### NOVA SCOTIA
SAILORS WERE WALKING THE STREETS
OF HALIFAX TWO HUNDRED YEARS AGO

### NEW BRUNSWICK
SAINT JOHN'S KING STREET DIPS
DOWN TO MEET FUNDY'S BIG TIDE

### NEWFOUNDLAND
OLDEST COLONY, NEWEST PROVINCE,
GROWS A PROUD AND STURDY PEOPLE

A turbellarian worm—one twentieth of an inch of ferocity—glides into view and gulps down the water bear in a puff of mud dust.

Nearby, a microscopic worm—*Aeolosona*—is snuffling like a raccoon along the bottom, grazing on decaying fragments of plants and fine debris which have fallen from the surface. It moves among a small group of tubes which look like chimneys. From these sprout the waving, questing bodies of tubifex worms which duck into the chimneys when danger threatens. Nearby, a mayfly nymph is thrusting its bladelike forefeet into a patch of sand, scooping out a shallow hole into which it digs two large tusks and rapidly disappears from view. A foot away, a horsefly larva collects blood at the rear of its spindle-shaped body, then drives one pointed end into the mud. It pumps the blood forward, enlarging the hole. It drives down again, repeats the process and disappears from view. Just above the disturbance it has made in the mud a great diving beetle, nearly two inches long, is swooping down on a dragonfly nymph which has incautiously ducked up from its sandy hiding place. The beetle grabs the nymph with two large hollow mandibles. A tiny pump in the beetle's body sucks the carcass dry. The beetle returns to the surface to pick up another supply of air under its wing covers.

The dragonfly nymphs, some of them nearly two inches long, dull colored, slow and clumsy in their movements, are easily overlooked by their prey. One of the nymphs makes its home among the duckweed meadows in the shallows where tadpoles and other creatures are plentiful. A young fat-bodied tadpole, about three inches long, comes angling down from the surface, moving steadily closer to the motionless nymph. Suddenly the nymph pumps a jet of water from its rear end and, as it shoots unexpectedly forward, rapidly ejects a hooked apparatus from under its chin. This reaches even farther forward and seizes the wriggling tadpole. The tadpole is too big for the nymph to handle comfortably and both creatures tumble among the weeds, flailing and lashing. Clouds of disturbed mud rise from the scene of battle. In the extremity of their concentration both creatures have ignored the fundamental rules of pond safety—caution, stealth and cunning. The fight ends abruptly when a bulky body shoots into the mud cloud and emerges clutching both creatures in its enormous mouth. It is an eight-inch-long bullfrog.

It is a law of the pond, and of all nature, that every creature has an enemy. Later in the summer the bullfrog dies, caught by a young-ster with a net, watched by a gardener working in the rock garden. Its legs may end up on a restaurant table in Toronto.

By following the trapped bullfrog to the surface it is surprising to look again at the pond above the water. The motorists are still grinding back and forth across the bridge in a pattern of life that changes little. But the pond has changed radically. The overhanging trees have the full rich look of late summer. The weeds have half-covered the surface of the water. The rose-pink flowers of marsh smartweed have wilted into seed heads. Submerged plants are gently casting their seeds on the bottom. A thousand young spiders, airborne on threads of silk, fall to their deaths in the water. The placid surface is continually broken by strange ripplings and splashings. Insects dart and weave across the water.

As the lazy summer days pass easily, the great exodus from the pond gets under way. The same creatures that shrugged off the sleepiness of hibernation and plunged down to the water now must leave their summer home. A dragonfly nymph crawls laboriously up the stem of a bulrush. It bursts from its larval case, reveals a shrunken body with stubby wings. It gulps air, pumps blood into its wing stubs and then flashes away across the pond and disappears.

A great diving beetle humps out of the water onto a tiny beach and begins hollowing a small cell in the damp earth. It will either quickly pupate and a fledged beetle will fly back to the pond, or it will winter in its cell. Millions of mayflies which hung under their egg rafts are bursting from the water, their massed nuptial dances a feast for birds, dragonflies and fishes. A hundred types of fly are creeping, crawling, swimming and jumping from their larval existences in the water to their brief airborne lives. The leopard frogs are ranging far through the trees in search of food. The tree frogs are singing in the elms.

For nighthawks, flycatchers, swallows, chickadees, titmice, warblers, sparrows, raccoons, skunks and snakes, the pond during the summer is such an overflowing storehouse of food that they are attracted and held in its vicinity. They, in their turn, play their part in keeping the pond's population under control.

As larvae emerge from the water they face sudden death. The skunks dig up the pupating grubs and the raccoons scoop up molluscs and snails in the shallows. The birds help in this balancing process by eating scores of millions of beetles, larvae, pupae, worms, slugs, snails and flies.

41

Meanwhile as summer wanes, a brief but fantastic upsurge of life begins under the water again. The microscopic creatures—rhizopods, crustaceans, algae—must build up their numbers to ensure some chance of survival through the bitter winter. They must do this against the combined efforts of the larger creatures to eat them. The urge of life in the pond is to gain strength for the winter, to hunt fattening protein food, to acquire as much resistance as possible to the oncoming crises of cold, lack of oxygen and starvation.

Then suddenly the proliferation of life in the pond wanes. The summer is dying too and the water is slowly clearing, losing its rich reddish-green color as the life in it disappears and the silt settles. The exodus from the pond slows, the mists of early summer mornings are replaced by the threatening chill of fall and the trees frame the pond with a border of changing color. This is the sad time. The gay dragonflies go, leaving their empty larval husks studding the wilting water plants. Insect and beetle transform to semidormant grubs, waiting patiently under the water or earth for

spring. The algae are dying in billions, literally blanketing the bed of the pond with their invisible bodies.

Through the fall, to the accompaniment of impatient honks morning and night from the bridge, the browning vegetation dies, rots, retreats from the water. The creatures, large and small, decrease their metabolism and their appetites so there may be enough food to last the winter. The birds stream overhead for the warmth of the south and the leaves rain down on the passive water.

Toward the end of the year, with the curtain of life nearly drawn, the raccoon and skunks are sleeping soundly in the surrounding woods. The muskrats have built their submerged homes of stalks and leaves and will spend the winter eating them. The frogs are buried in the mud, hidden under logs with the salamanders, sleeping among the leaves.

The ice forms slowly and the familiar silence of seeming death begins again. The long winter months stretch ahead to the pulsing touch of spring and the miracle of the pond.

## W. O. MITCHELL

# The Golden Jubilee Citizen

One thing I noticed: it's after the ice has gone out of the curling rink and before they can get on the land for spring drilling—that's when folks seem to stir up stuff they let lie all summer and fall. Holgar Petersen remembers the fight he had with Pete Snelgrove over that hay deal back in Nineteen Fourteen. Repeat Godfrey gets sore all over again the way Chez Sadie's put in that barber chair instead of just giving women permanents the way they're supposed to do. Jake starts licking old wounds too.

Jake's our hired man, helps Ma and me

farm our farm down Gover'ment Road from Crocus. Some of the wounds give Jake the worst twinges are the ones he got off of Miss Henchbaw that teaches us kids out at Rabbit Hill. She is a stickler for the truth; like Jake says, she stickles worse than anybody in Crocus. When she isn't stickling she is running Crocus. She doesn't run Jake.

Miss Henchbaw is the one organized the Crocus Preservation of Historical Shrines and Historical Landmarks Society—her and Repeat Godfrey. That put her in the saddle you might say, so when we run up against Saskatchewan's Jubilee Year, she's all set to run that too.

Take the day last fall when Jake and me were in Repeat's barber shop. I already had my hair cut and Jake was laying back in the chair while Repeat's razor went snickering up and down his strop. "She didn't invent the Golden Jubilee, Repeat." It came out sort of muffled the way the towel was wrapped all around Jake's face except for the tip of his nose.

"No one says she did—didn't say she did." Repeat left off stropping and took Jake's nose between his thumb and finger with the little one up like women do with their teacup. "But without Miss Henchbaw—without her—there'd be no Golden Jubilee Committee." Repeat wiped his razor on the square paper on Jake's wishbone. "To her and her alone goes the credit—most the credit—for the program to mark our province's fiftieth birthday."

Jake grunted. He can get a lot into a grunt.

"That woman," Repeat was saying to Jake, "that woman has a great sense of history. Great sense."

"No sense."

"How's that, Jake?"

"Nothin'!"

Repeat plugged in the clippers. "Most the reading I do is historical reading. You might say I revel in history." Repeat bent his knees the way he does, lowered his head, started his first swath through Jake's hair. "Fabulous new best seller set in the time of Louis Quinzy." He lowered his voice to a whisper. " 'In Felice Gagnon's lovely body flowed warm Basque blood—spiced with a fiery Castile strain—she charmed the crowned heads of Europe—held kingdoms in her graceful hands . . .' "

"That's nice. Take some off the top, Repeat."

" '. . . but her spirit was completely pagan.' " Repeat turned off the clippers—picked up his comb and scissors. "Learn quite a lesson from history. As the history is bent so the nation groweth."

"Uh-huh," Jake said.

"Crocus and Saskatchewan has—have had—a colorful past. Colorful."

"Thunderin' hooves the mighty fur traders—like of that." Jake said.

"Wild elements—bred in the blood and bone of Crocus citizenry. Blood and bone."

"Don't forget the top, Repeat." Jake squinted up to him. "Most the folks I know—early days—hail from Ontario. They come out for free land or a chance to start out a general store from scratch. They just got Ontario in

their blood an' bone. Kind of thin on the wild elements you was . . ."

"Can't take it too literally, Jake," Repeat said. "We all got Ontario in our blood. Isn't much can be done about that."

"No," Jake said. "I guess not." He looked kind of thoughtful.

"Let us not underestimate Miss Henchbaw. Her part—major part in the coming Golden Jubilee Celebrations. Sheer stroke of sheer genius—Crocus Golden Jubilee Citizen. Thanks, Jake."

I knew all about that. Repeat meant the essay contest where you had to tell who you thought was Crocus District's Golden Jubilee Citizen, the one person Crocus couldn't done without during the last fifty years. That was what I was working on.

It didn't go so good; I noticed it's not so easy to get your words to pull together in the harness the way you want them to. Besides—it isn't so easy to figure out a thing like that. First off I thought of Old Daddy Johnston that's a hundred and seven. Jake said:

"Not Daddy, Kid. Daddy's already famous in a way. Way I see it—when they tell you to pick your Golden Jubilee Citizen, I figger they mean somebody a person wouldn't think of offhand. Somebody that's bin goin' along, doin' his job so you—well—sort of like you was holdin' up a lantern an' there he is—Crocus Golden Jubilee Citizen. Bin there all the time—till your lantern shone on him an' showed what he was really like."

"Mmmmmh."

"Now—I like Wing. Sanitary Café. All the folks thinkin' of Merton Abercrombie, bank manager—MacTaggart, mayor Crocus. Me—I like Wing in the Sanitary Café."

"How come, Jake?"

"Well—all durin' them dirty Thirties when he fed the bindle stiffs an' the stew bums—the scen'ry hogs an' the gay cats an' the lump bums that swung down off of the freights behind Hig Wheeler's Lumber Yards. Wing never let one of 'em go away hungry. You take the hockey outfits—Peewees, Juniors, Intermediates—ain't a year Wing didn't put up the money for their uniforms. Then all them baskets of fruit he sends to anybody sick in the hospital. Go a long ways, Kid—before you find a better Golden Jubilee Citizen than Wing."

You never catch Jake following other folks' tracks very far. If you tried a hundred years you would have an aitch of a time to replace Jake. It was Jake taught me to hold a twenty-two and touch off a gopher. He's made me all kinds of things, because he's kind to kids. I never known him to thin a kid's hide once. When I was very young he used to hide the Easter eggs in the straw-stack for me. You take in the olden days:

"I never picked my friends outa race ner politics ner religion," Jake says. "I was fussy about Wilf—Sir Wilf—an' I drunk Catawba wine with Sir John A. After we settled a little misunderstandin' me an' Looie got along well too."

All kinds of fellows got into the history books, but Jake didn't. You don't find about him rassling Louis Riel on the banks Cutknife Crick, but he did, whatever Miss Henchbaw says. She doesn't believe he knew Sir Wilfrid Laurier and Sir John A. Macdonald personally either.

But I know this about Jake. He's honest and he's straight through. He has worked hard all his life and like he says: "Every day my life I twanged the bedsprings at sundown an' kicked the dew off of the stubble with the rooster. I never had a holiday long as I can remember. Who the hell ever heard of a hired man takin' a holiday!"

Jake could have been a politician. Like he told me once: "I could of bin in the Senate—walked in velvet up to the fetlocks—smoked House of Senate cigars an' spit into gold goboons like the rest of 'em down there. I ain't. I'm a hired man. Except for a couple times in the year when she gets piled to the barn windows—it's cleaner."

I guess it was along about March this spring, after I been chewing away at that essay, it suddenly dawned on me who ought to be Crocus Golden Jubilee Citizen. Like Jake said, it was like I held up a lantern and there he was in the circle yellow light: the man that made Looie Riel say uncle three times—once in English, once in Cree and the third time in French; the man that invented hay wire; far as I was concerned the man the country couldn't have got along without. Jake Trumper —the Golden Jubilee Citizen and our hired man.

That essay just rolled along like tumbleweed. I put down all about how Jake can tell the weather and witch water wells. I told how he could call mallards and geese, moose, deer and pigs. I wrote how he could play the mandolin and sing My Wild Rose of the Prairies so you had a lump in your throat—how he was the fastest runner in the whole Northwest in his stocking feet.

It took five pages to tell the way he saved Chief Weasel-tail and his whole band South Blackfoots from starving to death. I had her

crackling and the pages scorching with the awful prairie fire of Nineteen Ten when he lost his horse, Buttermilk. I filled a whole scribbler with Jake.

It took three arithmetic periods and two nights to copy her all out in another scribbler. I turned the first one in to Miss Henchbaw. I wrapped up the other one and mailed her to Mr. Lambert that's editor of the *Crocus Breeze*.

One thing about Miss Henchbaw—she rips right through your stuff when you hand it in to her. She said she wanted to see me for a minute after the bell. My scribbler about Jake being Crocus Golden Jubilee Citizen lay on her desk next to the saucer of crocuses.

"I've read this." Her mouth got thinner. "You've done a commendable amount of work on it." She shifted Trails through the Garden of Numbers a little to the south. "It's too bad your subject matter couldn't have been a little more worthy of your effort." I waited for her whilst she took a piece of green chalk in her fingers and kind of fiddled with it. "Truth," she said and her face was red all the way to her hair she piled up like one of those round loaves of bread.

"Truth," she said again, "is like a pure spring welling from the ground. It must not be adulterated or contaminated. Its sparkling clarity can be so easily dulled and muddied."

I was wondering when she was going to get to my essay.

"We must strive after truth in word and deed." She picked up my scribbler with one hand whilst the other sort of tapped the green chalk on her desk top.

"This is not truth!" The chalk snapped like an old chicken bone. I watched the pieces roll off the desk and onto the floor.

When I looked up, her eyes were enough to give a gopher the heartburn. "I thought—I think it is," I said. "Jake . . ."

"Louis Riel . . ." she was shaking her head, determined ". . . did not have dangling from his vest chain a rabbit's foot watch fob!"

"When Jake rassled him on Cut Knife . . ."

"Nor did General Middleton wear a bobcat fur vest throughout his Eighteen Eighty-five campaign."

"Jake saw it!"

"I doubt it very much."

I stared at her and she stared at me and I guess you could call it a tie. She cleared her throat sort of exasperated.

"This year—especially this year—our anniversary year, we cannot stand for impertinence with our province's history. I certainly can't agree with your selection for the greatest Golden Jubilee honor our district has to bestow."

I can't ever remember when I talked back to my Ma or a grownup in my life let alone Miss Henchbaw. Same time I can't remember getting mad as quick as I did then—sick mad! "I figure he's a good . . ."

"I don't."

"Jake he built the country—he . . ."

"By my calculations your nomination for Crocus Golden Jubilee Citizen—had been barely born by the time Louis Riel was hanged. He could hardly be a dignified symbol for our fifty years of history! He could hardly . . ."

That was when it happened—just like that green chalk snapping in her fingers. "He sure as aitch could! Maybe he doesn't smoke House of Senate cigars an' eat Winnipeg Goldeye three times a day an'—an' spit into gold goboons an' wipe his mush with a silk napkin —but he is the greatest livin' human bein' I ever knew in my whole life!" I guess I even pounded on her desk because I was staring at my fist and it was all stuck up with a wad of yellow plasterseen.

When she spoke it was real gentle. "Then your choice is as valid as mine would be." Her mouth wasn't thin any more; her eyes were funny like something hurt her—not a lot— some. "But I can't turn this in for possible publication to Mr. Lambert in the *Crocus Breeze*. You will have full credit for your English assignment." She brushed some of the green chalk crumbs off the desk top. "There are other crystal springs," she said. "That's all," she said. "You can go," she said.

Jake had already milked Noreen and Mary and Naomi and moved on to Ruth when I told him. "She just said my Golden Jubilee Citizen wasn't any good, Jake."

"Did she?" The milk went on saying some-fun— some-fun into the pail.

"Nobody can be right but her," I said.

"Uh-huh." Jake turned his head up at me. "Who'd you pick?"

"Well—I—right now—I didn't intend to let this person know I picked him."

"Oh." The milk quit some-fun—some-fun and started saying fun-fun-fun as Jake stripped Ruth. "I guess it won't make much difference if you tell me." He got up to move the pail and stool down to Eglantine. "I won't breathe a word."

"You," I said.

"Huh!"

"I filled a whole scribbler all about Chief Weasel-tail and his South Blackfoots and Sir Wilfrid Laurier and Sir John A. I really . . ."

"No!" Jake straightened up so quick he knocked the milk pail flying. "Kid! You didn't."

"Sure. Her saying all about being impertinent with our history!"

"Not alla that—that . . ." Jake looked like his teeth were hurting him. "Stuff!" He swallowed and he sort of leaned back against Eglantine. Then his face brightened up. He let his breath all go out of him. "But she said she was damned if she was gonna send it in to Chet at the *Crocus Breeze*!"

"Yeah," I said, "I didn't tell her."

"Tell her what?"

"What I did."

"What did you do?"

"Made another scribbler full word for word and sent it into Mr. Lambert myself. I wasn't taking any chances."

Jake was leaning up against Eglantine again. He looked like he needed to. He kind of brushed at his face with his hand like he had spider web tickling across his forehead. "Now," he said, "that's nice, ain't it!" I've seen Jake look that way before: time our fifty-bushel crop got hailed one hundred per cent.

The *Crocus Breeze* eight-page Golden Jubilee Edition came out May 24, because the town council figured that was the day to announce Crocus' Golden Jubilee Citizen. My essay wasn't in it.

Mr. Lambert had his own essay. It took the whole front page. He called it: HOLD YOUR LANTERN HIGH. This is what it said:

"We are an agricultural province celebrating our Golden Jubilee Year. Our fortunes have been tied to the land and to the grain that land grows for us. Today we wish to salute the man who for fifty years has been a living symbol of our grain-growing province. We wish to hold a lantern high and reveal that man in its golden light."

I had about lifting the lantern in my essay.

"Let us salute today the man who has seeded other peoples' grain when the summer fallow steamed under the spring sun, who has driven other men's teams when the meadow larks sang from the fence post. He has run other men's threshing machines and other men's binders. He has stooked other men's bundles when the strawstacks smoked against the far horizon. He has milked other men's cows, stretched other men's fences, done other men's chores."

I had in about chores and harvest.

"His fortunes have been tied to the land as surely as those of his employer, and to the vagaries, cruelties and generosities of prairie nature. This man suffered during the blue snow of Nineteen Six and Seven; he thirsted and went without during the dry Thirties. Hail hurt him as did grasshoppers and cut-worm and sawfly and low wheat prices. If he has walked through a field last fall, his overall pants turned blood red with rust.

"We venture to say that the bulk of our farm owners and operators today started out at some time in the past fifty years as hired men. If not as hired men then as boys who looked to the status of hired man as one of dignity, a place in farm life to be attained, a time to be reached when they could measure themselves against the worth of a grown hired man, a time when they could stook just as many stooks in a day as the hired man—a time when they could match him bundle for bundle when the threshing machine exhaled its slant plume of chaff and straw.

"This man eats at the same table as his employer and his employer's family, enjoying a social equality unknown in other parts of the world and in some other parts of our own country. He is a hay-wire mechanic, veterinarian, stock man, who answers to the name of hardtail, sod-buster, stubble-jumper, hoozier, or john.

"His genesis roves the world. He comes from Ontario, Galicia, Poland, Bohemia, Ukraine; he comes from south of the border, from Ireland, Wales, Scotland, Denmark, Norway, Sweden, Holland, Belgium. He wears flat-soled boots, has chores in his blood, straw in his overall bib and binder twine in his heart.

"He is in the pool of our lantern light now. You know him. Crocus' Golden Jubilee Citizen, without whom there could have been no fifty years of history, no Province of Saskatchewan:

"His name is Jake Trumper."

On Wednesdays the *Crocus Breeze* building sort of shimmies between Barney's Vulcanizing and Chez Sadie's: that's because Mr. Lambert is printing his paper for Thursday.

It wasn't shimmying the twenty-fourth of May, when Jake and me walked in; there wasn't a soul on Main Street, them all being out at the fair grounds for the harness races and the Golden Jubilee Celebrations.

Mr. Lambert was all alone at the back by that machine that flips the round plate up and back and over again while he shoves sheets underneath and they print: NO SHOOTING or NO TRESPASSING or JUST MARRIED. He didn't hear Jake and me come up, but he turned when Jake tapped him on the shoulder with the rolled-up Golden Jubilee Issue of the *Crocus Breeze*.

"Well, Chet," Jake said.

"Jake, Kid."

"I just come to tell you, you got the wrong man in your lantern light, Chet."

Mr. Lambert squeezed out a black snake of ink onto the roller. "I don't think so."

"Me either," I said.

"Anyways," Jake said, "I figgered it was polite to come in an' tell you—uh—thanks."

"Don't thank me, Jake." He looked across the machine at me. He smiled a little. "Him."

"Partly," Jake said, "you polished her up."

"No, I didn't," Mr. Lambert laid a new sheet down careful and reached up his hand. "I had enough to do with the special issue as it was. *Crocus Breeze* had a guest editor for the Golden Jubilee Issue."

"He wrote it up then," Jake said. "I'd like to . . ."

"*She* wrote it," Mr. Lambert said, "with certain discreet deletions and additions to the original piece." He looked over at me again.

Jake looked startled. "She?"

"Miss Henchbaw."

Jake swallowed.

I swallowed.

Once before I saw Jake looking that way. It was the time he knocked down nine grey Canada honkers in Tinchers' smooth-on barley field and Axel Petersen walked in on him.

That was two years ago, the fall Jake had forgot to get his license. Axel Petersen is game warden for Greater Crocus District.

PHYLLIS LEE PETERSON

# My Old McGill

To the casual sightseer from bus or horse-drawn calèche, Canada's most famous university is an impressive but incongruous jumble of buldings sprawled around the green horseshoe of its campus in the heart of Montreal. To those who know and love it well as past students—and I am one of them—it is more, much more. It is the humanity of Osler, the laughter of Leacock, the genius of Penfield. It is the past and the present—the relics of the Nor'West fur traders housed a stone's throw from the only cyclotron in Canada. It is a research station in the Barbados, a lonely outpost in the lonelier north, the Montreal Neurological Institute—hospital, school and world centre of study on the human brain. It is the flaming backdrop of Mount Royal in autumn, the founder's grave under a snow-wreathed ginkgo tree, fluorescent lights shining through the soft spring dusk from Edwardian mansions on adjoining streets. (McGill, like Topsy, just grew.) From here and its affiliated college, Macdonald, twenty miles away, have come the thousands of scientists, doctors, lawyers, teachers, agronomists, engineers, whose degrees rank high anywhere. Here, in a city predominantly French-speaking, Scot, English, American have blended to produce something truly international yet typically Canadian. McGill was a wonderfully exciting place when I went there twenty-five years ago. It is a wonderfully exciting place today.

The excitement is, of course, subdued. If one may make the special and necessary exceptions of fraternity rushes and the student cheering section at the football games, nothing at McGill is ever blatant. McGill still asserts its position as one of the world's greatest and most useful universities in its own way—cool, cautious and conservative. "Proceed, produce, and don't publish," advised a research head of the past. McGill still employs no public-relations counsel. It shuns publicity, as it did when an unknown New Zealander named Ernest Rutherford occupied its Macdonald chair of physics. Here, in a series of brilliant experiments from 1898 to 1907, Rutherford carried on from Roentgen, Becquerel and the Curies to explore uranium radiation and advance the transformation theory of radioactivity which paved the way for tomorrow's atomic world. When this information leaked out, a high-placed McGill official shuddered. "For God's sake, tell him to stop making wild statements to the Press. He's bringing discredit on the University."

Without fuss or fanfare McGill conducted the radar research that resulted in the McGill Fence, forerunner of the Distant Early Warning line. It operates an international weather station at Knob Lake on the Labrador border, the only one of its kind run by a university for the safety of aviation. It has fathered such diverse offspring as the Canadian Officers Training Corps, the University of British Columbia, and football as played on this continent today. And in its dusty archives the name of its first bachelor of arts is also that of Manitoba's first chief justice, then the lieutenant-governor—Alexander Morris—who helped found another university there.

McGill reserves one-third of its medical school for Americans, a tradition strongly entrenched since 1852 when a youth named Thomas Blake hitchhiked north by stagecoach and boat from Cohoes, N.Y., and said he wanted to be a doctor. (In return, Americans have contributed generously to the support of a university depending on private endowment for its existence and receiving less than 10 per cent of its income from any government source.)

Today McGill's internationalism is not confined to the United States. Strolling across its campus recently I caught the gleam of a sari, the scarlet spot of a fez, the white twist of a turban.

I had walked this greensward off Sherbrooke Street, listened to the American voices on the marble steps of the Medical Building, gone tea dancing with a boy from Nebraska. When I did, twenty-five years ago, I was the complete cosmopolite. Now, peering wide-eyed through bifocals at Greek, Bulgarian, Hindu, I knew how small my world had been. McGill's enrollment now numbers men and women from every province of the dominion, every state in the union, every country in the British Commonwealth, and forty-nine others as well. Why? What brings them here?

The answer lies not in statistics. This is not Canada's largest university, nor is it the oldest. King's College in Halifax was founded in 1789. It is not the wealthiest; its whole history has been a financial struggle for life. It is certainly not the most beautiful, with buildings erected as they were needed and ranging from Greek through Gothic to split-level modern. But there is something about it—what? Atmosphere, tradition, achievement? The more practical considerations of low fees in a private university? Small classes, a high standard of teaching, the close relation between student and staff? All these—and something more. The indefinable spirit that *is* McGill.

If that spirit could assume shape it would, I think, be a benevolent elderly gentleman, a trifle eccentric, a little crotchety at times, but with a heart as wide as the world for youth. He would be a bachelor—or if married, negligibly so—and would pour his frustrated fatherhood on every student who came his way. He would carry a turnip watch that never kept time and would wear clothes as though he'd forgotten to button them. He would teach Shakespeare so you saw him, and the Punic Wars so you took sides. He would smell of tobacco and chemicals, with a possible downwind of good whisky. This portrait, I hasten to add, bears no resemblance to anyone living or dead. Yet, in a way, it is a composite of all the McGill professors I ever knew.

I remember other things too: yellow slickers and coonskin coats, Stutz roadsters and the annual Meds Ball where the anatomical exhibits were no more pickled than certain embryo doctors. Coffee at Murray's with the first cup costing a nickel and the rest on the house. The Red and White Revue at His Majesty's Theatre, the hard slugging in the Redpath Library until 2 a.m. with spring exams lower-

ing. The hangover of Scottish Calvinism that made coeds wear flapping black gowns over gym tunics and forget what a geisha could do with a kimono. The inexorable process of weeding out and the abrupt departure of "Christmas graduates." The aftermath of the Depression, and the kindness of the dean when I told him I had to leave—like thousands of others.

Just what middle-aged impulse made me turn through the Roddick gates recently I'll never quite know. It may have been yearning for the past. It may have been the future and two sons rapidly approaching college age. Being English-speaking Montrealers, they will never consider going anywhere else. What, I wondered, would they find of my Old McGill?

My children will discover few landmarks I knew. The founder still sleeps in the green triangle outside the Arts Building. The original Union still stands on Sherbrooke Street, smelling of old sneakers and providing space in its depths for the production of the oldest college daily in the Commonwealth. They will also find the same gentle kindness, the same dour emphasis on hard work, and less intellectual spoon-feeding than they ever had in their lives. Apart from that, everything I remember has gone with the cold wind of progress. Nothing stands still in this world, least of all McGill.

The pessimism of the Thirties is gone, the apathy, the self-searching and soul-probing for Why Are We Here, What Is It All For. McGill, like Canada, is moving in a straight line toward the future, pioneering new frontiers, developing new industries, contributing her full share to East and West. It has opened new graduate schools in education, social work, fine arts, to name a few; new institutes in Arctic research, pulp and paper, Islamic studies. It has imported the first faculty member of the Azhar in Cairo, centre of orthodox Islamic learning, ever to teach in a Western university. And if a lawyer wants to become an expert on aviation he will come to the Institute of International Air Law, the only one on this continent.

In spite of all these departures, there is something as English as tea and crumpets about McGill. Fraternities have flourished for almost half a century but were frowned on as un-Oxonian until they lately received official recognition. In this McGill maintained the English attitude of not seeing anything it didn't want to. When fond alumni refer to Old McGill, they are not using the term in a sense of antiquity but rather with that shattering of British reserve which calls you "Old Thing" or "Old Bean," the ultimate in comradely affection.

Montreal is sentimental about McGill. Town and gown are bound by its graduates—doctors, lawyers, teachers, dentists, ministers and top-flight executives. ("Why go away to university when we've got it all here?") The sentiment is not confined to English-speaking citizens. In a community where French outnumber others three to one, the Gallic spirit glows with pride, and honors heaped on McGill are so many pats on the civic shoulder. Even the cops are kind. If a student gets into trouble, he is usually brought quietly home. If the trouble is bad, a red-faced gendarme holds a whispered conference with campus authorities. The only arrest rumored in my time was that of an elderly professor discovered near the gates in the small hours of a wintry morning, well fortified with whisky and down on his hands and knees in the snow. To the policeman who asked what he was doing, he courteously explained he was looking for goldfish. He was too. He'd brought three of his hostess's ailing pets home in a wet handkerchief from a dinner party and forgot them when he took out the handkerchief to wipe his spectacles. He was booked as a suspicious character and bailed out by the dean—or so the story goes.

Exiled Scots are a breed rational about everything except Scotland, and they laid a heavy hand on McGill. The founder was a partner in the North-West Company. Having made his pile in furs from the uncharted north, James McGill retired to Burnside, his country estate outside Montreal's walls, where he tended his meadows, planted orchards and "this day cut a dozen melons & all of them good." After he died in 1813, McGill left forty-six acres and £10,000 sterling for the formation of a university. But he set a ten-year limit on the gift. The will was bitterly contested by his French-Canadian stepsons and precious years slipped by. Four Montreal doctors from Edinburgh came to the rescue in 1829 by affiliating their medical institute with the nonexistent college, thus establishing McGill and the faculty that gave it glory. By 1871 the university had stumbled through vicissitude, acquired a formidable student body and erected an Arts Building where classes were also held in science.

Now the spirit of McGill began to emerge in its donors, its buildings, its staff. William Dawson, its principal, taught geology, envisioned a great hub of Canadian learning, and was not above climbing three flights of boardinghouse stairs in his seventies to assure a sick student he'd pass. Well-heeled Montrealers like the Molsons (beer) and Redpaths (sugar) sent their sons and were generous. In 1871 two students, engaged in one of the endless financial campaigns, bearded the shy eccentric little bachelor who headed the Macdonald tobacco empire. To their surprise, Sir William Christopher Macdonald responded with a handsome contribution and found an interest for life.

Born of Highland stock in Prince Edward Island, this unusual benefactor laid the foundation of a fortune in plug tobacco during the American Civil War. He went on to millions, closeted in a dingy office on Notre Dame Street and conducting his business strictly for cash. The tight fist opened for McGill and, once opened, never closed. It poured out $15,000,000; buildings mushroomed under golden rain. Believing firmly that a nation's strength came from its farms, its homes and its schools, Sir William established the daughter college that bears his name at Ste. Anne de Bellevue, twenty miles from Montreal, and founded separate faculties for agriculture, household science and teaching. To McGill he gave land, the Students' Union, and an entire east block for chemistry, mining and physics. He endowed chairs, established scholarships and ran like a startled fawn when anyone tried to thank him. And as the years closed in on this tobacco king who never smoked, he was wont to wander the campus by night, reflecting perhaps—like Mr. Chips—on the thousands of sons a childless old man could leave behind.

McGill was on its way. In 1872 a slim dark-eyed son of an Ontario manse graduated in medicine to become "The Baby Professor." His students adored him, as did all who ever knew him. William Osler had a gift for life, a joy he wore like a shining cloak through toil and grief and the years. The stories about him are legends at McGill. How he gave his only overcoat to a seedy beggar and two weeks later received it back with a hob-nailed liver bequeathed to "my good friend William Osler." How he comforted a patient in the wards with "You poor Scotch body, thole it a bit now. Thole it," and saw her smile through her tears. ("Oh sir, I hanna heerd sic talk since I parted frae Edinboro', bless ye.") How he could never resist a child. How he came from death, whistling "that I may not weep." William Osler, who went on to Johns Hopkins, Baltimore, and Oxford, and became the Beloved Physician.

In 1896 the school board in Vancouver applied for affiliation with McGill under the Public Schools Act of British Columbia. Mc-

Gill granted the affiliation as it had already done for three Quebec colleges, Morrin, Stanstead Wesleyan and St. Francis. A few years later the affiliation was extended beyond matriculation to first and second year arts. By 1908 the McGill College of Vancouver was firmly established with ninety pupils, a staff of eight and McGill supplying financial footing. From these humble beginnings sprang the separate and distinct U.B.C., which now rivals McGill in size.

By 1910 the mother of colleges had set her own build-as-you-need style of architecture and planted a forest of Greek temples, Gothic cathedrals and Victorian fortresses north of Montreal's Sherbrooke Street. Its peculiar providence continued to smile with the combination that has never failed it—a faculty with enthusiasm plus public-spirited citizens with money. Walter Stewart (Macdonald Tobacco) and J. W. McConnell (Montreal *Star*) carry on the princely tradition.

McGill's principals, too, were a varied lot and the job seemed prescribed ambassadorial training: Sir Auckland Geddes left in 1920 to represent Britain in Washington; Lewis W. Douglas left in 1940 and was later ambassador to Britain. Diplomacy suffered a setback in my time; the principal, Sir Arthur Currie, who led the Canadian forces during World War I, had no way with words but brimstone. When a distinguished scholar replied in eloquent Latin to his memorized speech for the honorary degree, Currie won the skirmish with "*Pax vobiscum!*" Old Guts and Gaiters, he was called in a scurrilous poem circulated through the Faculty Club. It took a good soldier to march the University through the Depression.

Revisiting the campus of one's youth can be a saddening experience, a disillusionment. For me it was neither, but rather the rediscovery of certain small quiet voices I first heard here. The Arts Building, my particular bailiwick commanding the main avenue, has not changed much in twenty-five years—or a century. A melee of students surges out to the steps as the clock strikes the hour. In the milling hall a notice board proclaims an evening of Polish song, a program of sixteenth-century music. Someone has lost his rubbers. The Players' Club is doing *Hedda Gabler* and a more arty group tackles Musset's *Marianne*. A solemn-faced freshette is selling the *Fig Leaf*, which she assures me is "a new magazine dedicated to humor." (How do they get that way at eighteen?) The hubbub fades, the flame-shaped torches blur in their sconces, and I can almost see Stephen Leacock through murky brown shadows.

Leacock. My old gentleman in the flesh, who taught economics and political science but rarely mentioned either. Canada's greatest humorist and a character out of his books. As with Osler, there are a thousand stories about him. How he would allow only an honor student to hold his dreadful dog outside the building when Bill Gentleman, custodian, refused it admittance. How he involved the whole mathematics department in an abstruse problem until they discovered it related the cubic space of his cellar to beer. How he talked to us about everything under the sun, revealing the glittering facets of a mind that never forgot anything it read, opening up vista after vista of enchantment while one thing led to another. How he clung to a strict policy of *laissez-faire* and, when the dean informed him the entire graduate class had failed because 60—not 40— was the pass mark, replied with a brief note, "After careful revision, I have discovered all these gentlemen obtained 60, not 40!"

Are there still humanists at McGill? I think so, but outlined in fluorescent light instead of a yellow shaft through a dusty window, wearing correct dark suits instead of the shapeless tweeds I remember. In this free air the belief that the world exists for man and not man for the world cannot help but flourish.

I found the credo everywhere. In Dr. Cyril James, its principal, who stresses the McGill aim toward the well-rounded individual. I found the belief in student zip, in research enthusiasm, in minds marching ahead, with hope, with faith and good cheer. I found it in Dr. Penfield's statement when he flew to Moscow for lectures before the Soviet Academy. "In the field of the brain there can be no narrow interests or prejudice. Any discovery must benefit all mankind."

Whether Rutherford's discoveries fifty years ago fall in this class remains to be seen. Certainly they are not forgotten in the Physics Building which, like all Macdonald's gifts, was built of the best, in this case, copper. Copper nails, copper sheathing—and "dead Ernest" (later the Rt. Hon. Lord Rutherford, Cavendish Professor at Cambridge) experimenting with alpha radiation on equipment he improvised for three hundred dollars. Today a modest plaque outside the building records his achievement. Inside, a Geiger counter still registers activity—which has faded to one-fifth what it was in 1904—and certain experiments must be done elsewhere.

Science has sprawled out from its original block like a giant amoeba ingesting everything north to the mountain. The Donner Building for Medical Research, the Eaton Electronics Laboratory, the Radiation Laboratory and Cyclotron, the Physical Sciences Centre—all are new since my day. In them I found the same sparkling optimism (which did not prevent my being discreetly screened), the same warm feeling for McGill.

I walked through the glory of fall, thinking over all I'd seen. The kids themselves, fresh-faced, roaring around with youth busting out all over, yet with a purpose that scared me. The dearth of rich men's sons—oh, there are still scions of wealthy families, the snazzy sports cars in the parking lots, but no one pays much attention. The playboy I knew with his own rented house, his own staff including a valet, wouldn't cut as big a swath now as the University Scholar with a consistent 80 per cent. The razzle-dazzle seems to have faded from the fraternities.

I had tea in the bowels of the Redpath Museum while the Indian relics, ethnological collections and Palaeozoic fossils—all beautifully displayed—drew crowds upstairs. The staff discussed murals and cycloramic lighting for the new North-West Company exhibit, and I kept on remembering the showpiece of my time. A four-foot eel that disappeared from its murky tank in the main hall until a University Street landlady required emergency treatment for shock after finding it in her bath.

The Redpath Library has been extended and streamlined to house a million and a quarter volumes, including Sir E. K. Chambers' Shakespeare collection, Canada's finest William Blake library, and the largest gathering of Lincolniana outside the United States. Smocked attendants scurry at your behest; 650 students can read in a variety of rooms, with chairs kind to their backs and light that considers their eyes. (My generation didn't have backs or eyes. We just had faces.) With deep inarticulate sentiment, McGill has installed a special room for my old gentleman. Leacock has never really left the campus but I think he approves the paneling from his own library, his books, his worn pipe, the familiar tobacco jar close to his hand.

Divinity is around the corner on McTavish Street with colleges for Anglican and United while the Presbyterian stands firmly apart, rock-ribbed, Gothic-arched and with the smoke of Auld Reekie clinging invisibly to its ramparts.

All along McTavish, millionaires' mansions have been converted into laboratories. The same thing is happening on surrounding streets, inundated by fluid growth and this thundering wave of vitality.

Dusk muted autumnal flame as I came again to the gates and turned for another look at the campus. Beside its daughter college, Macdonald—with spreading acres, gold of willows, brown of stone and red roofs blending into October haze—there is nothing beautiful here. Nothing but time, kindness. The intensely personal quality that binds all who knew it with what they have shared—the rustle of elms in lamplight, laughter through an open window, the sudden sharp stabbing realization of a meaning to life, the glory of blood surging through veins.

My old gentleman.

Crackling optimism. A belief in essential goodness. The wisdom of experience. Something called love.

Whatever the future holds for McGill, these things will never change. They are as old as truth, as deep as the roots, as fresh as a wind on the heather.

A good place, this, for my sons to find the strength of their country and manhood.

MORLEY CALLAGHAN

# Keep Away from Laura

A big chestnut tree in front of the Herberts' corner house spread its branches across the windows and sheltered it from the noisy new apartment house and its balconies across the street, where the Stanowskis lived with their Polish, Jewish and Ukrainian neighbors. It was the last of the fine old houses on the street. All the other old places had been torn down or broken up into flats. Mr. Herbert, a leather-goods manufacturer in a small way, lived there with his daughter.

Joe Stanowski hadn't had a chance to meet the Herberts. When his mother and younger brother, Pete, had moved into the apartment, he had been working in Detroit, and now he had been home only a few days. On Saturday afternoon he was coming home from work when Mr. Herbert and his daughter were approaching their shined-up old Cadillac on the drive to the left of their tree. The daughter looked so slim and pretty in her tailored blue suit that Joe slowed down to watch her get into the car. Leading the way to open the door for her, her father had a slow commanding stride, his pearl-grey hat square on the top of his head, and Joe didn't like his dark, proud, gloomy face. Nor did he like the way he wouldn't deign to notice the Jewish woman on the stoop next door, who bowed to him as she shook out her floor mop. But Joe did like the glimpse he got of the daughter's legs as she stepped into the car. Her father drew on his yellow gloves, then pressed the starter. It spun loudly, but the motor didn't start. After waiting gravely for a moment he gave it another spin. Nothing happened. So Mr. Herbert kept his foot on the starter while the slow whirring sound filled the street.

Crossing the road slowly, then hesitating, Joe waited, hoping he might be helpful and then have a chance to speak to the girl, and the Jewish woman, leaning on her mop, also watched with interest. For some reason then, Mr. Herbert took off his gloves and tried again and, as the loud and futile spinning continued, Joe's own mother, plump and jolly-looking, and his younger brother, Pete, came out on their balcony to watch. They waved to Joe. Three little kids in torn sweaters who had crossed the street moved under the chestnut tree and gaped at the car.

"Having some trouble?" Joe called, but apparently Mr. Herbert didn't hear him, for he got out of the car, chased the kids away irritably, circled the car with great deliberation, readjusted his hat, scowled at the row of apartment houses, and got into the car and spun the starter until the kids he had chased had come back again.

As Joe approached the car confidently his eyes were on the little dark curls at the back of Miss Herbert's neck. "Just a minute," he called. He had a slow lazy smile and a fine head with thick fair hair. "You'll have no juice left in that battery." Raising the old car's hood he reached for the choke, closed it and held it. "All right, try it again," he said calmly.

Eying him grimly Mr. Herbert deliberated and tapped the dashboard with his fingers and, as their eyes met, Joe knew that he resented him raising the hood of the old car and he resented him walking on the lawn under the old tree.

"Yes, try it again, Daddy," the girl said.

At the first spin the motor started. "Thank you," Mr. Herbert said, and the tone was so clipped and curt he might just as well have asked Joe why he didn't mind his own business. It was insulting and as the car backed away Joe reddened and cursed softly. Then Miss Herbert waved and smiled gratefully. Feeling better, he stood watching until the car went down the street and turned the corner, then he crossed to his own place and asked his mother about the Herberts.

Mr. Herbert was an old bear who ought to have moved out of the neighborhood long ago if he didn't like it, she said. Instead, he stayed there with his daughter in his big old house behind his big old tree, driving his silly old car, and looking down his nose at everybody and always making trouble for the kids who climbed the tree and knocked down the chestnuts.

Coming home Monday evening Joe went into the corner drugstore to get a coke, and there was Miss Herbert at the counter buying some aspirin. She was carrying a big folio. The counter lights gleamed on her long black hair parted in the centre, and he saw that she had soft shy brown eyes.

"Oh, hello," he said.

"Why, hello," she called as she turned to go. "Have you started any more cars?" Forgetting about his coke he went out with her. "I go this way too," he said, falling in step. She held aloof until he asked what she was carrying in the folio, then she told him she was going to art school studying design and wanted to do interior decorating. And he told her he was at an airplane factory but was studying draftsmanship three nights a week at night school. He talked easily. He had the fine European manners of his Polish father. As she kept glancing at him he didn't know how it happened, but suddenly they started laughing and slowing down and her shy stiffness vanished, and he felt exuberant, then almost shy himself.

At the big chestnut tree she said reluctantly, "Well, I'm afraid I leave you here."

"Well, what's your first name?"

"Laura."

"Laura. Laura. That's a nice name. Say, why don't we go to the movies some night?"

The shined-up old Cadillac came turning in at the Herbert drive and stopped at the garage. Mr. Herbert got out and stood there watching them.

"But you haven't told me your own name," she said.

"Joe Stanowski."

"Stanowski."

"Yeah, that's a Polish name. I just live across the street."

"Oh. There."

"Well, I'll call you," he said uneasily, for she looked embarrassed, and he thought it was because her unsmiling father was approaching with his slow deliberate stride, scrutinizing them boldly.

Just before the streetlights came on Joe was in the front room playing some records when he heard an angry shout coming from across the street. He looked out the window and saw Mr. Herbert on his steps waving his arms. A kid ran across the lawn and down the street. Another was swinging from a branch. His own brother, Pete, came running across the road heading for home with chestnuts dropping from his pockets and bouncing on the pavement, until he realized he was betraying his identity, then he circled away and went on down the street.

Coming down the steps slowly Mr. Herbert stood on the lawn, looking up at the tree, then he put his hands on his hips and surveyed the litter of sticks and stones the kids had thrown at the chestnuts, and the leaves they had knocked down. He began methodically to pick up the sticks and stones, then suddenly he straightened and glared at the apartment house. Dropping the sticks he came striding across the street.

"Mother, Mother," Joe called. "Here comes Mr. Herbert. Pete has been at his tree."

"Oh, my. You speak—No, you keep out of it. I'll speak," she said, hurrying from the kitchen and smoothing her grey hair. She tried to pull off her apron, had difficulty with it and grew flustered, but she was at the door when Mr. Herbert knocked.

"Ah, Mr. Herbert," she said, with her broad Polish accent.

"Madame," he began, but he couldn't maintain his enormously superior tone with his dark gloomy face full of violence. "That boy of yours," he snapped at her. "That little vandal—" When Mrs. Stanowski tried to interrupt him he lost his temper completely. "None of you people have any respect for a man's property. Why don't you keep to yourselves?"

"Such a way to talk over a few chestnuts," Joe heard his mother say. When she spoke slowly she spoke very good English and he hoped she wouldn't get excited; then suddenly words poured from her in Polish and broken English. "Mother," Joe called anxiously, and then he was standing behind her, and Mr. Herbert had shifted his eyes to him. "The police, no doubt, will understand you better than I do," Mr. Herbert said sharply. "In the meantime," he added, his eyes meeting Joe's, "keep away from my tree. Do you understand?" And he walked out . . .

Joe and his mother stood at the front window and watched him cross the road and begin to clear his lawn of the sticks and leaves. That was for me—that speech, Joe thought. He threw it right at me. He means keep away from Laura.

The streetlights came on and radios blared from open windows and, as they watched Mr. Herbert circling around, Joe was sure he knew what he was thinking; every time he stooped down Mr. Herbert was hating what had happened to the neighborhood. "We're all just dirt to him," Joe thought bitterly. He wished his mother hadn't got so excited.

Turning away restlessly from the window he looked around the room at the cheap furniture his mother had scrimped and saved for, but when he glanced at her and saw that her jaw still trembled he felt ashamed and hated Mr. Herbert. "Just the same," he said harshly, "if Pete doesn't keep away from that tree and stop humiliating us I'll beat his ears off."

He had told Laura that he would telephone her and he did so next evening. "How about that movie?" he asked.

"Really," she said, sounding embarrassed, "I hardly ever go to the movies. Thank you just the same."

"Maybe I could meet you down at the corner some night . . . we could walk up . . ."

"I have no fixed time for coming home." She spoke gently, as if trying not to hurt him, and he knew her father had talked to her and told her she should look down her nose at him.

"Look here," he said angrily, "for thousands of years kids have been knocking down chestnuts. They've got a right to do it. Your tree is no different from anybody else's and if your old man comes charging across here again insulting my mother I'll throw him out."

"Why—the idea of you talking to me like that," she gasped haughtily.

"I get the point," he said. "I won't even bother you." And he hung up.

That night he sat on the front balcony in the cool of the evening watching the lights in the Herbert place shining through the thick leaves of the tree. Their ground-floor window was open and someone was playing a piano. In a little while it became a duet. Old Herbert and his daughter were playing a little Bach. "Listen how stiff it is," he thought contemptuously. "Mechanical and stiff. My mother could go over there and play rings around both of them." But he couldn't stop watching the lighted windows behind the tree.

Later a whole gang of older boys came down the street and, as they usually did, they stopped under the Herbert tree and loafed there, laughing and talking and whistling, and their voices sounded loud and reckless on the quiet street. They made lewd jokes and jeered at each other. In a little while a police prowl car came along,

a cop got out and made the boys go home, and Joe knew Mr. Herbert had phoned the police station. Suddenly Joe was glad the tree was there for, although it spread its branches protectively across Laura's windows, it seemed to him that it also spread the city life around her house and tormented her.

Getting up, he went out, loafed across the road and walked up and down under the branches spreading over the sidewalk. He began to whistle softly. While he whistled he watched the upstairs window. At last he saw her shadow against the window shade. He laughed. He got pleasure out of jeering at her savagely. You think you're hidden up there and peeking out, eh, lady? That's just right for a girl like you. Keep hidden, lady. No friends. Never a guy with you. Keep hidden and you'll stay superior. Sauntering up and down he made sure she would recognize him, and he felt good, thinking, Wouldn't you be embarrassed if you knew I had spotted you? Isn't your old man pulling at your dress? What a lousy life you lead behind your tree.

Still whistling softly, knowing she could see him plainly, he crossed the road to his own place.

Next night he saw her coming home, walking on the other side of the street, aloofly self-conscious, ignoring him, and he felt sore, and he whistled that tune he had whistled under the tree, mocking her aloofness.

Early Sunday evening he heard that angry shout from across the street and the sound of kids running. At the front window he watched a kid he didn't know duck up an alley two doors below the Herbert house, and then Mr. Herbert, who had shouted from his open door, came leaping down the steps to grab a kid who was swinging from a branch. The kid, who had got his sleeve caught, was trying to free himself. "I'll fix you this time, you scamp," Mr. Herbert shouted. His arms wide open, he lunged at the swinging kid, who had jerked his sweater free, and who half fell, then staggered away from Mr. Herbert's grasp and ducked and dodged across the lawn. "Oh, no you don't," Mr. Herbert yelled, lunging again at the kid, who twisted away and eluded him and darted down the street. Like a sprinter Mr. Herbert took three leaping strides after him, then fell flat on his face and lay there, stunned.

It was a warm Sunday evening and the neighbors were on their balconies. Someone tittered, another guffawed, then there was a burst of laughter. Everybody was happy. Everybody enjoyed the comic performance. A silly fellow two doors away from the Stanowskis clapped and shouted, "Bravo." Joe, at the window, laughed heartily. It was perfect. Flat on his face.

But Laura had come out and when she saw her father lying on the lawn she ran to him and knelt down. Bewildered by the jeering laughter she looked over at the balconies.

Her bewilderment suddenly hurt Joe and he ran out and crossed the road and knelt down beside Mr. Herbert. "What's the matter with him, Laura?"

"Maybe it's his heart. It must be his heart."

"Have you any pain, sir?"

"No," said Mr. Herbert, white-faced and gasping for breath as he rolled over on his side. "My legs just . . . just suddenly fell away." Still enormously surprised and scared he let Joe take his hand and hoist him to his feet and, as he stood there, slowly brushing the twigs and grass from his coat, his strength returned. Then a young fellow on one of the balconies, seeing that Mr. Herbert was all right, yelled mockingly, "Speech. Speech."

Trembling with outraged pride Mr. Herbert swung around and glared at the balconies, and then he turned to Joe. "Thank you," he said in the same supercilious tone he had used when the car had been started for him. Feeling like a fool for being there Joe started to go.

"Joe," Laura called.

"What?" he asked gruffly.

"Don't go," she began timidly. "You, you've been very kind." She looked distracted and ashamed. After a nervous glance at her father she blurted out, "Won't you come in with us? We could—we could have a cup of coffee."

"What is this?" Joe asked as he saw her father glance at her sharply. Then he was sure he knew what she was up to. She was going to use him to help her father recover his dignity. Under the eyes of the mocking neighbors she would have her father walk him into the house and show he was unruffled and superior and not miserably alone and against everybody on the street.

"No thanks," he said abruptly, and as he started to walk across the street and some kid in hiding yelled, "Oh, Mr. Herbert, I'll race you down to the corner," he grinned. Again the neighbors laughed.

Then he heard Mr. Herbert say, "Laura. Please." It was her father's shocked worried tone that made him turn. There was Laura, looking harassed and lonely, her fists clenched as she muttered and took a defiant step toward the neighbors on the balconies. Half-crying, her face twisted, she was ready to denounce them and invite them all to jeer at her too. "Laura. No. Please keep out of this," her father pleaded, as if he realized he was drawing on her some lasting humiliation in the neighborhood.

"Let them stew in their own juice," Joe thought as he kept on going. But Laura's white tormented face seemed to follow him and cry out to him that she had not been trying to use him, she had only tried to grasp at the moment, had seen it was the one ready vulnerable moment to open the way to her, and that now, while his back was turned and he retreated, her life, which her father had made twisted and lonely, was being further warped into a lasting loneliness, and he couldn't stand it. Wavering, he turned and hurried back.

"Laura," he called.

"Oh, I'd like to tell those—"

"Laura, you asked me in."

"What? Yes. Why, yes," she said, looking confused.

"Well, come on then."

"Well, if you'd like to—" Her arm was trembling when he took it. Under the eyes of the watching neighbors they crossed the lawn, Mr. Herbert trailing awkwardly behind and, when they were under the big tree, Joe stopped a moment and looked up, and she wondered why he had such an odd reflective frown.

HUGH MacLENNAN

# Christ vs. Sputnik

When the news first broke about Russia's mechanical moon I was grimly glad, even though I lamented the coming of the day when our pleasant old earth will be as outmoded by colonized planets as the old culture-cradles of Europe are now outmoded by Russia and the United States. But since Sputnik was bound to be invented by somebody, I was glad that the first working model was produced by Russians and not by our friends.

If Sputnik does nothing else useful, it should at least rouse this mentally lazy continent to an activity which has been considered bad form for many a year: it may once again make it respectable for an honest man to think, even to think aloud. For already Sputnik has made public nonsense of the mythology foisted on North Americans by politicians, publicists and advertisers, who worship science without understanding the first important thing about it except that it is wonderful.

The average North American, who is one of the least scientifically minded types alive, has been thinking of science as a cushion for his body and a drug for his mind. Science, he has been encouraged to believe, will always look after him. When the first atomic bomb exploded over Hiroshima, the initial reaction of the average American citizen was what might have been expected: once again, our scientific boys had done it.

Informed Americans understood perfectly well that the role played by *our* scientific boys in tapping nuclear power was relatively slight. The two pioneering geniuses had been a New Zealander and a German Jew. Even in the Manhattan Project itself, the two most important scientists involved had been a Dane and an Italian. The atomic bomb was not the product of a single nation's genius, even of a single nation's know-how; it was a by-product of science itself. That the American government put up the money to build the bomb was not a scientific act, it was a political one.

But, with a thunder of propaganda, American myth-makers have insisted the public believe that the United States legitimately owned what in fact was an international property. When Russia made a bomb of her own, and made it years before the American government expected she would, the myth-makers pretended that her success was entirely caused by the activity of traitors who had given her the secrets. Right up to the day Sputnik was launched the public was told that Russia could not keep pace with America in science and technology because—such was the argument of Dr. Vannevar Bush—science and technology will always flourish better in free states than in countries like Russia.

I am grateful to Sputnik and its successors for having made it possible for millions of democratic citizens to understand how they have been duped, and to consider a few facts about science which the scientists themselves have been stating for years.

The first of these is that science does not regard any one nation as *chosen*.

The second is that science, especially the branches of it dependent on mathematics, flourishes in totalitarian states. Mathematics is without morals or ideology.

The third is that technological ability has no necessary connection with a nation's maturity.

The final truth is one I am almost afraid to mention lest I be accused of giving comfort to communists. In an all-out technological race, Russia is sure to defeat the United States because her society is totalitarian and communist while that of the United States is democratic and capitalist. In short, communism is better suited than democracy for success in a Rube Goldberg competition.

Look at some of the evidence: The educational system of the Soviet Union, entirely controlled by the state, has been a forcing house for the development of scientists and technologists. With her huge population, Russia is now turning out more engineers than the rest of the world put together. Nor is this solely 'a matter of superior organization; it is also a matter of mental attitude. The Russian's Bible is Marx, his ideology is dialectical materialism, and he has few lingering values from Christianity to disturb the official doctrine that the chief end of man is to produce, break records, win championships and move large objects from place to place. Uncontaminated by any anxiety that it profits a man nothing if he gains the world and loses his soul, the Russian expert is able to enter a technological race with an integrity far purer than his American competitor.

In contrast, North American technology appears confused in the extreme. While it is perfectly true that the average North American today lives a materialistic existence, the fact remains that materialism is an invader of his real heritage, and that his materialistic habits still trouble the conscience of his elite. Nor is this all. While the purpose of technology in the Soviet Union is to strengthen the state, the purpose of most technology in North America is to make a profit for the corporation which pays for it. This the Russian scientists smugly pointed out in Washington when they told American newsmen that American designers are better at producing fish-tailed automobiles, while Russian designers are better at producing machines to explore space.

From all this it follows—I don't see how anyone can seriously dispute it on the evidence —that the only way in which America can win a technological race with the Soviet Union is by scrapping the capitalist system and turning herself into a full-fledged totalitarian state. Nor would I be astonished if I heard that certain of the competitively minded men in the Pentagon would consider this a good idea, though of course they would not express it as baldly as I express it here.

Fortunately, it is an impossible idea. For in order to win a long-term technological contest with Russia, America would have to do a lot more than vest her government with dictatorial powers. She would, in the last analysis, have to abandon her entire heritage of civilization. She would have to close her churches and ban the Bible, lest the teachings

of Jesus disturb the minds of the people. She would have to forget about Jefferson and his doctrine of individualism. She would have to squelch all her best writers. She would have to turn Harvard into a carbon copy of the University of Moscow.

Since North Americans can do none of these things, no matter how hard they try, why do we allow so many of our spokesmen to assert that our sole hope of survival depends on winning the technological race with Russia? Why don't we take a good look at ourselves and compute our assets and our debits and begin an adventure long overdue on this continent, namely the working out of a philosophy of life which is based on current realities and not on the comfortable mythology inherited from the past? Why not admit what every foreigner assumes of us, that our present society is sick?

It is sick, I believe, because it has permitted itself to become schizophrenic, and the schizophrenia so obvious in the life of the modern United States is equally endemic here in Canada. It manifests itself in almost everything we say, think and do. It makes us nervous, insecure, at times hysterical and often contemptible in the eyes of older countries. Its continuance without check is more likely to destroy us than the ICBM's of the Soviet Union.

Specifically, we North Americans are schizophrenic because we are attempting to be Christians in one part of our minds and materialists in the other. Publicly we insist that religion is the backbone of our civilization and the author of our freedom. Yet at the same time our advertisers, who must earn a living in a competitive system, endeavor to make us believe by conditioned reflex that our chief end is to consume their products and that we can't be happy without that new car or suit of clothes or what have you.

The disease spreads downward and outward with symptoms too numerous to count. Seldom have there been more books about religion than are being published now, yet almost all of them discuss religion as though they were selling a patent medicine. Norman Vincent Peale writes about God as though He were a raw material to be exploited, and Billy Graham once described God as the most valuable product in the world, which ought to be sold more efficiently than soap. Humanitarians wish to abolish the disease of cancer, but the slogan they use is Fight Cancer—not heal cancer but fight it—thereby injecting an act of love with a dose of hostility. The same manufacturer who shouts that all must be done to outbuild Russia, screams like a stuck pig if anything is done to interfere with the profits of private companies. The same newspaper which insists that the loyalty of scientists be scrutinized by committees, has no hesitation in publishing secret scientific information if its editors believe it will make a good story. On a Canadian highway I have seen an advertisement for a 240-horsepower car facing another sign which warned Speed Kills! The same people who insist that the survival of their country depends on the use of its brains, saw nothing inconsistent in electing a political party which scornfully labeled all men of brains eggheads.

No man can serve two masters simultaneously, as was pointed out a long time ago and as we affect to believe. Neither can any society serve with equal devotion the philosophy of materialism and the religion of Jesus Christ.

On the basic levels of decision, from time to time, there come moments when a clear choice must be made. And it is a matter of record that at such moments, however grudgingly, our governments decide on the basis of Christianity. Soon after World War II it would have been technically possible for the United States to have destroyed Russia before Russia acquired atomic bombs of her own. Some people thought she should have done so. But in the moment of decision it turned out to be morally impossible. At the sticking point the American government was Christian, and it still is.

Since this is the kind of people we are, why not admit it above the propaganda level? Why not admit further that we have neither the ability nor the desire to beat Russia in technology merely for the sake of beating her? Why not let Russia win this technological race and keep our heads while they do so?

This is not the advice of a suicide or even of what used to be called a pacifist, for I do not believe it essential to Christ's teachings to offer your throat to a murderer. But I do believe it essential not to be so afraid of death as we now are, not to be as aggressive as we now are, not to be so full of hate and fear as we now are. I do believe that wars are caused more by fear than by the desire to dominate, more by competition than by, at times, a refusal to compete in collective madness. We have great deterrent power at the moment; so much that only a madman would dare draw its fire. Even if the Russians win the technological race, in the sense that they can do more damage than we can, we would be in no more danger than we would be if we were their equals in the capacity to do more damage. For wars, to repeat, are caused by fear, and in the modern world vast technological power has ceased to be a defense. Little Ecuador is safer than the United States or Russia.

I am not advocating an abandonment of our scientific and technological tradition. I *am* advocating that we pursue science as it should be pursued, as a search for truth and not a race for power.

R. S. McLAUGHLIN

# How the Auto Beat the Horse

as told to Eric Hutton

When I turned twenty-one in 1892 my father repaid me the $2.50 a week he had taken from my $3 salary for room and board during my three-year apprenticeship with the McLaughlin Carriage Company. He repaid me with generous interest, I should say, since he made me a partner, along with my older brother George.

My father had started with nothing but his hands, in a little shop in a forest clearing at

Tyrone in the Durham County of Ontario, and built the first McLaughlin vehicle, a cutter, in 1867—which makes us exactly the same age as Canada. The Governor wanted working partners—certainly George and I brought nothing into the business but willingness to work and such skills as we had acquired in the carriage shop.

Bank credit, essential for operating an expanding business like ours, was very difficult to secure in those days. It was fortunate that my father's reputation as a reliable and devout man, an elder of the church, made it possible for us to get a reasonable line of credit. With our working capital problem eased we were ready for the expansion necessary to meet increasing orders for McLaughlin carriages. But there remained a major bottleneck: our plant was a considerable distance from the Oshawa railway freight yards. We had to load all carriages at the factory on flat wagons, then team them down to the railway, unload them, and reload them on the railway cars. The streets were unpaved, deep in mud in wet weather, heavy with dust in dry weather.

The boxcars used by the railways in those days were dinky things, too small for the economical shipment of carriages. So we loaded our carriages twenty-five at a time on flat cars, which were much longer than boxcars, and we kept a crew of men building "houses" right over the carriages, closing them in solidly. It was a costly, time-wasting way of getting our products from factory to purchaser. Then came Oshawa's great street-railroad issue. There was strong opposition, speeches for and against, friends quarreling with lifelong friends over the issue. Finally it was put to a vote—and the railway won. The breaking of this bottleneck soon led to one even more serious.

The McLaughlin Carriage Company finally reached the point where it could not add another foot of badly needed work space to the crowded buildings on the half-lot my father had bought twenty years before. We either had to move or hold down production. Looking for new quarters, we considered a much bigger factory which had been built by the Honorable T. N. Gibbs to manufacture furniture. That business failed and the building had been taken over by the Heaps Manufacturing Company, another furniture concern, which also failed, leaving the building empty. We made an unusual deal for that building, trading in our old plant on it. We were warned by some people that the building was "jinxed," and by others that we were biting off more than we could chew.

"You will be lost in that big building," people told us. "You'll have to rent out some of it." But in two years we were up to our usual tricks: we were busy building extensions.

In 1896 we spread further by opening our first branch office in Saint John, N.B., where our carriages had become popular.

As I look back on those last years of the nineteenth century I think I can honestly say that I was the busiest young man in North America. After I returned from "testing my apprenticeship" in the United States I became foreman of the upholstery shop for a year or two. Then I went into the office and, in addition to handling my share of the business end, I became the designer for all McLaughlin carriages. It was to be one of my jobs—and my real labor of love—for the next twenty-five years, on all our early automobiles as well as the carriages. Today a motor manufacturer who puts out half a dozen different basic body designs feels he is offering a full line, and he is. But at the turn of the century, to keep abreast and ahead of the stiff competition, McLaughlin's was offering no fewer than 143 separate body designs of carriages and sleighs, with new models in many types every year.

Every part of the country had its own ideas about the carriages it wanted. Quebec wanted Concord bodies, for example, but Ontario preferred square boxlike bodies. The Northwest and other frontier areas must have their buckboards and democrats. Then there was the city stuff, phaetons, stanhopes and fringe-top surreys. The Maritimes insisted on the fanciest design of all. We were developing an export business too; Australia was buying our carriages. Road carts, the simplest type of conveyance then in existence, two-wheeled and low in price, were in great demand not only locally but in South America as well. Once we shipped five hundred road carts on one vessel bound for South America, then received a message from the buyer: "Ship lost with all carts; please repeat the order immediately."

The automobile generation, which recognizes the buggy in sweet old-fashioned songs, may think of it as the simplest form of machinery; but to us and to our customers it was a complex mechanism requiring considerable maintenance. Here, for example, are the first two of a dozen "rules for the care and preservation of wagons and carriages" we issued in 1896:

> *Carriages should be kept in an airy, dry coach house. There should be a moderate amount of light, otherwise the*

*colors will be affected. The windows should be curtained to avoid having direct sunlight strike upon the carriage.*

*There should be no communication between the stable and the coach house. The manure pit should be located as far away from the coach house as possible. Ammonia fumes crack and destroy varnish, and fade the colors of both painting and lining. Also avoid having a carriage stand near a brick wall, as the dampness from the wall will fade the colors and destroy the varnish.*

The carriage owner had problems the motorist never heard of: moths in the upholstery, for example. We recommended turpentine and camphor if the woolen linings became infested. We promised carriage buyers that the care we outlined would result in long life. How long, we did not know at the time. One of the rewards of long life has been for me to see for myself how well our promise has been kept. For many of those stoutly built McLaughlin vehicles survive to this day and give good service more than fifty years after they were made.

A little less than a year after my marriage to Adelaide Louise Mowbray the biggest disaster of our history struck. On December 7, 1899, the McLaughlin Carriage Company buildings burned to the ground. We were helpless; we could only stand and watch our life's work go up in flames, not only we McLaughlins, but the six hundred men who depended for a living on the carriage works.

If we were dismayed, the Governor, George and I, we didn't stay that way long. For the ruins of the McLaughlin Carriage Company were still smoldering when a telephone call came through from Belleville. The city was ready to float a bond issue, we were told, to provide us with a big cash bonus if we would rebuild our factory in Belleville. In quick succession, by telegram, telephone and letter, similar offers came from *fifteen* other Ontario cities and towns. How could we remain discouraged in the face of that kind of confidence in our ability to re-establish our business?

But we wanted to stay in Oshawa. We felt a loyalty to the town in which we had now been established for nearly a quarter of a century, a loyalty which amounted to the feeling that Oshawa owned the business as much as the McLaughlins did. And we soon had heartening evidence that Oshawa reciprocated that feeling. The town offered us a loan of $50,000, to be repaid "as convenient." We accepted.

But what were we and our workers to do while the plant was being rebuilt? And what about our markets?

At Gananoque, 150 miles east of Oshawa, I came across an empty two-story factory that we could rent, and grabbed it. I suppose the next six months were the most hectic of my life. Remember, we were going back into the carriage business with nothing except what we had in our heads. I took as many of our Oshawa workmen as I could use along to Gananoque, and we found billets in boarding houses and private homes.

By keeping that double-decked plant running two shifts every twenty-four hours we really rolled those carriages out: by the middle of July 1900 we turned out three thousand carriages. That was enough to supply our most urgent orders, and more important, to establish beyond any doubt that the McLaughlins were still in business. We all returned to Oshawa in midsummer and pitched in to help finish the new plant—and we were making carriages in Oshawa again before the roof was on. The new plant was built on such an ambitious scale that it is still part of General Motors.

Those were wonderful years for the carriage business. Everybody in Canada seemed to want a McLaughlin carriage or cutter. Our volume rocketed to the 25,000-a-year mark, our sales passed the million-dollar volume. There was only one small cloud on the horizon; a cloud caused by the appearance on Ontario's dusty roads of a strange contraption called the automobile.

I don't remember the first time I saw an automobile. It might have been the one that was the pride and joy of our bookkeeper, Oliver Hezzlewood. Certainly Hezzlewood's was the first car I had any personal contact with, the first I ever worked on. I don't even remember its make. I think it ran on one cylinder and was chain-driven. I know it had no doors, top or windshield. I know for this reason: one day Hezzlewood complained to me that his car, in spite of its many virtues, was a little inconvenient in inclement weather. What he meant was that when it rained he and his passengers got soaked to the skin.

"Can't you do anything about that?" he asked me. I talked with one of the foremen and we devised a top. It wasn't really a top, but a rubberized sheet that fitted over the body, with four holes cut in it for the heads of the driver and his three passengers. It was the darnedest-looking contraption you ever saw but, used in conjunction with sou'wester hats worn by the occupants, it did keep them dry. And Hezzlewood was immensely pleased with it. He had me drive his car—and from then on I had a new kind of wheels in my head: motor-driven wheels.

By 1905 there were a couple of dozen cars in Toronto. The nearest one to us was in Whitby. They were still much of a curiosity, a sporting proposition for adventurous people. In the United States the Ford Motor Company was two years old. The Buick Motor Company, also two years old, had just been taken over by a carriage builder named William C. Durant and in this year would produce 750 cars. Cadillac, three years old, was offering a one-cylinder car with the motor under the front seat. Among other cars for sale were the Locomobile, Mobile, Winton, de Dion, Columbia and Gasmobile. But the real titan was R. E. Olds, whose curved-dash one-cylinder Oldsmobile outnumbered all other cars on America's dirt roads and rutted gravel highways. Up to 1905, Olds—who was later to give his name to another car, the Reo—had produced nearly 12,000 cars. In that year he was to make a record 6,500 runabouts, and Gus Edwards was to write that priceless piece of publicity—the song, "In My Merry Oldsmobile."

I started a campaign to persuade my brother George that automobiles had a place in the world, and pretty well convinced him. We never did convince the Governor, though. He honestly believed that the automobile would never replace the horse-drawn carriage; certainly not for many years; certainly not in his time.

In keeping an eye on this intriguing new idea in transportation I had to move warily. I had to wait until my holidays before I could visit the United States and learn more about what was being done in the automobile field. I can imagine what the Governor's reaction would have been if I had said: "I want to take time off to learn how to go about replacing carriages with automobiles in the McLaughlin plant."

So when my vacation came I went to Buffalo, where Richard Pierce was making a car that was beginning to be heard about. Mr. Pierce took me to lunch at his club and afterward showed me around his plant where the Pierce-Arrow was being manufactured, painstakingly by hand operation, piece by piece, part by part. This stately courteous gentleman of the old school then made a startling statement in a quiet matter-of-fact voice: "Cars like this have no future, Mr. McLaughlin. I would advise you against trying to make them."

He explained that it was his belief that large cars would never find a considerable market; that McLaughlin's should use its experience in mass production of carriages to enter the low-priced car field. And, when I considered the $2,000 to $3,000 price of the Pierce-Arrow in comparison with our own price range for carriages—from $50 for our low-priced models to $165 wholesale for the largest and most elaborate carriages—I was inclined to agree with him. In a sense, Mr. Pierce was forecasting the fate of his own products. He continued to make his fine cars for many years, and they acquired great prestige. But they never sold in sufficient quantities to enable the company to survive adversity, and in the Thirties Pierce-Arrow went out of business.

I went over to the E. R. Thomas Company, also in Buffalo, for a look at the Thomas Flyer. Mr. Thomas couldn't talk business with me, he said, because he already had commitments with the Canada Cycle and Motor Company in Toronto. This fact made me all the more interested in getting a line on some arrangement to make cars in Canada, before competitors got the jump on us in our own country.

I also visited the Peerless Company in Cleveland, the Reo works and the Thomas Detroit factory, without coming to any conclusion about making cars in Canada. Back in Oshawa, I told my father what I had seen on my trip. He did not approve of my interest in cars, but he did not forbid it either. I think he considered it a youthful enthusiasm which I would outgrow much as I had outgrown bicycle racing.

Not long afterward we had a visit from a great friend of my father's, a Mr. Matthews, of Gananoque. He told us that a man he knew, Charles Lewis of Jackson, Michigan, had been in the spring and axle business and was now making automobiles. He suggested that we talk to him. So I took the train to Jackson with Oliver Hezzlewood, who was now an executive of the company. We called on Mr. Lewis. He was a fine old gentleman, genial and courteous, and ready to do anything in the world for us. He was enthusiastic over the possibilities of our manufacturing cars in Oshawa, and outlined how it could be done. We could manufacture the engines and many of the parts; he would supply us with an engineer and certain parts. He proposed an arrangement whereby we would pay him a certain amount in cash for the benefits we would derive from our connection with him. He was confident that the Jackson car was for us, and pointed out that one of his cars, driven by the great Bob Burman, had recently won the hundred-mile Vanderbilt Cup race on Long Island.

All in all, the proposition sounded good, I went home feeling that we were probably in the automobile manufacturing business at last —provided, of course, we could persuade the Governor to let us try it. Fortunately, I made one reservation before committing ourselves: I ordered two cars from Mr. Lewis for testing, one a chain drive, the other shaft driven. As soon as they arrived, Mr. Hezzlewood took the wheel of the former and I climbed into the latter. Off we went down the macadam highway . . .

I will draw a curtain over the events of the next hour. Suffice it to say that as automobiles they were a poor job of plumbing. We broke down several times. If we had not been optimists we would have gone contentedly back to carriage making. Certainly if the Governor had been along on either of those rides we would have been out of the automobile business before we entered it.

But there was still one bright spot. While we had been eating breakfast in Jackson before going to the Lewis works, William Durant and his factory manager had walked into the dining room. "Sam, what on earth are you doing here?" Durant asked. I told him. He thought for a moment, then said: "Charlie Lewis is a dear friend of mine. You get his story, then if you're not satisfied, come and see me."

I had known Durant for ten years, having met him at conventions of carriage manufacturers. He and his partner, Dallas Dort, had built a fifty-dollar stake into Durant-Dort, then one of the biggest carriage and wagon companies in the United States, with a production up to 150,000 units a year. Like my father, Durant wanted no part of the automobile business, which was then blossoming in his home town of Flint and nearby Michigan cities. Yet just about the same time I started to get interested—and concerned—about cars, Durant had been persuaded to buy the Buick company.

Before accepting Durant's invitation to "come and see me," I bought a Model F two-cylinder Buick in Toronto for $1,650. Before I was halfway to Oshawa I knew it was the car we wanted to make in Canada. I wired Durant and went to see him.

Durant greeted me with: "Well, there's no doubt this is the car for you." I agreed with him. He turned me loose with his factory man-

ager and accountants, and for two and a half days we went over every detail of the Buick operation. We worked out a tentative plan we thought would be fair to both sides. Then Durant and I got together, sharpened our pencils, agreed on most points—and then reached an impasse. We just couldn't agree on final details of the financial arrangements. We weren't far apart, but we just couldn't get together. I guess we were both stubborn.

I went home to Oshawa and told the Governor and George about my failure. I half-expected my father to say, "All right, that's over; now let's get busy making carriages." But he didn't. He listened while George and I worked out our alternative plan—to make our own car. All the Governor said was, "If you think you can make a go of it, go ahead."

We needed a first-class engineer to supervise the manufacturing and assembly processes, and of the many I interviewed my choice was Arthur Milbrath. We brought him to Oshawa and installed him in one of our buildings, on the west side of Mary Street, which had been set aside as the automobile shop. We equipped it with automatic lathes and other machine tools, planers and shapers—dozens of machines. From a Cleveland firm we ordered cylinders, pistons and crankshafts to our own specifications, and engine castings to be worked in our own shop. I put all I had into designing the most beautiful car I could dream of—the bodies, of course, would be made by the same artisans who had been making our carriages for years. The car was to be more powerful than the Buick.

We had everything we needed for our first hundred cars, and had the first car all laid out and practically ready for assembly, down to the beautiful brass McLaughlin radiator on which I had spent many hours, when disaster struck. Milbrath became severely ill with pleurisy.

Without an engineer we were helpless. The automobile shop, so nearly ready to produce its first harvest of McLaughlins, lay idle . . . dead. In this plight I thought of William Durant. I wired him, explaining what had happened and asking him if he could lend us an engineer. His answer came back promptly: "Will you be home tomorrow? I'm coming over."

Durant arrived, not with an engineer but with two of his top executives. He took up the discussion of our last meeting—when we had failed to get together on a manufacturing arrangement—just as if we had merely paused for breath. "I've been thinking it over," he said, "and have the solution to the problem we couldn't overcome in our figuring." The deal he suggested was pretty close to what I had in mind in the first place, and I said, "That will work." Durant nodded. "I thought it would," he said in that voice of his that was always so gentle—and always so much to the point.

In five minutes we had the contract settled. It ran just a page and a half and was a model agreement for lawyers to study. Chiefly it covered the terms under which we had fifteen-year rights to buy the Buick engine and some other parts. We would build and design our own bodies as we had always built carriages.

Nothing was said about the McLaughlin car, the hundred cars lying stillborn in the Mary Street building. Our contract with Buick meant, of course, that we would have to abandon those plans—and the partly built cars. We sold off the lathes and some other equipment, but much of the material and parts we had invested in had to be scrapped.

I have heard people regret that the coincidence of an engineer falling ill should have put an end to the project to produce an all-Canadian car. I may say that any regret on my part is tempered by the hard facts of the automobile industry, by the very great probability that if our engineer Arthur Milbrath had not become ill and we had proceeded with our plan to make our own cars, we almost certainly would have taken a header; and once having failed in our first effort we might never have got back into the automobile business.

No, the coming of Durant to Oshawa, not with an engineer to lend us but with a plan for co-operating with us in building cars, was a blessing. Even with the Buick connection we had to be lucky to succeed. We just happened to pick a car that was destined to make good. I have often wondered why some cars succeeded and some failed. One of the strangest facts about the automobile business in North America is that in its fifty-odd years no fewer than 2,400 different makers have manufactured and offered cars for sale; in each case the designers and engineers put the best they knew into the car; each was launched with high hopes—and today you can count on the fingers of two hands the car manufacturers who have survived.

PIERRE BERTON

# How the Klondike Rush Began

The man in the poling boat slipped silently down the river, moving swiftly with the stiff current of the grey Yukon, keeping close to the shoreline, where martens darted from the high clay banks and willows arched low into the water. Beneath him the waters hissed and boiled. Above him thrush and yellow warbler fluttered and caroled. And all around him the blue hills rolled on toward the rim of the world to melt into the haze of the horizon. Between each line of hills was a valley, and in the bottom of each valley a little creek gurgled its way down to the river. Below the wet mosses of some of those creeks, the man in the poling boat knew, there was gold. But, in this summer of 1894, he had no more stomach for it. For twenty-three years he had been climbing the hills of the world and trudging down the valleys, picking away at quartz and panning the black sand of a thousand creek beds. Always, the gold had eluded him.

He was a lighthouse-keeper's son from Big Island, off the tattered coast of Nova Scotia, and he could scarcely remember the time when he had not thought of gold. As a child he had read Alaskan histories and wandered about Nova Scotia searching for gold but finding only white iron. "Well," he would console himself, "it's a *kind* of gold." As a youth of fourteen he made the deliberate decision to spend his life seeking it.

First he signed aboard a sailing ship to search the seven seas, panning and picking to no avail in New Zealand and Australia and other corners of the globe. Then, after five years, he tried the northern hemisphere, working his way up through the Rocky Mountain states to the mines of Colorado, and then, after fourteen years, he was borne north with the human tide flowing toward Alaska. It was characteristic of his nature that while other men rushed to familiar creeks where earlier gold strikes had been made, he had chosen to press his search in unknown country on the upper reaches of the Pelly. But he found no gold on the Pelly; and now, out of funds and out of grub, with two equally disconsolate companions, he was drifting.

His name was Robert Henderson. He was tall and lean, with a gaunt, hawk's face, fiercely knit brows and piercing eyes. His full mustache, drooping slightly at the edges, accentuated the dour look that betrayed his Scottish ancestry. He wore his broad-brimmed miner's hat proudly all his life, as if it were a kind of badge.

Henderson and his companions had drifted for about one hundred miles when they reached the mouth of the Sixtymile River. Here, on an island, they espied a pinprick of civilization—a few cabins and tents, a saw-mill and a big two-story trading post of square-cut logs.

The trader, Joseph Ladue, was on the bank to greet Henderson—a swarthy, stocky figure of French-Huguenot background, and a veteran of the river since 1882. He too had been obsessed with the idea of gold for most of his life. It had a very real meaning for him, because without it he could not marry his sweetheart, Anna Mason, whose wealthy parents continued to spurn him as a penniless drifter. She was waiting faithfully for him three thousand miles away while he sought his fortune here in a starkly furnished log post on the banks of the Yukon.

Ladue's post lay roughly one hundred miles upstream from the mining camp of Fortymile which had been producing gold since 1886. Between the two settlements, two other rivers flowed into the Yukon from the opposite side: the Indian River, about thirty miles downstream from Ladue, and then the Thron-diuck River, another thirty miles farther down. La-

due had explored the Thron-diuck in the old days, and had gone so far as to take out an affidavit swearing that there was no gold on its streams. In spite of this, he now professed to believe that the neighboring Indian River country was ankle deep in nuggets, and had been extolling its possibilities to every prospector who stopped at his post.

"Let me prospect for you," Henderson said. "If it's good for me, it's good for you. I'm a determined man. I won't starve." His two companions were less enthusiastic. They chose to quit the north and return to Colorado.

For the next two years Henderson stubbornly combed the Indian and its tributaries for gold. He found gold, but not enough to satisfy him. On the surface bars of the main river he found gold as fine as sifted flour. On Australia Creek he found gold as delicate as lace. He dragged his sled up Quartz Creek and here he found gold as coarse as sand. It still was not what he was seeking. It is possible, indeed, that had he found a cache of twenty-dollar gold pieces, or a mountain of solid gold, he would have felt a vague chagrin, for with Henderson it was the search that counted.

Occasionally he would raise his eyes northward to examine a curious rounded mountain whose summit rose above the other hills. The creeks of Indian River flowed down the flanks of this dome, and Henderson guessed that on the other side more nameless creeks flowed into another river—probably the Thron-diuck, or "Klondike" as the miners mispronounced it. At last his prospector's curiosity got the better of him. He climbed the dome to see what was on the other side.

When he reached the summit a breath-taking sight met his gaze. To the north a long line of glistening snow-capped peaks marched off like soldiers to vanish beyond the lip of the horizon. In every other direction the violet hills rolled on as far as the eye could see, hill upon hill, valley upon valley, gulch upon gulch —each hill of almost identical height with its neighbor, so that the whole effect through half-closed eyes was of a great plateau creased and gouged by centuries of running water. From the summit on which Henderson was standing, the creeks radiated out like the spokes of a wheel, with himself at the hub, three falling off toward the Indian River and three more, on the far side, running to some unknown stream. He could not know it, but these were six of the richest gold-bearing creeks in the world.

Almost at his feet a deep gorge dropped off. He walked down a little way and dipped his pan into a small creek. When the gravel and sand washed away there was about eight cents' worth of gold left behind. Eight cents to the pan! This was a good prospect; he felt that he had found what he was looking for. Back he went over the divide to the Indian River where about twenty men, lured by Ladue's tales, were toiling away on the sand bars. He persuaded three to return with him to the creek which he named "Gold Bottom" because, as he said wistfully, "I had a daydream that when I got my shaft down to bedrock it might be like the streets of the New Jerusalem."

By midsummer of 1896 the four men had taken out seven hundred and fifty dollars, and it was time for Henderson to head back to Ladue's post for more supplies. To each man he met, he told the story of a V-shaped valley back in the hills; for this free interchange of information was part of the prospector's code to which Henderson fiercely subscribed. He not only told strangers of the gold, but he also urged them to turn back in their tracks and stake claims. In this way, he emptied the settlement at the mouth of the Sixtymile.

His order filled, Henderson drifted back the way he had come, in his skin boat. It was late summer and the water was low. The Indian River was so shallow that Henderson, fearing he might tear his craft to shreds trying to navigate it, determined to continue on down the Yukon toward the Thron-diuck, guessing correctly that Gold Bottom Creek must flow into it. Thus, on a fateful summer's day, he approached his historic meeting with a man named George Washington Carmack. The memory of that moment, bitter as gall, was to haunt Henderson all the days of his life.

The two men who now faced each other on the bank by the river mouth, who would later be dubbed "co-discoverers of the Klondike," and around whom so much controversy was to swirl, were opposites in almost every way. Henderson, lean and spare, with his keen-chiseled features, serious and intense, bore little resemblance to the easygoing, ever-optimistic Carmack with his heavy jowls, his sleepy eyes and his rather plump features. But they had one trait in common: an incurable restlessness had dominated their lives.

Carmack was the child of an earlier gold rush. His father had crossed the western plains in a covered wagon in '49, heading for California, and Carmack had been born at Port Costa, across the bay from San Francisco. He had gone to work at sixteen aboard the ferry boats, shipped to Alaska as a dishwasher on a man-of-war, jumped ship at Juneau and pushed steadily north.

Within a few years Carmack could speak both the Chilkoot and the Tagish dialects, and was exerting considerable influence over the Stick Indians from the interior or "Stick" country. At a time and place when every man was a prospector, Carmack appeared to be a misfit. He alone of all men did not want gold. Instead he wanted to be an Indian in a land where the natives were generally scorned by the white man and the word Siwash was a term of opprobrium. His wife, Kate, a member of the Tagish tribe, was the daughter of a chief, and it was Carmack's ambition to be chief himself. He had grown an Indian-type mustache that dropped over his lips in Oriental style, and when anybody said to him, "George, you're getting more like a Siwash every day," he took it as a compliment. While other men scrabbled and mucked in the smoky shafts of Fortymile and Birch Creek, Siwash George was slipping up and down the river with his Indian comrades. At the Klondike he was netting salmon to sell for dog feed when Henderson encountered him. His Tagish friends had joined him: Skookum Jim, a giant of a man supremely handsome with his high cheekbones, his eagle's nose and his fiery black eyes—straight as a gun barrel, powerfully built and known as the best hunter and trapper on the river; Tagish Charley, lean and lithe as a panther and, in Carmack's phrase, "alert as a weasel"; the silent, plump Kate with her straight black hair, and Carmack's daughter known as Graphie Gracey because no white man could pronounce her real name. It was this group that Henderson approached with news of the strike at Gold Bottom.

Carmack asked him: "What are the chances to locate up there?"

Henderson glanced over at the two Indians who were standing nearby. Then he uttered the phrase that probably cost him a fortune. "There's a chance for you, George, but I don't want any damn Siwashes staking on that creek."

He pushed his boat into the water and headed up the Klondike. "What's matter dat white man?" Skookum Jim asked, speaking in Chinook, the pidgin tongue of the traders that prevailed on the river. "Him killet Inchen moose, Inchen caribou, ketchet gold Inchen country, no liket Inchen staket claim, wha for, no good."

"Never mind, Jim," said Carmack, lightly. "This is a big country. We'll go and find a creek of our own."

And, as it turned out, it was to be as simple as that.

Carmack did not immediately follow Henderson's suggestion. He was less interested in gold than he was in logs, which he hoped to chop on Rabbit Creek, a tributary of the Klondike, and float down to the mill at Fortymile for twenty-five dollars a thousand feet.

It was as much Carmack's restless nature as his desire for fortune that took him and the Indians to the site of Henderson's strike some days after the meeting at the Klondike's mouth. They decided to strike up the valley of Rabbit Creek, which led to the high ridge separating the Klondike and Indian watersheds. Leaving their boat in a backwater, they shouldered their packs and began to trudge through the wet mosses and black muck and the great clumps of grass "niggerheads" that marked the mouth of Rabbit. As they went they prospected, dipping their pans into the clear water which rippled in the sunlight over sands white with quartz, finding minute pieces of gold, wondering whether or not to stake. They came to a fork in the frothing creek where another branch bubbled in from the south and here they paused momentarily.

At that instant they were standing, all unknowing, on the richest ground in the world. There was gold all about them, not only beneath their feet but in the very hills and benches that rose on every side. In the space of a few hundred feet there was hidden gold worth several millions of dollars. The south fork of the creek was as yet unnamed but there could be only one name for it: Eldorado.

But they did not linger here. Instead they hiked on up the narrowing valley, flushing a brown bear from the blueberry bushes, panning periodically and finding a few colors in every pan, until they reached the Dome that looked down over the land of the Klondike. Below, in the narrow gorge of Gold Bottom Creek, a pale pillar of smoke marked Henderson's camp. "Well, boys," said Carmack, "we've got this far; let's go down and see what they've got."

Exactly what happened between Carmack and Henderson has long been in dispute. Carmack later insisted that he urged Henderson to come over to Rabbit Creek and stake a claim. Henderson always swore that it was he who urged Carmack to prospect Rabbit—and if he found anything to let Henderson know. Two facts are fairly clear. First, Carmack did promise Henderson that if he found anything worthwhile on Rabbit he would send word back; Henderson offered to compensate him for his trouble if the occasion arose. Second, the Indians tried to purchase some tobacco from Henderson and Henderson refused, possibly because he was short of supplies but more likely because of his attitude toward Indians,

since it was against his code to refuse a fellow prospector anything. The trio headed back over the mountain almost immediately. They came wearily to the forks of Rabbit Creek once more, and pressed on for about half a mile before making camp for the night. It was August 16, the eve of a memorable day that is still celebrated as a festive holiday in the Yukon Territory. Who found the nugget that started it all? Again, the record is blurred. Years afterward, Carmack insisted it was he who happened upon the protruding rim of bedrock from which he pulled a thumb-sized chunk of gold. But Skookum Jim and Tagish Charley always claimed that Carmack was stretched out asleep under a birch tree when Jim, having shot a moose, was cleaning a dishpan in the creek and made the find. At any rate the gold was there, lying thick between the flaky slabs of rock like cheese in a sandwich. A single panful yielded a quarter of an ounce or about four dollars' worth. It was an incredible find.

The three men began to perform a wild dance—a sort of combination Scottish hornpipe, Indian foxtrot, syncopated Irish jig and Siwash hula, as Cormack later described it. They collapsed panting, smoked a cigarette apiece, and panned out some more gravel until Carmack had gathered enough coarse gold to fill an empty Winchester shotgun shell. Then they settled down for the night, the Indians chanting a weird song of praise into the embers of the fire while Carmack, staring at the dying flames, conjured up visions of wealth. In that instant of discovery something fundamental had happened to Siwash George; suddenly he had ceased to be an Indian. And he never thought of himself as an Indian again.

The following morning the trio staked claims on Rabbit Creek. Under Canadian mining law no more than one claim may be staked in any mining district by any man except the discoverer, who is allowed a double claim. Carmack blazed a small spruce tree with his hand axe, and on the upstream side wrote with a pencil:

TO WHOM IT MAY CONCERN

*I do, this day, locate and claim, by right of discovery, five hundred feet, running upstream from this notice. Located this 17th day of August, 1896.*

G. W. Carmack.

The claim, also by law, straddled the creek from rim-rock to rim-rock. Carmack then measured off three more claims—one additional for himself, by right of discovery, *One Above* discovery for Jim and another below for Charley which, under the claim-numbering system, became *Two Below.*

This done, and with no further thought to Robert Henderson waiting for news on the far side of the hills, the three set off through the swamps to emerge five hours later on the Klondike again, their bodies prickling with thorns.

They had moved only a short distance downriver when they came upon four beaten and discouraged men wading knee deep in the mud along the shoreline and towing a loaded boat behind them. These were Nova Scotians who had come to the Yukon Valley by way of California and had since tramped all over the territory without success. They were starving when they reached the Klondike looking for salmon, but here they had heard of Henderson's strike and now, in the intense August heat, their hunger forgotten, they were dragging their outfit upstream, searching once again for gold.

The leader, Dave McKay, asked Carmack if he had heard of Henderson's strike.

"I left there three days ago," Carmack said, holding his boat steady with a pike pole.

"What do you think of it?"

Carmack gave a slow, sly grin. "I don't like to be a knocker but I don't think much of it."

The faces of the four men fell: all were now at the end of their tether. "You wouldn't advise us to go up there?" Dan McGillivery, one of the partners, asked.

"No," said Carmack, still grinning, "because I've got something better for you." With that, he pulled out his nugget-filled cartridge case, like a conjurer plucking a rabbit from a hat.

As the Nova Scotians' eyes goggled, Carmack gave them directions to his claim. Without further ado, the four men scrambled upriver, the towline on their boat as taut as a violin string. This chance meeing with Carmack made fortunes for all of them.

"I felt as if I had just dealt myself a royal flush in the game of life, and the whole world was a jack pot," Carmack later remarked, when recalling the incident.

He reached the salmon camp at the Klondike's mouth and here he hailed two more discouraged men—Alphonse Lapierre, of Quebec, and his partner, another French Canadian. These two had been eleven years in the north and now, en route downriver to Fortymile, almost starving, out of flour and bacon, their faces blistering in the sun, they had reached the nadir of their careers.

"If I were you boys I wouldn't go any farther," Carmack told them as they beached their boat. "Haven't you heard of the new strike?"

"Oh yes, we know all about heem. I tink hees wan beeg bluff."

"How's this for bluff?" Carmack shouted, producing the gold. Again the effect was electric. The two men unloaded their boat, filled their packs and fairly ran across the flat, gesticulating with both hands and chattering in a mixture of French and English. The abandoned boat would have floated off with the current if Carmack had not secured it.

As Carmack made preparations to set off for the old mining camp of Fortymile to record his claim, he continued to tell anyone he encountered about the gold on Rabbit Creek. He made a special trip across the river to tell an old friend, then sent Jim back to guard the claims and drifted off with Tagish Charley down the Yukon, still spreading the news. He told everybody, including a man who on hearing the tale called him the biggest liar this side of hell.

Only one man Carmack did not tell. He sent not a whisper back to Robert Henderson.

Up and down the Yukon Valley the news spread like a great stage whisper. It moved as swiftly as the breeze in the birches, and more mysteriously. Men squatting by nameless creeks heard the tale, dropped their pans and headed for the Klondike. Men seated by dying campfires heard it and started up in the night, shrugging off sleep to make tracks for the new strike. Men poling up the Yukon toward the mountains or drifting down the Yukon toward the wilderness heard it, and did an abrupt about-face in the direction of the salmon stream whose name no one could pronounce properly. Some did not hear the news at all but, drifting past the Klondike's mouth, saw the boats and the tents and the gesticulating figures, felt the hair rise on their napes, and then, still uncomprehending, still unbelieving, joined the clamoring throng pushing up through the weeds and muck of Rabbit Creek.

Trader Joe Ladue already was on the scene. His quick merchant's mind had swiftly grasped the essence of the situation. Others were scrambling to stake claims, but Ladue was more interested in staking out a townsite on the swamp below the tapering mountain at the Klondike's mouth. It was worth all the gold of Bonanza; within two years lots sold for as much as five thousand dollars a front foot on the main street. Ladue named it Dawson City, after George M. Dawson, a government geologist.

By this time Rabbit Creek had an new name. A miners' meeting hastily convened on a hillside had given it the more romantic title of "Bonanza." Carmack's strike was scarcely five days old but already the valley was a scene of frenzied confusion. Men were ramming their stakes in anywhere, jumping their neighbor's claims, arguing and scrambling for ground and convening mass meetings which, in spite of their grass-roots democracy, served only to produce more anarchy. It took six months to straighten out the tangle.

At the Klondike's mouth the boats piled up on the beach, day and night, arriving as if by magic from the silent forests of the upper Yukon Valley. Many who tumbled from them and floundered up the river acted like madmen in their desire to stake and this was strange for there were few who really believed that any gold lay in the region of the Klondike. They staked from force of habit, as they had staked so often before, and once this ritual was completed, often enough they forgot about it, or failed to record their ground, or sold it for a trifle. A Klondike claim was considered virtually worthless.

Uly Gaisford, a barber from Tacoma, passed by the Klondike, still sick at heart over the infidelities of his wife, which had driven him to Alaska, and stunned by the boat wreck on the Pelly River that had cost him everything but the clothes on his back. He staked on Bonanza, but thought so little of the claim or of his own personal prospects that he went on to Circle City to take up barbering. To his later astonishment, his property produced for him fifty thousand dollars within a year.

It was the old-timers who were skeptical of Bonanza. The valley was too wide, they said, and the willows didn't lean the proper way and the water didn't taste right. It was too far upriver. It was on the wrong side of the Yukon. It was moose pasture. Only the cheechakos were too green to realize that it could not contain gold, and this naïveté made some of them rich. In that first winter, two-thirds of the richest properties in the Klondike watershed could have been purchased for a song.

Carmack himself could not start work at once. He was forced to cut logs for the sawmill Ladue had floated in to earn enough to feed himself; even then he was so short of funds that he could build only three lengths of sluice box. He had no wheelbarrow so he carried gravel in a box on his back for one hundred feet to the stream to wash out the gold. In spite of this, he cleaned up fourteen hundred dollars from surface prospects in less than one month.

But by the end of August all of Bonanza Creek had been staked, and new prospectors, arriving daily, were fanning out across the Klondike watershed looking for more ground. None realized it, but the richest treasure of all still lay undiscovered.

Down Bonanza, in search of unstaked ground, trudged a young Austrian immigrant named Antone Stander. For nine years, ever since he had landed in New York City from his home province of Unterkrien, Stander had been seeking his fortune in the remote corners of the continent, working as a cowboy, as a sheep herder, as a farmer, as a coal miner and now as a prospector. When he arrived in the New World, unable to speak a word of English, he had just one dollar and seventy-five cents to his name and after mastering the language and walking over most of North America on foot, he was no richer. All his funds had been spent on the trip north in the spring of 1896. Now, on this last day of August, he was embarking on a final gamble.

He was a handsome man, just twenty-nine years old, with dark curly hair and sensitive, romantic-looking features. As he reached the south fork of Bonanza Creek, a few hundred feet above Carmack's claim, he stopped to examine it curiously. The narrow wooded ravine, with a trickle of water snaking along its bottom, still had no name. The prospectors referred to it in Yukon parlance as "Bonanza's pup." It was soon to be known as Eldorado.

Stander arrived at the forks with four companions, all of whom had already staked on Bonanza. They had little faith in their property but, on an impulse, they walked up the pup in a group and one of them sank a pan into the sand. Like Stander, each had reached the end of the line, financially. Now they stared into the first pan and to their astonishment saw that there was more than six dollars' worth of gold in the bottom. They had no way of knowing it, but this was the richest creek in the world and each of the claims staked that day eventually produced one million dollars or more.

Gold lying in the gravels on the creek's edge did not necessarily mean that the valley was rich. Before that could be determined, someone would have to go through the arduous labor of burning one or more shafts down at least fifteen feet to bedrock, searching for the "pay streak" (which might not exist), hauling the muck up by windlass to the surface, and washing it down to find out how much gold there really was. This back-breaking labor could easily occupy two months. And until the spring thaw came and the rushing creek provided enough head of water to wash thoroughly the gravels drawn up the shaft all winter, no one could really say exactly how rich Eldorado was—if, indeed, it was rich at all.

To most men, then, Eldorado was as much

of a gamble as the Irish sweepstake. Some, such as Stander, determined to take the gamble and hold their ground and work it to see whether it really did contain gold. Nobody knew that this was the richest placer creek in the world, that almost every claim from *One* to *Forty* was worth at least half a million and that some were worth three times that amount and that a quarter of a century later dredges would still be taking gold from the worked-over gravels.

So the roulette wheel spun around on Eldorado. Al Thayer and Winfield Oler had staked out *Twenty-Nine* and believing it worthless returned to Fortymile, looking for a sucker on whom to unload it. They found their quarry in Jimmy Kerry's saloon in the person of Charlie Anderson, a thirty-seven-old-year Swede with a pinched face, who had been mining for several years out of Fortymile. Anderson was so doubtful of the Klondike that he had delayed his trip to the new field until all the ground was gone. Now he was drinking heavily, and Oler, a small and slender man from Baltimore, saw his chance. Anderson woke up the next morning to find he had bought an untried claim for eight hundred dollars. He went to the police post to try to retrieve his money; but the deal was legal. Anderson glumly headed for Eldorado. He had no way of knowing yet that a million dollars' worth of gold lay in the bedrock under his claim and that for the rest of his life he would bear the tag of "the Lucky Swede." As for Oler, he became the butt of so many jokes that he fled the country in disgust.

Next door to Charlie Anderson, on *Thirty*, the groundwork for the most staggering fortune of all was being laid. The claim had been staked by Russian John Zarnowsky, who thought so little of it that he let half of it go for a sack of flour and a side of bacon. The purchaser was an elephantine Nova Scotian known as "Big Alex" McDonald, who until this moment had known neither weal nor leisure. But the pay-streak on *Thirty* was forty feet wide and a man could, and did, pan five thousand dollars from it in a single day.

With this purchase, McDonald began his lightning ascent from unlettered day laborer to Klondike aristocrat. Any ordinary creature would have been content with this single piece of ground, but McDonald was not ordinary. While others sold, he bought—and he continued to buy as long as there was breath in his body. Within a year he was famous, hailed on three continents as "the King of the Klondike," sought out by pope, prince and promoter.

And yet, who is to say which were the lucky ones in the Eldorado lottery? Many who sold out and left the country ended their lives in relative comfort. Many who stayed behind to dig out fortunes lost all in the end. William Sloan, a Nanaimo dry-goods merchant who sold his interest in *Fifteen* for fifty thousand dollars and turned his back on the Klondike forever, invested his money wisely and rose to become a cabinet minister in British Columbia's provincial government. His son became chief justice of the province. But the King of the Klondike died both penniless and alone.

All this while, on the other side of the Bonanza watershed, Robert Henderson continued to toil at his open cut on the creek he had wistfully named Gold Bottom. Boats were arriving daily at Dawson; shacks were being clapped together helter-skelter; Bonanza was staked for fourteen miles and Eldorado for three; and men were spraying across the whole of the Klondike country searching for new discoveries. Henderson knew nothing of this: he had seen no one but his partners since that August day when Carmack had gone off, promising to send word back if he found anything on the other side of the blue hills.

Then one day—some three weeks after the strike—Henderson looked up and saw a group of men coming down from the divide. He asked them where they had come from, and they replied: "Bonanza Creek." The name puzzled Henderson, who prided himself on a knowledge of the country. Where was Bonanza Creek? The newcomers pointed back over the hill.

"Rabbit Creek! What have you got there?" Henderson asked, with a sinking feeling.

"We have the biggest thing in the world."

"Who found it?"

"McCormick."

Henderson flung down his shovel, then walked slowly over to the bank of the creek and sat down. It was some time before he could speak. McCormick! Carmack! For the rest of his life the sound of that name would be like a cold knife in his heart. The man was not even a prospector . . .

Years later Henderson accepted a two-hundred-dollar-a-month pension from the Canadian government as "co-discoverer" of the Klondike goldfields. This was his sole reward.

ROBERT THOMAS ALLEN

# What I Remember Most about School

Now that the kids are off to school again, I notice questions being raised. Should we teach more science? Are we neglecting the gifted child? Is PTA doing a job? Sometimes all this makes me wonder if anybody remembers what school is all about. You'd think it was a place where you tried to learn something, instead of a place you tried to forget, keep out of as long as possible, make disappear with games, dreams and magic.

Not learning anything at school was a mark of manhood, like not being neat. The kid who stood thirty-first in my class, before standings were abolished on the ground that they made backward students feel insecure, wore a beam of triumph on his face that made you feel like a sissy. He was a fat good-natured kid who chuckled his way through predicate adjectives, the French explorers, decimals, compound and complex fractions and singing, which was taught once a month by a mysterious soft brown woman who smelled of moth balls. I've noticed that some people seem to occupy a particular few square feet of the world's surface a lot more permanently and comfortably than other people, and this boy was one of them. He just sat there chuckling and flipping elastics, pins and spit balls, and waiting for the whole thing to blow over.

Standing first was something done only by a little girl in a clean white middy who looked at boys as if they'd got off a leash somewhere. Occasionally you were in love with her and if you happened to get a desk near hers you sat there stunned and grinning through entire eras of world history. In this condition you'd get vague impressions that England was made up of churchly old buildings that smelled a bit like the Royal Ontario Museum, and was occupied by rather admirable men who worked everything out by stabbing little dukes and cutting off women's heads; or that Canada was a green carpet miles wide with here and there men with hats on talking to bald Hurons.

Being in love didn't last long, but then we didn't spend long on a country. I remember we took the United States during two weeks when I had tonsilitis, and for years the entire nation appeared to me as twenty-one blank pages in my geography. When I came back without my tonsils, we'd somehow got onto Sir Wilfrid Laurier, with his high collars and parted hair and Parliament, and I began wondering if summer holidays would ever come—a feeling about politics that, by and large, the years haven't altered.

But, at best, school was just something that temporarily barred the way to the real world which, for me, was located about where that curved line cut the tops off the provinces: a world of snowshoes, trap lines and birchbark drinking cups. This was where I lived mentally for the biggest part of eight years and through every educational method devised by the Ontario Board of Education. It was a world filled with a sort of spiritual gas, like a Christian's heaven, which left no room for pain, duty, past participles, shame, fear or sifting ashes on Saturday morning.

Slit-eyed, peering out from my parka hood with beads of ice on my beard, the only living thing in a frozen land, I got the mails through. You could depend on Bob Allen. He knew the north country. He was indestructible, tight-lipped, tough; entirely unlike my teacher, a fat, pale, intellectual man named Mr. Kew, who never stopped talking in a voice that sounded as if he were crawling out of a fight. He'd make incredible jokes, like "Greenland's chief export is icebergs," and turn his lips inside out and grin horribly. He was as far as you could get from being a trapper. I've noticed that the older I get the closer I come to catching up with Mr. Kew: in fact, this morning when I looked in the mirror, I think I passed him.

Somewhere, psychologically, between the real world and the world of the classroom with its smell of ink, chalk and wet wool mitts on hot radiators, was the schoolyard, a barren waste of baked clay with occasional islands of pigweed and plantain, where life, although undeniably real, somehow didn't always work out the way it did for the characters in James Oliver Curwood.

For instance, there were the schoolyard fights, the salty taste of getting whacked on the nose and the dreadful cries of the spectators who, for some incredible reason, were cheering for some strange boy with a dirty face and no lips to take another poke at that favorite and all-round sterling character—you.

Fights were never connected with rage. They may have started with rage. But you soon were left with nothing to sustain you but the dread of not behaving like Hoot Gibson when you heard the distant cries of "Fight! Fight! Fight!" and the sounds of kids running from all corners of the schoolyard to encircle you and your foe with a ring that I remember as about the size of the Plains of Abraham. When that happened, there was nothing left to do but pull your head down into the collar of your overcoat and start swinging and praying that it would soon be over. If you got licked it was days before you could again see yourself bearded, indestructible and tough.

As I remember it, I had an average number of wins and losses. But there was one boy I wanted to lick, a kid named Art Sweeny—a boy with a bland smiling face, an air of calm reservoirs of power, and a distant look in his blue eyes as if searching for a worthy opponent. My life's ambition was to lick Art Sweeny, although I had nothing against him. It was something the same feeling as that of the mountain climber who, asked why he wanted to climb a mountain, said, "Because it's there."

But I never had a fight with Art. I met him recently on Yonge Street in Toronto. He had evidently stopped growing shortly after I knew him, because he was even shorter than I am—a dapper, friendly, wistful little bond salesman with a black pencil-line mustache and an appointment with a psychiatrist. Yet, after thirty-five years, during which I've forgotten everything from who came after Queen Elizabeth to which was Hochelaga and which was Stadacona, when Sweeny spoke to me there on Yonge Street in the same quiet, breathy voice I remembered, I caught myself wondering whether I could lick him if I did exercises every day for a month and got my stomach down and stopped smoking.

There were times, too, when you got into such trouble that you would have given anything to be anywhere where life was normal again, even sitting listening to one of Mr. Kew's jokes about icebergs. Like when the teacher in charge of seeing that we stood perfectly still and silent before starting to march into school caught you shouldering the kid next to you, or knocking the books out of a girl's arms ahead of you. He'd give his handbell a ring, grab the clapper, which strangled off the sound, and point with the wooden handle.

"That boy. Go to the principal's office."

There would be a petrified moment when you looked completely innocent and tried to tell yourself that he meant someone else.

"You. You there."

You'd lower your head, look up at him and point at your chest. "Me?" you'd say, forming the word silently with your lips.

"Yes, you. You there. No, no, no, no." He'd never give up once he'd started. "The second boy from the right. That boy with the round hat."

My mother used to cut the peaks off my brother's caps when they got V-shaped and I'd wear them like a sort of tweed beret. I could kid myself for just so long that I wasn't the one the teacher was pointing at. Then there'd be the long lonely walk across the planks toward the office of the principal, who received these visits in complete silence, not even asking what you'd done. He'd just open his desk drawer, take out a big ledger with the right place marked by a leather strap, and neatly enter your name, by which time you'd be in such a trance that the strap wouldn't hurt at all. You'd have the further consolation, when you got back to your class among friends, of being able to hold your hands against the cast-iron sides of your desk, making a great production of cooling the unbearable heat, and grinning in a worldly way at the nearest girl.

In fact, a school as I remember it was pretty much the way life has been ever since. There were triumphs, fears, defeats and humiliations, friends and enemies. And there were occasional disturbing feelings about the human race, like one time, I remember, when a fat homely girl in thick glasses came to school in a grotesque fur coat her mother had made for her and within a few minutes every kid in the schoolyard was following her, jeering.

The sight of her red, distraught face, as she looked for a place to hide, remained with me long after I'd forgotten the dates of every battle from Harcourt to Waterloo.

You didn't have to address sales meetings but you had oral composition. You'd get up, grin at your co-students, who wore various expectant expressions, the boys busy fixing catapults of elastic bands and bent pins, and go into your speech: "The moose. The moose lives in the far-off wastes of Canada. It is our biggest animal. At certain times hunters shoot the moose. This is called the moose season. Sometimes hunters shoot one another." You'd keep at it with an idiotic grin until the teacher said that was just fine.

You didn't try to get out of work with businessmen's luncheons and coffee breaks. You put your nose down into your textbooks and smelled them, or drew birchbark canoes around the margins and put mustaches on everyone from Columbus to General Currie. You spent hour after hour carving tracks in the desk top with your pencils, naming them after streetcar lines and deepening them a bit every day until you could switch from one track to another without having to look at the desk. If you did it carefully and quietly, you could tap a pin with the edge of your ruler until it was about a quarter of an inch through the top of your desk, or you could hold your ruler tight on the desk with one hand and flip it with the other till it vibrated, making a sound similar to the one I hear after four martinis.

There were dark, brown, wet Monday mornings after a weekend of fun, when you didn't exactly have a hangover but just the thought of parsing a sentence made you keep yourself late playing with the water from the melting ice, chopping new channels to the gutter with your heel. But there were also bright, wind-swept mornings that made the school flag crackle, when all the wonderful things that were going to happen didn't seem far away, and the boys all tried to see who could climb and jump the highest, and the girls gathered to gossip over the raised side of the school-yard, silhouetted against the rooftops and chicken-wire netting and looking as if they were in another world.

You didn't look forward to the last payment on your car or read *The Power of Positive Thinking* in those days, but there was a better world just ahead all the same, where things would be different and everything easy. I'm still looking for it, and sometimes think I may be just on the verge of finding it. I haven't yet.

COLIN  McDOUGALL

# The Firing Squad

He was the first Canadian soldier sentenced to death, and rear headquarters in Italy seethed with the prospect of carrying it out. At his marble-topped desk in Rome Major-General Paul Vincent read the instructions from London with distaste. The findings of the court martial had been confirmed by Ottawa—that meant by a special session of the cabinet, the General supposed—and it was now the direct responsibility of the Area Commander that the execution of Private Sydney Jones should be proceeded with "as expeditiously as possible."

The hum of voices and the quick beat of teletypes in the outer office marked the measure of Rome's agitation. No one had expected this confirmation of sentence. Not even the officers who had sentenced Private Jones to death. For them, indeed, there had been little choice: Jones had even wanted to plead guilty, but the court had automatically changed his plea, and gone on to record its inevitable finding and sentence.

The salient facts of the case filed quickly through the neat corridors of General Vincent's mind. This Jones, a young soldier of twenty-two, had deserted his unit, had joined with a group of deserter-gangsters who operated in Rome and Naples, and had been present when his companions shot and killed a U.S. military policeman. All this Jones admitted, and the court could pass no other sentence. The execution of a Canadian soldier, however, was more than a military matter: it touched on public policy; and higher authorities had never before confirmed a sentence of death.

General Vincent sighed. He preferred to think of himself as the business executive he happened to be rather than a general officer whose duty it was to order a man's death. An execution was something alien and infinitely distasteful. Well, if this thing had to be done under his command, at least it need not take place under his personal orders. From the beginning he had known just the man for the job. Already the teletype had clicked off its command to Volpone, the reinforcement base where Private Jones was imprisoned, and a staff car would now be rushing the commander of that base, Brigadier Benny Hatfield, to Rome. The General sighed again and turned to some more congenial correspondence on his desk.

A dirt track spiraled out of Volpone and mounted in white gashes upon the forested mountainside. Fifty infantry reinforcements, fresh from Canada, were spaced along the first two miles of zigzag road. They carried all the paraphernalia of their fledgling trade: rifles, machine guns and light mortars. Some were trying to run, lurching ahead with painful steps; others stopped to stand panting in their own small lakes of sweat. One or two lay at the roadside, faces turned from the sun, awaiting the stabbing scorn of their sergeant with spent indifference. But they all spat out the clogging dust, and cursed the officer who led them.

Farther up the hillside this man ran with the gait of an athlete pushing himself to the limit of endurance. Head down he ran doggedly through the dust and the heat; he ran as though trying to outdistance some merciless pursuer. Captain John Adam was going to run up that mountainside until he could run no more. He was running from last night, and all the nights which still lay ahead. He was running from his own sick self. Almost at the halfway mark, he aimed himself at a patch of bush underneath the cliff and smashed into it headlong. He lay quite still; he had achieved exhaustion: the closest condition to forgetfulness he could ever find.

For Captain John Adam found it unbearable to live with himself and with his future. He had lost his manhood. As an infantry company commander, he had drawn daily strength and sustenance from the respect of his fellow fighting men. They knew him as a brave leader, a compassionate man. He had been granted the trust and friendship of men when it was all they had left to give, and this he knew to be the ultimate gift, the highest good. And then, one sun-filled morning, he had forfeited these things for ever. He had cracked wide open; he had cried his fear and panic to the world; he had run screaming from the battle, through the ranks of his white-faced men. He had been sent back here to Volpone in unexpressed disgrace while the authorities decided what to do with him.

Now Captain John Adam rolled over and then stood up, a tall young man, looking brisk and competent. His sunbrowned face, his blue eyes, the power of his easy movements, even the cigarette dangling negligently from his lips, all seemed to proclaim that here was the ideal young infantry officer.

"Sergeant Konzuk," Captain Adam called now. "Get these men the hell back to barracks, and leave me alone here!"

The sergeant did not look surprised. He was used to such things by now, and this was no officer to argue with. Sure, he'd take them back to barracks, and let Adam do his own explaining. "All right, you guys—on your feet!" said Konzuk. It was no skin to him.

It was late afternoon by the time he had smoked the last of his cigarettes and Adam came down from the mountain. Striding through the camp he frowned with displeasure when he saw the hulking form of Padre Dixon planted squarely in his path. Normally, he knew, he would have liked this chaplain but he made a point of refusing the friendliness which this big man was trying to offer.

"Mind if I walk along with you, son?" Adam was forced to stop while the Padre knocked his pipe against his boot.

The two men walked on together through the dusk, picking their way between the huts and the barrack blocks. As they neared the officers' mess the Padre stopped and his fingers gripped Adam's arm. He pointed to a small grey hut just within the barbed-wire of the camp entrance. "That's where poor Jones is waiting out his time," the Padre said.

"Well?"

The Padre shrugged and seemed busy with his pipe. "No matter what he's done he's a brave boy, and he's in a dreadful position now."

"He won't be shot." Adam repeated the general feeling of the camp without real interest. "They'll never confirm the sentence."

The Padre looked him directly in the face. "Adam," he said. "It has been confirmed. He is going to be executed!"

"No!" Adam breathed his disbelief aloud. He was truly shocked, and for this instant his own sick plight was forgotten. This other thing seemed so—improper. That a group of Canadians could come together in this alien land for the purpose of destroying one of their own kind . . . And every day, up at the battle, every effort was being made to save life; there were so few of them in Italy, and so pitifully many were being killed every day. This thing was simply—not right.

His eyes sought for the Padre's. "But why?" he asked, with a kind of hurt in his voice. "Tell me—why?"

"The boy's guilty, after all."

"Technically—he was only a witness. And even if he is guilty, do you think this thing is right?"

The Padre could not ignore the urgency in Adam's voice. He spoke at last with unaccustomed sharpness. "No," he said. "It may be something that has to be done—but it will never be right."

The two men looked at one another in the gathering Italian night. For a moment their thoughts seemed to merge and flow together down the same pulsing stream. But then a new idea came to Adam. "Padre," he said, "why are you telling me about this?"

Then they both saw the figure running toward them from the officers' mess. It was Ramsay, the ever-flurried, ever-flustered Camp Adjutant. He panted to a stop in front of them. "Adam," he gasped out. "The Brigadier wants you at once!"

Brigadier Benny Hatfield waited patiently in his office. He liked to feed any new or disturbing thoughts through the mill of his mind until the gloss of familiarity made them less troublesome. Early in his career he had discovered that the calibre of his mind was not sufficiently large for the rank he aspired to, and so deliberately he had cultivated other qualities which would achieve the same end. He emphasized an air of outspoken bluntness, his physical toughness, a presumed knowledge of the way the "troops" thought, and his ability to work like a horse. Indeed the impression he sometimes conveyed was that of a grizzled war horse, fanatic about good soldiering, but with it all intensely loyal, and a very good fellow. Now he sat and considered his interview with General Vincent. He understood his superior's unexpressed motives perfectly well: it was a straight question of passing the buck. This execution was a simple matter of military discipline, after all, and he would ensure that it was carried out in such a way that no possible discredit could reflect on himself. The General, he believed, had made an intelligent choice, and he had an equally good selection of his own in mind. Ramsay was ushering Captain Adam into his presence.

The Brigadier looked up at last. "Well," he stated, "Captain John Adam." His eyes bored steadily at Adam's face and he waited in silence. He knew that in a moment his unwavering stare would force some betrayal of guilt or inferiority. He waited, and at last he was rewarded: the sweat swelled on Adam's forehead, and the man before him felt it essential to break the intolerable silence. "Yes, sir," Adam had to say.

The Brigadier stood up then. "Well," he said again. "It can't be as bad as all that, can it, boy?" His mouth lifted the straggling mustache in a grimace of affability, and despite himself Adam felt a small rush of gratitude.

But then the smile died. "It does not please me," the Brigadier said coldly, " to receive the worst possible reports about you." He consulted the papers on his desk. "You have read this report from Colonel Dodd?" It was a needless question. Adam knew the report by memory. It was an "adverse" report: It was the reason why he was back here at Volpone. That piece of paper was his doom. "Not fit to command men in action," it read; "not suitable material for the field."

With ungoverned ease Adam's mind slipped back to that sun-filled morning on the Hitler Line. They were walking through a meadow —slowly, for there were Schu mines in the grass—and they moved toward a hidden place of horror: a line of dug-in tank turrets, and mine-strewn belts of wire. And then the earth suddenly erupted with shell and mortar bursts; they floundered in a beaten zone of observed machine-gun fire. A few men got as far as the wire, but none of them lived. There was a regrouping close to the start line, and Adam was ordered to attack again.

The first symptom he noticed was that his body responded to his mind's orders several seconds too late. He became worried at this time lag, the fact that his mind and body seemed about to divide, to assume their own separate identities. Then the air bursts shook the world; no hole in the ground was shelter from the rain of deafening black explosions in the sky above them. Then he remembered the terrible instant that the separation became complete, that he got up and shouted his shame to the world. He got up from his ditch, and he ran blubbering like a baby through his white-faced men. And some of his men followed him, back into the arms of Colonel Dodd.

"Yes," Adam said now, his face white. "I've read the report."

Brigadier Hatfield spoke softly. "If that report goes forward from here you'll be in a bad way—at least returned to Canada for Adjutant General's disposal, some second-rate kind of discharge, the reputation always clinging to you . . ." The Brigadier shook his head. "That would be a pity."

If the report goes forward . . . A pulse of excitement beat in Adam's throat. What did he mean—was there any possibility that the report could be stopped here?

"Adam!" The Brigadier pounded a fist upon his desk. "I have confidence in you. Of all the officers under my command I have selected you for a mission of the highest importance."

Adam blinked his disbelief, but the hope swelled strong inside him.

"Yes," the Brigadier said steadily. "You are to command the firing squad for the execution of Private Jones!"

Adam blinked again and he turned his head away. For a moment he was weak with nausea the flood of shame was so sour inside him. "No," he heard his voice saying. "I can't do it."

The Brigadier's smile grew broader, and he spoke with soft assurance. "But you can, my boy. But you can." And the Brigadier told him how.

It was all very neat. Adam had his choice, of course. On the one hand, he could choose routine disposal of his case by higher authorities. Colonel Dodd's report, together with Brigadier Hatfield's own statement, would ensure an outcome which, as the Brigadier described it, would cause "deep shame to his family and friends," and Adam was sure of that. On the other hand, if he performed this necessary act of duty, this simple military function, then Colonel Dodd's report would be destroyed. He could return to Canada as soon as he desired, bearing Brigadier Hatfield's highest recommendations.

The Brigadier went on to say that the man Jones was a convicted murderer—that Adam should have no scruples on that score . . . Adam listened and each soft word seemed to add to his degradation. This was the inevitable consequence of his lost manhood.

The Brigadier's voice was kindly; his words flowed endlessly like a soft stream of liquid. Then the voice paused. "Of course," the Brigadier said, "it is a task for a determined and courageous man." His glance darted over Adam's bent head and flickered around the room.

Adam broke the silence at last. He spoke without looking up. "All right," he said. "I'll do it."

The Brigadier's response was quick and warm. "Good," he said. "Good fellow!" His smile was almost caressing. "Your sergeant must be a first-rate man, and—it is most desirable that he be a volunteer. Do you understand?"

Adam forced himself to nod.

The Brigadier stared directly in Adam's face. His voice now rang with steel of command. "All right," he said. "Bring me the sergeant's name and a draft of your parade orders by 1100 hours tomorrow." He leaned back and allowed the smile to possess his face. He had selected exactly the right man for this delicate job.

By next morning the news had raced to every Canadian in Italy. At the battle up north men heard about this execution with a dull kind of wonder. Advancing into the attack it was brought to them like bad news in a letter from home; they looked at each other uneasily, or they laughed and turned away. It was not the death of one man back in a place called Volpone that mattered. It was simply that up here they measured and counted their own existence so dear that an unnecessary death, a planned death of one of their own fellows seemed somehow shameful. It made them sour and restless as they checked their weapons and ammunition loads.

In the camp at Volpone it was the sole topic of conversation. It was soon known that the news had reached the prisoner also, although, to be sure, it did not seem to have changed his routine in the least. All his waking hours were busied with an intense display of military activity. The guard sergeant reported that he made and remade his bed several times a day, working earnestly to achieve the neatest possible tuck of his blanket. The floor was swept five times a day and scrubbed at least once. His battle-dress was ironed to knife-edge exactness, and his regimental flashes resewn to his tunic as though the smartest possible fit at the shoulder was always just eluding him. At times he would glance at the stack of magazines the Padre brought him, but these were thrown aside as soon as a visitor entered his room. Private Jones would spring to a quiveringly erect position of attention; he would respond to questions with a quick, cheerful smile. He was the embodiment of the keen, alert and well turned-out private soldier.

The truth was, of course, that Private Jones was a somewhat pliable young man who was desperately anxious to please. He was intent on proving himself such a good soldier that the generals would take note and approve, and never do anything very bad to him. The idea that some of his fellow soldiers might take him out and shoot him was a terrible abstraction, quite beyond his imagination. Consequently, Private Jones did not believe in the possibility of his own execution. Even when the Padre came and tried to prepare him, Private Jones simply jumped eagerly to attention, polished boots glittering, and rattled off, head high: "Yes, sir. Very good, sir."

A surprising amount of administrative detail is required to arrange an execution. The Brigadier was drawing up an elaborate operation order, with each phase to be checked and double checked. There were the official witness, the medical officers, the chaplain, the guards, the firing squad, of course; and the conveyance and placing of all these to the proper spot at the right time.

Captain Adam's first problem was more serious than any of this: his first attempts to recruit the sergeant for his firing squad met with utter failure. After conferring with the Brigadier he decided upon a new approach, and he went in search of Sergeant Konzuk.

The sergeant was lying at ease on his bed reading a magazine. When Adam came in, Konzuk scowled. He swung his boots over the side of the bed and he crossed his thick arms over his chest. Adam wasted no time. "Konzuk," he said, " I want you as sergeant of the firing squad." The sergeant laughed rudely.

"Never mind that," Adam said. "Wait till you hear about this deal."

"Look," Sergeant Konzuk said. He stood up and his eyes were angry on Adam's face. "I done my share of killing. Those that like it can do this job."

Adam's tone did not change. "You're married, Konzuk. You've a wife and two kids. Well, you can be back in Winnipeg within the month."

Konzuk's mouth opened; his eyes were wide. His face showed all the wild thoughts thronging through his mind. The sergeant had left Canada in 1940; his wife wrote him one laborious letter a month. But his frown returned and his fists were clenched.

"Look," Konzuk said, fumbling with his words. "This kid's one of us—see. It ain't right!"

"Winnipeg—within the month."

Konzuk's eyes shifted and at last his glance settled on the floor. "All right," he said, after a moment. "All right, I'll do it."

"Good." Adam sought for and held the sergeant's eyes. "And remember this, Konzuk —that 'kid' is a murderer!"

"Yes, sir."

The ten members of the firing squad were detailed the same day. Adam and Konzuk prepared the list of names and brought the group to be interviewed by Brigadier Hatfield in his office. And after that Sergeant Konzuk had a quiet talk with each man. Adam did not ask what the sergeant said; he was satisfied that none of the men came to him to protest.

Adam found his time fully occupied. He had installed his ten men in a separate hut of their own; there were some drill movements to be practiced; and Sergeant Konzuk was drawing new uniforms from the quartermaster's stores. Ten new rifles had also been issued.

Crossing the parade square that night he encountered Padre Dixon, and he realized that this man had been avoiding him during the past two days. "Padre," he called out. "I want to talk to you." The Padre waited. His face showed no expression.

"Padre—will you give me your advice?"

The Padre's glance was cold. "Why?" he asked. "It won't change anything."

And looking into that set face Adam saw that the Padre was regarding him with a dislike he made no attempt to conceal. He flushed, and his anger slipped forward. "What's the matter, Padre—you feeling sorry for the boy-murderer?"

Adam regretted his words at once; indeed he was shocked that he could have said them. The Padre turned his back and started away.

Adam caught at his arm. "Ah, no," he said. "I didn't mean that. Padre—is what I'm doing so awful, after all?"

"You've made your choice. Let it go at that."

"But—my duty . . ." Adam felt shame as he used the word.

The Padre stood with folded arms. "Listen," he said. "I told you before: no matter how necessary this thing is it will never be right."

Adam was silent. Then he reached out his

hand again. "Padre," he said in a low voice, "Is there no way it can be stopped?"

The Padre sighed. "The train has been set in motion," he said. "Once it could have been stopped—in Ottawa—but now . . ." He shrugged. He looked at Adam searchingly and he seemed to reflect. "There might be one way—" After a moment he blinked and looked away. "But no—that will never come to pass. I suppose I should wish you good luck," he said. "Good night, Adam."

That meeting made Adam wonder how his fellow officers regarded him. In the officers' mess that night he looked about him and found out. Silence descended when he approached a group and slowly its members would drift away; there was a cleared circle around whichever chair he sat in. Even the barman seemed to avoid his glance.

All right, Adam decided then, and from the bar he looked murderously around the room. All right, he would stick by Benny Hatfield— the two of them, at least, knew what duty and soldiering was! Why, what was he doing that was so awful? He was simply commanding a firing squad to execute a soldier who had committed a murder. That's all—he was commanding a firing squad; he was, he was—an executioner!

His glass crashed to the floor. Through all the soft words exchanged with Brigadier Hatfield, all the concealing echelons of military speech, the pitiless truth now leaped out at him. He was an executioner. Captain John Adam made a noise in his throat, and the faces of the other men in the room went white.

When he left the mess some instinct led him toward the small grey hut standing at the camp entrance. Through the board walls of that hut he could see his victim, Jones, living out his allotted time, while he, Adam, the executioner, walked implacably close by. The new concept of victim and executioner seized and threatened to suffocate him.

Brigadier Hatfield had the most brilliant inspiration of his career: the place of execution would be changed to Rome! There was ample justification, of course, since the effect on the troops' morale at Volpone would be bad to say the least. No one could dispute this, and all the while the Brigadier relished in imagination the face of General Vincent when he found the affair brought back to his own doorstep.

The Brigadier was in high good humor as he presided at the conference to discuss this change. All the participants were present, including one newcomer, an officer from the Provost Corps, introduced as Colonel Mc-

Guire. This colonel said nothing, but nodded his head in agreement with the Brigadier's points. His eyes roamed restlessly from face to face and his cold glance seemed to strip bare the abilities of every person in the room.

Colonel McGuire, the Brigadier announced, had been instrumental in finding the ideal place for the affair. It was a former Fascist barracks on the outskirts of Rome, and all the—ah, facilities—were readily available. Everyone taking part, and he trusted that each officer was now thoroughly familiar with his duties, would move by convoy to Rome that very afternoon. The execution—here he paused for a solemn moment—the execution would take place at 0800 hours tomorrow morning. Any questions? No? Thank you, gentlemen.

Adam was moving away when the Brigadier stopped him. "John," he called. He had slipped into the habit of using his first name now. "I want you to meet Colonel McGuire."

They shook hands and Adam flushed under the chill exposure of those probing eyes. After a moment the Colonel's glance dropped; he had seen sufficient. As Adam moved off to warn his men for the move he felt those cold eyes following him to the door, and beyond.

Adam kept his eyes closed while Sergeant Kozuk drove. In the back of the jeep Padre Dixon had not spoken since the convoy was marshaled; it was clear that these were not the traveling companions of his choice. Although Adam would not look, all his awareness was centred on a closed three-ton truck which lumbered along in the middle of the convoy. The condemned man and his guards rode inside that vehicle.

The concept of victim and executioner filled Adam's mind to the exclusion of all else. He had tried throwing the blame back to the comfortable politicians sitting at their polished table in Ottawa, but it was no use. He knew that it was his voice that would issue the last command. He was the executioner. . . . Then another thought came to torment him without mercy: How did his victim, Jones, feel now?

They stopped for ten minutes outside a hilltop town, where pink villas glinted among the green of olive trees. Adam followed Padre Dixon to the place where he sat in an orchard. The Padre looked up at him wearily. "How is he taking it?" Adam demanded at once.

The Padre scrambled to his feet. His eyes flashed with anger. "Who? The boy-murderer?"

"Please, Padre—I've got to know!"

The Padre stared at Adam's drawn face. Then he passed a hand across his eyes. "Adam —forgive me. I know it's a terrible thing for you. If it makes it any easier . . . well, Jones is brave; he's smiling and polite, and that's all. But Adam—the boy still doesn't understand. He doesn't believe that it's really going to happen!" The Padre's voice shook with his agitation.

Adam nodded his head. "That other time, Padre—you said there might be a way of stopping it. . . ."

"No, forget that—it's too late." The spluttering cough of motorcycles roared between them. "Come. It is time to go." And the Padre laid his hand on Adam's arm.

Adam and Konzuk stood on the hard tarmac and surveyed the site gloomily. The place they had come to inspect was a U-shaped space cut out of the forest. The base of the U was a red-brick wall, and down each side marched a precise green line of cypresses. The wall was bullet-pocked because this place had been used as a firing range, although imagination balked at what some of the targets must have been. On the right wing of the U a small wooden grandstand was set in front of the cypresses. Adam looked around at all this, and then his gaze moved over the trees and up to the pitilessly blue sky above. "All right, Konzuk," he said. "You check things over." And he went away to be alone.

At midnight Adam was lying on his bed in the darkness. His eyes were wide open but he made no move when he saw the Padre's big form stumble into his room. Then the Padre stood over his bed, eyes groping for him. He was breathing loudly. "Adam—he wants to see you!"

"No!"

"You must!"

"I couldn't!" Now Adam sat up in bed. His battle-dress tunic was crumpled. His face was protected by the dark, but his voice was naked. "No, Padre," he pleaded. "I couldn't."

"Look, son—it's your job. You've no choice. Do you understand?"

There was silence. Adam made a noise in the darkness which seemed to take all the breath from his body. "Yes, I understand." He was fumbling for his belt and cap in the dark.

The provost sergeant came to attention and saluted. His face was stiff but he could not keep the flicker of curiosity from his eyes. Adam saw that this was a real prison: concrete flooring, steel doors and iron bars. They stood in what seemed to be a large brightly lit guardroom. A card game had been taking place, and there were coffee mugs, but the guards stood now at respectful attention.

"Where is he?" Adam turned to the sergeant.

A dark-haired young man stepped from among the group of guards. A smartly dressed soldier, clean and good looking in his freshly pressed battle-dress. "Here I am, sir," the young man said.

Adam took a step back; he flashed a glance at the door.

The sergeant spoke then, apologetically. "He wanted company, sir. I thought it would be all right."

"It was good of you to come, sir." This was Private Jones speaking for his attention.

Adam forced himself to return the glance. "Yes," he said. "I mean—it's no trouble. I—I was glad to."

The two men looked one another in the face, perhaps surprised to find how close they were in years. Jones's smile was friendly. He was like a host easing the embarrassment of his guest. "Would you like to sit down, sir?"

"Yes. Oh, yes."

They sat in Jones's cell, on opposite sides of a small table. Because he had to, Adam held his eyes on the prisoner's face and now he could see the thin lines of tension spreading from the eyes and at the mouth. It was certain that Jones now believed in the truth of his own death, and he carried this fact with quiet dignity.

"It was good of you to come," Private Jones said again. "I have a request."

Surely, Adam thought, it took more courage to act as Jones did now than to advance through that meadow to the Hitler Line. . . .

"Well, sir," Jones went on, his face set. "I'm ready to take—tomorrow morning. But one thing worries me: I don't want you and the other boys to feel bad about this. I thought it might help if I shook hands with all the boys before—before it happens."

Adam looked down at the concrete floor. Well, he had to say something. The thing was impossible, of course.

Jones read the working of his face. "Never mind, sir—maybe you'd just give them that message for me—"

"I will, Jones. I will!" Adam stood up; he could not stay here another moment.

Jones said, "Maybe—you would shake hands with me?"

Adam stood utterly still. His voice came out as a whisper in that small space. "Jones," he said, "I was going to ask you if I could."

It was a softly fragrant morning. The dew was still fresh on the grass and a light ground mist rolled away before the heat of the climbing sun. In the forest clearing the neat groups of soldiers looked clean and compact in their khaki battle-dress with the bright regimental flashes gleaming at their shoulders. The firing squad stood "at ease," but with not the least stir or motion. Captain Adam stood several paces apart at the left. The grandstand was filled with a small group of official witnesses and in front of it stood Brigadier Benny Hatfield. A step behind the Brigadier was Ramsay, his adjutant; then Padre Dixon, and the chief medical officer. The assembly was complete—except for one man.

Somewhere in the background a steel door clanged, a noise which no one affected to hear. Then there came the sound of rapid marching. Three military figures came into view and halted smartly in front of Brigadier Hatfield. Private Jones, hatless, stood in the centre, a provost sergeant on each side. The boy's lips were white, his cheeks lacked color, but he held his head high, his hands were pressed tight against the seams of his battle-dress trousers. It was impossible not to notice the brilliant shine of his polished boots as they glittered in the morning sun.

Brigadier Hatfield took a paper from Ramsay's extended hand. He read some words from it but his voice came as an indistinct mumble in the morning air. The Brigadier was in a hurry. Everyone was in a hurry; every person there suffered an agony of haste. Each body strained and each mind willed: Go! Go! Have this thing over and done with!

The Brigadier handed the paper back to Ramsay with a little gesture of finality. But the three men remained standing in front of him as though locked in their attitudes of attention. Seconds of silence ticked by. The Brigadier's hand sped up to his collar and he cleared his throat with violence. "Well, sergeant?" his voice rasped. "Carry on, man!"

"Yessir. Left turn—quick march!"

The three men held the same brisk pace, marching in perfect step. The only sound was the thud of their heavy boots upon the tarmac. They passed the firing squad and halted at the red-brick wall. Then the escorting NCO's seemed to disappear and Private Jones stood alone against the wall. A nervous little smile was fixed at the corners of his mouth.

Again there was silence. Adam had not looked at the marching men, nor did he now look at the wall. Head lowered, he frowned as he seemed to study the alignment of his ten men in a row. More seconds ticked by.

"Captain Adam!"

It was a bellow from Brigadier Hatfield and it brought Adam's head up. Then his lips moved soundlessly as though rehearsing what he had to say. "Squad," Captain Adam ordered. "Load!" Ten left feet banged forward on the tarmac, ten rifles hit in the left hand, ten bolts smashed open and shut in unison. Ten rounds were positioned in their chambers.

There were just two remaining orders: "Aim!" and "Fire!" and these should be issued immediately, almost as one. But at that moment a late rooster crowed somewhere and the call came clear and sweet through the morning air, full of rich promise for the summer's day which lay ahead.

Adam took his first glance at the condemned man. Jones's mouth still held hard to its smile, but his knees looked loose. His position of attention was faltering.

"Squad!" Adam ordered in a ringing voice, "Unload! Rest!" Ten rifles obeyed in perfect unison.

Adam turned half right so that he faced Brigadier Hatfield. "Sir," he called clearly, "I refuse to carry out this order!"

Every voice in that place joined in the sound which muttered across the tarmac.

The Brigadier's face was deathly white. He peered at Private Jones, still in position against the wall, knees getting looser. He had a split second to carry the thing through. "Colonel McGuire!" he shouted.

"Yes, sir!" McGuire came running toward the firing squad. He knew what had to be done, and quickly. The Brigadier's face turned purple now; he appeared to be choking with the force of his rage. "Colonel McGuire," he shouted. "Place that officer under close arrest!"

"Sir?" McGuire stopped where he was and his mouth dropped open. Private Jones began to fall slowly against the wall. Then a rifle clattered loudly on the tarmac. Sergeant Konzuk was racing toward the wall and in an instant he had his big arms tight around Jones's body.

"McGuire!" The Brigadier's voice was a hoarse shriek now. "March the prisoner away!"

Padre Dixon stood rooted to the ground. His lips were moving and he stared blindly at Adam's stiffly erect figure, "He found the way!" he cried then in a ringing voice, and he moved about in triumph, although no one paid him attention. At his side Ramsay was spluttering out his own ecstasy of excitement; "Jones will get a reprieve after this! It will have to be referred to London, and then to Ottawa. And they'll never dare to put him through this again. . . ."

Ramsay looked up as he felt the Padre's fingers bite into his shoulder. He laughed nervously. "Yes," he chattered on. "Jones may get a reprieve, but Adam's the one for sentencing now." He peered across the tarmac where Adam still stood alone, his face slightly lifted to the warmth of the morning sun. He looked at Adam's lone figure with fear and admiration.

"Yes," he said, suddenly sobered. "God help Adam now."

"Don't worry about that, son," said the Padre, starting to stride across the tarmac. "He already has."

# THOMAS H. RADDALL

# How General Washington Lost Canada

In the whole of its turbulent history, the fate of Canada as a future nation united sea to sea probably never hung more finely in the balance than it did one summer day in 1775. That day in his army headquarters near Boston, George Washington had two proposals before him. One called for a minor campaign to capture Nova Scotia; the other was Benedict Arnold's scheme for an overland blow at Quebec.

The first plan was much the sounder. Aided by native anti-British rebels, an American force of one thousand men could have easily crushed the main stronghold of Halifax where only 126 of the garrison were fit for duty. They would have held the key to the Gulf of St. Lawrence, and Nova Scotia would eventually have become the fourteenth star in the new American flag.

Washington, of course, chose to be swayed by the colorful Arnold and lost five thousand men—mostly to hardship and disease—in the futile St. Lawrence adventure.

At the time, Nova Scotia included the whole of New Brunswick, much of the Gaspé peninsula, and part of the state of Maine. It was, in fact, the old French province of Acadie under another name. Aimed like a cannon at their Boston heart, it had been a menace to generations of spirited Yankees and for generations they strove to abolish it. In 1710 they captured the ancient Acadian capital (Port Royal, which they renamed Annapolis) only to see the French retire to Cape Breton and build a bigger and more dangerous sea-fortress at Louisburg.

In 1745 the New Englanders went on to capture Louisburg, a feat that astonished Europe, the first hint of the new power rising in America. An absurd government in London traded it back to France for concessions elsewhere, a bit of empire shuffling that enraged the American colonists. The British Parliament felt obliged to set up a military and naval base on the Nova Scotia peninsula as an offset to Louisburg. The chosen site was a magnificent wooded fiord known to the Indians as Chebucto, and there in 1749 a strong expedition of British settlers and troops created the town of Halifax, the new capital of the province.

Soon the British and their American colonists saw the real significance of their prize. It was the key to Canada, for it commanded the Gulf of St. Lawrence. In any strategy for the defense or conquest of British North America it had the sinister importance of a two-edged dagger, for its ports and hinterland commanded not only the throat of Canada but the main sea approach to New England. For that reason, lest the French plan a reconquest, the British maintained after 1763 their garrison and naval base at Halifax, the only establishment of its kind in North America.

As the years went by, with the British flag snapping in every breeze from Hudson Bay to Florida, the lesson of history faded into a peaceful feeling of assurance. When the American revolution sent a violent ripple along the colonial chain, the significance of the fourteenth and last link was so far forgotten that the British shipped their Nova Scotia garrison to Boston, while for their part the Americans devoted themselves to the wild-goose chase to the St. Lawrence.

The future of Canada hung upon what happened in Nova Scotia between 1775 and 1783. The only people among Nova Scotia's twenty thousand whites and three thousand Indians with a fixed loyalty to the king were some newly arrived Yorkshire settlers at the isthmus, some Scots at Pictou and in Cape Breton, a scatter of British army and navy veterans discharged in the country after the last war, and the small circle of Halifax officials and merchants whose fortunes were bound up in British government salaries and perquisites.

The predominant Yankee population of the province lived chiefly on the western shores of the peninsula, where they traded freely with Newfoundland, Labrador, the West Indies, and with their friends and relatives in New England, visiting back and forth across the mouth of Fundy and smuggling their rum, tea and other luxuries in the accepted American fashion. They governed their settlements in the New England way, by town meetings at which any man could have his say, and by elected committees whose word was law.

The province was ruled by a governor and council appointed from London; and it was financed from London, partly by direct subsidy and partly by the sums spent every year on the Halifax garrison and fleet. Most of this money eventually found its way into the pockets of the officials and their merchant friends. In this favored group there was one man notable for his difference. Michael Francklin had come to Halifax as a young Englishman with a few pounds in his pocket determined to make a fortune. In his business and political dealings he was as greedy as any other; but he had something the others lacked: a genuine interest in the country. He traveled the province widely in a time when it was dangerous to do so; indeed he had once been captured by Indians and held a prisoner for months. He had married a Yankee wife, a granddaughter of Boston's famous Peter Faneuil. He had a country mansion at Windsor and maintained a horse-breeding farm in the meadows of Minudie beside the Bay of Fundy. When the impending revolution began to throw its shadow across the mouth of Fundy he was the one man in the province who could claim trust from both crown and people.

In 1773, however, a new actor stepped upon the Nova Scotian scene, Francis Legge, a British army officer whose kinsman, the Earl of Dartmouth, had secured him the post of governor. He was an honest but stupid man, ugly and obese, more used to scaring soldiers of the line than dealing with smooth knaves of the Halifax sort or with colonial settlers who dis-

liked the Halifax knaves as much as he did but who also despised him for a bully and a fool. His investigations proved the ruling group in Halifax to be a gang of pompous thieves; but the thieves were very loud in their loyalty to King George at a time when His Majesty's government had begun to feel a sudden need for friends in America, and London hesitated.

Legge and the Nova Scotians, especially those natural democrats, the Yankee settlers, were natural allies in the struggle against the clique at Halifax. But in '75 the news of Lexington and Bunker Hill turned Legge's suspicions to the whole province.

He did not cease his vendetta against the parasites of Halifax, but now he extended it to the people of the province, butting fiercely in all directions like the honest but bewildered goat he was.

The shrewd rogues of Halifax were quick to see their opportunity. In January 1776 a delegation went to London to press for Legge's recall, pointing out that his policy was driving the Nova Scotians toward revolt, which was the truth; and London, suddenly alarmed, gave in. Legge was recalled. Michael Francklin, the lieutenant-governor, was the obvious man to take his place. But London had determined to make a clean sweep. Francklin was deposed also, and his post went to a naval officer, Arbuthnot, who knew nothing of Nova Scotia or its people, whose view, indeed, seldom went beyond the Halifax dockyard gate.

Soon after the outbreak at Lexington the busy Committees of Correspondence in Massachusetts got in touch with the Nova Scotians, urging open revolt. Later on, with the sanction of George Washington, the Congress sent agents to sound out the feelings of the Nova Scotians and to examine the state of the garrison. These went no farther than Machias, a hotbed of revolt on the vague borderland between Nova Scotia and what is now the state of Maine; but there they found people in close contact with the Nova Scotians, all urging that the province was ripe for rebellion.

In reality the Nova Scotians were in the painful dilemma that had ruined the Acadians before them, caught as they were between two powerful and opposed national interests; and they well remembered what had happened to the Acadians. Of all the continental colonies theirs was the nearest to England and so the most exposed to the British fleet and to troops coming in by sea.

There were hotheads among them like Jonathan Eddy of Cumberland and Parson Seccombe of Chester, ardently preaching rebellion; but more typical were Malachi Salter, the Yankee merchant of Halifax, and Simeon

Perkins. These were cautious, measuring their American sympathies against the British strength by sea, and hoping that somehow the Nova Scotians could stay neutral.

In the late summer of 1775 George Washington at his Cambridge headquarters outside Boston debated the two proposals before him. One was Arnold's scheme for a blow at Quebec. The other, known as Colonel Thompson's plan, was for the seizure of Nova Scotia. The Thompson plan required one thousand troops, four armed ships and eight transports, moving from an advanced base already established in Maine by the ardent revolutionists of Machias. The American troops would proceed up the Bay of Fundy and into Minas Basin. There they would seize the port of Windsor (where they could rouse and arm the American settlers of the Annapolis Valley and Cumberland, and the Ulstermen of Truro and Cobequid) and thence march on Halifax.

The Thompson plan was much more sound than Arnold's, in spite of Washington's caution about any scheme that depended on movement by sea. The British fleet at that time was too busy convoying supplies to the besieged army in Boston to give much attention elsewhere, and in any case the British naval commanders had a healthy aversion to the upper parts of the Bay of Fundy on account of its dangerous fogs and tides. In Nova Scotia the Americans would find themselves among a friendly people who spoke their own tongue and had small respect for His Majesty's government. Most important, there were no British troops left in the province except the guard at Halifax, and as late as November 4, 1775, the garrison of Halifax consisted of 390 men, of whom only 126 were fit for duty.

The voice of the dashing Arnold prevailed, however, and when the British army withdrew from Boston to Halifax in the spring of '76 the would-be rebels among the Nova Scotians had to lie low. Another opportunity came that summer, when Howe went off with all his forces to New York.

This time, other than three hundred British soldiers in Halifax, there was a single company of the Royal Highland Emigrants posted at Windsor and a weak battalion of the Royal Fencible American Regiment guarding the isthmus at Fort Cumberland. A single regiment of well-armed rebels could have overrun them all.

Again Washington was urged to send such a force to bring the fourteenth colony into the continental fold. Nova Scotian emissaries Jonathan Eddy, John Allan, and their Acadian colleague Isaiah Boudreau visited Boston and pointed out the ease with which it might be done, pledging the support of hundreds of Nova Scotians who only awaited arms and ammunition. But Washington was now concerned with New York, and the costly failure of Arnold's venture was fresh in his mind.

All that appeared in the autumn of 1776 was a small band of reckless frontiersmen from Machias, guided by Jonathan Eddy. They visited the settlers on the St. John River en route, and turned up in Cumberland in the last days of October, announcing themselves as the advance party of a strong American army. The intention of this army, they declared, was to liberate Nova Scotia, and they called on all "friends of America" to rise and take up arms in their support.

Fort Cumberland with its guns and bastions, its earthen ramparts built in the favorite star shape of French engineers in the old regime (it was the famous Fort Beauséjour of former times) guarded the Nova Scotia isthmus on a ridge in the Fundy marshes. It was held by Colonel Joseph Gorham, an indifferent soldier, with his shabby battalion of Royal Fencibles.

Eddy's rebels were armed mostly with fowling pieces, swords and pistols—relics of the old French war. They had no cannon. Nevertheless they captured fifty of Gorham's men, seized a ship laden with his winter food supplies, besieged him and his garrison for three weeks, and in the dark of one November night made a wild and badly managed attempt to storm the fort.

There was great alarm among the Loyalists at Halifax. Michael Francklin tried to raise the militia of the Annapolis Valley and Minas Basin for Gorham's relief, but even his influence could not move them. For a time it seemed that Eddy's bold enterprise would take Fort Cumberland and roll on to Halifax like a snowball in March.

General Massey at Halifax took a chance. The only reliable troops on hand were two companies of Royal Marines, landed from warships in the harbor. These he sent through the woods to Windsor, where they joined the little company of Highland Emigrants for a voyage up Fundy Bay to Cumberland. The Highlanders' ship went astray in bad weather, but the Marines landed secretly at night on the marshes below the fort.

The Cumberland rebels kept a careless watch in the winter weather. Gorham had shown no desire to attack their crude siege lines, and after the failure of their own attempt to rush the fort they were content to wait for Gorham's food and fuel to run out. The Marines and the pick of Gorham's men, led by Major Batt, stole along the edge of the marshes before dawn, passed the flank of the poorly manned rebel line, and at daylight fell on the camp where most of them were asleep. In an hour the Cumberland "Army of Liberty" was flying through the woods, and the vengeful redcoats were burning farm after farm along the ridge.

The chief leaders of the revolt, Eddy and Allan, had escaped to the St. John. The British soldiers gathered up some lesser culprits and sent them to Halifax for trial, but there a wise clemency prevailed. In various ways the trials were abandoned and the prisoners were allowed to escape. One of them, young Richard John Uniacke, eventually became attorney-general of Nova Scotia and a power in the land.

Eddy did not stop his flight until he reached Machias. John Allan, a man of better fibre, halted on the St. John River with some other refugees from Cumberland and began to recruit another force among the settlers at the river mouth and in the villages upstream. He also sought aid from the Malicete Indians of the St. John and the Micmacs of Miramichi. These activities went on undisturbed through the winter and spring of 1777.

There was still no sign of the promised American troops, but Massachusetts was alive to the importance of keeping at least some of the Nova Scotians in revolt, and of winning the Indians who were masters of the forest between the Bay of Fundy and the St. Lawrence. Hence Allan received some arms and ammunition for his followers, and belts of wampum, blankets and other gifts for the savages.

The British authorities at Halifax had their eyes wide open after the Cumberland affair. During the winter and spring General Massey recruited vigorously amongst the Scottish settlers of Nova Scotia and Newfoundland and called ashore the marines of every warship that came into Halifax. By the early summer of '77 he had six hundred marines and four hundred Royal Highland Emigrants, besides Gorham's garrison at Fort Cumberland. In June Massey despatched a mixed force of well-trained men to the St. John in the warships, Vulture, Mermaid and Hope.

The blow fell suddenly. Allen's little "Army of Liberty" made a brief stand at the mouth of the St. John and then fled up the river. British troops under Major Studholme followed swiftly in boats and canoes. Here and there a party of the rebels halted on the bank of the broad stream. All were attacked and overrun, and again the soldiers burned every farm that sheltered them.

Allan had sent a last desperate appeal to Boston, but it was hopeless. A gaudy pageant had begun to move down Lake Champlain and the forces of New England were scrambling inland to meet it. If Massachusetts had ever intended sending troops to Nova Scotia the intention blew away on the brassy wind of Burgoyne's trumpeters.

Allan made his last stand at the site of an old French settlement afterward known to the Loyalists as King's Clear. His Malicete Indian allies deserted him, and the British troops fell on the remnant of Nova Scotia's "Army of Liberty" and destroyed it. Allan and a few others managed to escape to Machias, where they arrived in mid-August. Even there they had no rest or safety. Machias had been the base from which the Nova Scotia rebellion was plotted and sprung, and the British command at Halifax was well aware of it. Over the seaward horizon came Sir John Collier with a squadron led by his big flagship Rainbow, and when his ships departed Machias was a smoking ruin. Thus ended the lone armed rebellion of the Nova Scotians.

The failure of the rebellion and the emptiness of all the promises from the other colonies caused the Nova Scotians to reflect sombrely on their position. The old ties of blood and trade with New England were strong. But a new factor had entered the problem. The successful rebels of New England, now that the tide of war had rolled away to New York, were sending armed ships to prey on British sea-borne trade. Some of these privateers had the written sanction of the Congress or their own states; most were, in fact, pirates.

These began to harry the Nova Scotia coast. The pretext was that their Bluenose cousins had not sent a representative to the Congress and therefore must be enemies of the United States. It was an excuse of thieves. The marauders began by seizing Nova Scotia trading vessels bound to or from the West Indies. From this they turned their attention to the shore itself, robbing the defenseless towns and settlements. The chief outports, Charlottetown, Lunenburg, Liverpool, Yarmouth, Annapolis, all were attacked at various times and most of them pillaged, together with many small hamlets of the fishermen. In the autumn of 1776, at the very time when Nova Scotia rebels were besieging Fort Cumberland and watching in vain for armed help from New England, the celebrated John Paul Jones was seizing unarmed vessels along the east coast of Nova Scotia and burning small sloops, sheds and cod-oil barrels of the poor fishermen of Canso.

Vainly the Nova Scotians wrote misspelled but earnest protests to the state legislatures and to various committees of safety and other local bodies in New England. Vainly they traveled in person to plead before those bodies. All was useless. The state legislatures were helpless to control their privateers, and in most cases the local committeemen were themselves actively sharing in the loot.

In self-defense the Nova Scotians had to muster their militia to fight off the raids. The next step was obvious. A fleet of Nova Scotian privateers, armed from the naval stores at Halifax and furnished with "letters-of-marque and reprisal" by the governor, began to prey upon the coast of New England. By the war's end the Nova Scotian Yankees were embittered and veteran enemies of the United States.

Thus, instead of a fourteenth American state commanding the Gulf of St. Lawrence, which would have doomed Canada in 1812 if not in 1783, there remained a solid British bastion on the Atlantic coast of North America.

McKENZIE PORTER

# The Last Stronghold of the Longstockings

After dressing for dinner in the bush for nearly a century, Canada's most die-hard community of old-fashioned British aristocrats is finally petering out. The scene of their valediction to the Kipling age is the Cowichan Valley, halfway between Nanaimo and Victoria on the east coast of Vancouver Island.

In the western background a range of snow-covered peaks rising to six thousand feet and in the middle distance a series of fir-clad foothills are essentially Canadian in character. But along the gentle slopes of the valley, which carries the Cowichan River some twenty miles from Cowichan Lake to Cowichan Bay, there are neat hedged meadows, vegetable gardens, small herds of cows, chicken runs, tennis courts and formal villas. All these suggest the softer scenes of rural England.

The lake, the river and the bay offer some kind of fishing almost every day in the year. Throughout the fall and winter a giant fighting trout called the steelhead builds for the Cowichan River a world-wide reputation among anglers. During spring and summer rainbow trout abound in Cowichan Lake and salmon run in the bay. In the uplands of the valley hunters find pheasant, grouse, partridge and deer. Around the mouth of the river they bag duck and a succulent species of goose called the brant. It was these opportunities for sport and the enrichment of their larders that first attracted well-bred English families.

Until the outbreak of the last war the economy of Duncan, the capital town of the Cowichan Valley, was based almost entirely on the private incomes of surrounding residents. Today the influence of these funds has been overshadowed by the payroll of an expanding logging industry and the profits of dairy farmers, mink ranchers, bulb growers, oyster cultivators and resort owners. English accents, common in sleepy old Duncan, are rare in bustling modern Duncan.

A newish city hall, fire hall and liquor store, a two-story Eaton's store, and a modern high school make Duncan look like any other small up-to-date Canadian town. The old frame Tzouhalem Hotel, which used to put up titled visitors from England, now competes with the new Commercial Hotel for the business of traveling salesmen and tourists.

The most significant sign of change is the growth in Duncan of a miniature Chinatown. It is inhabited by the old Chinese houseboys whom the landed English families can no longer afford to employ.

84

Yet something of the old spirit remains. In Duncan's four business streets there are still a few shops that might have been picked out of Stow-On-The-Wold. There are also a few men who might have stepped straight out of a joke in *Punch*.

These are the heads of the old English households, mostly retired British officers. In any other part of Canada they would be described as Colonel Blimps. They are inclined to hold strong views about the privileges of birth and rank, the dubiety of art and literature, the importance of rod and gun, the vulgarity of trade and politics and the superiority of the British. But because they usually keep their opinions to themselves they live on peaceful terms with their neighbors and are known somewhat affectionately as Longstockings. The nickname stems from their habit of wearing knickerbockers, often with a squashed felt hat, a shaggy tweed jacket, short puttees and sturdy ankle boots.

A few of them, probably in reaction against years of spit and polish, have given the whole community a reputation for eccentric dress. In Duncan, George Ferguson, the editor of the Montreal *Star*, once saw a plump elderly major wearing a deerstalker hat, a Norfolk tunic, khaki drill shorts and a pair of those thigh-high cavalry boots worn by the Life Guards. Another visitor saw an aged colonel in a black snap-brim fedora, soldier's greatcoat, flannel trousers tucked into the tops of scarlet rugger hose, and a pair of mountaineering boots.

Usually the dress of the Longstockings suggests exactly what they are: old warriors who have been touched by the midday sun from Khartoum to Rawalpindi and from Kowloon to Mandalay. At the annual Battery Ball, run by a reserve unit in the Duncan Agricultural Hall, they turn up looking as spruce and gallant in white ties, tails and medals as Sir Aubrey Smith in *The Four Feathers*.

Longstockings have been settling in Duncan, Cobble Hill, Quamichan Lake, Maple Bay and other parishes of the Cowichan Valley since the Seventies. The hyphenated names of many indicate that they are the younger sons of younger sons of titled English families. Born landless and poorer than their kinsmen, they chose the Cowichan on retirement because in climate, landscape and blood sports it offered a substitute for the country gentleman's life they could not afford back home.

And so for seventy-five years the Cowichan Valley became a Canadian facsimile of the huntin', shootin' and fishin' shires of the Old Country. Aristocratic English accents were passed on to Canadian children and grandchildren. Military traditions took young men back to the regular army in England. Eventually the nickname "Longstockings" was applied not only to the old men in knickerbockers but to their families as well.

On small estates, rarely more than fifty acres, the Longstockings did a little mixed farming. But they spent most of their time at hunting, fishing, cricket, tennis and social gatherings. For money they relied on pensions, legacies and small private incomes from England. The idyll was brought to an abrupt end in 1939 by the war. The local weekly paper, the Cowichan *Leader*, claimed that the town of Duncan recorded the highest rate of voluntary enlistment in Canada. Today more than one third of the names of the war memorial are hyphenated.

Will Dobson, the editor of the *Leader*, estimates that in 1939 in the valley about four hundred families (fifteen hundred individuals) were Longstockings. Now there are fewer than half that number. The changed status of India and Pakistan has cut off the flow of new Longstockings from the Indian army. Capital export restrictions in England have kept other brass hats at home. The income of the present community was almost cut in half when the pound was devalued after the war. Some, unable to meet dollar costs of life on drafts of pounds, shillings and pence, went back to England. Some followed their children who had taken jobs in Eastern Canada and became assimilated there. Many died off. Of the dwindling number who are left, some have become living legends.

The average Longstocking family lives at the end of a long winding muddy lane in a rambling villa situated picturesquely among clumps of oak trees, gorse bushes and bluebells. Usually these villas are heated by an open fireplace in each room. The architectural style reflects a divided nostalgia. On three sides the homes are fussy with the gables, leaded windowpanes and turrets of the typical English house. But on the sunny side most have the sort of long verandas found in the outposts of what their owners still call "the Empah."

Visitors may be startled by the snarling heads of tiger-skin rugs in the big square halls or by sheafs of Zulu assegais, Malayan kris, Gurkha kukris and Bedouin scimitars suspended from the paneling of the dark curving staircases. Some Longstockings sleep in fourposter beds. At breakfast they often eat a kipper or grilled kidneys instead of bacon and eggs. Every afternoon, tea with toasted crumpets and fruitcake is a rite. It is served around log fires in sitting rooms furnished with ample chintz-covered chairs and sofas, and with occasional tables and cabinets carved exotically by Asian and

African tribesmen. The Longstockings dine off steak-and-kidney pudding and home-brewed ale at long oaken refectory tables in rooms hung with brass, chinaware and oil paintings of their ancestors.

Every Friday and Saturday they go shopping in Duncan, the women being just as tweedily dressed as the men. For their benefit Mann's drugstore calls itself a chemist shop; the Duncan Home Bakery makes those mysterious disks of puff pastry and currants known as Eccles cakes; and Staples' rod-and-gun shop goes in for a curious sideline: English pipe tobaccos.

On sale in several stores are English magazines such as the *Tatler* and *Sketch* in which Longstockings find pictures of their relatives attending Ascot race week, the Queen's garden party, Covent Garden opera or the Four Hundred Club. As evidence of their interest in the seamier side of British life it is also possible to buy the *News of the World*. In the weekly edition of the *Manchester Guardian* or *The Times* they also find news of their favorite team sport —cricket.

The Cowichan cricket team enjoys an unusual fame in the United Kingdom and in other Dominions. It was so good in 1932 that the Australian test-match team, on its way to England, stopped off for a game. The sensation of the day was the failure of Sir Don Bradman, the great Australian batsman, to make his customary century. When he had made sixty G. G. Baiss, star of the Cowichan side, bowled to him. Bradman drove the ball straight back down the pitch. Like a bullet, it flew back to Baiss, who caught and held it. At that time Baiss was over fifty. He was still playing for Cowichan in his seventies.

Admiring observers pick Colonel Maxwell Edward Dopping-Heppenstal, C.B.E., D.S.O., Croix de guerre, late of the Gurkhas, as the "most typical" Longstocking. Short and wiry, with nut-colored features and snowy hair, mustache and eyebrows, this lifetime bachelor instantly evoked memories of poems by Kipling. After serving in Aden, India, China and Burma he fought in Mesopotamia and France during the First World War. He was wounded three times. Even after 1918 he was still fighting in the Afghan campaign of 1919 and the Waziristan campaign of 1922.

When he retired in the early Twenties he couldn't afford to live in England, so he settled at Quamichan Lake in the Cowichan Valley. His first home there burned down and he lost most of his souvenirs. But he managed to save his precious collection of kukris, the short curved knives with which a Ghurka can decapitate a bullock at one stroke.

When George V went to India to be crowned Emperor at the last Delhi durbar in history, Dopping-Hepenstal was one of the officers assisting at a royal tiger shoot. Six hundred and fifty elephants were gathered to carry the King and his retinue. In ten days the party bagged thirty-nine tigers; twenty-one fell to the King, who was a splendid shot. Then the Maharajah of Nepal, the host, said: "I think that will be enough tigers for the time being. There'll be other things, you know."

When he was sixty, after a decade of retirement, Dopping-Heppenstal heard that a Quamichan Lake boy-scout troop was disbanding for lack of leadership. He became scoutmaster and was soon promoted to district commissioner. Until a few years ago he often strolled through the hills with a string of panting scouts at his heels. When they complained they couldn't keep up he never lost his temper. The strongest words he was ever heard to utter were: "Oh, shut up, you chaps!"

Other leading Longstockings included, for instance, Colonel Ireton Eardley-Wilmot, who established in Duncan a group of British Israelites. This sect believes that historians made a mistake—the British, not the Jews, are God's chosen race. A less militant personality was Colonel Arthur Broome who delighted in making dolls' houses. He was so keen on a lifelike reproduction that even the plumbing worked. For tiger-skin rugs he used the painted pelts of mice.

One of the most beloved characters was Captain F. R. MacFarlane who, during the Twenties and Thirties, when he was in his eighties and nineties, was the oldest junior officer in the British Army list. He used to brew his own beer and consume it in such quantities that for forty years local abstainers claimed woefully that he was drinking himself to death. Then at eighty he took up cycling and survived a 45-mile-an-hour spill when his brakes failed on a hill.

Colonel L. Oldham regretfully gave up his tennis at eighty. His wife drowned while swimming at seventy.

The St. Patrick's Night Dinner was one of Oldham's favorite do's. "We've no right to run a St. Patrick's Night Dinner," he once said, "for there isn't an Irishman for miles around. What we should be running is a Burns' Night Dinner as we've scores of Scots. But Burns' Night is in January and that's such a terribly wet month here it's not fit for man nor dog. So in March, when it's clearing up a bit, we have a St. Patrick's Night instead."

Colonel Oldham owned the biggest tiger-skin rug in the Cowichan Valley. He bagged it himself, of course. Instead of having it on the floor he hung it on the wall. He retired from the

British Army in 1911. "Nobody can say I haven't had my whack at the pension fund," he chuckled a year or two back.

One of the most fiery of the Longstockings, Major L. C. Rattray, fished almost every day until rheumatism prevented him from wading. He used to visit Duncan to collect his mail, wearing his fishing boots, his old fishing hat stuck full of flies and his fishing basket slung around his shoulder. A stickler for the niceties of rank he gave "Sir" to men several ranks senior to himself and expected "Sir" from several ranks lower. The Mayor of Duncan was a sergeant in the army so all he got from Major Rattray was his surname: Wragg.

James Wragg always paid the Longstockings a lot of deference. They in turn helped him. He was born in a public house in Derby, England, and emigrated to Canada when he was sixteen. He worked as a cook in logging camps and went to World War I with the Canadian Army. He came back wounded, with the rank of sergeant, married and eventually opened a bakery in Duncan.

Besides his cakes and pastries, he used to sell sweaters and pipe tobacco to the Longstockings, but most of all he prospered because they liked his chirpy ways. He retired from the bakery before the last war and became Duncan's biggest real estate owner and perennial mayor.

"I used to feel sorry for the ladies just in from China, India and Africa when I was running my shop," he once confessed. "They had been used to a houseful of native servants, and they were lost when they got to Canada. Why, they couldn't even bake a rice pudding! They'd come into the shop with all the mixings—rice, sugar, milk and so on—in a basin and plead with me to make a pudding. I always did."

The Longstocking men would complicate his life in another way. Every day a dozen or more would pop into the shop and say: "Wragg, old boy! A present for you!" And they'd dump a large salmon on his counter. He'd get so many he couldn't even give them away to customers.

In 1951 it was announced that Princess Elizabeth and the Duke of Edinburgh would drive through Duncan without stopping. Wragg wrote a letter of protest to Buckingham Palace but the timetable could not be altered. He then made a radio speech in which he said he would "throw a human chain across the road" and halt the royal car. Scores of old colonels and brigadiers offered to put themselves under *Sergeant* Wragg's command for this operation. All over the world newspaper photographs were published showing Mayor Wragg and his supporters linking arms across the highway in illustration of how they intended to carry out the threat.

On the day of the royal visit ten thousand Cowichan Valley people gathered in Duncan to see what would happen. The publicity had had its effect. When the Duke of Edinburgh, who was driving, approached the outskirts of the town, he grinned and slowed down to walking speed. There was no need for the blockade because everybody got a good view of the pair. Later in Nanaimo the Princess, with dancing eyes, said to Mayor Wragg: "That was an exciting reception you prepared for us in Duncan."

It was a woman who put the idea for a road block into Wragg's head, a woman who is a bulwark of Longstocking tradition. Her name is Miss Norah Denny and she is the headmistress of the Queen Margaret's School for Girls. Although she's likely over sixty Miss Denny, with her short hairdo, blue blazer, brief tweed skirt and stout brogue shoes, has the brisk appearance and actions of a girl who has followed the beagles across the Yorkshire dales.

Like James Wragg, she arrived in the Cowichan after World War I, during which she served in the British WAAC's. For a year she scrubbed floors in Duncan because there was no other work for a single woman. Then she went into partnership with Miss Dorothy Geoghegan, a second-generation Longstocking; they opened a school in a small rented house. Miss Denny named it after her alma mater, the swanky Queen Margaret's School in Scarborough, Yorkshire. Since then, their school has educated two generations of Longstocking daughters with as many as 450 boarders attending. Many girls from British families in Hong Kong and the Pacific colonies attend, because it's closer than England.

Before World War I there were so many single men in the community that a Bachelors' Ball was started. Most of them were young Englishmen sent out by their families to learn farming. They were called Mud Pups. The parents would pay $500 a year to the Cowichan Valley expatriates to look after their sons. When the war started the Mud Pups joined up to the last man and the bachelor population of Duncan vanished overnight.

Longstocking society has provided congenial shelter at times for many men and women who left England after a breach of the conventions. There was, for instance, Teddy Hicks-Beach who was said to have been cut off by his father, a baronet, because he married a greengrocer's daughter. Walter Rudkin, an English gardener, married the daughter of a duke and brought her to the Cowichan Valley where they grew those sweet russet apples named Cox's Orange Pippins. E. W. Cole sang as a boy in the choir at Sandringham Castle and later married a Miss Bowes-Lyon, a member of the Queen

Mother's family. She was twenty years older than he. So they settled in the Cowichan and lived happily raising pedigreed dogs.

The Longstockings have also had literary and theatrical affiliations. Negley Farson based his novel, *The Story of a Lake,* on some members of the community. Rosamond Marshall, author of the best-selling *Kitty,* once lived in the valley. Charles Stoker, a brother of Bram Stoker, author of the horror story *Dracula,* and George Chaney, brother of Lon Chaney the actor, made their homes in the valley. Air Marshal Sir Philip Livingston, one-time chief of all medical services in the RAF and a consultant to the Royal Family, was born in the Cowichan and returned to it upon retirement. After fifty years' absence old families like the Shares, the Falls, the Leneys and the Corfields greeted him casually, "Hello, Philip," as if he'd been away for a week.

In the last war a third-generation Longstocking also achieved fame. As an officer in the Lincolnshire Regiment young Charlie Hoey won the Victoria Cross and lost his life in Burma.

Ex-officers of the British imperial forces still trickle into the Cowichan, but they are different from the old Longstockings. They have no scruples, for example, about going into trade. Commander John Lawrence, RN, who served in destroyers and was a friend of the Duke of Edinburgh, is the manager of Eaton's in Duncan. Colonel Ross Smith opened a restaurant named the Silver Bridge Inn and Commander George Windeyer, RN, works in a sawmill at Chemainus.

Even among those with the bluest blood time has wrought changes. Take the case of Robert Hew Fergusson-Pollok, an aristocrat who stands six feet four beneath strong iron-grey hair. Fergusson-Pollok can trace every one of his male ancestors back to the eleventh century. Born in British Columbia, he had to make his own living. He served as the mate and captain of coastal tugs and freighters. There was a time when he had to ask the mayor of Duncan for work on the roads. Then, in the early fifties, he inherited Pollok Castle at Newton Mearns, near Glasgow. It was built by his ancestors in 1028; since 1703 it had been the seat of baronets. The estate included thousands of acres on nineteen farms.

When he heard of his inheritance Fergusson-Pollok didn't even go to Glasgow to look the place over. "My wife," he explains, "didn't want me to." So he instructed his lawyers to sell the land and the castle and to send all the furniture out to a ten-room villa he bought in the Cowichan Valley. Shipping costs were $8,000. Now the Fergusson-Polloks and their caged pet birds live in a house so packed with antiques there is hardly room to move.

In the sitting room, Chippendale chairs, a whole Hepplewhite suite, a Jacobean solitaire table, a Queen Anne cabinet full of thirteenth-century Venetian glass and an Elizabethan writing desk are crowded among the department-store furniture the Fergusson-Polloks owned before they came into their fortune. A dozen Persian rugs are kept rolled up because there is no place to lay them. Claymores, *skein dhus,* pistols and shields of highland chieftains lie about the room. There are several sets of sixteenth-century playing cards; a quill pen used by Mary Queen of Scots when she visited Pollok Castle; a pair of silver candlesticks as thick as a man's wrist and each weighing fifty-six pounds and ancient oriental vases embossed with patterns of solid gold.

Among the dozens of ancestral portraits are three believed to have been painted by Sir Joshua Reynolds and one by Holbein. In the dining room, near a great oak table and matching chairs dating from Charles I, are giant stacks of red-and-yellow boxes, containing the Fergusson-Polloks favorite pastime—jigsaw puzzles.

If he wished Fergusson-Pollok could build the most beautiful home in the Cowichan Valley and lead the sort of aristocratic life all the other Longstockings have dreamed about. But he's not interested in Longstocking society. With some of the money he received from Scotland he bought a new Cadillac. He put thirty thousand dollars into a baseball club.

Fergusson-Pollok's attitude to the Longstockings reflects the gradual decline of this unique society. It is reflected, too, in the attitude of many native Canadians who have become openly anti-Longstocking.

Bobby Evans, a member of a Cowichan Bay family descended from pioneers, came home from the last war in a satirical mood. All along the Maple Bay Road, where he lives, there are rural mail boxes painted with the lengthy titles, ranks and decoration initials of old brass hats. Most of the inscriptions end up with the word "Retired" in brackets. On *his* mailbox Evans painted the following:

ACTING UNPAID LEADING SEAMAN
ROBERT EVANS
*(Just Tired)*

THE FIRST CANADIAN TO FLY WAS **J. A. D. McCURDY** OF THE MARITIMES IN 1910

## A GALLERY OF FAMOUS CANADIANS

THE BELOVED CANADIAN WHO SET THE WORLD LAUGHING: **STEPHEN LEACOCK**

TOBY ROBINS: BEAUTY AND BRAINS ON TELEVISION AND STAG

WILLIAM SHATNER: FROM STRATFORD TO BROADWAY

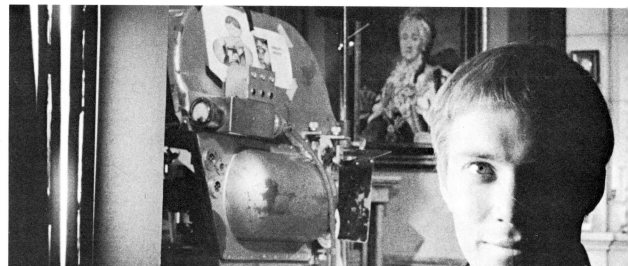

ENN GOULD: PIANO MAGIC IN HIS LONG FINGERS

MELISSA HAYDEN: INTERNATIONAL BALLET TRIUMPHS

THE CABINET OF LOUIS ST. LAURENT ALERT IN
THE CHAMBER OF THE PRIVY COUNCIL, PHOTO-
GRAPHED BY YOUSUF KARSH

A. R. M. LOWER: ANGRY MAN OF LETTERS

JOHN DIEFENBAKER: A MAN OF VISION

ACADEMIC KNIGHTS OF THE ROUND TABLE:
UNIVERSITY OF TORONTO PONDERS THE MODEL
OF A GREATER CAMPUS (CENTRE)

LOIS SMITH AND DAVID ADAMS:
NATIONAL BALLET STARS

**JOHNNY LONGDEN:** GREATEST JOCKEY OF THEM ALL

**WAYNE AND SHUSTER:** TORONTO COMEDY TEAM

MAZO DE LA ROCHE: HER JALNA IS
LOVED BY MILLIONS OF READERS

DORA MAVOR MOORE (IN CLOCHE) IS GRAND DAME
OF A STRUGGLING CANADIAN THEATRE

VINCENT MASSEY'S GIFT (HART HOUSE AT THE
UNIVERSITY OF TORONTO) RINGS TO CHRISTMAS
CAROLLERS

CHRISTOPHER PLUMMER (HIS ST. JOAN IS JULIE
HARRIS) SAVORED BROADWAY FAME

SAMUEL BRONFMAN DAZZLED NEW YORK WITH
HIS GLEAMING SEAGRAM SKYSCRAPER

LOUIS ARCHAMBAULT: RENOWNED SCULPTOR

RED PELLAN'S COMPELLING CANVASES BRING
RELS TO MONTREAL

ERTSON DAVIES:
TOR, NOVELIST, PLAYWRIGHT AND CRITIC

OSCAR PETERSON:
A NEW SOUND IN JAZZ

STEPHEN BOSUSTOW:
CREATOR OF THE
MAGOO CARTOONS

**PAUL EMILE CARDINAL LEGER:** PIETY, GRACE AND LEADERSHIP

**ALAN JARVIS:** FORMER DIRECTOR OF THE NATIONAL GALLERY

LESTER B. PEARSON:
UNITED NATIONS PROPOSAL WON HIM THE NOBEL PRIZE

MSGR. RÉNÉ LUSSIER, UNIVERSITÉ DE MONTRÉAL

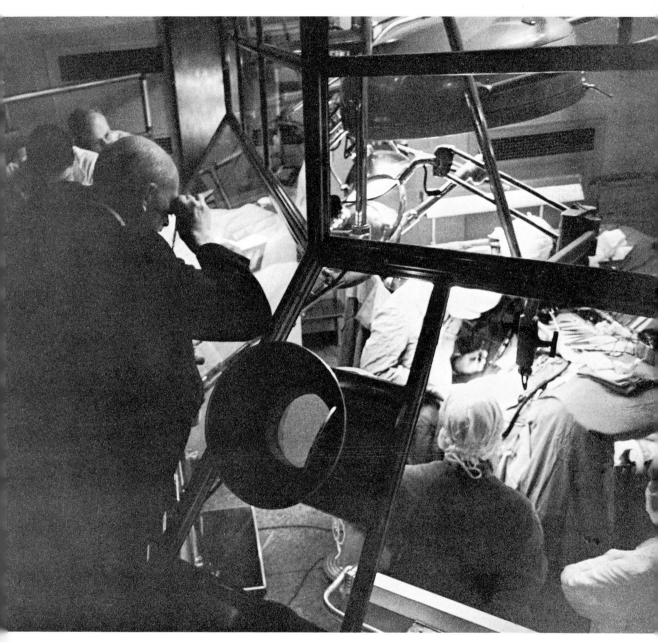

**ILDER PENFIELD:** THE HIGHEST HONORS IN MEDICINE

POLITICS: NEWFOUNDLAND'S **JOSEPH SMALLWOOD**    BIG BUSINESS: FOOD TYCOON **GARFIELD WESTON**

JOHN   NORMAN   HARRIS

# Tutelary Genius

Back in depression days, which I recall without the faintest tremor of nostalgia, I met a youth who called himself Forbes Radford. I met him in a Toronto rooming house, not far from the hockey gardens. In meeting him, I became party to a felony, or a misdemeanor, I don't know which. Mrs. Marler, the landlady, was just showing me a second-floor bedroom and had left for a minute to get the electric light bulb, which she removed for reasons of economy whenever the room was vacant. During the brief pause, Forbes swam into my ken.

"I say," he said, as he slipped into the room, "the chaps would appreciate it if you'd keep her talking here as long as possible." Without another word, he slipped out again.

I haggled with Mrs. Marler over every possible detail and kept the good lady away from her housework longer than the rental of a room for two-fifty a week could possibly justify. Just as we were closing the deal, another stranger appeared in the doorway behind Mrs. Marler, holding out an upraised thumb to indicate that I had now detained Mrs. Marler long enough.

As soon as Mrs. Marler had waddled out, both strangers reappeared, with a couple of others.

The reason I had been asked to delay Mrs. Marler, they explained, was that she had impounded a large locked suitcase belonging to Forbes, for nonpayment of rent. The suitcase contained Forbes's iron, not permitted in rooms by decree of Mrs. Marler, and an electric plate, also forbidden. For the welfare of the community, it was necessary to break into Mrs. Marler's private quarters and salvage these things, as well as some of Mr. Radford's most beloved garments, making up the loss of weight with suitable ballast.

Forbes had a wardrobe that would have done

credit to a man of distinction. His clothes were conservative and of the finest quality. He spent a great deal of time pressing them, folding them and generally taking care of them. He usually took part of his wage, when he was in work, in garments at wholesale price or less and he occasionally got a new suit, tailored to measure, by serving as a mannequin at a male fashion show.

Soon after my arrival at Mrs. Marler's, I had occasion to rent a tuxedo to wear to a dance. On my way downstairs, I told Forbes I was going out to rent a tux. A look of real pain flitted over his face.

"Old man," he said, "not for the world would I hurt your feelings, but 'tux' and 'tuxedo' are provincialisms of the most barbarous sort. I shall be happy to lend you my dinner jacket, so you can save two bucks."

Two bucks was two bucks. I accepted with pleasure, but I made another mistake in trying to put on a made-up bow tie, the only evening garment I owned.

"Only the veriest bounder would wear a made-up bow," Forbes told me severely. Meekly I let him tie a proper black bow about my throat and held my peace.

During the long winter months I got to know Forbes fairly well and was fascinated by the puzzle of piecing his background together. He was fastidious and correct in all things and was filled with a lot of odd prejudices. He seemed to know all about wines and clothes and the proper way to address the Governor-General. Much of this, I gathered, he had inherited from his father.

"My governor has never dressed for dinner in Canada," he once told me. "He says, 'when in Rome . . .'"

His governor, it appeared, was conservative, opposed to all swank, side and ostentation and a stickler for just about anything you can be a stickler for.

"In Canada," Forbes informed me, "my governor has always been known as plain Joseph Radford. He wants it that way."

Quite, I thought. My thoughts, unconsciously, were full of "quites" and "rathers" and other Forbesian expressions. Of course Radford's governor, after he'd lost his fortune, would want to live quietly and drop his titles. Simple pride would demand it.

One evening, when I was getting into my best blue suit to attend, on a free ticket, the Bastion Road Church Businessmen's Monthly Get-Together (any free meal looked good), I saw Forbes across the hall getting into his tux—beg pardon, his dinner jacket. He caught my eye and I raised my brows interrogatively, a trick I had picked up from him.

"A musical evening," he replied. "Meeting some men who would like to hear a little music."

This intrigued me and I forgot about the Businessmen.

"Hey, I'd like to hear some music, too," I said naïvely.

"My dear chap," he said in a kindly way I didn't like, "the sort of music we'll have tonight would mean nothing to you whatever."

I was wounded, and extremely annoyed at having walked straight into that, so when I found myself leaving the house with Forbes I didn't speak. Even when we both boarded the northbound Yonge streetcar, I didn't speak. When we both transferred to the westbound Bloor car a fleeting suspicion entered my mind, which I then dismissed, but after we passed Keele Street, the suspicion returned stronger than ever. I resolved to test it.

I drew the complimentary Get-Together ticket from my pocket and pretended to examine it carefully, all the while watching Forbes out of the corner of my eye. It took a little while, but at last I saw that it had hit him.

"I see we are attending the same function," he said, with all the dignity he could manage at short notice. Then he started to laugh. I believe it was the only sign he ever gave that there was any humor in his make-up.

Forbes and I were, indeed, attending the same function. He was furthermore hired, for two dollars plus a meal of ham and peas and scalloped potatoes, to play the piano for the singsong that filled the period between the meal and the speech, in which a hardware merchant was to coin a valuable phrase about every red-blooded Canadian putting his shoulder to the wheel. In addition, he was to play a solo ("Humoresque") and an encore ("The Parade of the Wooden Soldiers").

We walked home together, to save carfare, but in all the five miles we never mentioned the Businessmen's Get-Together.

By far the quietest man in the lodging house was the railway office worker, a husky young fellow called Ken. I don't think we exchanged more than a score of words all winter. He didn't seem unfriendly and he joined in all the Catawba parties, but he seemed to be busy most of the time, either studying company law or attending drills at the Spadina Armories. When the pharmacy students were too noisy he sometimes went in and told them they could learn to make chocolate malted-milk shakes without so much row, and when any of the residents started to get tough with Forbes, or guy him too much about his mannerisms, he would say, "Okay, now lay off him, you guys."

Otherwise, he minded his own business. I know that once he helped Forbes with his rent, because I could hear Forbes saying, "I'm most frightfully grateful, old chap," and Ken telling him to forget it and shut up.

On a day in early spring, the police came for Forbes. Two plain-clothes men called at the house and stood unflinching in the hall while Mrs. Marler kept insisting, shrilly, that Mr. Radford wasn't home. Ken heard the row and came down.

"What's he done?" Ken demanded curtly.

The plain-clothes men exchanged a glance. "He's forged a cheque, that's what he's done," one of them said.

"Okay, I'll find him," Ken told him.

I followed Ken down the cellar and there we found Forbes, huddled behind the furnace. His face was tear-stained. He told us he was sorry and he hadn't meant to do it.

It came out in court that Forbes, under the influence of early spring, had forged and uttered a cheque, payable to himself, over the signature of a well-known tycoon. His immaculate dress, his disarmingly offhand manner and the fact that he wanted to open a savings account with half the amount, had deluded the assistant manager of a branch bank into initialing the cheque with only a routine enquiry.

Forbes told the banker that he had sold his summer place to the wealthy man and this was the down payment to close the deal. Forbes had even given his correct address. With the money obtained he went on a buying spree, purchasing spring clothing that Solomon in all his glory wouldn't have sniffed at.

As soon as he could get his lick in, Ken gave the magistrate the relevant facts.

Forbes, he said, was really Alfred Radford. He came from Bannock, a small village, and Ken had gone to school with him there. He had always been a dreamy person and sometimes his dreams got a little out of hand. He had been in the Psychiatric Hospital twice for treatment. The name Forbes was itself part of the dream that Alfred was walking around in. He had found it in a book.

Forbes was remanded for examination by the alienist. Later Ken expressed surprise that I hadn't seen through the whole thing from the first.

"His mother asked me to keep an eye on him," he explained, "so I got him a room at Mrs. Marler's where I could. His old man is a drunken furnace installer and roofer who runs a little hardware store in Bannock. He never was in England in his life. All that stuff comes out of books. His mother was a schoolteacher and since she got married she's been teaching music. She taught me for a while. But she was always on to Alfie to be a gentleman, I guess because her husband disgraced her. They call him Dirty Joe."

I was transferred to another town a few days later, before the case was finally settled and, although I meant to write and find out what happened, I kept putting it off until I forgot about it.

The next time I met Forbes was some years later, at the Dorchester Hotel in London. It was at a tea dance "for officers," given by Lady Viola Somebody, and Forbes walked in with an English Guards officer. He was wearing the uniform of a Captain in the Canadian Army and it would be hard to find a better turned-out officer in any army, including the Scandinavian.

"Old man!" he greeted me. "Really, I'm delighted."

In our few minutes of private conversation, he told me that at last he had found his proper profession. Many of his governor's people, he said, had been soldiers and he certainly intended to stay in the Permanent Force after the war. To the Guards officer he expressed his regret at not having got over in peacetime for Hurlingham.

"Oh, do you play polo?" the guardsman beamed. "I say, what a shame we can't provide any! But really, you know, there's plenty of sport. I can give you a decent spot of shooting if you'll pop up to Scotland after the Twelfth."

Lady Viola considered Forbes a definite find. She found it her duty as a Christian noblewoman to entertain officers on active service, even "colonial" officers, but she could hardly conceal her feeling that colonial officers were not gentlemen. Here, at last, was a Canadian officer, tailored to measure by Dornford Yates.

I tried to get Forbes's address, so I could look him up later, but he was a little evasive.

"We're on maneuvres a lot," he explained. "Let me know where your squadron is stationed and I'll make it a point to visit you. I've not seen an air force station."

I gave him the address, but he never wrote and he never came. Instead, quite by accident, I found where *he* was stationed.

I had occasion to visit an old friend, who was with an infantry unit near Aldershot. On my way in to the adjutant's office in the Headquarters Building, I bumped into Forbes. He was wearing dungarees and was swishing a mop over the floor with a monumental lack of interest. From time to time he dipped the mop in a gingerly fashion into a bucket of dirty water.

I stood and stared, but when Forbes looked up and saw me he didn't bat an eye. He merely raised his finger in warning and beckoned me into the latrine.

"I can't talk here," he explained in the latrine. "A single word might give the show away. *Nobody must know that I'm an officer.* The War House sent me down to keep an eye on a certain friend of Herr Hitler's who has wangled his way into the Canadian Army. It would be funny if it weren't so serious, but the fellow is actually in command of the battalion! He doesn't know yet that we're on to him."

Promising discretion, I went on my way.

"What was 'Loopy' Radford talking to you about?" the adjutant asked me.

"Oh, he's an old friend from away back," I said. "What kind of a soldier does he make?"

"Well, now, that depends on what you mean by soldier. On the parade ground he's perfect, as he ought to be, because he spends a lot of his time there for one thing and another. Also, he's the best batman we have, except for his habit of borrowing your best tunic to go to tea on Sunday. In other respects, he's a trifle clueless."

"What do you do about the uniform business?" I asked.

"We overlook it completely," he replied. "He behaves so well when he's out that he gives the regiment a good name. I'm always being asked by dowagers around here to bring that lovely Captain Radford over for dinner. They say he's so *gentlemanly*. We keep this a deep, dark secret from the Old Man who, between you and me, is a Sherbrooke Street Englishman from Montreal. He is mystified by rumors that there is a really nice polite officer in the unit, but he hasn't yet connected them with Radford, who appears before him regularly."

I suppose I shouldn't have been surprised when, before lunch, I bumped into Ken in the mess. We exchanged hellos and then were a little stumped for a moment until I remarked, "You're still keeping an eye on the boy, I see."

He looked puzzled for a second, then said, "Yeah, sure."

"And, boy, he really needs some watching in the army," he added. "I got him into this outfit by telling the C. O. he'd make a good batman. It was a blow to Forbes, but I pointed out that he couldn't be an officer himself, which is what he wanted, because of his illness. At that time I had the naïve idea that insanity was a bar to commissioned rank. As a matter of fact, although he doesn't know it, one colonel actually put him up for it, and for the good of the army and for Forbes's sake I had to queer the deal."

My final glimpse of the mortal Forbes came as I left the army camp. Defaulters were lined up at the guardhouse awaiting inspection by the orderly officer. Forbes could be identified among them at some distance by the smartness of his turnout. All his gear and accoutrements gleamed and glistened above and beyond the call of army regulations.

The sergeant called his defaulters to attention as I came past and swung about to give me a terrifically military salute. While his back was turned, Forbes took the opportunity to wave to me and give me a Look which indicated that we both Understood.

I never saw Forbes again and the war had been over a couple of years before I saw Ken. The fortunes of peace had thrown us both into Montreal, a large and wealthy city with two languages and no rapid-transit system. We were both employed at the head offices of large firms and were both faced with the difficulty of getting home at night on streetcars packed to the doors, trying to butt through streets jammed with automobiles, most of which kept their horns blowing with Gallic fervor right through the period of heavy traffic.

We both hit on the same sensible expedient, a popular one in downtown Montreal, which is to head for a tavern and there pass the time until the traffic situation is improved. The taverns, like the streetcars, are crowded, but they serve beer.

I found Ken in a tavern. He was much stouter and his hair had thinned a lot. He looked middle-aged. He wore no sort of service button and even when others in his crowd were violently discussing some phase of the late war he showed no interest. The war for him was finished and done with. The fact that he had reached the rank of lieutenant-colonel and had received the Distinguished Service Order would never be mentioned by Ken, of that I felt sure. The others had all drifted away before I brought up the subject I wanted to question Ken about.

"What became of Forbes?" I queried.

"He got the chop."

"Where?"

"France."

"Oh, in '44?"

"No, in '43."

I tried vainly to think how Forbes could have been killed in France in 1943, in an infantry unit. Ken didn't look as if he wanted to talk, but gradually he relaxed.

"I never talk about this," he said at last, "because it's so incredible. But then you know Forbes. We got torpedoed on our way to Sicily and after we'd drifted around on a raft, four of us, for about four days, we got picked up by a little fishing boat. They landed us on the coast at night and told us how we could contact the Resistance, which we did without much trouble. The Resistance billeted us round in farmhouses near a small village, gave us civvies and generally treated us well.

"We were allowed to walk about quite freely, because the village was solid Resistance. They were hoping to move us toward the Spanish frontier shortly, as soon as a local panic died down. One day, in the village, I spotted Private Alfred Radford strolling down the road looking like a stage Englishman. He was wearing plus fours, a Fair Isle jumper, a real bookmaker's sports jacket, and a felt hat full of trout flies. He was also carrying a rough walking stick. On sight, I'd have arrested him as a Belgian traitor trying to imitate a British agent.

" 'What's all this?' I asked him.

"He was a bit vague, but later I learned he'd told the Resistance people he was Captain Forbes Radford, of the British Secret Service, and that he'd come to find out about German forces in the district. The Resistance thought all Englishmen were a bit loopy anyway, so they believed him and let him go on his own sweet way.

"Then one night a couple of the seventeen-year-old Resistance kids got a bit too keen and went beyond their orders. They used to be sent out to blow up railway lines and bridges with gelignite dropped by you RAF types. Spontaneous assassination of German personnel was strictly *defendu*. That was a policy matter, to be decided in advance by higher authority. Well, these two kids found a German staff car pulled up by the roadside while the passenger, a *Generalmajor,* was relieving himself. They knocked him and the driver off as quick as a wink.

"There was quite a fuss at the local Resistance H. Q. when the kids came in with cases and binoculars and revolvers taken from the staff car. The local chief chewed them up good and proper and then gave orders that we visitors were to push off at the short trail, pronto, into the woods, anywhere.

"One of our boys was a French Canadian, from St. Hyacinthe, so he elected to stay and brazen it out. I didn't have any choice, because I'd sprained an ankle on an expedition with those fool kids, so they buried me in an empty gas storage tank until the fuss was over.

"About ten o'clock the S. S. Sicherheitsdienst moved into the village in force. For my money they were the meanest Jerry outfit of all. Their job was security and counterespionage, but with an accent on brute force and bloody ignorance. Nothing subtle or clever about them."

What took place when the S. S. arrived was witnessed by Jean-Louis, the French Canadian. He told Ken that from the outset it had a nasty look about it, as if the Germans were about to perpetrate another Lidice. They beat through the houses and rounded up all the men of the village, Jean-Louis included, and herded them into the village square.

Jean-Louis was standing at the edge of the mob of villagers, watching the S. S. men conducting the women and children to some other point and removing certain portable goods from the houses, when to his horror he saw Forbes returning to the village.

Forbes was still wearing the felt hat with the trout flies, the plus fours, le sporting and the Fair Isle jumper, but in addition he had hung the Generalmajor's binoculars about his neck. He strolled into the square with such an air of insouciance that Jean-Louis half-expected to see him stroll right past the preoccupied Germans without being noticed. It was obvious that he had already lunched and only too well. There was the suggestion of a stagger about his gait, as if he were walking on air with pockets in it. Without doubt he had found an inn a few kilometres away and had been entertained royally. Under the influence of good food and too much wine he had completely forgotten about the impending crisis, but then again, Ken thought, he might just have lost his way and wandered back by mistake.

At any rate he strolled past several sentries without challenge and was approaching the mob of villagers when an S. S. officer saw him, strode briskly toward him and shouted something in bad French.

Forbes, according to Jean-Louis, nodded politely and raised his rough brier stick in greeting. Then he tried to stroll on past. *"Ein Mo-ment, bitte,"* the German said, seizing his arm, *"Comment vous appelez-vous? Wie heissen Sie?* What is your name?"

Forbes had a hazy eye. He seemed to be quite unaware of his surroundings. Floating on a pink cloud of the *vin du pays,* he was off in some lovely daydream.

"Oh, my name's Radford," he replied, according to Jean-Louis, "Captain Forbes Radford, D.S.O." Then he smiled knowingly at the simmering German and added, "British Intelligence, you know."

Outraged by the coolness of the thing, the S. S. officer tore the binoculars from Forbes's shoulder, opened the case and read the name inside.

Forbes just stood there, with a bewildered look, until the S. S. officer screamed with rage and struck him across the face with the back of his hand. That was too much for poor Forbes, who came out of it rather suddenly, turned in panic flight and ran like a deer until he was shot down by a dispassionate *Posten* at the edge of the square.

After his pockets had been emptied and inventoried, the clothes were removed, the body photographed, and then what was left of Forbes was driven two kilometres out of town and buried by two villagers detailed for the purpose. So far as the S. S. Sicherheitsdienst was concerned, the crime had been solved and necessary action taken. No further action against the village was needed.

"I saw the grave before I left for the Spanish frontier," Ken said. "People had planted a few flowers on it. But just take a look at it now!"

He handed me a snapshot of Forbes's grave. It was marked by a huge stone cairn, with heroic figures at the corners and a weeping angel bent over a dead British soldier. Occasional cherubim fluttered about and the plaque clearly read, "Captain Forbes Radford, D.S.O., British Secret Service."

"There was quite an argument between the graves registration people and the mayor of the village about that," Ken said. "But the graves boys saw they were playing with gelignite, so they let the whole thing drop. It's a pity his mother never lived to see it."

I see Ken sometimes in the tavern and now and then at lunch in a hotel. I often wonder how he feels without somebody to keep an eye on.

STEPHEN LEACOCK

# A Leacock Sampler

## ON LECTURING

Few people realize how arduous and how disagreeable public lecturing is. The public sees the lecturer step out onto the platform in his little white waistcoat and his long-tailed coat and with the false air of a conjurer about him, and they think him happy. After about ten minutes of his talk, they are tired of him. Most people tire of a lecture in ten minutes; clever people can do it in five. Sensible people never go to lectures at all. . .

The city in which I live, and I suppose for the matter of that, all Canadian cities, is over-run with little societies, clubs and associations, always wanting to be addressed. So at least it is in appearance. In reality the societies are chiefly composed of presidents, secretaries and officials who want the conspicuousness of office, a few members who hope to succeed to office, and a large list of other members who won't come to the meetings. For such an association, the invited speaker carefully prepares his lecture on Indo-Germanic Factors in the Current of History.

. . . Then comes the fated night. There are seventeen people present. The lecturer refuses to count them. He refers to them afterward as "about a hundred." To this group he reads his paper on Indo-Germanic Factors. It takes him two hours. When he is over the chairman invites discussion. There is *no* discussion. . .

But pass over the audience. Suppose there is a *real* audience, and suppose them all duly gathered together. Then it becomes the business of that evil-minded villain—facetiously referred to in the newspaper reports as the genial chairman—to put the lecturer to the bad. . . Some chairmen develop a great gift for it.

"Gentlemen," said the chairman of a society in a little village town in western Ontario to which I had come as a paid (a very humbly paid) lecturer, "we have with us tonight a gentleman" (here he made an attempt to read my name on a card, failed to read it, and put the card back in his pocket)—"a gentleman who is to lecture us on" (here he looked at the card again) "on Ancient—Ancient—I don't very well see what it is—Ancient—Britain? Thank you, on Ancient Britain. Now, this is the first of our series of lectures for this winter. The last series, as you all know, was not a success. In fact, we came out at the end of the year with a deficit. So this year we are starting a new line and we're trying the experiment *of cheaper talent*."

Here the chairman gracefully waved his hand toward me and there was a certain amount of applause. . .

Another time I arrived in a little town in eastern Ontario and found to my horror that I was billed to "appear" *in a church*. I was to give readings from my works, and my books are supposed to be of a humorous character. A church hardly seemed the right place to get funny in. I explained my difficulty to the pastor of the church, a very solemn-looking man.

He nodded his head, slowly and gravely, as he grasped my difficulty. "I see," he said, "I see, but I think I can introduce you to our people in such a way as to make that all right."

When the time came he led me up on the pulpit platform of the church, just beside and below the pulpit itself, with a reading desk with a big Bible and a shaded light beside it. It was a big church, and the audience, sitting in half darkness, as is customary during a sermon, reached away back into the gloom. The place was packed full and absolutely silent.

"Dear friends," the chairman said, " I want

you to understand that tonight it will be all right to laugh. Let me hear you laugh out heartily, laugh right out, just as much as ever you want to. Because"—and here his voice assumed the deep sepulchral tone of the preacher —"when we think of the noble object for which the Professor appears tonight, we may be assured that the Lord will forgive anyone who laughs at the Professor."

I am sorry to say, however, that none of the audience, even with the plenary absolution in advance, were inclined to take a chance upon it.

## ON HUMOR

Until two weeks ago I might have taken my pen in hand to write about humor with the confident air of an acknowledged professional. But that time is past. Such claim as I had had been taken from me. In fact, I stand unmasked. An English reviewer writing in a literary journal, the very name of which is enough to put contradiction to sleep, has said of my writing: "What is there, after all, in Professor Leacock's humor but a rather ingenious mixture of hyperbole and myosis?"

The man was right. How he stumbled upon this trade secret, I do not know. But I am willing to admit, since the truth is out, that it has long been my custom in preparing an article of a humorous nature to go down to the cellar and mix up half a gallon of myosis with a pint of hyperbole. If I want to give the article a decidedly literary character, I find it well to put in about half a pint of paresis. The whole thing is amazingly simple.

But I only mention this by way of introduction and to dispel any ideas that I am conceited enough to write about humor, with the professional authority of Ella Wheeler Wilcox on Love, or Eva Tanguay talking about Dancing.

All I dare claim is that I have as much sense of humor as other people. And, oddly enough, I notice that everybody else makes the same claim. Any man will admit, if need be, that his sight is not good or that he cannot swim, or shoots badly with a rifle, but to touch upon his sense of humor is to give him a mortal affront.

. . . But our sense of humor under civilization has been weakened. . . For me, as I suppose for most of us, it is a prime condition of humor that it must be without harm or malice, nor should it convey even incidentally any real picture of sorrow or suffering or death. There is a great deal in the humor of Scotland (I admit its general merit) which seems to me, not being a Scotchman, to sin in this respect. Take this familiar story (I quote it as something already known, and not for the sake of telling it).

A Scotchman had a sister-in-law—his wife's sister—with whom he could never agree. He always objected to going anywhere with her and, in spite of his wife's entreaty, always refused to do so. The wife was taken mortally ill, and as she lay dying, she whispered: "John, ye'll drive Janet with you to the funeral, will ye no?" The Scotchman, after an internal struggle, answered: "Margaret, I'll do it for ye, but it'll spoil my day."

In the whole domain of humor, we Canadians stand, as we do in all matters of art and aesthetics, as a middle term between what is British and what is American. We cannot fully participate in either. Indeed, our position is somewhat akin to that of the late Duke of Argyll, of whom it was said in Scotland that "his pride o' birth was sic' that he couldna' associate wi' men o' his ain' intellect, and his pride o' intellect was sic' that he couldna' associate wi' men o' his ain' birth."

It is possible to write humorous things *about* Canada, and it is possible to write humorous things *in* Canada (I try to do it myself), but there it is, in my humble opinion (reached after forty-six years of effort), no Canadian humor.

The deep background that lies behind and beyond what we call humor is revealed only to the few who, by instinct or by effort, have given thought to it. The world's humor, in its best and greatest sense, is perhaps the highest product of our civilization. One thinks here not of the mere spasmodic effects of the comic artist or the black-faced expert of the vaudeville show, but of the really great humor which, once or twice in a generation at best, illuminates and elevates our literature. It is no longer dependent upon the mere trick and quibble of words, or the old and meaningless incongruities in things that strike us as "funny." Its basis lies in the deeper contrasts offered by life itself: the strange incongruity between our aspirations and our achievements, the eager and fretful anxieties of today that fade into nothingness tomorrow, the burning pain and the sharp sorrow that are softened in the gentle retrospect of time, till as we look back on the course that has been traversed, we pass in view of the panorama of our lives, as people in old age may recall, with mingled tears and smiles, the angry quarrels of their childhood. And here, in its larger aspect, humor is blended with pathos till the two are one, and represent as they have in every age, the mingled heritage of tears and laughter that is our lot on earth.

## ON MARIPOSA

If you do not know Mariposa, my dear reader, the loss is yours, and the fault lies at your own door. For it means that you have

95

failed to see it by not having the eyes to see. There is no doubt that if you live in Ontario at all you have driven, numberless times, in your motor through the wide streets of the beautiful town; that you have drawn up outside the Continental Hotel, and have drunk two per cent beer, foaming over the bar; you have admired, or at least have had the opportunity to admire, the striking architecture of the Carnegie Library (opened 1902: the gift of A. Carnegie. J. Melville, Mayor); you have seen the imposing front of the new YMCA building (ANNO DOMINI MCMXIX), even if your urbane indolence has prevented you from inspecting the inside of it and viewing the swimming tank, which is said to be the largest of its size in North America, and is deep enough to drown any man under eight feet high.

If you have not seen these things the fault, I repeat, is all your own. It means that you have crawled wearily away in your motor after eating dinner at the Continental and have started back on your journey to the sordid city with the reflection, "How absolutely alike all these little towns are." You have perhaps applied to it the brutal and degrading epithet "one-horse"; and you may have said to your companions, "How awful it would be to live in a town like that all winter!" Such a man as you could hardly realize that in the wintertime—when the Mariposa Shakespeare Society is in full swing (meeting once every five weeks), when the Chess Club (over Hillis's store in the Oddfellows' Block) is a blaze of light every third Saturday evening, and when the Mariposa Opera House presents, every month or so such features as *Muggs Landing*, the Marks Brothers in *East Lynne*, and things admitted even on the handbills to be big New York attractions—that, in short, in point of intellectual life the wintertime is *the* season in Mariposa, just as June is the season in London, or March on the Riviera.

The springtime when it comes in Mariposa comes as the fitting and appropriate reward of the peculiar optimism that has carried its inhabitants through the rigors of winter. There never were such people as the Mariposans for persisting in the belief that the winter is not really cold, and that it is at any given moment about to "break."

In March, though the ice on the lake beside the town is two feet thick, the winter is declared to be "on its last legs," and there is an organizing meeting of the Mariposa Tennis Club which gives a touch of summer itself to the season. April blows wild great gusts of flying snow that come whirling down from the Hudson Bay. But the Mariposans sneer at it. Already they are planting beans under the snow

and patching up hen houses with an eagerness which means that the brief winter is over all too quickly and spring may be upon them, unprepared, at any moment.

Then all of a sudden comes the First of May and the winter is understood to be over. On which there is an immediate and peculiar change of opinion, a sort of right-about-face. All the people declare that it was the longest and hardest winter that they ever remember; that such a winter was never seen before; that their health is shattered by the severity of it; that the fall crops are destroyed; that the lambs are dead and that the fruit trees will never bear again. The farmers, it is freely claimed, are ruined—a fact admitted by all the farmers themselves.

## ON THE MONARCHY

A Loyal British subject like myself in dealing with the government of England should necessarily begin with a discussion of the monarchy. I have never had the pleasure of meeting the King—except once on the GTR platform in Orillia, Ontario, when he was the Duke of York and I was one of the welcoming delegates of the Town Council. No doubt he would recall it in a minute.

But in England the King is surrounded by formality and circumstance. On many mornings I waited round the gates of Buckingham Palace but I found it quite impossible to meet the King in the quiet sociable way in which one met him in Orillia. The English, it seems, love to make the kingship a subject of great pomp and official etiquette. In Canada it is quite different. Perhaps we understand kings and princes better than the English do. At any rate we treat them in a far more human heart-to-heart fashion than is the English custom and they respond to it at once.

I remember when King George—he was, as I say, Duke of York then—came up to Orillia, Ontario, how we all met him in a delegation on the platform. Bob Curran—Bob was mayor of the town that year—went up to him and shook hands with him and invited him to come right on up to the Orillia House where we had a room reserved for him. Charlie Janes and Mel Tudhope and the other boys who were on the Town Council gathered round the royal prince and shook hands and told him that he simply must stay over. George Rapley, the bank manager, said that if he wanted a cheque cashed or anything of that sort to come right into the Royal Bank and he would do it for him. The Prince had two aides-de-camp with him and a secretary, but Bob Curran said to bring them uptown too, and it would be all right. We had planned to have an oyster supper for the Prince at Jim Smith's hotel and then take him either to the YMCA poolroom or else over to the tea social in the church basement.

Unluckily, the Prince couldn't stay. It turned out that he had to get right back into his train and go on to Peterborough, Ontario, where they would have a brass band to meet him, which naturally he didn't want to miss.

But the point is that it was a real welcome. And you could see that the Prince appreciated it. There was a warmth and a meaning to it that the Prince understood at once. It was a pity that he couldn't have stayed over and had time to see the carriage factory and the new sewerage plant. We all told the Prince he must come back and he said that if he could he most certainly would. When the Prince's train pulled out of the station and we all went back uptown together (it was before Prohibition came to Ontario) you could feel that the institution of royalty was quite solid in Orillia for a generation.

## ON HOW TO SUCCEED

According to all the legends and storybooks, the principal factor in success is perseverance. Personally, I think there is nothing in it. If anything, the truth lies the other way.

There is an old motto that runs: "If at first you don't succeed, try, try, again." This is nonsense. It ought to read: "If at first you don't succeed, quit, quit, at once."

If you can't do a thing, more or less, the first time you try, you will never do it. Try something else while there is yet time.

## ON POLITICS

To avoid all error as to my point of view, let me say that I am a Liberal Conservative, or, if you will, a Conservative Liberal, with a strong dash of sympathy with the Socialist idea, a friend of labor, and a believer in progressive radicalism. I do not desire office but would take a seat in the Senate at five minutes' notice. I believe there are ever so many people with exactly this way of thinking.

## ON ROUGHING IT

The season is now opening when all those who have a manly streak in them like to get out in the bush and "rough it" for a week or two of hunting and fishing. For myself, I never feel that the autumn has been well spent unless I can get out after the moose. And when

I go I like to go right into the bush and "rough it"—get clear away from civilization, out in the open, and take fatigue and hardship just as it comes.

So this year I am making all my plans to get away for a couple of weeks of moose hunting along with my brother George and my friend Tom Crass. We generally go together because we are all of us men who like the rough stuff and are tough enough to stand the hardship of living in the open. The place we go to is right in the heart of the primitive Canadian forest, among big timber, broken with lakes as still as glass, just the very ground for moose.

We have a kind of lodge up there. It's just a rough place that we put up, the three of us, the year before last—built out of tamarack logs faced with a broad axe. The flies, while we were building it, were something awful. Two of the men we sent in there to build it were so badly bitten that we had to bring them out a hundred miles to a hospital. None of us saw the place while we were building it—we were all busy at the time—but the teamsters who took in our stuff said it was the worst season for the black flies that they ever remembered.

Still we hung to it, in spite of the flies, and stuck at it until we got it built. It is, as I say, only a plain place but good enough to rough it in. We have one big room with a stone fireplace and bedrooms around the sides, with a wide veranda, properly screened, all along the front. In the back part we have quarters where our man sleeps. We had an icehouse knocked up and water laid on in pipes from a stream. So that on the whole the place has a kind of rough comfort about it—good enough for fellows hunting moose all day.

The place, nowadays, is not hard to get at. The government has just built a colonization highway quite all right for motors, that happens to go within a hundred yards of our lodge. We can get the railway for a hundred miles, and then the highway for forty, and the last hundred yards we can walk. This season we are going to go the whole way from the city in George's car with our kit with us. Tom says that as far as he is concerned he'd much sooner go into the bush over a rough trail in a buckboard, and for my own part a team of oxen would be more the kind of thing that I'd wish. However, the car is there, so we might as well use the thing, especially as the provincial government has built the fool highway right into the wilderness. By taking the big car also we cannot only carry all the hunting outfit that we need but we can also, if we like, shove in a couple of small trunks with a few clothes. This may be necessary as it seems that somebody has gone and slapped a great big frame hotel right there in the wilderness not half a mile from the place we go to.

The hotel we find a regular nuisance. It gave us the advantage of electric light for our lodge (a thing that none of us care about), but it means more fuss about clothes. Clothes, of course, don't really matter when a fellow is roughing it in the bush, but Tom says that we might find it necessary to go over to the hotel in the evenings to borrow coal oil or a side of bacon or any rough stuff that we need; and there is such a lot of dressing up at these fool hotels now that if we do go over for bacon or anything in the evening Tom says we might as well just slip on our evening clothes and then we could chuck them off the minute we get back. George thinks it might not be a bad idea —just as a way of saving all our energy for getting after the moose—to dine each evening at the hotel itself.

George's idea is that we could come in each night with our moose—such and such a number as the case might be—either bringing them with us or burying them where they die— change our things, slide over to the hotel and get dinner and then beat it back into the bush by moonlight and fetch in the moose. It seems they have a regular two dollar table d'hôte dinner at the hotel—just rough stuff, of course, but after all, as we all admit, we don't propose to go into the wilds to pamper ourselves with high feeding; a plain hotel meal in a homelike style at two dollars a plate is better than cooking up a lot of rich stuff over a campfire.

One thing we're all agreed upon in the arrangement of our hunting trip, is in not taking along anything to drink. Drinking spoils a trip of that sort. We all remember how in the old days we'd go out into a camp in the bush (I mean before there used to be any highway or any hotel) and carry in rye whisky in demijohns (two dollars a gallon it was) and sit around the campfire drinking it in the evenings.

But there is nothing in it. We all agree the law being what it is, it is better to stick to it. It makes a fellow feel better. So we shall carry nothing in. I don't say that one might not have a flask of something in one's pocket in the car; but only as a precaution against accident or cold. And when we get to our lodge we all feel that we are a darn sight better without it.

If we *should* need anything—though it isn't likely—there are still three cases of old Scotch whisky, kicking around the lodge somewhere: I think they are kicking around in a little cement cellar with a locked door that we had made so as to use it for butter or anything of that sort. Anyway, there are three, possibly four, or maybe five, cases of Scotch there and if we should for any reason want it, there it is. But we are hardly likely to touch it—unless we hit a cold snap, or a wet spell, or if we strike hot dry weather. Tom says he thinks there are a couple of cases of champagne still in the cellar: some stuff that one of us must have shot in there just before prohibition came in but we'll hardly use it. When a man is out moose hunting from dawn to dusk he hasn't much use for champagne, not till he gets home anyway...

There's only one trouble about our plans for our fall camp that bothers me just a little. The moose are getting damn scarce about that place. There used, so they say, to be any quantity of them. There's an old settler up there that our man buys all our cream from who says that he remembers when the moose were so thick that they would come up and drink whisky out of his dipper. But somehow they seem to have quit the place. Last year we sent our man out again and again looking for them and he never saw any. Three years ago a boy that works at the hotel said he saw a moose in the cow pasture back of the hotel and there were the tracks of a moose seen last year at the place not ten miles from the hotel where it had come to drink. But apart from these two exceptions the moose hunting has been poor.

Still, what does it matter? What we want is the *life*, the rough life just as I have described it. If any moose comes to our lodge we'll shoot him, or tell the butler to. But if not—well, we've got along without for ten years. I don't suppose we shall worry.

## ON MODERN BUSINESS

Four businessmen were stranded, shipwrecked and penniless, upon an island in the South Seas. It was a beautiful island. Breadfruit grew on every tree, coconuts dangled at the tops of palms, while beds of oysters lay near the shore.

But for the businessmen it was useless. They had no "funds" to develop the island; with an advance of funds they could have gathered breadfruit and made bread. But without funds! Why, they couldn't! They must stay hungry.

"Don't you think," said the weakest among them—a frail man (he had never been able to raise more than a million dollars)—"Don't you think," he said to the biggest man, "you could climb that palm tree and throw down coconuts?"

"And who will underwrite me?" asked the other.

There it was! They were blocked and helpless; couldn't even get an advance to wade into the sea for oysters. So they sat there on the rocks—starving, dejected, their hair growing long. They couldn't even shave; there was no barber union.

On the fourth day the frail man, who was obviously sinking, said: "If I die I want you to bury me over there on that little hill overlooking the sea."

"We can't bury you, Eddie," they said. "We've no burial fund."

They fell asleep on the sands. But the next morning when they woke up an Angel was standing beside them. They knew he was an Angel although he wore a morning coat and a top hat, and had grey striped trousers with spats above his boots.

"Are you an angel?" they asked.

"Pretty much," he answered. "That is to say, I am a director of the Bank of England, but for you just now it is almost the same thing."

"Funds, funds!" they exclaimed. "Can you advance us funds?"

"Certainly," said the Angel. "I came for that. I think I see a fountain pen in your waistcoat pocket there. Thank you . . . and that ten-cent scribbler . . . much obliged. Now then, up you get! Light a fire, go and collect those oysters, go and pick some breadfruit, chase that wild goat and I'll arrange an advance of funds while you're doing it."

As they sat around the fire at supper the Angel explained it all out of the scribbler.

"I have capitalized your island at two million dollars (that's half a million each) and I have opened a current drawing account for each of you of a hundred thousand, with loans as required. . ."

What activity next day! Climb the coconut tree? Why, of course. The man was underwritten. Oysters? They wrote out an oyster policy and waded right in up to their necks. What a change the next week or so brought! There they sat at lunch in their comfortable Banyan Club House overlooking the sea (annual dues, $1,000 a year)—sat at lunch eating grilled oysters with coconut cocktails. . .

"To think," said the little man Eddie, "that only a week ago I wanted to die!"

So that's the allegory and, of course, the island is meant to be Canada, and the shipwrecked men its population. But perhaps you almost guessed that, anyway.

It's almost a pity to mention the sequel. A little later, four laboring men tried to land on an island. The others undertook to fight them off with shotguns. That started civilization. But the pity was that if they had only had the Angel with them, he would have told them to let the laborers land and to multiply all the figures in the book by two, and add a little extra, because in developing a country blessed by ample resources twice four is ten.

DORIS DICKSON

# Dr. Locke and His Million-Dollar Thumbs

On a steaming July afternoon in 1932 a couple from Kentucky were driving into a little village in northeastern Ontario called Williamsburg and they were startled to find themselves entangled in a bizarre traffic jam. A maze of automobiles, wheel chairs and stretchers on wheels clogged the road, while thousands of pedestrians, many on crutches, spilled from the maple-shaded sidewalks onto the highway, got in the way of automobiles, dodged hot-dog and souvenir stands and made driving a nightmare. More misshapen bodies were in the shuffling crowd than would likely be found any-where outside a hospital.

After one stricken glance at the snail-paced traffic, the woman burst into tears. "We're too late," she sobbed. "The doctor's dead and they are having his funeral today."

But that was ten years before the doctor's death in 1942 and was an almost daily occur-rence for every one of those ten years. It was a procession of, literally, the lame, the halt and the blind, making their pilgrimage on fallen arches and tortured arthritic limbs to the shrine of Canada's world-famous "miracle healer," Dr. Mahlon W. Locke.

Outside Williamsburg today Dr. Locke is best remembered as the designer of a shoe which has a special arch support and carries his name. But from 1928 to 1942 grateful pa-tients hailed him as a miracle man who could cure everything from hives to multiple sclerosis by twisting their toes and pressing fallen arches back into place. Although sufferers from every disease (including curiosity) came to his clinic, Locke's reputation was based chiefly on his treatment of arthritis.

Thousands swarmed into Williamsburg, mostly from the United States but also from every province in Canada, from the Yukon Territory, South America, Holland, Norway, South Africa, Germany, Australia and Eng-land. Many had joints so swollen, frames so cruelly twisted and bodies so emaciated when they arrived that no one but themselves and Locke had any hope they could be cured. They traveled in private planes, private railway cars and limousines; they hitchhiked; a red-haired cowboy from Alberta with a crippled ankle rode the brake-rods across the prairies in win-ter to arrive in Williamsburg with twelve cents in his pocket. One woman survived the trip from California on a cot in the back of an an-cient half-ton truck.

A list of Locke's patients reads like a page out of *Who's Who*. Mrs. F. D. Roosevelt, Louis B. Mayer, Lady Eaton, Faith Baldwin, Ernie Pyle, Eva Tanguay, Mrs. James Donahue (heiress to the Woolworth millions) and Sir Robert Borden were among them. Mackenzie King returned year after year for treatments. A merchant prince from Bombay, India, brightened the landscape one summer with his red fez, brown jodhpurs and brilliantly gowned wife following at his heels. He brought his pri-vate physician who was reported to be inter-ested in starting a similar clinic in India. Screen siren Jean Harlow was said to be a patient but Locke wasn't sure he had treated her. If he were alive today he probably wouldn't recog-nize Marilyn Monroe as she passed through his hands. His specialty was feet.

A graveled road through Williamsburg to Ottawa forty miles northwest began to go to pieces under the heavy traffic, and had to be hard-surfaced. Transcontinental trains made unprecedented stops at the nearest railway sta-tion, Morrisburg, six miles south of Williams-burg on the St. Lawrence River. The ferry, crossing from Morrisburg to Waddington, N. Y., stepped up its hourly schedule of runs to a quarter-hourly schedule, added another ferry and kept both operating until midnight. Six hundred cars a day often crossed on the ferry. Williamsburg took on a cosmopolitan air as a dozen foreign languages were heard.

While the rest of Canada fearfully groped its way through its worst economic depression, Williamsburgers "never had it so good." Mon-ey poured into the village and surrounding countryside. Every house bulged with paying guests and farmers' sons slept in the haymow and rented their beds. Two hotels (one with 125 rooms) were built to help house the crowds, and the "Rapids Queen," a liner with sixty-five staterooms and a ballroom, was an-chored at Morrisburg to accommodate the overflow. Frame cottages sprang up and were rented at high rates. After the boom was over they were sold for chicken houses. Twenty-three restaurants operated where there had been three. Even the children were in business; they carried lunches, held places in the line-up and ran errands. Young men earned a dollar a day per patient for pushing wheel chairs and carrying stretchers to and from the Circle, as Locke called his lawn on which he worked his wonders. News and tobacco stands took in as much as $1,500 a week.

It was by no means all fun. Guests com-plained about the lack of toilet facilities until plumbing was installed. Wells went dry. House-wives worked from early morning until late at night serving meals, house cleaning and doing laundry. It was impossible to make reservations as the patients never knew when Locke would send them home. The children had no room on the streets to play, and whole families tired of sleeping in their kitchens. One man declared, "It was the happiest day of my life when the last guest left."

It was the first acquaintance with high living that many of the young people, and the older ones too, had known and in some instances it went to their heads. Only Locke and a few other canny souls finished up the years much wealthier than before. Gamblers followed the crowds and set up floating crap games in the hotels. Predatory women looking for wealthy husbands considered the village a happy hunt-ing ground. Locke tried to control the situation, in order to keep the villagers from exploiting the sick and the gamblers from exploiting the villagers. He spread the news among his patients that he wouldn't treat any who stayed in homes or hotels of which he disapproved. He earned himself a reputation as a czar but for the most part his wishes were respected. A newcomer to the village, Miss Flora Griffiths, brought a lawsuit against him for ruining her livelihood by refusing to treat patients who stayed in her rest home. She asked for a hearing without a jury, claiming it was impossible to get an impartial jury in the district. Her request was denied and the suit, for $50,000, dismissed.

For fourteen years Williamsburg was like a circus merry-go-round revolving about Dr. Locke's Circle, a wooden platform on what had once been the Lockes' west lawn but was now covered with concrete—thousands of aching feet had worn it bare and each rain left it a sea of mud. The Women's Institute, to Locke's disgust, had a canvas canopy erected over the platform to protect the patients from the weather. (Later the patients took up a collection and replaced this with a wooden structure which still stands.) Iron pipes, radiating like the spokes of a giant wheel, marked out fourteen runways down which patients moved on camp stools until they reached the wooden chairs at the centre. Two of the runways were for wheel chair and stretcher cases.

Housewives, socialites, doctors, farmers, businessmen and ministers chatted together democratically while waiting for the doctor's appearance. When the runways were filled, they lined up in the streets and milled about on the lawn next door. They talked, read, sang and knit. They vied with each other to show how they had improved. People, harassed and tense at home from too much work or play, relaxed in the cheerful atmosphere.

As Locke made his way to the centre of the Circle from his modest frame house nearby, the crowd cheered him. The first impression he gave was of power—physical and mental. Although he was little more than average height, his head and shoulders were massive and he weighed 250 pounds. His physical strength and endurance are legendary in Williamsburg. His serene bright-blue eyes probed deeply. This glance, together with what he learned through handling their feet, gave him the only information he obtained about his clinic patients.

As Locke seated himself in his low swivel chair at the hub of the wheel, he looked more like the farmer he was at heart than a successful doctor. Always a little untidy, he worked in shirt sleeves, often without a collar or tie, his baggy grey trousers anchored by both belt and suspenders. In his early fifties, at the height of his fame, he had thin light-brown hair, an engagingly open countenance and a singularly sweet smile. He was ambidextrous. His powerful hands with well-muscled thumbs and stocky tapered fingers, moved with incredible speed and sensitivity. X-ray hands, his patients called them. He grasped each stockinged foot as it was thrust forward and pressed up the arch with one quick movement of the thumb while he twisted the toes down and out with the other hand. Occasionally a loud "crack" sounded and the patient jumped. Stuffing the proffered bill in his pocket, Locke whirled on to the next patient and the next dollar. With occasional stops to unwind his chair, or go into the house to empty his pockets, he treated as many as ten patients a minute. After a full day of this he painted his aching thumbs with iodine before retiring and followed the same routine next day. As long as his health and time allowed it, Locke continued his local practice also, and when he was forced to give it up he was jealous of anyone else coming into his territory.

According to his admirers, Dr. Locke scorned advertising and cared nothing for money. Yet so many millions of words were published about him in the United States and Canada during the early Thirties (in newspaper columns, magazine articles, several biographies and a novel), that in his busiest summers he treated as many as 2,700 people twice daily for a dollar each and, as he said himself, he was probably the only man in the world who made a million dollars with his own two hands (more likely three million, his neighbors estimated).

Although he seldom spoke unnecessarily and discouraged questions in the line-up, Locke's friends delighted in telling him jokes as they passed by. His huge body would jiggle up and down with suppressed laughter. "Like Santa Claus," remembered Mrs. A. J. Casselman, of Williamsburg. His rare remarks were usually humorous or sarcastic. To a woman who demurred when asked to remove her shoes, saying the pain was in her shoulder, not her feet, he replied, "When you step on a dog's tail, which end yelps?" A reporter was told: "Other doctors pull their patients' legs, I pull their toes." A richly dressed woman who tried to push her way to the front of the line, protesting, "But, doctor, I'm a millionaire," was squelched with his biting, "Get back in line, madam, so am I."

He said he turned down a lucrative offer to move his headquarters to the Mayo Clinic, Rochester, Minnesota, because they "wanted me to work like a mule in the back room while they sat in the front with a cash register. Here, I run my own show."

A story, probably apocryphal, circulated

through the line-up that Locke had torn up a $10,000 cheque from a wealthy American patient, accepting only his usual dollar-a-day fee. At another time he refused $50 for preferential treatment in the line-up with, "My fee is a dollar, madam," then turned to a shabbily dressed woman in the inner circle and asked, "Is it worth $49 to you to give up your turn?"

This was good showmanship and boosted the morale of his patients but, according to those who knew him, it was also genuine. His sympathies were all with the underdog, they say. He took a certain perverse delight in embarrassing distinguished visitors. If one felt it beneath his dignity to wait in the general line-up, he was at liberty to wait in the Lockes' living room, but he would cool his heels there until everyone in the line-up was treated. Andrew W. Mellon, when he was United States Ambassador to Great Britain, had an appointment but was "forgotten" and kept waiting for hours.

For the dollar fee Locke gave his patients a treatment in the morning and in the afternoon, told them whether or not they had a goiter (he believed that goiter and arthritis were related in 90 per cent of the cases and sold thyroid pills made to his own prescription for fifty cents a box), recommended that they have their shoes fitted with "cookies," which he called the special arch supports, or buy Dr. Locke shoes. Depending on their condition, he would suggest they take a further treatment in the driving shed at the rear. Here, his young woman assistant, Aurlien Weegar (later Mrs. J. Tewsley, of Toronto), exercised arthritic limbs and gently twisted stiffening bodies to hasten the breaking down of adhesions on the joints. For a time, before a shoe store was opened in the village, salesmen also fitted patients with shoes in the shed, or even on the front steps of Locke's office. More than nine thousand pairs of shoes at ten dollars a pair were sold in the village.

Reporters sparked into life a fiery controversy between laymen and doctors about the efficacy of Locke's treatments. They wrote reams of copy for big city dailies, reporting fabulous cures of blindness, deafness, muscular atrophy and paralysis, saddling him with the title of "miracle-man," which he hated. Most doctors, and some reporters, ridiculed the "hoof-doctor," attributing his successes to mass hysteria and hypnotism. A Detroit paper referred to the outdoor medical clinic as the "barnyard clinic." (Lack of sanitation was a serious problem in the pre-septic-tank days and probably the biggest miracle of all was that no epidemic started in the village.)

A report of an investigation published in the *Journal of the American Medical Association* in November 1932 virtually called Dr. Locke a quack. Dr. Morris Fishbein, editor of the *Journal,* wrote: "As nearly as we can determine from the available evidence, Dr. Locke practices the laying on of hands." Patients hotly denied that "faith-healing" was a factor in the cures. Samuel Silver, of Toronto, went to Locke's clinic in desperation, his leg so painful he couldn't walk. Five Toronto doctors, unable to find anything organically wrong, had dismissed him from a hospital with the admonition to forget it. Silver scoffs at the suggestion that faith in Locke was necessary. "Faith, what faith had I?" he asks. "I'm not a man with much faith. All I believe is what I see. He helped me."

Canadian doctors, on the whole, ignored the furore, or commented mildly, as did Professor Duncan Graham, then head of the Department of Clinical Medicine at the University of Toronto, "We've had patients back in the hospital after they've been to his clinic, still suffering from arthritis."

An Alexandria, Ontario, doctor whose patient, against his advice, went to Locke and came back apparently cured, railed, "Why, man, he's got you hypnotized!"

"He could put a ring through my nose and lead me up and down the streets and I wouldn't care," replied the impenitent one. "I'm better."

On the other hand, Dr. Leonard Keene Hirshberg, a graduate of Johns Hopkins University, came to Williamsburg to scoff and remained to praise the doctor's methods. A few doctors who observed the treatment attempted to imitate him. Rex Beach, American novelist, wrote: "To me he is the personification of drama. One man fighting barehanded against a score of creeping diseases. One man breaking canes and crutches! One man upon whom rests the last hope of an army of crippled people."

Even more emotional were some of the women patients. "I just worship the ground he walks on," said one.

Locke's theory was that fallen arches press on the main nerve leading into the foot, irritating it. This constricts the arteries and the blood, moving sluggishly, becomes full of impurities, particularly uric acid which attacks the places of least resistance (in the case of arthritis, the joints). Outgrowths of cartilage eventually "fix" the joints in any position they would normally assume. Bone tissue enlarges and distortion results. He felt that forcing the arch back into place relieved the pressure on the nerve and speeded circulation of the blood, which would in time rid itself of impurities, honeycomb the tissue that had formed on the joints and restore the patient's health. Specialists to-day, as they did in his time, say that this is much too simplified a version of a complex disease. They say that arthritis is only one of the conditions included under the broad term rheumatism and that there are over a hundred different types of arthritis. In only one of these, gout, does uric acid play any part. Present-day treatments vary greatly for each type of arthritis but Locke, in his "manipulative surgery," did not differentiate between them.

Jock MacDonald was one of Locke's most spectacular and publicized cases. Jock was sixteen when he was brought to Williamsburg from Unity, Saskatchewan, on a cot in a baggage car, as the least painful way of moving him. He weighed a scant ninety-one pounds and could barely turn in bed. His left arm was rigid at his side, his fingers deformed and one leg was drawn up and locked at his hip. The other leg was also slightly affected. He lay on his cot in excruciating pain, unable to brush away the flies that settled on his face.

After Locke's first arch treatment, Jock felt a tingling sensation. His feet, cold before, began to feel warm, then burned like fire. After a week of treatment he became violently ill, with much vomiting and diarrhea. (This was a common reaction and, according to Locke's theory, was nature's way of ridding the system of poisons.) Jock's fingers loosened up at first, then his legs, until in six months he could walk using crutches, and after two years could ride a bicycle for miles and walk with only a cane. Jock's father, James MacDonald, who had been a newspaperman in Unity, remained in Williamsburg to publish a weekly paper, the Williamsburg *Times,* devoted almost entirely to news of the Circle. He also lauded Locke in a book called *Dr. Locke, the Healer of Men,* which sold at newsstands about the clinic.

Helen Foley, a nineteen-year-old girl from Florida, was another patient whose recovery was praised as miraculous. Helen, a polio victim, couldn't stand without her legs buckling under her. Mrs. John Tewsley, Locke's former assistant, related that after several years of treatment Helen was "a perfect cure."

It is difficult to assess the proportion of patients who were helped by Locke's treatments. Those who were had their stories printed and reprinted. Those who after a few treatments went home discouraged remained anonymous. A doctor whose sister-in-law took treatments for several months for arthritis, says that rather than being helped, she was considerably worse. Others could not stand the pain occasioned by the treatment nor the violent physical reaction afterward and left. Many, however, remained

for two or three years. One girl stayed ten years. Although still sadly deformed, she was confident Locke's treatment not only arrested the disease but helped her materially in regaining some of the mobility she had lost.

Born at Dixon's Corners, seven miles west of Williamsburg, on St. Valentine's Day 1880, Mahlon Locke was forced to take responsibility early when his father died in 1888, leaving three small sons (Mahlon, the eldest, Peter and Duane) and a farm. The boys attended public school at Dixon's Corners and high school at Iroquois, often shabbily clothed and walking the seven miles to and from Iroquois on weekends.

Because of the pressure of seasonal farm work, Mahlon never spent a full term at high school and left without matriculating. After two years on the farm, influenced by his mother and a young student minister, he enrolled at Kemptville high school, twenty-five miles away, and completed his matriculation in a month. At twenty-one, he entered Queen's University, spent every summer at farm labor and most evenings in Kingston working at odd jobs, one of which was plucking partridges for a hotel. At twenty-five he graduated from Queen's as a medical doctor and returned to Brinston, a few miles from Dixon's Corners, where his mother, now remarried, was living. Here the young doctor began his first practice with his step-father, Dr. G. W. Collison. It was hard going. In six months he earned only fifteen dollars and was thoroughly discouraged. A college friend, Dr. M. E. Grimshaw, was working for the Algoma Steel Corporation north of Lake Superior, and Mahlon joined the firm as a company doctor at Sault Ste. Marie for a hundred dollars a month.

A year later Grimshaw and Locke interned at the Royal Infirmary in Edinburgh, Scotland, for a postgraduate course. Here Locke earned his cherished triple licentiate from the Royal College of Surgeons, Edinburgh; Royal College of Physicians, Edinburgh; and the Royal Faculty of Physicians and Surgeons, Glasgow. Years later he said he learned more in six months in Edinburgh than he had in four years in Kingston. In Edinburgh he conceived the theory that was later to make him famous.

City life had no charms for Locke. He liked the peace and freedom of the country. He fitted like a hand in a glove into the prosperous dairying community of Williamsburg, famous for its cheese and McIntosh apples. From the day he hung out his shingle on June 1, 1908, his success as a country practitioner was assured.

Except for a few short holidays Locke scarcely moved outside a twenty-mile radius of the tiny village. By his skill at diagnosis and treatment, as well as his kindliness and capacity for work, he won his neighbors' unswerving loyalty. To all ages he was known as Doc, or the Old Doc. He kept five horses steadily on the go. No call was too much trouble. Delivering three babies in one night under primitive conditions was not unusual. Mrs. Locke said that in winter his overcoat seldom dried between calls. One night as his team broke trail through deep snow, his cutter upset, dumping the doctor into a snow bank. He rolled himself up in a blanket and slept out the rest of the night there.

He was always especially interested in bones, and in a community where the chief occupational hazard seems to have been falling out of haymows he had plenty of practice setting broken bones and dislocated shoulders and hips. Innocent bystanders were called in to sit on the patient while the doctor, by main strength, pulled a dislocated hip back into place. Since he had little faith in anaesthetics the operation was bound to be painful.

His fees for general practice were arrived at by a system of computation known only to himself. He sent no bills, and unless a patient asked he'd never know how much he owed. If the family were poor or had had a run of bad luck there would be no charge. Even the well-to-do found his charges surprisingly low. One woman who started her family late in life says that for her first delivery the doctor charged ten dollars, for the next eight dollars and for the next (in the same year) six dollars. When asked why his fee kept going down he laughed, "If you have another baby within the year I'll deliver it for nothing."

In 1914 when he was thirty-five Locke married 21-year-old Blanche McGruer at her parents' home near Williamsburg. Because of unexpected patients he was an hour late for the ceremony. The couple settled in the white frame house in Williamsburg where the doctor had lived for seven years. Here their four children were born, three girls and a boy.

Locke's treatments for arthritis began in 1908—the first year of his general practice in Williamsburg. He thought too many of his patients suffered from both flat feet and rheumatism for it to be coincidence. His chance to test his nebulous theory came when Peter Beckstead, a blacksmith in Williamsburg, was so severely crippled by rheumatism that he was unable to continue his heavy work. Locke began pressing the blacksmith's fallen arches back into place. After several treatments, Beckstead found that the pain was lessening. To keep the arches in place, and strengthen the

foot muscles, the doctor had the local shoemaker place leather cookies in the blacksmith's shoes. Beckstead recovered and continued shoeing horses until he died a quarter of a century later. Pressing fallen arches back into place and recommending cookies for shoes became a regular part of Locke's work and in 1931 he claimed there wasn't a case of arthritis in Williamsburg Township. Gradually his reputation spread to surrounding towns.

As more people heard of him Locke found it profitable to have office hours every Tuesday at Prescott, twenty-five miles away on the St. Lawrence River. A few Americans came across the river for treatments. Once a Roman Catholic priest, Father Kelly, from near Lockport, N.Y., came to Williamsburg so crippled by arthritis that he could no longer conduct Mass. Six months later, after Locke's treatments, Kelly literally ran up the path to the doctor's office to show how he had improved. A Lockport newspaperman, Frank Coughlin, himself about to undergo an operation as a last resort against arthritis, heard of Father Kelly's improvement and came for treatments. He was so impressed that he wrote a glowing account of the clinic. This was reprinted in several American newspapers, and the boom was on. That was in 1928. Ontario papers took up the cry and articles were printed in magazines.

In 1930 from two to three hundred people were taking treatments each day. In the summer of 1931 the number had swelled to almost a thousand. About this time Locke sold the patent for the shoe he had designed to a Perth manufacturer for $30,000.

In following years he must often have wondered if he had a lion by the tail. In August 1932 *Cosmopolitan* magazine printed an article by Rex Beach describing the Williamsburg clinic and Locke in warm terms. He, Beach, had been staying at the Château Laurier in Ottawa, golfing. Fallen arches made walking a misery, and someone half jokingly suggested he visit the doctor at Williamsburg. Beach took the advice, had a foot treatment, talked to the crowds and wrote his article. The next summer the crowds reached an all-time record of 2,700 persons treated a day.

"I always say that Rex Beach killed him," commented Lewis Schell, one of Locke's old cronies. "He had plenty to do right around here without all those people." Although 1932 and 1933 were the peak years crowds continued until Locke's death in February 1942.

Besides the strain that treating thousands of people daily placed on Locke's strength, his private life was sadly disrupted. Patients invaded his living room, his dining room, and on one

A. Y. JACKSON ADDS A NEW WORK TO THE GROUP OF SEVEN'S ACHIEVEMENT

## THE PAINTER'S CANADA: HER FACE, HER FIGURE, HER MANY MOODS

THE STORYTELLERS LIKE KRIEGHOFF, THE
NATURALISTS OF THE GROUP OF SEVEN, AND THE
MODERNISTS WHO FOLLOW A DOZEN NEW CHAL-
LENGING ROADS—ALL HAVE HAD THEIR "PRIVATE
SHOWS" IN MACLEAN'S PAGES. OVER THE YEARS,
THE PUBLIC HAS CONDEMNED AND CHEERED AND
OCCASIONALLY BEEN PRODDED OUT OF ITS APATHY
TOWARD THE ART OF THIS STILL-YOUNG NATION.

**THE SLEIGH RACE,** CORNELIUS KRIEGHOFF
AFTER A CENTURY HIS NEGLECTED FOLK ART WAS WORTH A FORTUNE

**THE JACK PINE,** TOM THOMSON
POSSIBLY THE MOST "CANADIAN" OF THEM ALL

ALGOMA, NOVEMBER, A. Y. JACKSON
TURNING HIS BACK ON EUROPE, HE FOUND A LIFE-WORK ON HIS DOORSTEP

"PAINTING IN CANADA HAS ALWAYS BEEN A PRECARIOUS WAY OF MAKING A LIVING. ONLY THE POETS RANK LOWER THAN THE PAINTERS IN THE FINANCIAL SCALE. IT MIGHT WELL BE ASKED WHY ANYONE SHOULD DEVOTE HIS LIFE TO ART. THE ANSWER IS SIMPLE: THE TRUE ARTIST CANNOT HELP HIMSELF. HE WILL CONTINUE TO PAINT EVEN IF HE HAS NO SALES AT ALL."

A. Y. Jackson, in *A Painter's Country*

NORTH SHORE, LAWREN HARRIS

PRESENCES IN A THICKET, JACK SHADBOLT.
THIS, AND OTHER WORKS SHOWN HERE, WERE COMMISSIONED BY MACLEAN'S

"IF THE MODERN ARTIST SWAYS ON HIS
TIGHTROPE AND SO OFTEN FALLS, HAVE
MERCY ON HIM FOR YOU ARE ON THE
TIGHTROPE TOO."

Jacques de Tonnancour

GABRIOLA ISLAND, ED HUGHES

CENTENNIAL REGATTA, B. C. BINNING

LAURENTIAN HEAVE, JACQUES DE TONNANCOUR

AUTUMN, GHITTA CAISERMAN

DREAM AT A WHITE VILLAGE, ALFRED PELLA

YESTERDAY, THE CANADIAN PAINTER, TURNING HIS BACK ON EUROPEAN TRADITION, DEVELOPED A DISTINCTIVE ART WHICH REACHED ITS HIGHEST FORM IN THE GROUP OF SEVEN.

TODAY, THOUGH THE INFLUENCE OF THIS GROUP REMAINS STRONG, MORE AND MORE ARTISTS ARE ENTERING THE MAINSTREAMS OF INTERNATIONAL ART AND MANY—INCLUDING SOME OF THOSE WHOSE WORK APPEARS ON THESE PAGES—HAVE ACHIEVED INTERNATIONAL REPUTATIONS.

ONE OF THESE, JOHN LYMAN (RIGHT) HAS ACHIEVED THIS, EVEN THOUGH HIS SUBJECTS ARE ALMOST INVARIABLY FOUND IN QUEBEC.

"I DON'T LOOK FOR THINGS TO PAINT—BUT PAINT THE THINGS I MEET IN LIFE" HE SAYS. "I TAKE MY PROVINCE AND ITS PEOPLE FOR GRANTED AND FEEL NO NEED TO RIG UP ANY INTERPRETIVE THESIS OR ANY KIND OF ROMANTIC NONSENSE."

**FARMER'S DAUGHTER**, JOHN LYMAN

**TANGLED LANDSCAPE**, GORDON SMITH

RECLINING NUDE, FREDERICK H. VARLEY

occasion when he was ill with blood poisoning in his leg, his bedroom. Every meal was interrupted a dozen times by the telephone ringing or someone at the door. Locke began his treatments at eight in the morning (except for the mornings when he began at five) and continued until eleven at night, so the Circle was seldom empty. Sometimes the line-up started as early as 1 a.m. To have a few minutes to himself during the day he would visit one of his farms.

Locke's farms were his only hobby. He bought his first one near Williamsburg in 1913. He said he wasn't sure he could make a living as a doctor but knew from experience he could as a farmer. He bought what everyone else considered a worn-out but pure-bred Holstein bull for thirty dollars and began raising pure-bred cattle. One of his Holsteins set a world record for 101 pounds of milk in a day and 142 pounds of butter in thirty days. Locke also raised Percheron horses and standard-bred race horses. He was lawyer, general counsel and adviser to many of his older patients. He gave advice on business deals, on legal matters and wrote their wills (but died without one himself).

A man of strange contradictions, he often reached in his pocket and passed over a handful of bills to a needy patient. Yet he enjoyed telling of the time he dressed up in patched clothing to fool a cattle-buyer into thinking he was a poor man so he could get a better price. He'd lend money to anyone he knew without interest or fuss, but at a time when his earnings were well over a thousand dollars a day, he paid hired men on his farms a dollar a day.

He took no interest in civic improvement or politics. When approached by the Ontario Liberal leader, Mitchell Hepburn, an onion farmer, to stand for election, he laughed him off with, "You go home and grow your onions and I'll peddle my pills." Except for a week's holidays at Christmas Locke had little time for anything but work. He read magazines, a few novels, his medical journals and, every day, a chapter or two from the Bible, of which he knew large sections by heart. He always found social contacts on his own intellectual level difficult and preferred spending his leisure with men he could dominate. In July 1938 a group

of former patients, who called themselves the Friends of Dr. Locke Committee, organized a testimonial banquet for him at the Château Laurier in Ottawa with more than one hundred guests present. A bronze cast of Locke's hands made by Italian sculptor Deno Buralli was presented to him, and he made what was probably the first speech of his life. The family was in a cold sweat for him but if he was nervous he didn't show it.

Another gift from the Friends of Dr. Locke Committee was a huge red leather-bound book with thousands of letters from grateful patients. These ranged from short notes from people who wore Dr. Locke shoes, but had never met him, to testimonials saying, "I was doomed to spend the rest of my life in a wheel chair but after six weeks' treatment by Dr. Locke, and after six or seven years, I am still walking and able to attend to my work."

During the last few years of his life Locke's health was poor. His weight dropped from 250 pounds to 190. He was tired much of the time and had several severe colds, verging on pneumonia. After he was unconscious for two or three days in a Montreal hospital, he began taking insulin injections for diabetes and watching his diet more closely. He tried to work fewer hours but 500 to 600 patients were still attending the clinic each day in the summer of 1941. At that time he also owned seventeen farms, including some which had been reforested. He planned all the work himself for five farms under cultivation, shouting instructions each morning from his bedroom window to the hired men as they passed on their way to work.

On the morning of February 7, 1942, feeling a little better, Locke left his home at 8:30 to drive to one of his farms. There had been a fresh snowfall and the car, a 1942 Cadillac, slid into the ditch. He tried at first to push the car out, then, when a neighbor came to help, he slid behind the wheel to steer. The neighbor found him slumped over the wheel, almost unconscious, and drove him home. When Mrs. Locke came to help carry him into the house Locke pointed to his head, indicating he had suffered a stroke. He never regained full consciousness and died about midnight.

## FRANK HAMILTON

# The Case Book of Antoine Rivard

"The income from a criminal law practice," Antoine Rivard remarked, "is very uncertain. Many clients can pay nothing, so we try to make the rich pay for the poor. But a murder case is never a paying proposition. The money invariably runs out before the case is finished. An appeal can cost $1,000 a week or more, exclusive of the lawyer's fee. In many cases, I've had to foot the bill myself. But the rewards are publicity and prestige, and for that reason a criminal lawyer must keep in the limelight at every assizes. Since I began practicing I have always had at least one capital case at every assizes."

For *Maître* Rivard his dozens of murder cases have more than paid off. He has enjoyed the satisfaction of being Quebec's best known, most successful criminal lawyer. He owns two massive eleven-room houses, one a baronial-looking place with brass-studded oak doors in Quebec City, the other on a country estate at Rivière du Loup. He can afford to smoke two packs of Du Maurier cigarettes and a handful of Havana cigars a day. His gold-and-diamond cuff links and his wardrobe of three dozen hand-tailored suits are as much a part of his trademark as his dumpy, five-foot, five-inch figure.

Rivard's case book runs the gamut from civil cases (including long historical disputes over the legality of a property deal made 300 years ago) to criminal cases from armed robbery, safe-cracking and bootlegging to mass murder and espionage.

There are those who regard Rivard as a sinister figure, a backstairs intriguer; others who consider him a brilliant lawyer and an astute politician. (When one admirer referred to him as "that fabulous mouthpiece," the Opposition immediately shortened it to "that fabulous mouth.") But he has never deserted the credo

that a criminal lawyer must keep in the limelight. He has always succeeded in handling cases in which the dramatic element is present.

One of these was the Lamothe case—the "Case of the Seduced Servant"—which provided acres of newspaper headlines in the autumn of 1936. It was a particularly difficult case and Rivard won it in a particularly dramatic way.

A seventeen-year-old girl, the daughter of a Provincial Police official named Lamothe, had been shot to death in her bed. Rivard's client was the Lamothes' maid who when arrested had been standing over the murdered girl's body with a smoking gun in her hand. She admitted to the police that she had fired four shots into the sleeping girl.

She was a poorly educated country girl of nineteen who had come from the farm to Quebec City to work as a servant girl in the Lamothe house. Lamothe, it was admitted by all concerned, had seduced her and had then tried to break off the relationship. As Rivard imaginatively put it to the jury, "This poor, ignorant country girl was seduced by her master and then tossed casually aside like an empty beer bottle, and left alone with her dishonor."

For three days the little defense lawyer waged an eloquent tear-wringing battle. But no one knew better than he that his whole defense was based on sentiment and not on law. He had not even attempted to deny that his client had shot and killed her employer's daughter. In fact he had even put her on the stand and had had her admit it, a move that had stunned the court.

It was, Rivard told the jury, the old story of hell having no fury like a woman scorned—with a new twist. His client, he admitted, had a "righteous temper," was jealous of her virtue and her virginity, and was narrow-minded because that was the way she had been educated. With passionate words he painted the picture of the young girl seduced by a man more than twice her age, a man who had a daughter of his own around the same age, a man who was a provincial policeman and sworn to uphold the law. "Devoutly religious, this violated virgin was racked with shame, haunted with fear, obsessed with hate."

In a long and passionate elaboration in which he argued that "this is not a man's crime, it is a woman's passion," Rivard argued that "this little country girl shot the daughter of the beast who had seduced her—shot not to kill, but to hurt, and in hurting the daughter, revenge herself upon Lamothe who had so grievously wronged her." It was not the daughter that the accused saw when she pulled the trigger, Rivard insisted, but Lamothe himself.

Rivard's reconstruction of the case moved the entire courtroom. Even the Hon. Mr. Justice Lucien Cannon, a former crown prosecutor who had often opposed Rivard in earlier years and who was not known for any partiality toward or sympathy for the defense in the cases he heard, seemed touched. The jury and many spectators wept openly.

But, despite Rivard's tearful plea, the crown prosecutor in his summing up methodically and skilfully supplanted the defense argument with the cold irrefutable fact that the defendant had committed an act of murder by her own admission. He hammered it home to the jury that they were there not to judge the man Lamothe, but merely to decide whether the accused girl was guilty of murder or not. The prosecutor concluded his long summation with a final burst of oratory: "You have heard the defendant admit that she took her master's service revolver and, coldly and deliberately, fired not one but *four* bullets into his sleeping daughter! That was *murder!* In cold blood, she wilfully and premeditatedly *murdered* a young girl who she admits had never done her harm. For that awful crime she must pay with her own life!"

An excited buzzing filled the courtroom. In the prisoner's dock the pallid young woman wept silently. To just about everyone in the courtroom it looked as if Rivard had bitten off more than he could chew. It was obviously an open and shut case of murder. The crown prosecutor strode confidently back to his desk, sat down and gave the tubby defense attorney a triumphant look.

Now it was time for Rivard to make his final address to the jury. It was the critical moment of the trial, Rivard's last chance to save his client's life. Everyone sat back, prepared for the same long, tearful argument Rivard had made in his opening address and all during the trial. All of them realized that the crown prosecutor had succeeded in breaking the spell, and that even the great Rivard could hardly use the same old material again with the same results. But what else could he say?

Slowly Rivard rose from his chair. His head was down, his shoulders sagged and he looked, for once, like a defeated man—no longer cocky or confident. Slowly he walked over to the jury as the court stenographers poised their pencils. Slowly he passed a small, chubby hand over his round face and through his hair. Then, slowly and with studied deliberation, he took off his black horn-rimmed spectacles and he looked strangely nude in his black robes without them. His unhurried, deliberate movements seemed to hypnotize the jurors and the spectators alike. His timing was superb. For nearly a minute he just stared at the jurors. Then, without introduction, or even a "gentlemen of the jury," the paunchy little lawyer waved his spectacles and shrugged his shoulders expressively.

"All right," he said quietly in a resigned but slowly rising voice. "All right! Find her guilty. Let her be hanged! One day soon, over your coffee, you will read in your morning paper that she is dead. And perhaps as you walk down Grande Allée that morning on your way to work, you will see Lamothe. . ." He pronounced it La-*mutt* and made it sound like a spit. And he turned slowly and pointed at the provincial policeman. ". . . Yes, perhaps you will see Lamothe walking up Grande Allée . . . *with another girl*." Without saying another word Rivard turned, walked back to his desk and sat down.

Rivard's amazing plea and its unexpected brevity (it is one of the shortest ever delivered) left the court bug-eyed. The judge enquired incredulously, "It that all you have to say, *Maître* Rivard?" "Yes, your Honor," Rivard replied quietly.

After the judge's routine remarks the jury filed out. In less than two hours it was back. The verdict: Guilty of manslaughter, with a strong recommendation for mercy. Justice Cannon sentenced her to four years in prison (she served only two), and another victory was chalked up for the remarkable little lawyer.

Obviously, Rivard's veiled implication that Lamothe would go out and do the same thing again was the spark needed to switch the juror's thoughts back to his earlier emotional argument and convince them that Lamothe's act was sufficient provocation. But many of Rivard's legal friends break out in a cold sweat when they think of this case. They consider that Rivard took a tremendous chance—a chance few other lawyers would dare to take

—when he staked his case and the life of his client on a fifty-eight word summary.

Rivard is always dramatic—even in minor cases. He once saved a client by taking a leaf from the case book of the famous nineteenth-century Parisian lawyer Lachand. In this case Rivard knew that if the crown prosecutor succeeded in emphasizing a certain piece of evidence during his summation to the jury his client wouldn't stand a chance.

When the crown prosecutor began his summary Rivard became lost in thought, his fingers idly drumming on his desk. As the prosecutor neared the dangerous part of his address Rivard absent-mindedly, and without appearing to notice, dipped his left forefinger in his inkwell. With the air of a man in deep thought, his round face screwed up in concentration, his eyes staring straight ahead, he began to run his finger down the left side of his forehead and down his left cheek, leaving an ink mark. Then slowly and with studied casualness he quietly drummed his hand up the desk once more and again dipped his finger in the ink.

As Rivard straight-facedly traced ink designs on his left cheek, chin, ear and neck, he could feel the jurors, one by one, beginning to stare at him. Soon the jury was completely engrossed in what Rivard was doing and the prosecutor's words were going over their heads. The jury was on Rivard's left and all of them could plainly see him. The prosecutor was too engrossed with his own oratory to notice what was going on, although neither he nor the judge, both of whom were in front of Rivard, could have seen the ink marks because Rivard's head was turned slightly to the left and they could only see the clean right side of his face.

When the prosecutor had passed the dangerous part of his summation Rivard suddenly appeared to notice what he had so absent-mindedly been doing and quietly left the courtroom to wash his face, returning in a few minutes to give his own summation.

The ink trick not only diverted the jury's attention from the dangerous part of the prosecution's case but, because it was a joke on himself, put Rivard in a sympathetic light in the eyes of the jurors. Rivard's client was acquitted.

To Rivard, such diversionary maneuvres are all part of the game. "A lawyer," he says, "is sworn to fight with everything he's got, to defend his client as though he were defending himself, whether his client is guilty in the eyes of the law or not. A lawyer is justified in using every conceivable method to get his client acquitted. Anyone who thinks lawyers should only successfully defend innocent persons is foolish. In the first place it would be impossible; in the second, we'd need another 10,000 penitentiaries."

He is fond of talking about his cases and of the methods which have made him successful. "Do you know what it takes to make a great criminal lawyer?" he will say, leaning forward in his swivel chair and jabbing at a visitor with his black horn-rimmed spectacles. "It takes psychology, acting ability and a little law. A civil court case is all logic and law, but a criminal case is 10 per cent law and 90 per cent mob psychology. I say *mob* psychology because in a criminal case the lawyer does not plead to the judge but to the jury of 12—and you know, three's a crowd.

"A criminal defense lawyer starts his plea to the jury the moment he enters the courtroom by the way he enters. His conduct throughout the trial is part of his plea. He can appear sore, for instance, but he must never really lose his temper. At the outset he must immediately attract attention and hold it. He must be the pivot about which the trial revolves. He must let the jurors guess in advance what his basic defense will be so that they feel it is a resumé of what *they know*. At the same time he must keep enough little surprises up his sleeve to hold their interest.

"A great criminal lawyer must be an actor. He must use tragedy sparingly and know when and how to use it. And, above all, he must be a good comedian. I think a lawyer, before he studies law, should study under a great actor as did the great lawyers of France a century ago."

To understand Rivard's position in Quebec it is necessary to understand the personality of the Canadien. He is more interested in court cases than his fellow Canadians. He follows crime news with avid attention and prefers, if possible, to be on hand in the courtroom. To the Canadien the courtroom is a theatre where real people enact real drama. In this theatre he appreciates a talented performance. Rivard has never let him down.

One of Rivard's murder trials, "The Case of the Weeping Wife," illustrates the point.

Early in 1944 a young family man named Plante was charged with killing a friend at a riotous Mardi Gras party by beating him over the head with an axe. Several prosecution witnesses were later to testify that they had witnessed the crime. Rivard undertook to defend him. The only defense he had was sentiment.

Rivard's client was what he calls "a sympathetic character." Plante was young, handsome, had a good job and an excellent reputation. He also had a beautiful young wife and two young children. The victim, on the other hand, had been a bachelor of rather unsavory reputation.

When the trial opened in Beauce, Rivard knew that he could not put Plante on the stand. In the first place, he stuttered badly; in the second place, he would make what Rivard calls "damaging admissions." So, instead, he put Plante's pretty wife in the witness box, as his main witness.

She did not say a word. She simply wept. When Rivard asked her questions such as, "Did not the dead man make improper advances to you?" and "Did not the dead man pick a fight with your husband?" she did not admit or deny. She only cried more. When the crown prosecutor tried to browbeat her into talking on cross-questioning she wept louder than ever, which put that embarrassed and exasperated man in a bad light with the jury.

Rivard backed up Mrs. Plante's "testimony" with a series of emotional character witnesses and an impassioned, heart-rending address, during which copious tears rolled down his fat round cheeks. The jury tearfully acquitted Plante.

A few days later the victim's brother told a lawyer friend of Rivard's in Quebec: "I went to the trial sure that the man who killed my brother would hang. I wanted him to hang. But as soon as I heard that bright, young so-and-so (Rivard) speaking, I knew he'd get off. Why, he had the spectators, the witnesses, the jury and even the judge crying all through the trial. And do you know what! *I was crying with them!*"

Although he won Plante's acquittal with sentiment only, and against the undeniable fact that Plante had killed the man, Rivard is firmly convinced that the verdict was not only just but the best possible one that could have been returned. He points out that the Plante family have since been happy, model citizens.

"If that young fellow had hanged or gone to jail what would have happened to his young wife and his children?" he asks.

Hardly a year has passed when Tony Rivard has not held a human life in his hands. He once defended a man charged with murdering his wife in a doorstep quarrel late one winter's night—the man got off with a fifty-dollar fine for assault. Another time, in less than seven hours, before two juries, Rivard won acquittals for two clients who had *signed* confessions of murder.

Once a known sex pervert took a young boy canoeing. The boy's nude body was later washed up on the shore and medical evidence showed that he had been criminally attacked. The man was tried and sentenced to death. But Rivard, after careful on-the-spot detective work, was able to show that the two had had intimate relations before the fatal trip. The second trial lasted only a few minutes. The accused was sentenced to ten years for manslaughter.

All these are marked down as victories in the Rivard case book. As a Quebec crown prosecutor who earlier sent twelve out of fourteen men to the gallows he was equally successful. But there was one case Rivard would just as soon forget. That was in 1936 when his first job as public prosecutor was to send his best friend to his death.

Early that year Hughes Lanctot, a mining prospector in northern Quebec, had pulled a revolver from his pocket and shot a Pole between the eyes because he believed the man had been making improper advances to Lanctot's twelve-year-old son.

The prospector was the son of Charles Lanctot, for thirty years deputy attorney-general of the province and actual boss of the Quebec crown attorneys and Provincial Police. The case was full of political implications. Maurice Duplessis, still not in power, charged that the Taschereau government was "protecting" the young Lanctot. The government promptly caused Lanctot to be arraigned for murder. But before the trial could go on an election had swept Duplessis into office.

As the new prosecutor, Rivard was called in to handle the case. He tried to duck the job. Hughes Lanctot and he were the same age, had played together as children, had grown up as brothers. He told Duplessis he'd rather be defending Lanctot. But *Le Boss* gave him little choice: take the case or be banned to political limbo.

The trial opened in Quebec in the autumn of 1936. Rivard started the fireworks even before the jury was selected. He demanded the Provincial Police be barred from the trial. He argued that the defendant's father had been their boss for thirty years and that they were still loyal to him. The debate lasted all day, but Rivard won. The RCMP were called in to take charge of the jury.

The case was bitterly fought. The defense proved that the dead Pole had made advances to the accused man's son. But Rivard produced scores of witnesses to the killing who testified that Lanctot had shot the Pole between the eyes without giving him a chance to say a word. A death sentence seemed certain. But Rivard had a last-minute surprise. In his summation he painstakingly reviewed all the evidence and, to the surprise of everyone, asked the jury to pay particular attention to the fact that the dead Pole *had* molested the defendant's son and that

Lanctot had been under great mental stress. "The Crown does not ask you to return a verdict of murder in this case," he concluded. "The Crown will accept a verdict of guilty of manslaughter."

The jury did as Rivard requested, and Judge Cannon sentenced Hughes Lanctot to twelve years for manslaughter. Rivard had effected a compromise. He had appeased Rivard the lawyer by winning the case; he had appeased Rivard the politician by sending Lanctot to prison; and he had appeased Rivard the man by saving his friend's life.

On a foggy fall morning a few years ago Lanctot finished serving his sentence, with time off for good behavior. As the penitentiary gates clanged behind him he saw the short, fat little man through the fog. "Tony!" he exclaimed.

"Hello, Hughes," Rivard greeted him. "Are we still friends?"

"I hold no grudge against you, Tony," Lanctot replied. "You only did your duty. And besides, I think you probably saved my life."

And Antoine Rivard and Hughes Lanctot walked out into the fog arm-in-arm.

JUNE CALLWOOD

# How Marilyn Swam the Lake

The day that sixteen-year-old Marilyn Bell swam across Lake Ontario was a cold, sunny ninth of September. The small, tousle-haired Toronto schoolgirl swam forty miles from a log retaining wall in Youngstown, New York, to a slimy concrete breakwater off Sunnyside, Toronto, and thereby collected for herself whatever immortality awaits pioneer marathon swimmers, plus approximately $50,000 in contracts, prizes and gifts from Canadians who were moved by her courage.

While the lustre of her achievement cannot suffer, the swim will be best remembered, by those who watched it firsthand, for the petulance and undignified bickering of the officials and for the weird newspaper war it provoked between the Toronto *Star* and the Toronto *Telegram*. No other human-interest event in Canada since the Moose River mine disaster has stirred a reading and listening public so deeply and no other event has had such a bizarre and hectic setting for its drama.

At one point, with the girl's heavy, aching arms flogging the water between them, and her brain almost unconscious with exhaustion, a Canadian National Exhibition official and Marilyn's trainer engaged in a sharp, shouted debate over the most advantageous spot for her to land. At another point, *Star* and *Telegram* reporters pushed and connived for possession of the stretcher and ambulance that would carry the pale, shaking swimmer from the dock. Every now and then, rarely and wonderfully, someone showed real concern for Marilyn Bell.

The swim had been planned by the Canadian National Exhibition sports committee as a crowd-drawing spectacle to demonstrate the prowess of Florence Chadwick, a 34-year-old American considered by many to be the world's greatest woman swimmer. The CNE paid Miss Chadwick a $2,500 advance of the $10,000 she was to collect if she succeeded in swimming the lake. Two Canadian swimmers, Winnie Roach Leuszler, 28, who had swum the English Channel three years before, and Marilyn Bell, 16, dived into the lake behind Miss Chadwick to demonstrate something or other to themselves and their friends. Neither expected any reward if she failed but Mrs. Leuszler had hopes that a large hat would be passed among CNE spectators if she succeeded. Marilyn Bell, who was the first woman to complete a twenty-five-mile swim eight weeks before off Atlantic City, expected nothing.

The expenses of both Canadian swimmers, including a $700-a-day boat rental, were being paid by the Toronto *Star*. Marilyn's coach Gus Ryder, had offered the *Telegram* an opportunity to sponsor his swimmer at the same time as the *Star,* but the paper refused.

Around four o'clock in the afternoon of the day it happened Toronto suddenly seemed to awake to the fact that Marilyn was the only swimmer left in the lake. Half-hour bulletins on two Toronto radio stations, CKEY and CKFH, relaying broadcasts from boats beside the swimmer, whipped the city into a frenzy of excitement. The highly vaunted Flo Chadwick had been pulled out of the water, sick and retching, at four-thirty in the morning; strong, heavily built Winnie Leuszler had quit in agony from cramps ten hours after her second start. A five-foot-one, 119-pound child was still swimming seventeen hours after entering the water at Youngstown, New York.

Offices began to empty and a traffic jam formed between downtown Toronto and the grandstand that the CNE had built overlooking the lake. Radios everywhere were tuned to those stations which offered live coverage. Toronto's two publicly owned CBC stations, which had remained aloof from the swim, began to pirate news bulletins. Marilyn Bell's Grade XII classmates at Loretto College School, who had been fretting through History, Latin, Geometry and French, had already been dismissed in the middle of Chemistry so they could buy flowers and take them down to the lakefront to meet Marilyn.

Down at the lakefront several thousand people were gathering on the plank seats of the grandstand. Most were in summer clothes, with their arms crossed over their chests to keep off the cold wind from the lake. Far out on the grey water was a smudge that some people thought was a group of boats. A newsboy cried: "Read all about it—Marilyn only an hour away!" Pink flares, sent up by the CNE, cracked high in the sky to guide the swimmer in. A pink *Telegram* fluttered in the stiffening wind. 2 MILES TO GO! screamed the headline.

Beside one of the grandstands was a floating wooden dock and a small square of lawn fenced off and guarded by policemen. Inside, reporters, cameramen and CNE officials were milling around in a swelling excited babble of conversation.

Rumors of the brewing newspaper battle kept *Telegram* reporters at the lakefront anxi-

ous. Marilyn was, they knew, accompanied by *Star* boats, and it seemed likely that an attempt would be made when she landed to keep her away from the *Telegram*. One story had it that a *Star* launch would pick her out of the water as soon as she touched shore and take her to a hiding place. The *Telegram* hired an ambulance to stand by and planned to have stretcher-bearers hustle her from the water when she touched the CNE jetty. They would take her to a *Telegram* hiding place. In the meantime the *Telegram* printed 3,000 extras with the headline MARILYN DOES IT! and hid them near the grandstand, to be sold as soon as Marilyn arrived. The *Star* had 10,000 extras, with the headline MARILYN MAKES IT!, hidden in *Star* trucks around the CNE grounds.

A loudspeaker blared "Marilyn Bell has been pushed west by the strong wind . . . for every hundred yards north she swims, the waves push her two hundred west but she's still in the water!"

George Duthie, CNE sports director, pushed through reporters as he climbed out of a motorboat. "I've just seen her," he said gloomily. "She's in bad shape. She'll never make it."

Seven miles out in the lake, across choppy water, being blown almost parallel to the shore, Marilyn Bell was ready to quit for the fourth time. She was treading water, swimming two strokes and stopping to tread water again. She could sometimes see the grey shoreline past the heaving waves and for hours it hadn't been getting any closer.

By now she had been in the water eighteen hours. Florence Chadwick's contract with the CNE had permitted her to pick her own time to make the swim. This meant that she also picked Marilyn's starting time and Winnie Leuszler's. Both Canadians had envisioned the swim as a race and they wanted to start at the same time as Florence Chadwick and touch Canada ahead of her. Miss Chadwick announced at nine o'clock Wednesday night that she would start at 10:30. Marilyn Bell, who hadn't slept all day, promptly climbed into the loose black silk-and-nylon suit distance swimmers always wear, low under the arms and high over the legs to reduce friction. Jack Russell, a professional boatman who was to operate the outboard motor on the lifeboat that would guide Marilyn, gave her a lucky four-leaf clover and she wrapped it in wax paper, put it on top of her blond, boyishly cut hair and pulled a white rubber shower cap over it. She was ready.

At eleven o'clock Florence Chadwick, escorted by a detachment of U.S. soldiers, had emerged from a U.S. Coast Guard building, walked sternly through reporters and Youngstown citizens who had collected in a drenching rain and slipped feet first into the water. She began swimming immediately, a strong, beautiful stroke that invoked cheers. Marilyn watched her as a spotlight followed her in the black water, then she slipped off her robe, kissed her parents good-by, walked to the edge of the Coast Guard lawn and dived off the retaining wall. It was 11:07.

Marilyn started off rapidly, like a sprint swimmer. Her simple purpose was to get ahead of Chadwick, and stay there. For a while the searchlights shone on the two women who were joined a few minutes later by Winnie Leuszler, and then they were lost in the blackness of the night.

This was the part of the swim Marilyn had dreaded most, swimming in darkness for the first time in her life. Ahead of her she could see only the flashlight held in her tender by Gus Ryder, her trainer and the outstanding swimming coach in the country. She had said earlier: "If I feel an eel on me, I'll scream!" but when the first eel, a little one eight inches long, struck her stomach and hung there she kept calm and punched it off with her fist. In the next few hours three more clamped to her thigh and she beat them off without any hysteria. Ahead of her, beyond the falling and climbing water, was the white pencil line of a CNE searchlight that burned all night as a guide to the swimmers.

What Gus Ryder later called the crisis came around four in the morning, at almost the same time that Florence Chadwick quit swimming. Marilyn, exhausted from fighting twelve-foot-high waves, stopped swimming and looked pleadingly at Ryder. "I'm cold, I'm numb," she called in her light child's voice.

"Marilyn," Ryder shouted back, "you've swum all night and that's really great. If you can do that you can do the rest. In another hour the sun will come up and it will be really nice." He fastened a paper cup into a ring at the end of a six-foot stick, poured corn syrup into the cup and passed it to the girl. She stood in the water, treading lightly to keep afloat. She sipped the nourishing drink and tried not to cry. Ryder didn't offer to take her out of the water and after a moment she let the paper cup float away in the darkness and started swimming again.

When dawn came Marilyn was fourteen miles into the lake. Ten feet away from her was the 24-foot lifeboat, "Mipepa," steered by Jack Russell and carrying Gus Ryder, a *Star* reporter-photographer named George Bryant, and a thirteen-year-old boy, Peter Willinsky, whose father owned the boat. Some distance away, and well behind the "Mipepa," was the yacht, "Mona IV," with Marilyn's parents and *Star* reporters and photographers aboard.

As the sky lightened, everyone in the lifeboat was shocked by Marilyn's appearance. Her normally pretty and gay face was haggard, the muscles around her mouth slack and her eyes glassy. She said later, "My arms were tired, my legs ached, my stomach hurt in one big awful pain and I couldn't get my breath. I wanted to quit. When it gets to your stomach, marathoners say, you're through." For more than an hour she had been swimming with her arms alone, dragging her legs motionless in the water behind her.

George Bryant noticed that she was crying and found himself crying too. "If it had been my decision," he later told friends, "I'd have got her out of there right then."

Ryder passed Marilyn more corn syrup, but her hand was shaking so much the cup spilled into the water. Next he passed her some liniment he had scooped out of a jar and dropped in a paper cup. Under his direction, she rolled over on her back and rubbed her legs with the liniment. She continued to cry.

"Swim over here, Marilyn," Ryder called. "We'll take you out."

The girl began to swim and Ryder watched her closely, noticing that her legs were moving again. "Pull away, Jack," he ordered. Jack Russell moved the throttle and the boat moved away from Marilyn. She kept on swimming, still crying.

"That's a bad sign," Ryder told Bryant. "If she keeps on crying, I'll have to take her out." After a while she stopped crying and as the sun began to climb she was swimming strongly.

The nautical phase of the battle between the Toronto *Star* and the Toronto *Telegram* began a few hours later. As dawn broke, *Star* and *Telegram* boats crossed paths as they attempted to find the ferryboat that Florence Chadwick had hired to follow her. They could find no trace of it. Four hours after Chadwick had been pulled from the water, both newspapers discovered her at the National Yacht Club in Toronto. After that it was Marilyn's swim, with Winnie Leuszler not a serious contender. At eight in the morning the *Telegram* contingent aboard the CNE press boat "Ja-Su" decided to get their first close-up pictures of Marilyn in the water. They found the schoolgirl swimming strongly beside the lifeboat "Mipepa" with Jack Russell at the helm. Gus Ryder was crouched beside him and red-haired George Bryant, legs astride and camera in hand, was standing in the middle. Flanking the "Mipepa" snugly were two *Star* yachts, "Mona IV" and "Manana III."

The "Ja-Su," carrying four *Telegram* reporters and photographers, was crowded to the rear by Marilyn's escort. A dinghy was lowered with the photographers and rowed to within camera distance of the swimmer. Later, when the *Telegram*'s second boat, "Commander," with two reporters and a photographer aboard, found the flotilla, tempers grew shorter. The *Telegram* sought to wriggle between the *Star* boats and there was talk of ramming. A woman on the "Mona IV" threw a pop bottle at the "Commander," missing a newsreel photographer by inches. The "Manana" and the "Ja-Su" lightly collided. The *Star* later explained that its boats had been trying to protect Marilyn Bell from "eager fools in powerboats" who were jeopardizing her safety.

The water temperature, which can be a bitter 50° even on a late summer day, kept between 60° and 70°, the only break the lake gave Marilyn that day. Though her navigators were unaware of it at first, currents were pushing her west of Toronto. Toward noon the waves began to quiet.

At 10:30 Ryder noticed Marilyn tiring again. He scribbled on a blackboard the news he'd been saving for such a crucial moment: FLO IS OUT. He held the board so she could read it. Marilyn, delighted to learn she had outlasted the world's greatest woman swimmer, swam with renewed vigor. When she faltered again, toward noon, Ryder wrote some more notes in chalk: SWIM FOR ME and DON'T LET THE CRIPPLED KIDS DOWN. Marilyn stared at the notes, put her face in the water and began swimming again. Her stomach was a steady pain and her legs ached. Ryder refers to his chalked notes to Marilyn as "blackboard psychology."

In Toronto, CNE President Robert Saunders announced that since Florence Chadwick was out of the water, forfeiting $7,500, any swimmer who finished would get "a substantial amount of money." Around four o'clock in the afternoon the *Star* boats heard the news on their radios that Winnie Leuszler was out of the water and that Saunders had announced Marilyn would get $7,500—the balance of the Chadwick fee—if she finished.

It seemed doubtful, to everyone but Ryder, that she could finish. She had been in the water for seventeen hours and she hadn't slept in thirty-one hours. The Toronto Harbor Commission, concerned that she might drown before anyone could reach her, dropped two dinghies into the water with lifeguards at the oars and

they began to row beside her, watching her steadily. As she swam, relaxing her arm when it was in the air and pulling it hard through the water, relaxing the other and pulling, relax and pull and kick, kick, kick, kick, she began to fall asleep. During the Atlantic City swim she had hummed "O Canada" and "The Happy Wanderer" to break the monotony; this swim she hadn't felt like humming at all. The voices in the boat began to seem far away.

"Marilyn! Marilyn!" shrieked Ryder. She opened her eyes and read the blackboard he was holding: $7,500 IF YOU FINISH. Her heavy bloodshot eyes read the figure as $750. "I'll split in with you, Gus," she called.

Earlier it had struck Ryder and Bryant that Marilyn needed extra encouragement. They asked the "Mona IV" to locate Marilyn's best friend, a tow-headed girl named Joan Cooke. One of the *Star* boats hurried to Toronto, picked up Joan and maneuvred a few hundred yards from the "Mipepa." There was no small boat to take Joan across, so she stripped off her shoes, jacket and watch and dived into the water wearing a blouse and knee-length slacks. Ryder and George Bryant pulled her into the "Mipepa" and she stood in the boat, shivering in her wet clothes and yelling, "Atta girl, Marilyn." Bryant remembered his duty to his newspaper and took a picture of Joan as she was hauled into the boat; it was the last picture he took that day as the anguish of rooting Marilyn home blotted out everything else. He neglected entirely to keep a notebook. He and Ryder and Russell stayed awake twenty-one hours in an open boat and forgot their own weariness to such a degree that it occurred to none of them to open the gallon thermos of coffee someone had provided. They ate nothing.

The summoning of Joan Cooke turned out to be fine strategy. Toward five o'clock Marilyn began to falter again, clawing the water with no strength. Her legs no longer hurt—they had no feeling at all—but the pain in her stomach was steady. Ryder asked Joan to jump in and swim beside Marilyn.

"I can't swim in slacks and a blouse," she protested.

"Take them off," suggested Ryder.

Joan looked around at the twenty large and small boats fanned out behind the "Mipepa"— most of them were festooned with photographers, their collars turned up and their hands gripping cameras. "They won't take a picture of you," Bryant assured her. She pulled off her clothes and dived into the water in her panties and a brassiere.

The splash of her dive woke Marilyn, who

had been dozing again. She looked at her friend and laughed. "Don't touch her, Joan, you'll disqualify her," screamed Ryder. Joan nodded and called briskly to Marilyn, "Come on, let's go." She began swimming quickly and expertly. Marilyn's stroke picked up and a tiny flutter of white water behind her showed that her feet were kicking. Joan stayed in the water a few minutes more, then climbed back into the "Mipepa" and wrapped herself in blankets.

At five o'clock Ryder pointed to the Toronto sky line and wrote on the blackboard, WE ARE TAKING YOU STRAIGHT IN. In spite of this, Marilyn's stroke slowed from the sixty-four strokes per minute she maintained at her best to fifty strokes a minute. She stopped twice in two minutes, staring dazedly at the boats collecting from Toronto and Hamilton. The wind grew stiffer and colder and the waves pushed her west of the pink flares popping over the Exhibition.

Two seaplanes dipped overhead and roared away: The *Star* had hired two planes to carry photographers and reporters with walkie-talkie sets and the *Telegram* had one plane. Newsmen covering the swim were beginning to realize they hadn't slept for two days and a night and they watched the child in the water with wonder.

To people listening in their homes and cars the radio coverage seemed a phenomenon in itself. "She's swimming now," the hoarse voice of the announcer would say. "Now she's stopped and Gus Ryder is holding up the blackboard. It reads 'One and a half miles to go' but we estimate it is closer to four. Probably trying to encourage the girl who . . ." Officials of CBLT, Toronto's television station, dallied with the notion of sending their mobile unit to the lakefront to photograph Marilyn's arrival but decided against it. The unit was needed to cover a scheduled prom symphony concert that night.

As the afternoon wore out Ryder huddled in his jacket in the stern of the "Mipepa." Bryant stood beside the blanketed Joan Cooke. The two lifeguards, one clad only in his bathing suit, pulled steadily at their oars. All of them unceasingly watched the rise and fall of the white arms in the water, the bathing cap that turned and became a grey face gulping air and then became a bathing cap again. Once, when she faltered, Ryder wrote on the blackboard: IF YOU QUIT, I QUIT.

Behind them now was the queerest collection of ships Toronto's harbor had ever seen: Sleek yachts, shabby motorboats, sailboats, the monstrous tug "Ned Hanlan" belching smoke, a motorboat carrying several adults and two star-ry-eyed boys of four and five, and another with several men in business suits, a woman and a year-old baby girl dressed in pink. On the fringe were kayaks and rowboats.

An air-force officer on the "Ned Hanlan" came away from the boat's radio and yelled into a megaphone to Ryder, "She's been offered another $6,000." Ryder prepared a new sign for his blackboard: NOW $15,000. Marilyn, close to unconsciousness again, didn't notice.

People in the boats could now distinguish trucks moving along the highway on the shore and each separate building of the Sunnyside amusement area, west of the Exhibition grounds. Some newspaper and newsreel photographers crossed from smaller boats to the more comfortable Harbor Commission launch.

"I don't think those *Star* guys are going to let her land at the Ex," one of the *Telegram* photographers said excitedly. "She's swimming straight for Sunnyside!"

"We'll get her all right," replied Allan Lamport, a member of the CNE Sports Committee. He yelled to Ryder a moment later: "Isn't it just as close to take her to the Ex? We've got a crowd waiting there for you."

"We can't get in there," Ryder hollered back, "she's going against the waves." The sun was gone by now and the moon was a cold oval in the sky.

"Poor girl," said Harbor Commissioner W. H. Bosley gently, "I hope this isn't going to hurt her."

"Gus, you're headed for the widest part of the bay!" cried Lamport.

Ryder leaned over the end of the "Mipepa." "Swim for the yellow building, Marilyn, the yellow building, Marilyn!" Marilyn opened her eyes, found the building and plodded on with her mechanical stroke. She had two miles more to go.

"No, no," shouted Lamport.

"Keep quiet," retorted Ryder fiercely, "we're running this."

Another motorboat, containing Robert Saunders, president of the CNE; George Duthie, sports director; and Hiram MacCallum, general manager, pulled up beside the *Star* yacht "Mona IV."

"Have her swim to the Ex," Duthie yelled. "We've got a pot of earth there she's to touch."

"She'll land wherever she can," a *Star* reporter shouted back.

"It this a Toronto *Star* swim?" asked Saunders indignantly.

"The CNE had nothing at all to do with this swim," answered the *Star* men. When CNE officials moved closer to the "Mona IV," Syd Bell,

Marilyn's father, screamed, "You get out of here!" The officials retired a distance away and regarded the "Mona IV" balefully.

At that moment, at 6:35, Marilyn stopped swimming and stood up, treading water.

"Come on, keep going," shouted Ryder.

"I'm tired," Marilyn wailed.

"Come on!" cried Joan Cooke, "Fifteen minutes more!"

"I can't go any farther."

"Come on," shouted Bryant, "only a little more!"

"I can't move!" Marilyn said, crying.

Her father, watching from the "Mona IV," called across the water: "Take her out, Gus."

Ryder, not hearing, shouted "Fifteen minutes more, Marilyn. Come on!"

Like an obedient child, Marilyn put her face in the water and started swimming. At that point her conscious mind blanked out and she had the feeling she was far away, floating bodiless and light. In the distance voices were whispering, "the yellow building, the yellow building," and her stomach ached dully.

Once again she stopped and Ryder passed her the last of the eight pounds of corn syrup and the package of uncooked pablum he had brought.

"Do you want to come out?" he asked when he saw her face.

"Which way do I go?" she muttered vaguely and started to swim again. She became aware of a feeling that if she stopped once more she would be finished. She never paused again.

"Gus has a mad on for the Ex, you can see that," commented Lamport furiously as he watched Ryder lead the girl toward Sunnyside. The Exhibition grounds, black with people, were a mile to the right. It was dusk and the buildings, the boats, the sky and the water were varying shades of blue. It became so cold that men in the boats shivered and it was hard to hold a pencil. The strange fleet showed running lights, like fireflies. The moon was brighter.

At 7:50 Ryder's hoarse voice could be heard shouting "Come on, Marilyn, ten minutes more!"

"If she touches the breakwater, that's sufficient," Bosley observed in the Harbor Commission launch. The shore was only 450 feet past the concrete breakwater.

A voice on the *Star* boat called to Ryder: "When your boat touches the sea wall, bring her right here. Don't let her get up, just touch!"

Ryder turned on his flashlight. The darkness along the shore ahead turned out to be thousands of people, screaming unintelligibly. A launch owner pushed on his horn and the fleet unleashed a cacophony of horns, whistles and sirens. Every man began to shout, and some to cry. The "Mipepa" pulled aside and let Marilyn go in to the breakwater alone. She touched it with her left hand and stopped. It was six minutes after eight. She had been in the water twenty hours and fifty-nine minutes. The lake is thirty-two miles across, but she had swum forty miles or more fighting the currents.

Marilyn Bell can't remember touching the breakwater. When the lifeguards tried to pull her into one of their dinghies she was furious. "Let me go!" she cried. She thought they were trying to take her out of the water before she had finished the swim. "I'm all right," she said firmly and pushed herself a few yards into the lake again. Ryder's boat came beside her and she became aware of the shouting thousands and saw rockets bursting in the sky.

"Are these people crazy or am I?" she whispered as Bryant and Ryder, weakened too after twenty-one hours on constant watch, laboriously pulled her into the "Mipepa." She was taken to the "Mona IV," where her parents hugged her and she was put to bed.

*Telegram* reporters sorrowfully watched the *Star* boat swallow the biggest news story of the year. The crowds around the Exhibition's lakefront grandstand continued to wait for the heroine, cheering the Harbor Commission launch hysterically when it docked. Through the din came the sound of Loretto students screaming, "One, two, three, four . . . Who are we for? . . . Marilyn, Marilyn . . . Rah, rah, rah!" The voice on the public-address system abruptly explained, "We regret that Marilyn Bell's condition does not permit her to receive her admirers."

Marilyn, lying in a bunk on the "Mona," was sipping cocoa when she was struck by the notion that her legs were paralysed. "I can't walk!" she cried anxiously. "I can't feel my legs." "Sure you can, honey," her mother assured her. The girl was not convinced so her mother put an arm around her and walked her around the cabin. Marilyn sank back in the bunk greatly relieved.

The "Mona" slipped into the Toronto Lifesavers' Station dock where an ambulance hired by the *Star* waited to take her to the Royal York Hotel suite and a *Star*-hired doctor and nurse. A line of parked taxis had been ordered for *Star* reporters. It was, however, the worst-kept secret of the day.

The *Telegram* knew, before the "Mona" came in sight of the dock, every detail of the *Star* scheme—including the room number of the hotel suite. Every available editorial employee was called to help separate Marilyn Bell from the *Star*. In case of a slip-up, one group waited at the National Yacht Club, another large group at the Lifesavers' dock near downtown Toronto and four more groups at the four entrances of the Royal York; and, as a precaution, a small delegation was at the King Edward and another at Marilyn's home.

The offense started with a *Telegram*-hired ambulance, which arrived ahead of the *Star*-hired ambulance at the Lifesavers' Station. The stretcher-bearers unloaded their stretcher and prepared to wait for the swimmer. The *Telegram* had rented a large bedroom in the Royal York Hotel for her.

*Star* men spotted the *Telegram* ambulance standing empty at the curb with the keys still in the ignition and quietly drove it a few blocks away, removing both the keys and the cap of the distributor. Two more ambulances replaced it at the curb, one hired by the *Star* and the other a mystery to both papers. The Lifesavers' jetty then held three stretchers, each complete with a pair of stretcher-bearers screaming at one another, "This is the *official* stretcher!"

Marilyn's father asked Ed Hopkins, official of the Harbor Commission, to clear the jetty of everyone but "friends, relatives and the *Star*." A few *Star* men got off the "Mona" to assist lifeguards in the identification. *Telegram* men resisted the order and twelve police constables from No. 1 precinct were called. The jetty was cleared, but only for an instant. *Telegram* photographers infiltrated back behind barrels and posts and waited for Marilyn.

The swimmer herself, catching the spirit of the occasion, suggested to a *Star* man: "Would you like me to put a blanket over my head so they can't get pictures?" It was a tempting offer, but he refused. She walked off the "Mona" wearing a two-piece sweat suit and climbed on the waiting *Star* stretcher, which someone fin-ally had identified. As she was loaded into the ambulance, the *Telegram*'s Dorothy Howarth climbed in beside her, assisted courteously by a somewhat-dazed *Star* man. He realized his error immediately and snarled, "Get outa there, you!" Dorothy backed out.

Joan Cooke climbed in beside the stretcher and squeezed the swimmer's shoulders. "That was wonderful, Marilyn," she said. "Congratulations."

"For what?" asked Marilyn blankly.

"For the swim," said Joan. "For finishing the swim."

"I did?" cried Marilyn incredulously. "I finished?" It hadn't occurred to anyone that the girl didn't know.

The *Star* ambulance eventually arrived at the Royal York Hotel's freight elevator, and Marilyn was carried aboard. The elevator descended to the basement, where a hundred waiters, bus boys, chambermaids, porters, cooks and waitresses clapped and shouted as her stretcher was taken across the basement to a waiting passenger elevator. The corridors of the fourth floor were filled with *Telegram* and *Globe and Mail* reporters and photographers, and the *Star* pushed the stretcher through the mob with difficulty.

Eventually the door of room 469, part of a three-room suite, closed behind her and she climbed into bed. The doctor who examined her, Dr. F. R. Griffin, remarked to the reporters in the hall that he expected Marilyn had lost twenty pounds during the swim.

Actually Marilyn's health, the subject of much gloomy conjecture that night, was so superb that Griffin was baffled. Her heart, pulse and respiration were normal. Except for bloodshot eyes and a rubbery feeling in her legs, she appeared to have suffered no harm at all. In fact, she had gained a pound.

ROBERT FONTAINE

# In the Long Run

When I was twelve I belonged to the YMCA. We sang songs, played ping-pong, tossed a basketball around and had lectures on living the good life. We did not care much for the lectures, but since they usually preceded a dinner with chicken and ice cream we always listened to them.

I used to wonder how my cousin Roy could do it. Roy was a collector of anything he saw lying around. He explained that his father was sick, his mother worked for less than nothing and the only way he could survive was to pick up a bit here and there.

Of course I could not agree with his theory, even if at times I admired his cunning and nerve. The point is that I was astonished at the way Roy could listen without blinking to all the lectures and then go right ahead and operate.

We would come from the lecture and Roy would take two five-cent chocolate bars from the supervisor's desk. Then he would put twenty-five cents in the cashbox and remove change for a dollar.

"I don't count very good," Roy explained whenever I caught him.

He was a good-looking, husky boy with dark hair, laughing eyes and strong white teeth. He looked young and innocent and no one suspected that when a detective opened his locker in the YMCA one night he would find seven track suits, nine pair of basketball kneepads, four pair of sneakers and a dozen other items. It was marvelous how Roy could get all the stuff in his locker, let alone the manner in which he acquired it.

The truth, which Roy told me once, was that he went around to all the lockers, row after row, and twisted the combinations this way and that way. Often some of the lockers opened. Roy would take one or two garments and lock up again. All the things were too big for him and he never sold them. I do not know why he picked them up. But he did.

Anyway, the detective took him up to the supervisor's office and he asked me to come along, too. I believe they suspected I was an accomplice, but I was as blameless as a baby.

We sat down on hard chairs and watched the gold desk clock ticking and listened to our hearts beating. I was very nervous, this being the first time I was ever involved in a larceny. Mr. Wakes, the boys' supervisor, was a gentle, pale-eyed man with a sharp nose and little hair. He paced around us for a time in silence. Then he said to me:

"What do you know about this?"

"Nothing, sir."

"Did you know your cousin was taking this . . . these . . . taking. . . "

"No, sir."

"Hmm." He turned to Roy who smiled at him so pleasantly that it was apparently difficult to find the words.

"Roy," he began, "you are one of the most active boys in this Y. You are a fine athlete. You have a good personality. When there is work to be done you do much more than your share. Tell me, why do you steal?"

"I don't steal," Roy said. At this, the detective sat up and blinked.

"How's that?" he asked sharply.

"You heard me," Roy said. "And we don't smoke cigars in the boys' department. We don't like to encourage them. Isn't that right, Mr. Wakes?"

Mr. Wakes smiled for a moment, rather pleased. "Yes, yes, Roy. Exactly." He turned to the detective. "You understand?"

The detective squashed out his cigar in the ash tray by the gold clock.

"Also we remove our hats immediately upon entering the department," Roy said. The detective looked daggers at Mr. Wakes, but he took off his derby.

"Listen," the detective said, "this kid is a thief. What are we standing here for, talking?"

"He said he didn't steal anything," Mr. Wakes said vaguely. "We . . . uh . . . we . . . can't judge the boy without giving him a hearing."

"Listen," the detective said to Roy. "Confess. Go straight. You'll get off with a suspended sentence in reform school."

"I have nothing to confess," Roy said.

The detective raised his hand as if to wallop Roy, but Mr. Wakes stopped him, gently. "Let us be . . . uh . . . uh . . . gentlemen about this."

"Look," the detective said, "I opened his locker. I saw the stuff lying there. I got a list of the stolen property. The stolen property was in his locker. It's an open-and-shut case."

"Nobody has preferred any charges yet," Roy said.

"What does that mean?" I asked him in a whisper.

"No whispering!" the detective shouted.

"In the boys' department we are polite to each other. We do not shout nor use bad English. We respect each other," Roy said.

The detective turned to Mr. Wakes who was swallowing a little nervously. "Listen, brother. You asked for a detective. You said property was disappearing. Now we have done our duty and discovered the criminal. Let us go down and prefer charges."

"Uh . . ." Mr. Wakes said weakly, "we must be sure."

"Holy Moses! . . . The stuff was all there in the kid's locker," the detective shouted.

"In the boys' department we do not use profanity," Roy said. Mr. Wakes smiled, glad to be back in his element a moment. "Yes," he agreed, "we discourage even circumlocutions."

"Look," said the detective, very exasperated, "I am not here for a lecture. I am here to make a pinch. The stuff was found in the kid's locker. . ."

Mr. Wakes sighed and waved his hand ineffectually.

"It's not my locker," Roy said calmly. The detective blinked. Mr. Wakes opened his eyes wide. I nearly fainted.

"Whose locker is it then, little man?" the detective said sharply.

"His," Roy replied, pointing to me.

"But I don't use it," I said. "I hardly ever use it."

"Yes, come to think of it, the boys have been doubling up on the lockers," Mr. Wakes said.

"This other young man is the soul of honor so I clear him instinctively. On the other hand, it is not Roy's locker. So the evidence, circumstantial as it is, cannot be used against Roy."

"Then who put the stuff in the locker?" the detective asked, running his hand over his hot face.

"I do not know," Roy said.

"Well, I'll be a monkey's uncle!" the detective declared.

"In the boys' department," Roy observed, "we are kind to animals."

The detective put on his hat, lit a cigar and went out, slamming the door. There was a long silence while Mr. Wakes looked out the window. In time he turned around and looked at us gently and a little wearily.

"Uh, boys . . . boys. I appoint you two boys to see that the stealing of . . . uh . . . garments, etc., is stopped. I have faith in you and I know you will apprehend the culprit and punish him in a proper fashion. Uh . . . I might add that crime does not pay. The man who begins in a small way ends up stealing large sums and is soon miserable."

"My uncle Joe stole ten thousand dollars from a bank and they haven't caught him yet," Roy said. "That was ten years ago. Every month or so we get a postcard from him in the Fiji Islands."

Mr. Wakes cleared his throat. "In the long run. In the *long* run, crime does not pay. The proof is that people at heart are honest. People are . . . uh . . . *really* good. . ."

"I know some awful stinkers," Roy said.

"Me, too," I agreed. Mr. Wakes sighed. "Yes, yes. But there is a trend toward goodness. In the long run we will all be good. Those of us who are bad must be considered ill. We must treat them for a disease of evil . . . and then one glorious day we shall all be well . . . and . . . uh, happy. In the long run. That is all, gentlemen."

We walked out slowly and down the stairs and toward the square. Roy was very solemn. After a while he spoke thoughtfully.

"You know, I feel bad for the first time in my life. Not because I stole the gym suits. They're no good anyway. I just didn't like all those senior guys shoving me around. I showed them it ain't enough to be big. You have to be smart, too. But something else. I mean I did something wrong."

"I talked about this old guy Wakes like he was crazy. But what happens? He knows I am poor so when I am not looking he puts a ten-dollar bill in my pocket. It makes me feel worse than stealing."

"I know," I said, as Roy reached in and took a ten-dollar bill from one pocket.

"I think I know what I'll do," he said reaching into the other pocket, removing from it a shiny gold object. "I'll go back when he isn't looking and put back his clock."

In the long run, however, Roy came out all right. He became one of the city's finest detectives, although I have no idea how.

GEORGE A. DREW

# The Unforgettable Billy Bishop

On August 4, 1914, there were 272 airplanes available to the British army and of these less than 100 were fit for military service; at the time of the Armistice, after thousands had been destroyed, worn out or become obsolete, there were 22,171, all of them infinitely more powerful, faster, and more reliable than the best of those in use at the beginning of the war. In August 1914 there were fewer than 250 officers in this new service; in November 1918 there were more than thirty thousand. During the period of this phenomenal expansion the British air forces accounted for more than eight thousand machines; destroyed nearly three hundred enemy balloons; fought more than fifty thousand fights in the air; fired more than twelve million rounds of machine-gun ammunition at enemy targets on the ground; took more than half a million aerial photographs and in doing all this suffered nearly eighteen thousand casualties.

In this almost incredible story of British achievement, Canadians played a tremendous part. It is true that it was some time before they joined the Flying Corps in any numbers, due to the apathy of our military authorities toward this new arm of the service, but once their interest was aroused they rushed to the air service in ever-increasing numbers, until by the end of the war one-third of the officers in the Royal Air Force were Canadians.

Canada's share, individually and collectively, was out of all proportion to her population. Not long after Canadians really took up flying in earnest it became apparent that they were at least the equals of any of the airmen in the war. Perhaps the wide horizons of life in Canada, the atmosphere of optimism, the confidence of individual opportunity, and the general adaptability to unexpected tasks, born of life in a still undeveloped country, all contributed to the qualities which so peculiarly fitted Canadians for success in this new and incalculably hazardous adventure. Whatever the reasons may have been, the simple fact remains that without any qualification Canadians proved the greatest air fighters in the world, and the greatest of them all was William Avery Bishop. Stay-at-home Canadians read with pride—if not amazement—in August 1917 that Captain Bishop of Owen Sound had been awarded the most coveted decoration for valor in the world, the Victoria Cross, "for most conspicuous bravery, determination and skill." Unknown to most Canadians he had already won the Military Cross and Distinguished Service Order for deeds of great bravery. When he attended at Buckingham Palace late in the summer of 1917 to be invested with these decorations, King George V said that it was the first time he had been able to give all three to one person. It was only then that Canadians realized that in the air their men were gaining the same high reputation for courage and determination which they had already earned at Ypres, the Somme and Vimy.

In the course of time Bishop's record stood beside those of the great British aviators, Ball, McCudden and Mannoch, and finally well

119

above them. As the months of 1918 passed, other Canadians rose to claim a place in this select company. Collishaw, Barker and Mc-Laren were not far behind, and there were many others whose exploits ranked them among the greatest pilots in the war. The combined record of the four Canadian aces named surpassed that of the leading four war pilots of either Germany, France or the United States, as well as that of any other four British pilots.

Among the fighting airmen of the Allied armies in World War I Bishop stood supreme. There is no reason for false modesty about it. His official record of seventy-two enemy planes destroyed demonstrates this fact to the world. It is something to be shouted from the housetops, not whispered quietly among ourselves.

His record lifted him well above that of any other Allied airman. Captain Albert Ball, the greatest English pilot, was killed by Lothar von Richthofen just after his record had passed the fifty mark. Guynemeyer, the French ace of aces, whose name is engraved on the walls of the Pantheon and in the hearts of Frenchmen, met his death when his victories had reached fifty-three. Rickenbacker, the leading American, had twenty-one.

Nor was it in total victories alone that Bishop was their superior. On May 25, 1917, Guynemeyer destroyed four machines. Paul Deschanel, afterward President of France, in speaking of this event said: "This exploit, unique in the annals of military aviation, won for him the officers' cross of the Legion of Honor." Within a few months Bishop had not only equaled but surpassed this exploit by bringing down five German machines in a single day.

Bishop was far ahead of any American aviator, although his first fight as a pilot came just a few days before the United States declared war. In fact, his individual total of seventy-two was ten more than the combined total of the four leading Americans.

Only one man challenged Bishop's record and that was Baron Manfred von Richthofen, the Red Knight of Germany, with eighty victories officially recognized. He was the flower of the German flying corps, the idol of the whole nation and by long odds their greatest ace. Yet without in any way detracting from his record as a great fighter, a sportsman and a gentleman, it is necessary if the facts are to be understood to point out the vast difference in the circumstances under which he and Bishop fought. Whereas Richthofen scarcely ever fought alone, Bishop's greatest successes were achieved in solitary flights. Then, too, nearly all of the fighting during the time of Richtho-fen's and Bishop's activities was carried on well behind the German lines.

This had two important effects. In the first place, there could not fail to be uncertainty at times as to which pilot had fired the fatal shots when a whole squadron attacked a single machine, pouring thousands of bullets from their twin Spandau guns. Where such doubt existed it was only natural that the leader of the squadron should receive the credit. In the second place, nearly all the fighting took place behind the German lines. If a British machine was forced down it had little chance of reaching its own lines. If it landed in German territory it would be counted as a victory for the German officer engaged. A German machine might be forced to land under precisely similar circumstances, but would land well within its own lines. An examination of Richthofen's record shows several machines forced to land but not destroyed, which were counted as victories. On the other hand, Bishop forced many German machines to land on their own side. These were not counted as victories. This situation was not because of caution on Richthofen's part or superior bravery on Bishop's. Each adopted the role best suited to the policy dictated by their respective air forces. Richthofen was killed on April 12, 1918, by a Canadian, Roy Brown, but Bishop lived. (He died, from a heart attack, in Florida on September 11, 1956.) In the shell-torn skies over France, he took fearful chances, never hesitated to accept battle against the greatest odds and yet he was never wounded.

His was indeed a charmed life. Day by day death hovered over him, stretched out its hand with barking Spandaus and crashing high explosives and then withdrew. Time and time again he found himself in the midst of a whirling maelstrom of enemy machines, in which a greater danger than the flaming bullets was the chance of a collision such as had cost the life of Richthofen's teacher, the great Boelcke. Yet when the "dog fight" cleared away Bishop's machine, riddled with bullets, would wing its way safely home while a smoking heap of wreckage behind the German lines told the watching armies that the master marksman had won again.

There were several interesting similarities in the stories of Bishop and Richthofen. Both were young men when the war began. Bishop was twenty and Richthofen twenty-two. Both served first in the cavalry, Richthofen as an officer with a Uhlan Regiment, Bishop as an officer with the Mississauga Horse of Toronto. Both joined the air service as observers before becoming pilots.

Bishop was cadet at the Royal Military College at Kingston in 1914. Born at Owen Sound, Ontario, on February 8, 1894, he had passed through the ordinary educational routine of a Canadian boy until he entered the Royal Military College. There was nothing in his early life to suggest that he was soon to become one of the world's outstanding airmen.

He enlisted and went to England with the Mississauga Horse where fate, in the form of the British War Office, directed this unit to a particularly muddy training camp. Mud caused the death of many men during the war. Indirectly, it brought death to more than a hundred German airmen because it was mud that persuaded Bishop to join the Flying Corps. Bishop himself has told us the story in *Winged Warfare.*

> *Ordinary mud is bad enough, when you have to make your home in it, but the particular brand of mud that infests a cavalry camp has a meaning all its own. Everything was dank, and slimy, and boggy. I had succeeded in getting myself mired to the knees when suddenly from somewhere out of the storm appeared a trim little aeroplane.*
>
> *It landed hesitatingly in a nearby field as if scorning to brush its wings against so sordid a landscape; then away again up into the clean gray mists.*
>
> *How long I stood there gazing into the distance I do not know, but when I turned to slog my way back through the mud, my mind was made up. I knew there was only one place to be on such a day—up above the clouds and in the summer sunshine. I was going to meet the enemy in the air.*

Bishop applied immediately for his transfer and got it. A few months later he had qualified as an observer and was in France. He spent four months in action as an observer. During this period he carried out the customary routine of observation, photography and bombing. He was forced to return to England because of an injury to his knee when his pilot made a bad landing. He was laid up for several months on account of this—his only injury during the war—and then, his sick leave over, was given his chance to become a pilot.

He spent the winter of 1916-17 in training, during which he served on the Zeppelin patrols. Early in March 1917 he learned to fly one of the small and extremely fast single-seater fighting machines which had just been developed by the British aircraft designers. A few days later

he reported to the headquarters of the Royal Flying Corps for his orders to proceed to France as a pilot. At last he was ready for the great adventure.

In March 1917 he joined the 60th Squadron in France. It was equipped with the Nieuport Scout, a small fast single-seated machine designed essentially for fighting. It was fitted with a Lewis gun fixed immediately in front of the pilot. The firing of the machine-gun was synchronized with the speed of the engine in such a way that the bullets passed between the revolving propeller blades. This called for a nice balance of firing accuracy and flying skill, as the guns were fixed in a rigid position making it necessary to point the whole machine in the required direction to bring the sights on the target.

On March 25 he had his first real fight and very nearly his last. The great strategical retreat of the German armies to the Hindenburg line was in full swing and the British airmen were constantly at work observing enemy movements, bombing their supply centres, and photographing the country over which the advancing forces must pass. The scouts bore a vital part in this important work, protecting the slower observing and bombing machines from hostile aircraft during their flights over the enemy's lines. On the twenty-fifth Bishop was on a patrol with three other scouts when they encountered three German Albatrosses.

As the two patrols met, Bishop got "on the tail" of one of the German machines, dived down and fired twelve or fifteen rounds. Apparently the German airman was not seriously hit but dived steeply for about six hundred feet in an effort to get out of his dangerous position under Bishop's gun. Bishop followed him down, however, and as the lower machine flattened out closed to within forty or fifty yards and fired another burst of tracers into the fuselage which appeared to hit the pilot. The German machine then fell in a spinning nose dive. Bishop was taking no chances of letting his quarry escape, however. Down he went in a great dive of nearly seven thousand feet firing all the way, and then when he had reached fifteen hundred or two thousand feet he found his engine had filled with oil and would not work.

Well within the German lines, less than two thousand feet from the ground, with a dead engine and the enemy trenches bristling with machine-guns, there was every prospect that his first fight was to be his last and that the best he could hope for was to spend the remainder of the war in a prison camp. There was nothing to do but glide in the direction of his own lines and hope for the best. His luck, however, was with him when he needed it most. He glided just over the line.

On March 25, 1917, Bishop's record of one machine looked small beside those of the leaders of that time. Earlier on the same day Richthofen, who had been a fighting pilot for six months, had shot down his thirty-first victim. Guynemeyer, the great Frenchman, had thirty-five to his credit and Ball, twenty-nine. Probably Bishop was the last to think that he would very soon exceed those figures.

On Saturday, April 7, 1917, Bishop was ordered to destroy a particular observation balloon about five miles behind the German lines. As he was about to dive on the balloon, he was attacked by an enemy scout which he drove down after a short fight. Then he proceeded to finish the job he had started on. While he had been engaged with the enemy airplane the balloon had been hauled down, but he went down after it, firing bursts of tracer bullets into the bag and at the crew on the ground. Again his engine failed for the second time in a few days, and he was very nearly forced to land miles within enemy territory. When only a few feet from the ground, however, his engine came to life again and he was able to get safely home. It was learned afterward that the balloon had been completely destroyed by fire. Bishop won his first decoration for this exploit.

The day following that fight was Easter Sunday but it was not to be a day of rest, for Easter Monday was the day set for the great attack on Vimy Ridge. It was a beautiful, clear day and at nine o'clock in the morning he crossed the lines with an offensive patrol of six machines under his squadron leader, Major Scott. They flew for miles behind the German lines before meeting the enemy they sought. Bishop became separated from the others in the course of the first fight and his report for the day in a few words describes what most men would consider more than enough fighting for a lifetime, to say nothing of having it packed into about three-quarters of an hour on Easter Sunday morning.

SQUADRON:     *No. 60*
TYPE *and* NO. *of*
   AEROPLANE:    *Nieuport No. A-6769*
ARMAMENT:    *1 Lewis Gun*
PILOT:     *Lt. W. A. Bishop*
DATE:     *8-4-17*
TIME:     *9.30 to 10.15*
DUTY:     *Offensive Patrol*
HEIGHT:     *10,000 ft.*

REMARKS ON HOSTILE MACHINE:
TYPE, ARMAMENT, SPEED, ETC.

*1 Double Seater*
*1 Albatross Scout*
*1 Balloon*
*1 Albatross Scout*
*2 Single Seaters*
*2 Albatross Scouts*
    *and 1 Double Seater*

### NARRATIVE

*While on Offensive Patrol at 9:30, I dived after Major Scott, on a two seater, opening fire twice as he was already diving. Then I engaged a single seater, he flew away eastwards after I had fired 40 rounds at him, tracers hit his machine in fuselage and planes. I then dived at a balloon from 5,000 feet and drove it down to the ground. It did not smoke. I climbed to 400 and engaged an Albatross Scout, fired the remainder of my drum at him, dodged away and put a new drum on, and engaged him again. After two bursts he dived vertically and was still in a nose dive when about 500 feet from the ground. I then climbed to 10,000, and 5 miles N.E. of Arras I engaged 2 Single Seaters flying toward our lines. 3 more machines were above and behind. I fired the remainder of my drum into the pair, one burst of 15 at one and the rest at the 2nd one. The former turned and flew away with his nose well down, the 2nd one went down in a spinning nose dive, my tracers hit all round the pilot's seat and I think he must have been hit. Then I climbed and got behind the other three about the vicinity of Vitry, I engaged them and one double seater went down in a nose dive but I think partly under control, I engaged the remaining 2 and finished my third drum at them. They both flew away eastwards.*

               *W. A. Bishop*

It was afterward learned that two of these machines had been completely destroyed. Bishop's record was mounting fast and it was still only two weeks since his first fight.

Day by day Bishop's reports recorded fight after fight with an ever-increasing toll of German airplanes and balloons. At this time he was flying as much as seven and a half hours between sunrise and sunset and scarcely a day passed without several engagements. When one reads with astonishment today of some venturesome flight and wonders at the courage which such a risk demands, it is well to remember that men like Bishop were day by day and hour by hour for months at a time facing an almost certain prospect of death—and there was nothing beyond the flight but the recognition of a duty performed.

Bishop received notice of the award of the Military Cross and was promoted to the rank of captain only six weeks after he had joined the squadron. He signalized his quick promotion by shooting down another enemy machine in flames the next day.

He was now reaching the point where he might have some hope of overtaking Ball who had returned from leave in England and was adding almost daily to his record. This personal rivalry was a tremendous incentive in the flying corps and introduced a sporting element into the work which relieved it to a great extent of its more sombre aspect.

Bishop was now filled with ambition to become the leading British pilot and almost daily he spent as much time as possible when off duty practicing on the *Petit Bosche*. This was a target on the ground representing the vital parts of an airplane. The pilot would dive steeply at this target firing as he would at an enemy. He could see where his bullets hit, which gave valuable experience and an opportunity to correct defects in his sighting. It was necessary to plunge at full speed to within a few feet of the earth before flattening out, the whole procedure duplicating the course followed when a pilot was successful in getting "on the tail" of an enemy machine.

The nine fights recorded in Bishop's remarkable combat report for April 30, 1917, took place in a little more than two hours in the air. They not only set up a new high record of activity but also furnished a wide variety of fighting. The report is worth examining.

At ten o'clock he was leading an offensive patrol over the lines south of Lens at a height of ten thousand feet when he saw an enemy machine below him. Down he went after the enemy, firing fifteen rounds at close range with no apparent result. The enemy dived eastward for home and safety.

Ten minutes later he was north of Lens on his own side of the lines climbing up to two hostile aircraft at eleven thousand feet. He opened fire on one of these from underneath as he climbed up to it, but after fifteen rounds his machine-gun jammed and he found he could not adjust it in the air, so was forced to return to his airdrome some miles away. These were two very large machines which Bishop afterward identified as the first of the great Gothas which were later to become so well known in the daylight raids on London.

He was soon up in the air again and less than an hour later was back over the lines alone south of Lens attacking two-seated observation machines which were serving as eyes for the German artillery. He got ten rounds away at the leader, who then sought protection by diving under five Halberstadt scouts. Bishop then turned his attention to the scouts, firing twenty rounds as he dived at them, but without result. Having lost his advantage of height he flew away.

Only seven minutes later he again encountered the three artillery observation machines which had evidently decided it was reasonably safe to proceed with the work of ranging their batteries. Bishop immediately attacked, firing twenty rounds into the second of the three machines. It went down in a spinning nosedive completely out of control. As soon as his victim went down, Bishop turned and attacked the third machine. Evidently its pilot had lost heart as he dived away, and Bishop followed, emptying the remainder of the drum of bullets on his gun into him. The third machine also disappeared, so that in a few minutes' fighting the particular batteries which these machines were serving had lost their eyes and some target behind the British lines was for the time being relieved from enemy shell fire.

The record of these fights in Bishop's reports sounds so uneventful that it is well to remember that a fight with three enemy planes, each of which mounted two machine-guns to Bishop's one, was a very formidable undertaking because each of these German machines had an observer with a gun which he could fire in any direction and to which he was able to devote his whole attention while the pilot maneuvered for position. True, Bishop had an advantage of speed, but with bullets pouring at him from six guns, many of which passed through the wings and body of his machine, the odds were far from being wholly in his favor.

Having disposed of the artillery observers Bishop flew south to Monchy where ten minutes later he found the same five Halberstadt scouts, which he had already engaged, about to attack some British B.E.'s which were observing for the British guns. He was higher than the German machines and had the advantage of position. He dived at them, opening fire when very close, then zoomed up with the speed he had gained in his descent and dived again. This he repeated three times, when the German scouts found it too hot for them and turned for home, leaving the slow moving B.E.'s to continue their work for the artillery.

In those stirring days in the spring of 1917 a scout cruising over the lines at ninety miles an hour rushed from one incident to the next in less time than it takes to tell it, particularly if he sought battle as Bishop did. Only five minutes after he had driven off the five Halberstadts he attacked two two-seater machines observing for the artillery at a height of five thousand feet east of Wancourt. They flew to the rear and he followed them as far as Vitry, more than five miles behind the German lines where he again fired at them. They were persistent, however, and flew back toward the lines again, and this time he finished the remainder of his second drum of ammunition into one of them without apparent result.

After putting a fresh drum on his machine-gun he again attacked and, this time singling out one of the enemy, he flew at him head-on, both of them firing as they approached. This proved too much for the Germans who dived out of the fight and did not come back.

About twenty minutes later he had climbed to eleven thousand feet when he discovered another artillery observation machine below him south of Lens. He got above it and then dived vertically, opening fire at close range. The German dived steeply to the east and Bishop followed, firing in all some sixty rounds which finished his last drum. During this time the observer in the German machine was, of course, returning the fire. This machine was forced to land in a field not far behind the German lines.

In one hour, from 11:08 to 12:08, Bishop had, single-handed, engaged eleven different enemy planes, five of which were fighting scouts. The fact that in that length of time he had forced six enemy two-seaters to discontinue their artillery observation, destroyed one machine thus killing two of the enemy and forced another to land, at the same time making it possible for the British observers at Monchy to continue their flight by driving off the threatened attack of the five Halberstadts, gives some estimate of his immense value as an individual fighting unit in the British army.

Nor was his fighting over for the day. After lunch at his airdrome he and his squadron commander, Major Scott, went over the lines together at three o'clock. Before long they encountered four Albatrosses at a height of eleven thousand feet. Bishop climbed above them and then dived at the leader, firing short bursts of five rounds each. The fight continued, with Bishop and the Major firing as they saw their chance, but with no apparent result. Seeing four more machines diving from above, Bishop zoomed up out of the fight to see whether they were friend or enemy and found they were triplanes of one of the British naval squadrons which had just come to that part of the front. The four Albatrosses evidently decided the odds were too great and disappeared.

These German machines were painted a brilliant red which indicated that they belonged to Richthofen's squadron of skilled pilots. Bishop believed that Richthofen himself was the leader whom he had engaged and there is reason to believe that he was correct, as Richthofen at this time frequently flew with three others of his squadron, his brother Lothar, Schaeffer and Wolff. In any event it is almost certain that these two must have come together at some time during that month of April when both of them were fighting many times a day nearly every day on the same part of the front.

The following brief official citation appeared in the London *Gazette* on June 18, 1917.

*His Majesty the King has been graciously pleased to approve of the appointment of the undermentioned officers to be Companions of the Distinguished Service Order in recognition of their gallantry and devotion to duty in the Field:*

*Captain William Avery Bishop, Canadian Cavalry and R.F.C.*

*For conspicuous gallantry and devotion to duty. While in a single-seater he attacked three hostile machines, two of which he brought down, although in the meantime he was himself attacked by four other hostile machines. His courage and determination have set a fine example to others.*

May 7 was a favorable day for Bishop, but it was a blue day for the 60th Squadron and the whole Royal Flying Corps. Late in the afternoon Captain Ball, the leading British pilot at that time, was killed during a fight with Richthofen's squadron. He had more than fifty victories to his credit, was universally popular, had been idolized in England, was an inspiring figure to the younger pilots, including Bishop, and still stands out as one of the greatest airmen of the war.

A few days after Ball's death Bishop left for two weeks' leave in England, having destroyed more than twenty machines in a little over six weeks' fighting.

Before the end of May Bishop was planning an expedition which he had contemplated for some time. He had decided to make a single-handed attack on a German airdrome at dawn in the hope of surprising the enemy as they were preparing to take off for the morning's work. He finally chose June 2 for this extremely hazardous adventure.

He rose before sunrise and just as the first light of dawn was brightening the sky, he was speeding over the enemy lines. He flew straight to the airdrome he had decided to attack but, when he reached it, was disappointed to find no sign of life. He turned his machine to the southeast in the hope of finding a target. About three miles from the first airdrome he came to another. Passing over it at about three hundred feet he saw seven machines out of their hangars with busy groups of mechanics getting them ready for flight. Several of the machines already had their engines running.

Bishop swooped down, raking the length of the airdrome with his bullets as he passed over. When he turned he saw that one of the enemy was taxiing along the ground and about to take off. This was the very chance for which he had waited and often imagined while planning the flight. With his greater speed he was soon immediately above and behind the rising plane and a short burst of fifteen rounds was enough to send it crashing back to the ground. As he turned back toward the airdrome he found another machine had just taken off. This time he fired thirty rounds at a range of 150 yards and the German airplane crashed into a tree near the airdrome. As he turned back again he found two of the machines in the air. He had now lost the advantage of height but he did not hesitate to continue to fight. He attacked one of these machines at a height of one thousand feet, finishing his drum of ammunition into it before it crashed close to its airdrome. He then placed a fresh drum of ammunition in his gun and attacked the fourth machine finishing the whole drum before he flew away.

All the time that Bishop had been flying back and forth over the airdrome he had been subjected to terrific fire from machine-guns on the ground in addition to that which he faced from the machines in the air, and his faithful Nieuport was literally riddled with bullets. When he finally turned for home he was still far from safety, for his own airdrome was a good twenty miles away and his machine and engine had been under a severe strain. For some time he was followed by four enemy scouts which flew directly over him but to his surprise they did not attack and he landed without further incident.

This exploit won the Victoria Cross for Bishop. He was the first Canadian airman to wear the dull crimson ribbon.

When he returned to England in August 1917 he had a remarkable record. He had destroyed forty-seven enemy airplanes and several balloons, had driven down many more with which he was not officially credited, had numberless narrow escapes including a fall of four thousand feet with his machine in flames, and wore on his breast the ribbons of the Victoria Cross, the Distinguished Service Order and the Military Cross—a distinction which had been conferred on no other Canadian before him. A Bar to the Distinguished Service Order and the new Distinguished Flying Cross were to follow later. His record of forty-seven machines also placed him in the forefront of living British airmen.

A few days after his promotion to the rank of major he was granted leave to visit Canada and on September 27 he arrived in Toronto where he received a tumultuous civic welcome. He was continually before the public and his presence in person provided a tremendous stimulus to recruiting for the rapidly growing training-centres of the Royal Flying Corps. Canadians saw before them an amiable youth of twenty-three who, after less than six months with a fighting squadron, had risen from lieutenant to major, wore on his breast the three premier officers' decorations for valor, and now had more machines to his credit than any living aviator in the Allied armies. They saw before them in life the sort of fanciful hero usually only encountered in books of adventure of the type made popular by G. A. Henty, and they rushed to join this service which gave young men such unbelievable opportunity for promotion and honor.

Early in 1918 he returned to England and joined the School of Aircraft Gunnery. Then on May 22, 1918, he went to the front for the third time.

The great German offensives of the spring of 1918 were in full swing. For a while Bishop's work was part of the general routine which the close cooperation that now existed between the airmen and the land forces imposed upon the scouts, but after the British line became fairly well established, he started on a carnival of destruction which had no parallel in the annals of aviation.

He was only in France about four weeks on this final visit to the front and while he had many encounters from the beginning, in the last twelve days he seemed to go fighting mad, and the official citation accompanying the award of the Distinguished Flying Cross tells a story of indomitable courage, fighting spirit and sheer flying skill, beside which even the most daring of the postwar flights seem comparatively uneventful.

*London Gazette No. 30827*
*3rd August, 1918.*
*Air Ministry.*

*AWARDED THE DISTINGUISH-*
*ED FLYING CROSS Capt. (temp. Maj.)*

125

*William Avery BISHOP, V.C., D.S.O.,*
*M.C., (formerly Canadian Cavalry).*

*A most successful and fearless fighter in the air, whose acts of outstanding bravery have already been recognized by the awards of the Victoria Cross, Distinguished Service Order, Bar to the Distinguished Service Order and the Military Cross.*

*For the award of the Distinguished Flying Cross now conferred upon him he has rendered signally valuable services in personally destroying twenty-five enemy machines in twelve days—five of which he destroyed on the last day of his service at the front.*

*The total number of machines destroyed by this distinguished officer is seventy-two and his value as a moral factor to the Royal Air Force cannot be overestimated.*

In twelve days Bishop had destroyed four more machines than Rickenbacker, the leading American pilot, did in the whole of his five months at the front. On his last day in France, as many of the enemy fell under his guns as were brought down by the whole of the Royal Flying Corps in the first month of the war. The record of seventy-two machines, which no airman then living had equaled, did not include a very large number which had been driven down but not seen to crash, and there can be no doubt that many of these were also destroyed.

Bishop was appointed to the staff of the Air Ministry in June 1918. About this time it was decided to form a separate Canadian branch of the Royal Air Force and with the organization of this force in view he was transferred to Canadian Headquarters on August 5, 1918. Although plans had been completed, the Canadian Air Force did not come into actual existence before the Armistice, and Bishop therefore saw no more service at the front.

In the meantime he had been promoted lieutenant-colonel and on November 2, 1918, the London *Gazette* contained the following announcement.

*The undermentioned officer of the Royal Air Force has been awarded the Decorations specified, in recognition of distinguished services rendered:*
*Conferred by the Government of the French Republic.*
*Croix de Chevalier, Legion of Honor.*
*Croix de Guerre with Palm.*
*Lieutenant-Colonel William Avery Bishop, V.C., D.S.O., M.C., D.F.C., Canadian Cavalry and Aviation Service.*

Thus, when the war ended, Bishop at twenty-four was a lieutenant-colonel and had been awarded practically every decoration for valor conferred by the British and French governments.

RAY GARDNER

# How Percy Williams Swept the Olympics

On July 30, 1928, in Amsterdam, Percy Williams, a runner who a few weeks before had won the sprints at the Vancouver high schools' sports day, startled the world by winning the hundred-metre event at the Olympic Games. Two days later, just turned twenty and so light of build he was described as delicate, he won the two-hundred-metre sprint to become the World's Fastest Human. It was a triumph that stands today as Canada's brightest moment in Olympic Games history—perhaps in all the annals of Canadian sport.

There have been other great achievements recorded by Canadian athletes—Jimmy Mc-Larnin's winning of the world's welterweight boxing championship, Barbara Ann Scott's world and Olympic figure-skating victories, Marilyn Bell's triumph over Lake Ontario. But none has so thrilled the Canadian people—and held the centre of world attention—as did Williams' incredible sweep at Amsterdam in the fading Twenties.

Forty thousand spectators in Amsterdam's new Olympic Stadium went wild as the lithe Canadian breasted the tape in the two hundred metres to become a double champion. The Canadian athletes were almost hysterical with excitement. The British, South Africans and Australians were in an uproar. To them it was a triumph of Empire. In Canada the victory inspired a national rejoicing that wasn't to subside until weeks later when Williams crossed the country in triumph, to be lionized in Winnipeg, Calgary and, finally, Vancouver.

No other Canadian has ever taken the country by storm as did Percy Williams in those September days of 1928. His youth, his modesty and his achievement touched the national pride. The picture of Percy standing at ease and wearing his white track suit, the Maple Leaf emblem and "Canada" across his chest, became familiar to every Canadian who even glanced at a newspaper. "The day Percy Williams came home" is still recalled in Vancouver with a nostalgic sigh. The city gave him a sporty blue Graham-Paige coupé. Money (eventually $14,500) poured into a trust fund to provide for his education. Kids munched Our Percy chocolate bars, the product of a swift-moving Edmonton candy merchant.

What had thrilled the crowd at Amsterdam, made Williams world famous and in Canada a national idol, was the marvel of an unknown runner not only winning a double Olympic championship, but defeating one of the most brilliant fields of sprinters the Games had ever seen.

Only Percy Williams himself was able to take his victory calmly. He sat on his cot in Amsterdam's third-rate Holland Hotel and recorded in the pocket diary he had kept for his mother his own impressions of victory and the first rewards of fame:

*August 1—Well, it's done. Won the 200 M. Not so bad. Telegrams galore. The girls' team sent flowers to me. Hot dog! McAllister, Paddock, Scholz, Borah and Wykoff all congratulated me.*

Bob McAllister, Charlie Paddock, Jackson V. Scholz, Charles Borah and Frank Wycoff were the fastest and by far the most famous runners of the day. They were the United States stars rated by everyone a cinch to win the sprints. In four days the unknown Canadian had met and beaten them all. Paddock said of the Canadian who outran him that "the world has never seen a greater competitive sprinter"; and Will Rogers, the reigning humorist, suggested annexing Canada to acquire Williams.

Williams' times were not record-breaking; they were even considered slow: 10.8 seconds for the hundred metres and 21.8 seconds for the two hundred metres. The Olympic records then were 10.6 for the hundred (which he had equaled in winning a heat) and 21.6 for the two hundred. But this was of no real account, for Williams' strategy was always to beat the man, not the clock. Trained to a razor's edge, Williams weighed only 126 pounds, the lightest runner ever to win an Olympic sprint. After his victory in the hundred, they said he'd never last out the grueling preliminary heats of the two hundred. In fact, the great Paddock declared that "it seemed impossible for that skinny little sprinter to do it." Yet in four days Williams ran eight races, winning six and placing second in two.

His rout of the favorites was so stunning a blow that General Douglas MacArthur, then president of the United States Olympic Committee, felt it necessary to make a public explanation. Only once before had the United States failed to win at least one of the two sprints and never since have they failed to win both. "The Canadian, Percy Williams," said MacArthur, "is the greatest sprinter the world has ever seen and he will be even greater before his career is ended." He did run faster races—in 1930 he set a new world's record of 10.3 seconds for the hundred metres—but he never won greater glory than in those four days at Amsterdam.

The first Canadian to reach Williams as he flung himself across the finish line in the two hundred metres was Bobby Kerr, of Hamilton, who himself had won the event at the 1908 Olympics. "Won't Granger be pleased," Williams gasped. A few hours later he told the droves of reporters who sought him out, "Whatever I've done has been through my coach, Bob Granger."

It was not a routine tribute to a helper. Williams meant it literally. For just as Jimmy Mc-Larnin had the cagey manager Pop Foster behind him, and Marilyn Bell owed much of her success to coach Gus Ryder, so Percy Williams had his Bob Granger. Even today, Williams says emphatically: "Granger was everything. *Everything*."

A florid man with flaming red hair and a freckled face, Granger was thirty-three years old when he first saw Percy Williams run in the spring of 1926. Percy was then eighteen, to Granger "a puny 110-pound kid." Some time that year he decided the boy would win the 1928 Olympics. It was a decision, not a dream.

Dr. Harry Warren, now professor of geology at the University of British Columbia, knows the Granger-Williams story as well as anyone. Trained by Granger, Warren was Canada's reserve sprinter at Amsterdam and was one of three athletes who shared a small hotel room with Percy. "Granger *knew* that Percy would win the Olympics. He told me so in 1926. He was absolutely sure of it. Percy didn't love running—Granger drove him to it. Percy was a delicate boy and Granger wouldn't let him out of his sight for a minute if he could help it."

V. L. (Pinky) Stewart, a Vancouver advertising executive who, as a runner, was also trained by Granger, says, "He had Percy obsessed with the idea of winning the Olympics. He mesmerized him."

Born in New Westminster, B.C., of Scottish parents, Granger himself had excelled at rugby and swimming and was a fair track man. When his own playing days were over, he devoted all of his time, energy and whatever little money he had to developing schoolboy athletes. Oblivious to all else in life, Granger studied every technique of coaching and conditioning athletes, especially sprinters. He had a library of books on the subject, but he went beyond what the books taught to evolve his own theories. At Amsterdam the Swedish trainers were astounded by his knowledge of muscle therapy. Stewart says, "He was a genius in his own field. He was like a tin god to us kids. He could hold us spellbound for hours with his stories about track. He'd say to a youngster, 'Well, you're a regular little Charlie Paddock.' And the boy would be walking on air for hours."

In 1926 Granger was coaching rugby and track at Vancouver's King George High School. One of his protégés was Wally Scott, the city sprint champion. The students at King Edward High had promoted a match race between their star, Percy Williams, and Scott. Granger was amazed to see Percy run his own champion to a dead heat. Granger later commented that he had never seen worse style in a boy who could run like Williams did. "I think he violated every known principle of the running game," said the coach. "He ran with his arms glued to his sides. It actually made me tired to watch him."

From the summer of 1926 till the eve of the Olympics, Granger slaved over Williams to perfect his starting and running form. Day after day, in spring and summer, Granger got a group of boys together and had them demonstrate starts and arm motion. Mostly, Percy just watched—and learned. Granger called this "visualization." It was a way of conserving the boy's energy. At home, Percy practiced by the hour before a mirror. He did setting-up exercises to strengthen stomach and chest muscles. His hands were developed to give him an extra spring off the mark.

Even so, Granger always maintained that his runner didn't master the correct arm movement in his starts until the day before the Games were to open. Whenever it happened, Williams did become the fastest starter of his time. After the Olympics he was unbeatable in short dashes, forty to sixty-five yards, where a rocket-like start means everything.

At fifteen, Percy had been stricken with rheumatic fever and, the doctors said, left with a damaged heart. He was even warned to avoid excitement. In any case, he was extremely light and far from robust. His Amsterdam weight was 126 pounds, compared with Paddock's 175 pounds and McAllister's 170.

While heavier runners might work themselves into condition, Granger took infinite pains to bring Williams slowly up to racing pitch. He spoke of the boy's "precious energy." On a cold day, he would rub Percy before a race with cocoa butter and dress him in as many as three track suits and four sweaters to prevent loss of body heat ("precious energy"). He concocted an amazing variety of rubdown lotions. One was a mixture of olive oil, wintergreen and liniment. He gave him Finnish massages and Swedish massages. Granger set out to make the boy as confident of victory as he was himself. He called him the Vancouver Gazelle, after the world's fastest beast, and continually showed him how his times were beginning to compare with those of the world's fastest men.

Granger succeeded in making track enthusiasts of the boy's family and had them dreaming of Olympic victories. Percy, an only child, lived with his mother, Mrs. Charlotte Williams, who worked as a theatre cashier, and her parents. Williams has always been extremely devoted to his mother and even during the Olympics wrote her every other day. He has never married.

In the spring and summer of 1927 and the spring of 1928, Granger kept Williams running—and winning—in every local meet. He ran what were, for a schoolboy, some remarkable times: 9.9 seconds for the hundred yards, 22 seconds for the two-twenty. In June 1928 he took his first stride toward Amsterdam by winning the British Columbia Olympic trials. He tied the Olympic record of 10.6 seconds for the hundred metres, running against a breeze and on a grass track that dipped up and down like a roller coaster. On June 15, Percy and the other coast athletes went to Hamilton and the Canadian Olympic trials. Williams recorded it in his diary:

*June 15—Was there a crowd to see us off? Boy, and how! I only hope it will be for a good reason.*

Broke, Granger was left behind. But two days later he was on his way east as a pantry boy on a CPR diner.

Percy Williams became the unexpected star of the Hamilton trials. Against a field of top-notch Canadian sprinters, most of them trained in American colleges, he won the hundred metres in 10.6 seconds, again equaling the Olympic record, and the two hundred metres in 22 seconds.

*June 30—Well, the day of miracles is not passed. I can't quite understand yet but they say winning the 100 metres puts me on the boat for Amsterdam.*

But it didn't put Granger on the boat. The Canadian Olympic team—and Granger's luggage—sailed from Montreal on July 11 aboard the liner "Albertic." As the ship neared Quebec a search was made for a stowaway. Granger appeared at Quebec to retrieve his luggage— he had reached there, he wrote later, "by other means than the St. Lawrence River." The "Albertic" left without him, but the next day money arrived and he sailed on a CPR freighter, the SS "Minnedosa."

The crossing was painful for Granger. He had counted on nine days at sea to perfect Percy's starts. Eventually he reached Amsterdam and, in Percy's room at the Holland Hotel, he drilled the youth in his starting. A mattress was placed against one wall, as a buffer, and Percy would take off from across the room. The management, not sharing Granger's obsession, objected. But nevertheless it was there in the Holland Hotel, so Granger said, that the World's Fastest Human learned how to get off the mark in a hurry.

On Sunday, July 29, Percy Williams began his dash to glory. Eighty-seven sprinters were entered in the hundred metres. The overwhelming favorite was Frank Wykoff, an eighteen-year-old Californian schoolboy who four times had tied the Olympic record and had beaten

Paddock in a race billed as "the sprint of the century." Should Wykoff fail, there was Bob McAllister, the Flying Bowery Cop, and Claude Bracey, pride of Rice University. These three were specializing in the hundred-metre while other U.S. runners were saved for the two-hundred-metre.

Percy Williams won his first heat easily, in 11 seconds, but was forced to run his fastest race of the Games, 10.6 seconds, to win his second heat and enter the semifinals. His diary entry showed extreme modesty:

*July 29—My ideals of the Olympic Games are all shot. I always imagined it was a game of heroes. Well, I'm in the semifinals myself so it can't be so hot.*

At 2 p.m. on Monday, July 30, Bob Granger suffered a moment of supreme anguish when, for a split second, Williams was caught on his haunches at the start of the hundred-metre semifinal. He recovered brilliantly to finish four inches behind McAllister, who had to equal the Olympic record to win. Second place qualified Williams for the final.

There were now two hours to kill before the final. Granger took Williams to the dressing room and gave him a book to read. As race time neared Percy warmed up, and then Granger rubbed him down with the last precious piece of the cocoa butter he had brought from Canada. "Keep calm, it's only another Sunday-school race," he told the boy.

When they lined up for the hundred-metre final the young Canadian was dwarfed by the brawny Bob McAllister and Jack London, a two-hundred-pound British Negro. Frank Wykoff, George Lammers of Germany, and Wilfred Legg of South Africa completed the field. Thousands of Germans in the stands gave a mighty cheer for Lammers. The Canadians began to chant, "Williams, Canada! Williams, Canada!" and some of the crowd, perhaps taken by his size, joined in.

There were two false starts—first Legg broke, then Wykoff. Each time the crowd surged to its feet, then subsided again. The third start was perfect. Williams shot away with the gun, the rest on his heels. With thirty metres to go, Williams was still in front. Then London made a valiant effort to catch him, but missed by a yard. Lammers was third, Wykoff fourth, Legg fifth and McAllister sixth and last.

The stadium was in a riot. Granger, who later described the race as "ten seconds of breathless living," wept. P. J. Mulqueen, the Canadian Olympic chairman, rushed on the field and kissed the winner.

129

*July 30—Well, well, well. So I'm supposed to be the World's 100 M Champion. (Crushed apples.) No more fun in running now.*

Now began two days of grueling running in the two hundred metres. The favorite was the flaxen-haired California Comet, Charles Borah, who had won the United States trials in 21.6 seconds, equaling the Olympic record. To back him up, the United States had the veteran Paddock and Jackson V. Scholz, who had won the two hundred metres in the 1924 Games in the record time of 21.6. Germany had a strong contender in Helmut Koernig, an almost flawless runner.

Williams wasn't conceded a chance against these fresh, more experienced and, on the record, faster runners. His best time, 22 seconds, was two-fifths of a second off their pace. What no one could know was that Granger's tactics and Williams' "gear shift"—a unique ability to change running styles while in full flight—would single out Borah and Koernig, one at a time, and kill them off.

The secret of Williams' success was this ability to switch styles while running. Williams would take off with a driving start and keep driving until he had reached his maximum speed. Then he would shift into an easy, flowing style, a sort of overdrive. Near the finish, as his speed diminished, he would drive again, hitting the tape at top speed. "It was," Williams explains today, "like pedaling a bike downhill. There was no use trying to go faster; it would break my stride to try."

On Tuesday, July 31, Williams romped through his first heat of the two hundred metres and was resting in his dressing room when Harry Warren burst in with the news that, by luck of the draw, Borah, Koernig and Williams, with three others, were drawn to run in the next heat. "I can still remember my horror," says Warren. "It meant that one of these three great runners was to be eliminated even before the semifinals. Only the first two would qualify."

Granger gave Williams his instructions. "Don't try to win," he said. "Run to beat whoever is running second, Borah or Koernig." Then, to make the boy perspire without exertion, he smothered him under a pile of a dozen coats and blankets.

Koernig, the pride of Germany, flashed out in front from the start of the race, with Borah on his trail. At the halfway mark Williams was running third, four yards behind Borah. It was then that Williams, already traveling at top speed, tried to drive himself faster too soon. Momentarily he faltered, almost breaking his stride, and dropped farther behind. With sixty

metres to go it appeared impossible for him to catch Borah. Now he shifted gears again—and this time moved smoothly into his drive, flashing past Borah in the last two yards. Driven by Borah and Williams, Koernig had equaled the Olympic mark of 21.6 in winning.

*July 31—Miracles still happen. I'm in the semifinals. Eliminated Borah. One of the nicest fellows I have ever met. Ran two heats today. First one was easy. 2nd one against Borah and German champ.*

Granger, who had watched every race in agony, was now beside himself. He spent the night in the corridor outside Williams' room. At intervals he slipped notes under the door to Williams' roommate, Harry Warren. Percy had a habit of pulling the covers over his face as he slept—Warren was to pull them down. "He must have oxygen!" Granger wrote. In another note he asked, "Is he breathing easily?"

The afternoon of Wednesday, August 1, Williams won his semifinal race easily, with Paddock fourth. Only two years before Percy had shown his mother a picture of Paddock displayed in a Vancouver gas station and had told her, "There is the world's fastest human."

Now only one race stood between Percy Williams and a double Olympic championship. When they lined up for the final of the two hundred metres, Williams faced Koernig and Jacob Schuller, of Germany; John Fitzpatrick, a Canadian from Hamilton; Jackson Scholz, of the United States, the 1924 champion; and Walter Rangely, of Great Britain. Even before Amsterdam, Granger knew almost all there was to know about all the internationally known sprinters. Now, at Amsterdam, he had studied them in the flesh until, as Williams remarks today, "He even knew who their grandfathers were."

"Koernig is your man to beat," he told Williams. "He is a front runner—an inspirational runner—and if you come out of the curve even with him, or just ahead of him, you will kill his inspiration and win." This strategy, and Williams' ability to carry it out, was to beat Koernig, who could actually run the distance faster than Percy could.

As they came out of the curve, Koernig and Williams were in the lead, running neck and neck. They ran that way until the last fifty metres. The crowd came to its feet as the Canadian ran on even terms with the great German. Thousands of Koernig's countrymen urged him on. Then Williams shifted gears, out of his flowing stride and into a blinding driving finish. For an instant the amazed Koernig seemed to hesitate. The skinny kid from Canada flashed by him and won by a yard over Rangeley, the Briton, who had come up fast to place second. Koernig finished third, in a dead heat with Scholz.

The crowd broke loose in the wildest demonstration that ever followed an Olympic victory. Granger, who had mentally run every stride with Williams, was limp. In his excitement, he had clenched his hands on a barbed-wire barrier and they were drenched with blood.

At the Holland Hotel, the cables arrived in a deluge—from Prime Minister Mackenzie King, from almost every Canadian provincial premier and most mayors. There were offers for Williams to run in New York, Berlin, Stockholm, Britain and Australia. Reporters surrounded him. "It doesn't feel any different being Olympic champion," he told them. "My lucky coin in the race was a good start." Then he had a supper of salad and mineral water and went to bed.

When Peerless Percy—as the papers called him—came home in September, he was met by his mother in Quebec and together they traveled across the land in triumph, their arrival in each city the headline news of the day. Montreal's Mayor Camillien Houde told him, "You're a great kid, Percy. I say to you, stay Canadian." Hamilton gave him a golden key to the city. In Toronto thousands cheered Percy and his mother at the CNE. At Winnipeg the CPR station was packed with people, and it was Percy Williams Day at the Polo Park racetrack.

In Vancouver, the streets for blocks around the CPR station were a solid mass of people that morning of September 14 when Percy and his mother finally reached home. Granger had traveled on ahead and was there to meet them. The moment Percy stepped off the train, the sun broke through dark rain clouds. A schoolboy band struck up "See the Conquering Hero Comes." Two thousand schoolchildren marched ahead of the big touring car that carried Percy, Bob Granger, Mayor Louis Taylor and Premier S. F. Tolmie past cheering crowds to Stanley Park. There twenty thousand gathered to see Percy presented with a car and Granger with a purse of five hundred dollars in gold. Premier Tolmie said, "Oh, what a homecoming! Never has there been such joy and pride."

For the next three years Canada watched and marveled as the World's Fastest Human kept on running and winning. A few scoffers, mostly U.S. sports writers, said he had been favored by the soft, slow track built on Amsterdam's marshlands. In February of 1929 he invaded the hard, fast, indoor tracks of the United States and took New York, Boston, Philadelphia, Newark and Detroit by storm as he reeled off a series of truly phenomenal victories over outstanding runners, most of whom specialized in indoor running. He set a new world's record of forty-five yards (4.9 seconds) and equaled three other world's records. In Detroit he beat Eddie Tolan, the famous Midnight Express, in a forty-yard dash—and thereby began one of running's most intense rivalries.

Twenty thousand people jammed Vancouver's Hastings Park on July 13, 1929, to see Williams win over Tolan by two inches in the hundred yards. A year later, in the same setting, ten thousand spectators groaned as he ran third to Tolan in the hundred metres. On August 9, 1930, in Toronto, Williams ran his fastest race, setting a new world's record of 10.3 seconds for the hundred metres. His Toronto mark was half a second faster than his winning time at Amsterdam. A classic duel between Williams and Tolan was anticipated for the 1932 Olympic Games, to be held in Los Angeles. But Percy had run his last really great race.

The beginning of the end came on August 23, 1930, in the hundred-yard final of the first British Empire Games, at Hamilton. The day was cold and, after they had taken off their warm training suits, the finalists were kept standing in their flimsy track suits for almost ten minutes. It was the very situation Granger had always feared. Williams was flying almost certainly to a new world's record when, with thirty-five yards to go, he pulled a muscle in his left thigh. In agony, he kept running, staggering out of his lane at the tape. He won in the remarkable time of 9.9 seconds—and then crumpled to the track. His leg was never right again.

The end came—as fame had come—at the Olympic Games. He went to Los Angeles without Granger (they had quarreled over a petty matter) and certain he had only two good races left in him. He ran third in two hundred-metre heats and then, in the semifinal, ran fourth and out to Eddie Tolan. Tolan went on to become a double champion. After that Williams stepped deliberately out of the limelight and devoted himself to business and to golf.

Looking back over the years, Percy tries to remember how he reacted to sudden fame. "I was just like any kid of twenty," he says. "I was simply bewildered by it all. I didn't like running. Oh, I was so glad to get out of it all."

PIERRE BERTON

# Hindmarsh of the Star

In the ranks of that vast army of men who at one time or another worked for Harry Comfort Hindmarsh, the presiding genius of Canada's largest newspaper, the Toronto *Star*, there circulates an intriguing but untrue story that illustrates the awe in which he was held. The story has it that Hindmarsh has sent for an old employee to tell him he is fired. When the old man reaches Hindmarsh's office and hears the news he thanks him profusely.

"What are you thanking me for?" growls Hindmarsh. "It's Christmas Eve! You've been here forty years! Can't you see I'm cutting you off without a cent?"

"I realize that, Mr. Hindmarsh," says the old retainer, tugging at his forelock, "but when I first heard you had sent for me I thought you were going to *sell* me."

In some sections of the newspaper fraternity, where Hindmarsh was regarded as an ogre, this sort of thing was believed as gospel. In others where he was revered almost as a saint it was dismissed as calumny. Around this almost legendary figure, right up to and including the day he died in 1956, the winds of controversy blew with gale force. But if an occasional gust disturbed the impassive calm with which he viewed the world around him, he did not show it. As he rose from cub reporter to president, Harry Hindmarsh neither answered his critics nor coddled his admirers. Even to the closest members of his staff he was an unknown quantity, a creature of myth and fable, whose own picture appeared only once in his newspaper. Few men knew him well. But whether they respected or hated him, almost all newsmen who crossed his path were secure in one opinion: he was the greatest editor they ever worked for.

Under Hindmarsh's peculiar genius, the Toronto *Star* gained its reputation for a relentless coverage of the news, unequaled anywhere, as well as for some of the most erratic journalism extant. Money was no object to him; distance no obstacle. Reporters flew off to Persia on a whim or phoned Montevideo on a hunch. Under his aegis *Star* men hired everything from tugboats to airliners to get the news. One man hired a railway train and returned to the office aghast at what he had done. Hindmarsh raised his salary ten dollars a week.

Many hated his guts. One reporter tried to kill him with a foot-long pair of copy shears. Hindmarsh never changed expression or took his hands from his pockets as underlings leapt to his rescue. Ernest Hemingway wanted to punch him in the nose. When the *Star* building was erected in 1929 one wag suggested that a motto be carved around it: Every Man for Himself and The Devil Take the Hindmarsh.

But *Star* reporters always worked for him like beavers. "You really lived a story with the Big Guy," one ex-staffer recalls. "When a hot story was breaking he'd come out of his office to take control and a sort of aura would form around him." In moments of crisis he was the calmest man on the floor. As managing editor he used to deliver in his deep slow voice an unending series of instructions that might dispatch a dozen reporters to a key spot, some on a dead run. But he himself never spoke above a low conversational level. "It was like joining a religious order," another old reporter says. "When you worked for Hindmarsh you couldn't help yourself: you just lived, ate and breathed that goddam *Star*."

The *Star*'s greatest scoop occurred just after Hindmarsh became managing editor in 1928 and it illustrates the lengths his men went to get the news for him. The German aircraft Bremen had crash-landed off the Labrador coast after history's first successful east-west crossing of the Atlantic. Bush pilot Duke Schiller was expected to return to Lake St. Agnes in Quebec with first news and pictures of the event. It was the greatest story since Lindbergh, and the Press of the continent dashed to the lake to meet him. But the *Star* was ahead of them all. Before Schiller got away to Labrador it reached him with an offer of $7,000 for his story. To get his men to Lake St. Agnes at once, Hindmarsh hired a special train. The *Star* reporters fought off six American newsmen who tried to climb aboard. Then at Murray Bay, the nearest telegraph outlet, they tied up the line by ordering the operator to wire a copy of the *New Republic* back to the office.

Schiller finally flew in carrying one precious roll of film. For a single picture a New York tabloid was later to offer $20,000. An American reporter got the film first, but Fred Griffin of the *Star* seized him and physically tore it away. He put the film on a *Star* plane which flew off for civilization. The plane was forced down at Quebec. The *Star* hired a train to speed the film to Montreal. At Montreal it was printed, and Roy Greenaway of the *Star* hired a taxi to drive the 350 miles to Toronto. The taxi drove at sixty miles an hour through a raging blizzard. At one point the steering wheel came off. Greenaway and the driver rammed it on. At another point it hit an oncoming car. "We're from the *Star*," cried Greenaway. "It's all right," said the other driver, "I'm a friend of Mr. Atkinson (the *Star* publisher)." Shortly before 11 a.m. the pictures arrived at the *Star*. They appeared on the paper's front page that day giving it a twenty-four-hour beat on every paper in the world.

Hindmarsh's news imagination often nudged the bizarre. In July 1926 fifteen youths were plunged into Balsam Lake, northern Ontario, when their war canoe capsized. Eleven drowned. Hindmarsh's reaction was immediate. "Reconstruct the tragedy," he said to the first reporter back from the scene. Dutifully, thirteen reporters went out, hired a war canoe, paddled it into Lake Ontario, capsized it and plunged into the icy waters while photographers snapped the scene.

"News," Hindmarsh once said, "is the greatest gamble in the world." Once he sent Gregory Clark and photographer Norm James to British Columbia with orders to get a story—any story. They ran into a major air crash and came up with exclusive interviews with the survivors. Hindmarsh never had much sense of geography. One reporter remembers being in New Orleans on a story. He got a call from the *Star*: "Hop up to Chicago." In vain he protested it would be cheaper and swifter to send a man from the office.

Many of the *Star*'s great stories were the result of Hindmarsh's analytical mind. Once he sent a reporter to cover the murder of three little boys who had been shot in their sleep by their twelve-year-old sister. He was not satisfied with the reporter's story. "There's something behind this," he said. Further digging revealed the child had been fascinated by her father shooting pigs through the eyes. She had re-enacted the scene in her sleep. It was another *Star* scoop.

Hindmarsh's "hunger to know what is happening," as one of his reporters called it, his "childlike wonderment in the little things" was reflected in the heavily scrawled suggestions on the *Star* galley proofs, which he read carefully. His attention to small detail was a source of wonder. He gave his men explicit instructions on what to do, where to go, what questions to ask. During the kidnapping of brewer John Labatt, when Toronto was being combed for suspects, one *Star* man was assigned simply to stand across from the Royal York hotel until 4 a.m. and note whether anyone who looked like a gangster walked in the side door.

Hindmarsh always felt that a picture was worth ten thousand words. *Star* reporters ransacked the homes of the slain to get photos of the victim. One reporter was told by the widow of a man impaled on a picket fence that there was only one available photo of the victim showing him as a child. "It's all right," said the reporter cheerfully, "we'll paint a mustache on." Hindmarsh chose pictures with the speed of light from the stacks set before him. He chose the sugary *Star Weekly* cover paintings in similar fashion. One reporter once brought him a painting as a Christmas present. Hindmarsh thought it was for the *Weekly*. "Take it away!" he rumbled after a swift glance. At one point the *Weekly* decided to run reproductions in color of famous paintings. Hindmarsh selected a man to choose them. "But Mr. Hindmarsh," the reporter protested. "I know absolutely nothing about art."

"Fine," said Hindmarsh.

"But there's something else," the reporter added. "I'm color blind."

"Excellent!" boomed Hindmarsh. "You're the man."

This contempt for the public was apparent in another Hindmarsh innovation—the symposium. Reporters would select dozens of names at random from the phone book and ask such questions as "Do men make more fuss over pain than women?" The paper found this a useful tool in editorial campaigns. "Hindmarsh trained us to ring up people and get them to say, 'Yes, you are quite right,'" one former symposium expert recalls. His disdain for the public was matched by a cavalier attitude toward the great by-line writers who once worked for him. He was once asked why men like Hemingway, Morley Callaghan, Pierre Van Paassen, Gregory Clark, Jimmy Frise and Matthew Halton had all left his employ. "They all got too big for their breeches," Hindmarsh said.

One of the greatest legends surrounding Hindmarsh concerns the departure of Ernest Hemingway. Hemingway worked for the *Star* between 1920 and 1923 and there are several versions of the reasons for his departure. The popular version is that Hemingway, after returning from Spain, was assigned to write a promotion story on a white peacock and refused in a spectacular resignation which, when pasted together sheet by sheet and hung on the notice board, measured five feet in length. The authorized version differs. It says that Hemingway had received from an Italian diplomat he was interviewing some documents he promised faithfully to return. When he found that Hindmarsh had flung the papers in the wastebasket he quit. Hindmarsh's own version was that Hemingway was sent to northern Ontario to cover a labor dispute. His dispatches so favored the strikers that Hindmarsh wired him to start reporting the news. Hemingway returned in high dudgeon, stormed into Hindmarsh's office, gave him a half-hour tongue-lashing, and then quit.

There is probably some truth in all three versions. Hemingway seems to have quit over a variety of things. He did post a long critique of the *Star* on the notice board and he certainly hated Hindmarsh. "Working for him was like being in the Prussian army under a rather poor general," he once said. At one time he planned to write a novel about Hindmarsh called "The Son-In-Law" (Hindmarsh had married the daughter of *Star* owner Joseph Atkinson). Years after he quit the *Star* he wrote the struggling Newspaper Guild announcing that he was enclosing a cheque for $100 "to beat Hindmarsh." There followed four pages or so of comment and then a final sentence:"On second thought I'm making it $200."

A shy youth, who became a big man physically and financially, Hindmarsh had a gruffly paternal attitude to the men who worked for him. To the weak ones he was like a father, half indulgent, half stern. There are numerous instances of *Star* reporters whom Hindmarsh bailed out of debt. It was his custom to have all the man's bills brought to him. He totaled them all carefully, checked to make sure there were no more, then signed a cheque for the entire sum. His only stipulation was that the man involved keep quiet about it. Hindmarsh sent sickly wives of staffers to Arizona and paid for their children's operations. One woman prayed for him every night because he saved her husband from alcoholism and took him back on the paper.

But he insisted on doing things his way. When *Star* men got sick they often found Hindmarsh selecting the doctor and prescribing the treatment. Once he called in Morley Callaghan and told him in a fatherly way that he had been smoking too much and staying up late at nights. "But you're *wrong*, Mr. Hindmarsh!" said Callaghan emphatically. "You're fired!" rumbled Hindmarsh, who didn't like to be told he was wrong. Callaghan was fired five times from the *Star* but never actually stopped work. "The trouble with you, Mr. Callaghan," Hindmarsh said to him once, "is you've never been broken to harness."

When Matthew Halton wanted to write a book, Hindmarsh, who felt that a man's every waking moment should be devoted to the *Star*, refused him permission. Halton indicated he would anyhow and was fired. Then Hindmarsh made him a present of $10,000 and agreed to buy an article a week from him at a sum that exactly equaled his staff salary.

Hindmarsh never allowed anyone—man or newspaper—to get the better of him. When the late George McCullagh bought the Toronto *Telegram* and announced he would "push that Communistic rag (the *Star*) off its pedestal," the *Telegram* began to beat the drums for a serialization of Dickens's *Life of Christ*, an old circulation getter that the *Star* itself had published decades before. Hindmarsh promptly called a reporter. "Get me a life of Christ by 5 p.m.," he said in the same slow voice in which he had once told a city editor to "get me an elephant." The reporter got a life of Christ and the *Star* got in into print a full day before its rival.

The sharp edges of Hindmarsh's many-sided personality left their mark on everything with which he came into contact. The desire to dominate, the almost fanatic attention to detail, the insatiable and childlike curiosity—all had their effect on his family, his private life, the people who worked for him, the political party he supported, the church he went to and the town in which he lived. It was impossible to divorce his private existence from his newspaper, for the two were impossibly tangled.

He lived at Oakville, thirty miles along the lake from Toronto, and Oakville to the *Star* was the most important small town in Canada. It chronicled the town's events in minute detail. When British American Oil began building a refinery near the Hindmarsh home, *Star* reporters combed the area gathering critical opinions charging that it would pollute the beaches. Hindmarsh was a member of St. John's United Church, Oakville. Once when the church was looking for a new minister, teams of *Star* reporters combed the province for a likely candidate. The teams were usually three strong: a reporter, his wife and a shorthand man. The shorthand man took down the minister's sermon verbatim. The reporter wrote a memo on his appearance and popularity. The reporter's wife wrote a memo on the minister's wife. From this, the new man was chosen. When Hindmarsh became president of the Oakville Golf Club, he called in some of his executive staff and urged that they take things easier. "Get out in the fresh air. Play golf!" said Hindmarsh. They dutifully swelled the membership of the Oakville Club.

Many old-time reporters still recount memories of curious assignments involving homework problems for Hindmarsh's four children. One man had to comb through all English exam papers of the Oakville High for a decade and find out what six essay topics were assigned most frequently. He then had to prepare essays on all six topics, written in the style of a teenage girl. These were for the "guidance" of one of Hindmarsh's daughters who was having trouble with the subject. Hindmarsh went over this homework as carefully as he did *Star* galley proofs. Sometimes he would call in a second reporter and ask for a rewrite.

He was nothing if not meticulous. One reporter was called in to select a hired man for the Hindmarsh home. He interviewed sixty-three prospects before he got the right one.

One evening Hindmarsh visited the new home of his son-in-law Ab Fallon. He discovered one of the bookcases only partially full. He produced a tape and measured the gap. Next day he sent down to the *Star* library for four feet, eight inches of books.

He took a microscopic interest in the details of his reporters' private lives. One reporter sent him a memo announcing he was to be married. He got back four closely typed pages from Hindmarsh giving detailed advice on how to start a home: the exact brand of refrigerator to buy, the kind of heater to install, and the section of the city in which to settle. "He warmed his hands over the fires of other people's lives," a former employee said of him. Hindmarsh, who regularly sent people to the ends of the earth, seldom stirred from the steady day-to-day routine that took him from home to office and back again. Such was his isolation from the world and the men around him that few knew his history or background. Perhaps this was purposeful. One reporter was so terrified of Hindmarsh he was physically unable to speak to him. Then one day he was told Hindmarsh's nickname at school had been "Dogmeat." This regained him his voice.

Hindmarsh was born of Canadian parents in Missouri. His father's people came from Margate, England. His mother's family, the Comforts, were from New England. The father impulse was strong within him, possibly because he never knew his own father. He kept his own family closely around him on his twenty-two-acre estate. One son and two sons-in-law worked at the Star and lived nearby him. When his oldest boy John rebelled, quit the newspaper and went off farming by himself, it was a blow to his father.

Hindmarsh's mother was a strong-willed woman with a fierce, possessive love for her boy. After her husband's death from t.b. she moved back to her former home at St. Thomas, Ontario, where her father Hiram Comfort, a woolen merchant, was the richest man in town. She inherited his wealth and used some of it to indulge her son. (His was the finest cornet in the collegiate cadet band.) Years later when Hindmarsh moved to Toronto she moved with him. She couldn't bear to see him marry. When his betrothal was announced she conscientiously redecorated the house for his bride. The night before the wedding she fled to California.

In her later years she unaccountably took to drink and this too had its effect on her son. Around the *Star* there was a saying that if you took one drink you were fired; if you were a hopeless alcoholic your job was secure. All his life Hindmarsh tried to save his men from drink. Homewood Sanitarium in Guelph and Shadowbrook in Toronto have been called *Star* Annexes. At one time five *Star* reporters were taking the cure. Hindmarsh himself took only one drink in his life: once when he caught cold he accepted a glass of whisky.

In St. Thomas Hindmarsh, living alone with his mother, grew up a shy and somewhat lonely boy. He was fond of cats, dogs, and music and played the violin, bugle and clarinet. He was taunted for playing with girls and this his pride could not stand. He lay in wait for one girl and gave her a thrashing. He kept his love of music and when he instituted the *Star* Hour of Good Music on a Toronto radio station he personally selected the programs, mainly from pieces he remembered as a boy. The program was rehearsed and played daily into his office loudspeaker.

At the University of Toronto he became a

successful debater, president of the History Club, vice-president of his class, a member of the Literary and Scientific Executive and editor of the *Varsity*. Some of his classmates were later to provide grist for the *Star* mill. Two were hanged for murder, one killed himself, one absconded with a client's funds and one, Vincent Massey, became Governor-General. The quotation underneath his picture in the University yearbook baffled every reporter who ever worked for him: "For this," it read, "was the gentlest man and the meekest that ever sat in hall among ladies."

On graduation he went to work for the Toronto *Globe*. Once when a sensitive reporter balked at covering a hanging, Hindmarsh volunteered. On the gallows the prisoner confessed to two more murders. After he dropped, Hindmarsh leaned over the trap and watched fascinated as his toes and fingers twitched their last. Then he rushed below to watch the body cut down. His report was so enthusiastic that Toronto reporters have ever since been barred from covering hangings.

Hindmarsh joined the *Star* in December 1911. Two years later at twenty-six, he was city editor. In 1915 Joe Atkinson, disturbed at the young men flocking about his daughter Ruth, remarked that "Next Sunday I'll bring a *real* man out." The man was Hindmarsh. Ruth rebuffed him at first: she felt her father was thrusting him at her. But Hindmarsh courted her ardently. Eventually they were married and had a close and happy married life.

The gentlest man and the meekest had the iron boiled into his soul by John R. Bone, the *Star*'s scholarly looking but tough managing editor. Bone looked like an elderly Arrow-collar man with his pince-nez and slicked-down hair but his appearance belied him. The picture that dominated the wall of his office was anything but scholarly: a huge copy of a New York tabloid's famous photo of Ruth Snyder dying in the electric chair. He rode Hindmarsh hard. When Bone died in 1928 the new managing edi-

tor's character was cast in a permanent mold.

He was from that day, to all intents and purposes, the dominant personality on the dominant newspaper in Canada. But there was one man he could never dominate and that was his father-in-law. Atkinson was always as close as the buzzer on Hindmarsh's desk, and before the shrill, carping tones of the publisher, the big man was submissive.

The greatest division between him and his father-in-law was over money. Hindmarsh, brought up in comparative luxury, was a spender. Atkinson, who went to work for a living at fourteen, was a saver. When Hindmarsh plunged on a big story, Atkinson made him recoup next month. To do so he had to fire men and cut salaries. A proud man, he took the brunt on his own shoulders. "If you have something unpleasant to do, do it at once," he said. In 1930 he gave thirteen men their notice on Christmas Eve. The act plagued him for years. Each Yuletide a group of ex-employees sent him a Merry Christmas telegram, collect.

But a greater blow came in 1948. Unknown to Hindmarsh, the *Star*'s great writer-and-artist team of Gregory Clark and Jim Frise had decided to go to work for the Montreal *Standard*. Their names and faces were familiar to millions through their Greg-and-Jim feature in the *Weekly*. Their whole lives had been bound up with the paper. On the train back from Montreal one October evening the two old retainers sat glumly. The die had been cast; they were leaving the old sheet. Finally Frise broke the silence. "Greg," he said, "somebody has got to tell Hindmarsh."

"I suppose so," said Clark.

After another silence, Frise spoke again. "Would you tell him, Greg?" he asked.

"Okay, Jim," said Clark.

More gloomy silence. Finally Frise spoke. "Greg?"

"Yes, Jim?"

*"Tell him on Christmas Eve."*

136

HAROLD HORWOOD

# The People Who Were Murdered for Fun

The story of the Newfoundland Indian-hunters is one of the most brutal and little-known chapters in the history of Canada. Fishermen from England and France who colonized the island in the seventeenth century found it already inhabited by a race of tall, fair Indians, who called themselves "Beothucks" (pronounced *Bay-oh-thucks*). They were a gentle and peaceful people, who at first welcomed the white settlers as friends. Nevertheless, within a few years they were being hunted and shot as remorselessly as the wolves and caribou which roamed the interior barrens.

Beautiful Alexander Bay, lying partly within Terra Nova National Park on Newfoundland's east coast, is a spot where Beothuck stone tools may still be dug from the sands by souvenir hunters. Until recently this serene stretch of landlocked water was known as "Bloody Bay," because its waters once ran red with the blood of Indians slain there by white men.

The Beothucks, who were never armed with any weapons deadlier than bows and arrows, were hunted first because they were considered a nuisance, and later for the sport of pursuing and killing such elusive game. A Beothuck came to be regarded as the finest "big game" prize the island of Newfoundland had to offer, and it was a common saying among the fishermen that they would rather shoot an Indian than a caribou.

During the early years of the Indian-hunting period northern Newfoundland was settled by outlaws. Government of the colony was arranged to favor a floating population of fishermen from western England. These people arrived each spring and left each fall with cargoes of fish. They were forbidden to take up permanent residence in the island, and ships' captains were subject to a fine for each person they failed to bring back to England.

Every ship then carried a number of women crew members—usually from four to six. Both men and women lived lives of semi-slavery under indenture to their fishing "masters," and were often glad to escape, even to the wild life of the Newfoundland coast. So the island was gradually populated with families of deserters. The British navy was sometimes sent to round up such deserters, and as late as 1800 a few of them were caught and hanged from the yard-arm of a British man-o'-war.

In the wild northern parts of the island, to which these people fled, there was, for more than a century, no law whatsoever—no courts or police, nor any churches or schools. The settlers lived by catching salmon and trapping fur. They dressed mostly in sealskins, making their own boots, mitts and caps. There are people still living who remember wearing sealskin trousers as children. They lived by their guns —shooting their own meat at all seasons: seals in the spring, ducks and geese in summer and fall, caribou and partridge in the winter.

Trouble was inevitable between people so rough and lawless as the settlers and people so simple and unsophisticated as the Beothucks and there were clashes almost from the beginning. The organized killings began in 1613 and lasted until 1823. It is doubtful if any other native tribe anywhere suffered such systematic persecution for so long a time. During the first hundred and fifty-six years the murder of a Beothuck was not even a crime punishable by law and, even after the government declared it a breach of the King's peace, to be punished by hanging, the Indian-hunters continued to operate with complete impunity. No one was ever punished for killing a Beothuck.

This is how it started: John Guy of Bristol, who had founded the first official English colony in Newfoundland, established friendly trade with the Beothucks in 1612, and made an agreement to return by ship at a certain time the next summer to exchange trade goods for all the furs the tribe could collect.

Word was passed from band to band that winter, and all the Beothucks sent trading representatives, loaded with caribou hides and small furs. Several hundred Indians waited at the appointed place in Trinity Bay while the time for the meeting came and passed. About a week after Guy's expected arrival a ship sailed into the bay and hove to in the lee of the point where the Beothucks were gathered. Thinking Guy had returned, they began a wild celebration, dancing on the shore, launching their canoes, and paddling excitedly toward the vessel.

Into the midst of this sudden rejoicing fell sudden death. The Indians were met with a broadside of grape shot, which ripped their boats, killed some of the men, and sent the rest fleeing into the forest in panic, believing that the men who had made a treaty of trade with them the year before had turned traitors and murderers. Forever afterward the natives had a superstitious dread of firearms, and one or two white men armed with muskets could easily put a hundred Beothucks to flight.

The ship, of course, had no connection with Guy. The men on board supposed that the natives on the beach were doing a war dance, and assumed that those in the canoes were launching an attack. They congratulated themselves on having successfully beaten off the "murderous redskins."

Even this terrible mistake might have been put right in time, had it not been for a growing enmity between the two races. This enmity sprang from totally divergent views on property. The English and French were fiercely jealous of their possessions. To the Beothucks a man's stature was measured by his success in the hunt and his wisdom in the tribal council. "Personal property" to them meant only clothes, fire stones, and amulets. All other property was more or less public.

So the Beothucks started "borrowing" gear from the white men's fishing stages, just as they would borrow hunting gear from another Indians' camp. The white men organized expeditions to take back their lost property by force. To the uncivilized fishermen it seemed almost a law of nature that a man had a right to kill anyone who stole from him.

Thus the organized Beothuck-hunts began. The profit motive was soon added to the motive of revenge, for a raided Indian camp often yielded hundreds of caribou hides and other valuable furs. But what started as a dispute over property soon turned into a bloody and cruel sport. Settlers used to refer to the number of "head of Indians" they had killed, and the phrase "go look for Indians" became a sporting byword similar to "go look for partridge." Successful hunters cut notches on the butts of their guns to keep tally of the number of "head" they had killed. It was decided quite early in the game that a woman or a child counted equally with a man and deserved a full notch.

In a lifetime of killing Indians some of the musket-toting settlers rolled up an impressive total. One man named Rodgers, living at Twillingate, boasted that he had killed sixty Beothucks. This man's last successful Indian-hunt took place in 1817, when he and two other white men ambushed a party of nine. They maimed all but one of the Indians by discharging three loads of buckshot "into the thick of 'em." The one who was still able to run dived into the water and tried to swim to a nearby island. But Rodgers launched his canoe, gave chase, and killed the man in the water with his axe.

Meanwhile his friends were using their axes to finish off the other Indians, who were squirming in their blood on shore. All nine corpses were left in a heap, and the bones later viewed by a government agent, to whom Rodgers recounted the adventure. He was not punished, or even brought to trial, for his part in this atrocity.

A trapper named Noel Boss claimed the honor of being the most successful Beothuck-hunter, with ninety-nine men, women and children to his credit. He almost succeeded in killing his hundredth victim—a little girl named Shananditti, whom he hit with a load of buckshot as she fled across the Exploits River. She escaped, wounded, into the woods, and lived to become famous, several years later, as "the last Beothuck." Boss later fell through the ice of Grand Lake and drowned, much to the sorrow of his many friends in Notre Dame Bay.

Until recently most of the stories of Indian-hunting in Newfoundland were based upon traditions handed down for many generations in the families of settlers. However, when the archives of the first Earl of Liverpool went on sale, a most important paper came to light. Now known as "the Liverpool manuscript," it contains long, first-hand accounts of the Indian-hunters' adventures. Compiled in 1792, it shows that the stories preserved by word of mouth were in no way exaggerated.

A master fisherman and his "shareman" once surprised a Beothuck mother on a beach, as she carried her four-year-old boy on her back. They both fired at once, the double load of swan shot hitting her in the loins. She collapsed, and crawled into the woods, holding one hand over the mortal wound. The two fishermen then made off with the child.

They sold the boy, and he was sent to England where he was exhibited at several fairs in Poole and other western towns, for an admission price of tuppence. He was named John August, as August was the month in which he was captured. Later he was sent back to Newfoundland, and became the master of a fishing boat at Trinity. But like most Beothucks who tried to live in civilization, he caught tuberculosis. He died at thirty-eight.

This example of a child's life being spared was the exception and not the rule. Most fishermen believed in "killing the nits with the lice," as they used to phrase it. So after shooting a party of Beothuck men and women, they would round up the children and cut their throats. Atrocities of this sort are on the written record, attested by British naval officers sent on expeditions to Notre Dame Bay during this period.

Several cases of complete indifference to the sufferings of wounded children are recounted in the Liverpool manuscript:

John Moore of Trinity and a hunting party "surprised" a woman and two children in the woods. The woman knelt and exposed her breasts, as was the custom of Beothuck women when giving themselves up to death. The hunters killed her and wounded the two children, who ran into the bushes and hid. They made a search and found one child, "which died on one of the men's shoulders before they reached the brook."

Though most Beothucks were killed singly or in small parties, there were some killings which rank as full massacres. It was the custom of fishermen and trappers, whenever they came upon an Indian village, first to loot it of everything of value, and then to burn the *meoticks,* with all their contents. The greatest recorded exploit of this nature was undertaken by two men from Notre Dame Bay, who made a winter journey of more than a hundred miles to destroy the headquarters of the tribe at Red Indian Lake.

They took the Beothuck village completely by surprise, as the people lay asleep in the early morning. More than a hundred men, women and children were driven out on the frozen lake. Except for a few who had snatched up their sleeping furs as they ran, the Beothucks were stark naked. They retreated into the woods before the musket fire of the two white men, who then loaded a sledge with everything they cared to take from the *meoticks,* and finished by setting fire to everything that remained. The naked Indians were left to die of exposure and starvation in the dead of winter.

The largest massacre of Beothucks took place near Hants Harbor, Trinity Bay. There a group of fishermen, armed for hunting, managed to trap a whole tribe of Beothucks, driving them out on a peninsula which juts into the sea. They did not make an exact count of the number killed, but reported it to be "about four hundred."

In the early stages of this "war" the Beothucks fought back. They once organized a party of eighty men and descended upon the French fishermen of northern Newfoundland, who had armed a sloop-of-war for the express purpose of driving the Beothucks off the coast. At St. Julien's the Indians found a boat's crew piling fish, and killed seven of them. Cutting off the heads as trophies (the Beothucks seldom took scalps) they crossed the hill into the next cove, where they killed nine more Frenchmen.

Sixteen of the Indians then dressed in the fishermen's clothes, and next day appeared at Croc Harbor. There they found twenty-one men working at their fish, and slew the lot of them. They stuck the thirty-seven heads on poles, and went back to the woods. Not a single Beothuck had been killed in the raid.

So far as is known, the Beothucks never molested any man who had not taken up arms against them first. And in the whole two hundred years of their slow extermination by the whites, they never harmed a white woman or a white child.

Late in the eighteenth century the government adopted a "save the Beothucks" policy, but, apart from issuing proclamations, nothing was done until 1800. In that year a reward of fifty pounds sterling was offered to "him that shall bring a Red Indian captive." The plan was to entertain the captive in St. John's at government expense and then send him home, loaded with presents, and bearing the message of the white man's new-found good will. It was a plan which had worked well for Cartier a century and a half earlier in the St. Lawrence basin.

Fifty pounds seemed a fortune to the rude trappers of Notre Dame Bay, but no one ever managed to take a Beothuck man alive. Five women were taken at one time or another, and the reward claimed, but none of those women ever got back to the tribe. One was murdered by her captor on the way back, and the other four died of tuberculosis while in captivity.

Indeed, the government policy of taking captives was made the excuse for killing the last important Beothuck chief and his brother, at a time when their leadership seemed to have halted the tribe's march toward extinction. It happened in 1819, when John Peyton Jr. led an expedition to Red Indian Lake to take captives. Peyton surprised a small group of Indians out on the ice of the lake and managed to overtake one woman and seize her. This happened to be Demasduit, the wife of the chief, Nonosbawsut. The chief tried to rescue his wife, but was stabbed in the back with a bayonet and then shot through the chest. His brother, who also made a gallant rescue attempt, was cut down by a musket ball.

Nonosbawsut was a magnificent, bearded giant of a man. They measured him where he lay dead on the ice. He was six feet, seven and a half inches tall. His widow died after less than a year in captivity. Peyton and his gang were brought to trial for this murder and abduction, but the jury ruled that they had acted in self-defense. Peyton was appointed a magistrate, held court in Twillingate and lived to a ripe old age as "the first citizen of the north."

The last Beothucks were killed and captured in 1823, when the tribe was reduced to seventeen. The remnant were starving that winter, and with the approach of spring a small party, consisting of a man and his daughter, his sister and his two nieces, set out for the coast, to give themselves up to the white men, in the hope of receiving food.

On the coast they separated, the father and daughter going one way, the woman and her two daughters another. The man and the girl met two trappers named Curnew and Adams near a place called New Bay. The man approached them in an attitude of supplication. One of them raised his musket and shot the Indian through the chest with a ball. He collapsed on the snow, and died without a sound.

His daughter then came forward slowly, opening the deerskin robe which covered her breast. She sank to her knees and tore her dress to the waist. She remained in the attitude, eyes turned upward, hands holding back the torn flaps of deerskin, while the two men drew nearer, raised their guns, and shot her through the heart. Like her father, she died on the snow without a sound.

The other three women found a second hunting party headed by William Cull, a famous Indian-hunter who had discovered that a live Indian was worth a lot more than a dead one. He took them captive and claimed the hundred and fifty pounds reward. The old woman and her elder daughter died that summer. Indeed, they were not far from death when captured by Cull. The younger girl was taken to Twillingate and became a domestic servant in the home of John Peyton Jr., where she lived for five years. This girl was Shananditti, the last of the Beothucks, for the twelve people left in the woods had completely disappeared.

In 1828, when Shananditti was dying of tuberculosis, she was taken to St. John's. There, between bouts of illness, she recorded what she knew of the history and mythology of her people. She died in hospital in the spring of 1829. Though, like all her people, she had lived and died a pagan, she was nevertheless buried in the Church of England graveyard on the south side of St. John's.

Her grave was later dug up to make way for a new road, and even her bones were lost.

DUNCAN McLEOD

# Nineteenth-Century Niagara

When Wild Bill Hickok, the legendary western scout and gunfighter, arrived in Niagara Falls, Ontario, as the star of the world's first wild-west show, he looked like almost any other prosperous visitor in a neat business suit—without his colorful frontier trappings or his fabled pearl-handled .44's. But Wild Bill walked with both hands in his pockets where he carried two small but deadly derringers.

His caution was well taken. Hickok was the continent's most notorious target—he had killed eighty men—and the Front facing the Canadian Falls was, in 1872, the playground and workshop of some of the continent's worst scoundrels. It became so infamous that many tourists were afraid to go there. Visitors were so systematically humbugged, swindled, blackmailed and bullied that newspapers in both Canada and the United States tarred the resort with their blackest prose, vaudeville comics made wry jokes about it, poets wrote rhymes about the mulcting of the innocents, guidebooks warned of the dangers awaiting the gullible, and angry voices were raised against it in the New York state legislature.

From 1825 to 1888 the mile-long Front, stretching from what is now Oakes Gardens to Table Rock at the brink of the Falls, was one of the most ruthless and ingenious clip joints in history. Originally it was a military reserve of Upper Canada, but piecemeal—except for a government road—it was taken over by a group of businessmen and showmen. To attract customers to their taverns, hotels, museums, bazaars and curio shops they sailed wild animals in schooners over the Falls, staged an elaborate Indian burial ceremony and a farcical buffalo hunt—with Wild Bill Hickok in charge—and they encouraged or hired daredevils to jump into the raging river or walk across the

Gorge on tightropes. They also perpetrated some of their country's most blatant hoaxes.

Derby-hatted sharpers imported white pebbles from England and sold them to visitors as congealed Niagara spray. At Burning Spring, where natural gas bubbled through the water and could be set afire, tourists bought bottled water, and found out later of course that it didn't burn. One forgotten curio dealer launched the legend of Niagara Falls as a honeymoon resort by telling his customers the story of a beautiful Indian princess thrown into the Falls to become the bride of a god who dwelt in the mist and spray. He also sold them paintings and medallions of a bare-bosomed princess.

The Front itself, squeezed between the Niagara escarpment and the Gorge, was only three hundred yards wide, but in character it was almost as unbridled as its strange inhabitants. From the spidery suspension bridge spanning the Gorge to Table Rock, there were six large and, for those days, magnificent hotels—the Clifton House, Robinson House, Brunswick House, Museum House, Prospect House and Table Rock House. Scattered between them were souvenir stands, taverns, refreshment booths and a forest of Indian tepees. In the middle of the Front stood Colonel Thomas Barnett's Museum, a costly ($150,000) ornamental stone building filled with everything from Egyptian mummies to Mohawk arrowheads. In a park surrounding the museum were buffalo, rare flowers, rattlesnakes and raccoons, among other attractions."

At tollhouses guarding the roads to the Front along the escarpment, sightseers were charged a fee just to enter this curious Casbah, and inside they were boldly robbed and cheated on almost every side. Barkers dressed like Mississippi gamblers in checkered waistcoats, tight pants and carrying yellow Malacca canes

141

marched along the Front in raucous hordes, shouting the merits of this or that hotel or tavern, trying to lead visitors to tepees where Irish "Indians" in feather headdress and beaded leggings sold cheap and often spurious handicraft for whatever they could extract from their customers.

There were barkers for the rattlesnakes, the Egyptian mummies, Indian antiquities and Niagara spray, barkers for the firewater in the bars, for the false firewater sold at Burning Spring and for the battlegrounds of the War of 1812, just a few hundred yards from the Front. Other barkers lured the curious or the witless to see the Whirlpool and the Lower Niagara Rapids from Termination Rock at the base of the Falls, where guides charged you nothing to go down but made you pay a "ransom" to get up again. And through the dust and din of the whole Front, hackies drove visitors to the hotels and taverns or other stopping places, where they later collected a percentage of any money solicited or stolen from their passengers.

After a visit to the Front in 1871 Henry James, the American author, wrote in disgust: "The spectacle you have come so far to see is choked with horribly vulgar shops, booths and catch-penny artifices which have pushed and elbowed to within the very spray of the Falls. The inopportunities one suffers here amid the central din of the cataract from hackmen, photographers and vendors of gimcracks is simply hideous and infamous. Their cries at times drown out the thunder of the cataracts."

Often the cries of the victims were even louder. Some were beaten when they refused to pay a ransom to get out of the Front's more infamous establishments. The Table Rock House, a curio shop and hotel operated by "Old Sol" Davis and his several sons and daughters, was openly described as "the den of the forty thieves" by the Hamilton *Evening Times*. Davis sued the *Times* for libel, and at the trial several visitors to the Front, including women, testified that they had been threatened or beaten or forced to pay ransoms in Davis's place.

The Front, with its cupidity and crookedness, could not have survived in a more sophisticated era, but in the Canada of 1825 it would have been surprising if it had not flourished. For the hayseed with straw in his hair was not only a literal reality but, with the rube and the hick, he represented the average Canadian. It was an age of which P. T. Barnum later said, "There's a sucker born every minute, and two to take him." Upper Canada had only 130,000 people; Kingston was the biggest town (2,336); London had not yet been founded and Ottawa was still called Bytown. The United States fron-

tier had just reached the Mississippi and the midwest still belonged to the Indians.

In such a backwoods most of the social pleasures were improvised. A barn-raising, a wedding, an auction or a revival meeting was the occasion for a celebration. These affairs were usually accompanied by roisterous square dancing as fiddlers scraped out such tunes as "Money Musk," "Old Dan Tucker" and "Pop Goes the Weasel." Whisky was twenty-five cents a gallon, and fighting, gambling and drunkenness went with almost every public gathering.

Any excuse for a holiday from farm work or land clearing was seized eagerly, so when the enterprising tavern keepers and merchants at the Front began to stage their stunts thousands came by oxcart over muddy roads through the bush, by Lake Ontario schooners and by flatboats up the Erie Canal to join the fun.

The first man to appreciate the commercial possibilities of the Front was a farmer named William Forsyth. He owned land above the escarpment, and in 1817 he built a hotel on it and ran a fence down to Table Rock, overlooking the Horseshoe Falls. Only guests at the hotel were permitted inside the fence to view the Falls from this superior vantage point. When Sir Peregrine Maitland, the lieutenant-governor of Upper Canada, ordered him to remove the fence from military property, he refused. Maitland sent a squad of soldiers and they tore it down. Forsyth promptly sued for damages.

The suit dragged on and Forsyth, running short of money, sold his hotel and the property above the escarpment to Samuel Street, a wealthy and politically influential neighbor. From a later lieutenant-governor, Sir John Colborne, Street got a license to occupy the military reserve. The government kept only a sixty-six-foot-wide strip along the bank of the Gorge for a public road, but Street was told he could not place any obstruction along the Front.

Street's answer was to call together a group of businessmen and propose a City of the Falls. They built a railway to bring Americans down the Canadian side of the Niagara River from Buffalo, and they began putting up baths, hotels, souvenir stands, taverns and a museum. When Colborne heard about it he ordered the army to halt the work. The officer in charge, remembering the Forsyth suit, had his men remove only one stone from a fence. Street sued the government for trespassing, was awarded five hundred pounds, got a deed to the whole Front and the government was left with only its road.

That was the start of a wild tawdry seventy years on the Front. In addition to the cataract itself, the first big attractions at Niagara were the battlefields of the War of 1812. Nine hundred men had been killed at Lundy's Lane, about a mile from the Falls, and Street and his friends provided guides for visitors. Street also built a pagoda, a towerlike affair from which his patrons could view the countryside without walking or riding in a carriage. When the lure of the battlefields wore thin, the promoters groped for a new attraction. In the summer of 1827, in towns and villages on both sides of the border, handbills appeared with a startling notice: "The pirate ship 'Michigan' on the eighth day of September will sail down the deep and furious rapids of the Niagara and over the precipice and into the abyss below with a cargo of furious animals."

When the day came the Canadian bank of the Gorge and the rapids was black with sightseers. The excitement mounted as word swept down their ranks that the "Michigan" had been cast loose. On board were stuffed effigies of several notables, a buffalo, three bears, two foxes, a raccoon, a dog, a cat and four geese. All except the buffalo were loose on the deck.

On the ship's bowsprit was the American ensign; at her stern, the British Jack. People with field glasses could see the foxes running around the deck in terror; the two bears climbed a mast, didn't like it there and jumped overboard. The crowds cheered as they struggled to reach shore and shouted in glee as they finally climbed up the bank and vanished into the forest.

Then the "Michigan," her sails billowing, struck the rapids. She pitched and shook—and broke into pieces. A cry of disappointment went up from the bank. All that could be seen going over the Falls were bits of wreckage. These were later salvaged and sold as souvenirs.

Among those who witnessed the Michigan's last trip was Sam Patch, of Rochester, N.Y., who had made a local reputation by jumping off bridges and other high places into rivers. Patch announced he would jump off a hundred-foot ladder into the river below the Falls. The merchants on the Front quickly rushed out handbills and thousands gathered on the Front. Then the merchants announced that Sam had broken his leg. By that time it was too late for many to go home and they had to stay overnight in the expensive hotels and inns. The next day Sam appeared, sound of limb, and made his leap. But the Front had wrung two days' lodging and food out of thousands and many angry visitors cried "Hoax!"

It was one of the first, but far from the last, swindles worked on tourists at the Front. One guide showing a visitor around the base of the Falls picked up a white stone one day.

"What's that?" asked the tourist.

"Why," said the guide, suddenly inspired, "it's congealed mist. Very rare."

The tourist bought the stone for three dollars, and the Niagara Spray racket soon became one of the most popular and profitable at the Falls. When the guides could no longer find this variety of white stone, souvenir dealers found there were mountains of it in Derbyshire, England, and began importing it.

One souvenir dealer with a slow-moving supply of medallions and paintings of Indian maidens hatched the idea of building a myth around them. The maiden, he told customers, was a princess sent over the Falls as a bride for a god who lived there. Although North American Indians never have sacrificed human beings to their gods, the gullible public liked the story and romantic women took it to their hearts.

Soon honeymooners began coming to the Falls. The astute merchants encouraged the legend and named the spume of mist in the cataract The Bridal Veil. In 1846, when the first little boat sailed around the bottom of the Falls, it was named the Maid of the Mist, and so were all its successors. Oscar Wilde visited the Falls in 1883, observed the honeymooners and then the cataract, and wrote pointedly: "This must be the second major disappointment of American married life."

Many of these smaller hoaxes were in good fun, and it's almost certain the public helped them along to some extent, as people do today at carnivals. But organized robbery, extortion and swindling—often helped by hoodlums and strong-arm boys—was a different thing. It became the rule on the Front, brought the whole resort into ill repute and finally helped to kill it.

The key man in this skin game was the hack driver, usually an obsequious creature who picked up visitors on their arrival by train and offered to show them the sights for a small fee. He drove them to the Whirlpool and the Lower Gorge and finally landed them at Table Rock House, the headquarters of "Old Sol" Davis and his clan. From there, stairs led to Termination Rock; nearby were Burning Spring and Colonel Barnett's Museum.

Barnett, enterprising and honest, charged a straight fifty-cents admission, but at all the other places sight-seers were told there was no fee. Inside, however, tawdry saleswomen sold worthless knickknacks at fancy prices, and visitors had to pay pug-ugly doormen anything from fifty cents to two dollars to get out again. From the owners of these places the hackies collected fifty per cent of the money extorted from customers, and when the ride was over they charged their passengers whatever the traffic would bear.

As the systematic swindle continued through the Fifties tourists became more and more wary of the Front, and the merchants began to look for new lures. In 1859 they found a prize one in Jean François Gravelet, known as Blondin, a tightrope artist who did incredible things on his rope above the Gorge. He ran, turned somersaults, lay down, put baskets on his feet, while a hundred thousand people gasped and hundreds of gentlewomen fainted.

Blondin started a new golden era for the Front. Other tightrope experts and daredevils followed, though none were as expert as Blondin. Railway excursions came to the Falls from the American midwest and from New York. The merchants prospered and the crooks got even richer.

In 1867 the Front's reputation was blacker than ever. In the New York legislature a resolution was passed protesting to Canadian authorities "the outrages on American citizens at Niagara Falls." The Toronto *Telegram* countered that the worst outrages were perpetrated by a "Yankee and a scoundrel, Sol Davis."

Then the Hamilton *Evening Times* referred to "the robbers at Niagara—the cave of the forty thieves, otherwise known as the Table Rock House and kept by the notorious Sol Davis and his progeny." It was a dangerous locality for strangers, said the *Times*.

Old Sol promptly sued, and now, for the first time, the ruthlessness and crudity of the swindles and extortions on the Front began to come to light. At the trial witnesses came forward and told how they had been robbed and threatened, and sometimes beaten, if they refused to pay a ransom to get out of the Davis establishment.

"Enter . . . all is free," they had been told by an oily individual when they went in. Then . . .

Dr. E. P. Miller, New York City, said he refused to pay four dollars for going to Termination Rock, and he was caught by the whiskers by one man, the throat by another, pushed out of the door and thrown to the ground. He was in bed for six weeks.

S. L. Kilbourne, a lawyer from Lansing, Michigan, had to pay $4.50 for a photograph worth fifty cents. He thought it was a joke, but when Sol Davis gave a whistle and two "large Ethiopians and two equally large Irishmen" charged into the room, he changed his mind and paid.

John Crist, from Lockport, N.Y., when told he had to pay five dollars, made a dash for the door, but was caught and flung back. "Here is one dollar in my purse," he wailed. "It's all I have except a quarter. I'll give you all I have."

"You're a damned pretty fellow to come all the way to the Falls with only a dollar in your pocket," cried Davis. "You'll stay here until you pay."

"Is there no law in Canada that will give me redress?" cried Crist.

One of Davis's sons shook his fist in Crist's face and cried: "That's the law in Canada, and we're the officers to carry it out."

John Weir, a farmer near Peterborough, refused to pay four dollars and was threatened by Davis who said: "Damn you, I have something here that will put a window through you." Weir paid.

Even the American consul at Niagara Falls was a victim. W. Martin Jones told how he had gone to the Falls with his wife and a secretary of the Department of State in Washington. A man named Jess Burkin opened their carriage door at the Table Rock House and said: "Ladies and gentlemen, please step out. All is free."

Jones told him to close the door as he knew the character of the house. Burkin then "commenced to use language I would not like to repeat and threatened to throw me over the bank into the Gorge. He went away and returned with Edward Davis, son of the proprietor, who also threatened to throw me over the bank."

The jury took only three minutes to decide that the *Times* was not guilty of maligning Davis's reputation.

As a result of the trial the Canadian government, which owned the entrance from the road, canceled Davis's license to guide tourists to Termination Rock. Davis then made plans to blow off part of the rock so he could build a staircase outside the government's property. He had the dynamite ready when Colonel Barnett tipped off the authorities. Enraged, Davis sued Barnett for perjury, but lost again in the courts.

Now, like a disgraced and jaded rake, the Front became the butt of wits and rhymers—the last stop before oblivion. By 1870 many tourists were afraid to go there. Tightrope walkers had lost their appeal. Colonel Barnett thought he saw the solution in an Indian burial ceremony to attract sight-seers to his museum. He imported Indians togged out in ceremonial dress and painted to the eyebrows and he displayed a coffin reported to contain the ashes of twenty Indians unearthed from a mound near Queenston where they had lain for a thousand years. It was pretty tame fare for tourists accustomed to boatloads of "furious animals" and death-defying stuntmen, and what was supposed to have been a serious ritual was greeted with whimsical good humor by a small crowd. Barnett admitted the venture was a flop and looked around for something more exciting.

The great buffalo hunts of the western plains had excited public imagination in the United States. Barnett got the idea of staging a buffalo hunt at Niagara Falls and sent his son Sydney west to hunt buffalo and hire some performers. In Kansas City he met Wild Bill Hickok and engaged him to manage the show. He also hired some Sac and Fox Indians and Mexican cowboys.

When Wild Bill arrived at the Front, Blondin was forgotten. The frontiersman, with his long blond hair, broad shoulders, handsome features and his amazing record of gun victories, was quickly made a hero. He was not a show-off, but when one day he walked into a bar and saw a friend asleep in a chair, he fired between his feet with a derringer. When his friend didn't bat an eye Wild Bill roared with laughter and the incident became the talk of the town.

On August 28 about three thousand people gathered to see the Great Buffalo Hunt. The arena was an enclosure of about eighty acres above the Horseshoe Falls, fenced with ten-foot-high boards. In the centre two buffalo bulls grazed peacefully. In a far corner of the enclosure were four Texas steers. Cheers went up as Wild Bill, dressed in buckskin-fringed frontier costume, rode into the arena followed by four Mexican vaqueros and three Indians. After saluting the crowd, the little band rode out to do battle. The buffalo turned docilely and watched the cowboys riding about hallooing. Finally one stepped defiantly toward his adversaries. With his huge head and beard he seemed of enormous proportions in contrast to the prairie ponies. For a while he charged the cowboys, as the crowd gasped. Then a vaquero lassoed one of his feet. At that moment a second Mexican and his pony were knocked over by the enraged animal and it seemed to the horrified spectators as if the buffalo was only stopped from killing both rider and pony by the lasso, held by several straining cowboys. Another lasso was thrown over his horns and the struggle ended.

The other buffalo was lassoed in the same way but broke the rope. Indians approached him on foot and on horseback, shooting blunt arrows. For a time the buffalo pursued one of the vaqueros, but the sport degenerated into a farce when it became evident that he was driven by a motley crowd of Indians, white men and boys. At last he was left in his ignominy on the grounds.

The Great Buffalo Hunt received a bad press. One correspondent wrote that it was a mere sham. "Many of the Indian chiefs had to take a buffalo by the horns to make him run. Wild Bill managed by the aid of his satellites to secure a cow, which had to be goaded into desperation before it would run. The chase after the Texan cattle was also a farce, since the Indians were evidently chasing a cow that had been roaming about for the last two years in the pastures of some peaceful agriculturist."

A second hunt was held two days later, but the effect was no better. Four buffalo were turned loose, but they had to be goaded to gallop. Three, it turned out, were from Colonel Barnett's museum park. Artistically and financially, the whole venture was a flop, Barnett was forced into bankruptcy and his museum sold to his old enemy, Sol Davis.

For the whole Front, the Great Buffalo Hunt was also the end. The public felt it had been cheated once too often and refused to go back. In 1888 the Ontario government expropriated the Front and created a public park. Souvenir stands, hotels, taverns, tepees—all were torn down and flowers and grass planted in their place.

In 1901 Mrs. Anna Edson Taylor went over the Falls in a barrel, and lived, and there was a slight, renewed flurry of excitement, but it didn't last. For years she sat on a street in Niagara signing autographs for pennies, and eventually she died in a poorhouse. Four others—Bobby Leach in 1911, Charles Stephens in 1920, Jean Lussier in 1928 and William (Red) Hill Jr. in 1951—went over the Falls and Stephens and Hill died in the attempt. In each case the old memories of Blondin and Wild Bill were revived, but only for a day.

Today the raucous roistering Front is scarcely recognizable in quiet Queen Victoria Park with its green lawns and colorful flowers where even an Eagle Scout isn't permitted to sell an apple on Boy Scout Day. But in a nearby souvenir shop you can buy a little white stone for a dollar. It's really imported from England, but ask the salesgirl what it is and she'll tell you: "It's congealed mist from the Falls."

ERNEST BUCKLER

# The Quarrel

Do you know what quarreling is like between a man and a woman to whom the language of quarreling is an alien tongue?

When you go outside from the kitchen afterward, if you are the man, the leaves wave absently in the movement of the August air that is more heat than breeze; and everything you work with, the fork or the scythe or the handle of the plow, sags, heavy to the touch. Your thoughts stumble inside your head, and time comes inside and hurts there. You think it must be noon a dozen times, but scarcely an hour has passed.

If you are the woman, you reach into the corners of the zinc beneath the stove legs as carefully as ever with the broom, and stoop as carefully as ever to pick up the twist of white thread embedded in the raised roses of the hooked rug, but the rug doesn't seem like anything your own hands ever made. You were going to have a change for dinner, but it's too late now; there is a cast of irrevocable lateness about everything. You catch a glimpse of your face in the mirror over the sink, and it seems as if the mirror must be lying, to show it enclosed and with shape. You press the tip of the flatiron into the fancy points of rick-rack braid on the apron, but you don't feel the inner smile that was always there at a thing that was extra trouble to be made pretty.

The kitchen and the fields go dead, with a kind of singing remoteness. And when the hum of the anger has died completely away, there is nothing left—nothing but that curious drawing between you, as if you were tied together with an invisible cord on which all the minutes were strung to intolerable heaviness, but never to actual breaking.

I didn't know that all this was happening between mother and father that Saturday morning, of course, because I was only ten. But I knew the day was spoiled. And the next day. I knew what Sunday would be like.

It wouldn't be the perfect August Sunday, the first Sunday after the hay was cut, with the nice hiatus about it as if even the fields knew it was a day of rest, and the tail ends of all the jobs that weren't quite finished lacking the insistence they seemed to have on a weekday. My father would not drowse on the kitchen lounge in the long restoring forenoon, while mother wandered with that special Sunday leisure through her flower garden, pulling a weed here and there, stooping to hold a bright poppy in her hand like a jewel, bringing a dipper of water from the well and holding apart the spicy leaves of the geranium so the roots got all of it, and tiptoeing in past him with a bouquet of the splashy nasturtiums for each of the lamp rests on the organ.

And after dinner, father would not change into the striped drill pants with the size tag still on the waistband and his fine shirt and his fine shoes. Mother would not go upstairs and come down adjusting the wonderfully intricate coral brooch at the neck of her dress. And I wouldn't wait with the thrill of a minor conspiracy, though it was a simple thing, to walk together with them to the garden.

The hay was cut, but we wouldn't walk to the garden with that funny feel of freedom, because, though we could still see the darker-green line of the crooked path we had used through the stringy grass, now our feet could go anywhere they liked. Nor through the garden, where it lay exposed at last to the full kiss of the sun; looking for any cast of ripening in the tomatoes, parting the secrecy of the cucumber vines to see if any fruit lay on the ground beneath, gauging the number of days before the corn would be really yellow, or calling a greeting, smiling though our faces couldn't be

146

clearly seen that far, to a neighbor strolling through his garden the same way.

Father would not change his clothes at all tomorrow. As soon as he had milked and fed the pigs, he would fill his tobacco pouch and get a handful of matches from the canister behind the pantry door and go outside, without asking mother what time she planned to have dinner. She might be doing the chamber work or putting clean newspapers under the rows of preserves down cellar, but she seemed to feel the instant he left the house and I would see her come to the dining room window and watch, in that curious secret way, to see whether he went to the wood lot or the back meadows.

The whole kitchen would seem to catch its breath when his step sounded on the porch again, exactly at noon. As we ate silently, mother would seem to know, without watching, the minute he was ready for his tea; but she'd set it down where he could reach it, she wouldn't pass it to him. And if they both put a hand out for the sugar bowl at the same time, something so tight and awful would strain across the table that I'd feel like screeching.

Right after dinner, father would leave again. Mother would dress up a *little*—I don't think, if she were dying, she could have sat through Sunday afternoon in a housedress—but she wouldn't go outside. She'd be quiet with the catalogue for a bit, but just when I'd think her mind was taken up, she'd drop the catalogue and begin that awful wandering from room to room. As if each familiar thing promised her absorption and then failed her.

When I'd hear her swiveling up the organ stool, her intake of breath, caught before it became a real sigh, and then the first pitifully inaccurate chords of "Abide With Me," I'd rush outside, myself.

And no matter how late I played, or with whom, or at what fascinating game, or no matter how angry I got with myself that I couldn't be insensitive to my parents' quarrels as other kids were, I'd get that awful feeling in the pit of my stomach when I came near the house again that evening. Then we would sit silently, but each moving when another moved, with the Sunday hiatus stifling as a thunder pocket now.

I'd go to bed early, to escape it. But it was no use. I'd listen for the movement of mother taking the clock from the mantelpiece, and start when I heard it. I could see father then, sitting there in the loud-silent kitchen with even the tick of the clock gone, staring at the floor a minute after he had taken off his boots, before he followed her. I would hear the softer than usual pad of his woolen socks on the stairs and then there would be nothing. The very boards

of the old house would seem to sing with that listening stillness.

That's exactly how it turned out to be. I have no trouble to *remember* the particular torture of that day.

You see, that was the August Sunday which was to have been twice as wonderful as ever before because it had in it the looking ahead of a tomorrow more wonderful than any day I had ever known. Monday was the day that we, and we alone from all the village, were going to the Exhibition in Annapolis.

I had never been to the Exhibition before. There was to be a traveling show. (I had studied the poster so long I knew the face of Madame Zelda as well as my own, she who would tell my fortune though she didn't even know I existed.) There was to be a merry-go-round. ("Mother, do they really go as fast as an automobile?") There was to be the excitement of so many strange faces. There was to be ice cream. And those were the days when ice cream was something that made a high priest of the man who scooped it with such incredible nonchalance out of the deep freezer, and it didn't seem as if the ten cents you laid on the counter could possibly pay for it.

I should have had warning of the quarrel. The moments before it had been so perfect.

We had been wrapping the tablecloth of tiny, tiny, intricately mortised blocks, that mother was to enter in the fancywork class. She kept folding it, this way and that, trying to find a way it would not muss; even father hung about the table, wanting to be in on the thing; and I stood there, tingling with willingness to hold my finger on exactly the right place while mother tied the second knots.

She had made a great show of pretending that she'd never have dreamed of sending it in if the others hadn't kept at her, and we never mentioned the possibility of its winning a prize. But in our hearts, none of us had any doubt whatever that it would be the most beautiful thing there and would get first place.

When I took it out to the mailbox, the laborious lettering on the wrapper completed at last, there was that wonderfully *light* feeling in all of us. The moment was so perfect that even the consciousness of its perfection sprang into my mind.

Always before, when this had happened, I had thought of something sad at once, as a sort of protection. If only, I castigated myself afterward, I had not neglected to do that this time. . .

It doesn't matter how this quarrel started. The thing is, their quarrels always ended the same way. Actually, what happened, my father began poking about in the bottom of the dish closet where mother kept the wrapping paper.

"Did you see that sheet of paper with the lumber tally on it?" he said.

"What did it look like?" mother said.

"It was just a sheet of paper with some figures on it," he said.

"Where did you put it?" she said.

"I put it in here," he said. "It ain't here now."

"Let me look," she said. She went through exactly the same papers he had, but she didn't find it.

"It ain't there," father said, with the first hint of annoyance. "I ought to know it when I see it."

Mother looked through all the papers again.

"You didn't burn it with them scraps from the package, did you?" father asked.

"No," mother said, "of course not. I never burn anything that's any good." But she went and looked in the stove just the same. There was nothing but ashes there now.

"Well, what did you stick it *in* there for?" she said suddenly.

"I'd like to know where I'd put anything that—" father said. "You're always burnin' somethin'!"

"Ohhhhhh—" mother said. She sighed. "I wish I'd never bothered with that tablecloth."

"Ohhhhhh—" father said. He started to pace about the kitchen, the way he always did when he was angry. The cat brushed against his legs and he stepped on her tail. Her screech started him so he gave her a kick with his foot. "Git out from under my feet," he said. Mother put the cat outdoors, without saying a word, as if he were a man who was cruel to animals and she couldn't bear to watch it.

"Now I'll have to count that lumber all over again," father said.

"Oh," mother said, "you'd think that was going to kill you—"

I ran out of the house then, because I knew what the rest of it would be like. Now they were both angry beyond embarrassment or caution at their quarreling; whenever they could think of nothing else to say, they'd say something false and cruel. "Oh, no, no one ever gets tired but *you*—" "Well, what do you think it's like for *me*?" "I got feelings, too—"

I ran around in circles outdoors, the whole day burst and tumbling about me. They had broken it, like glass, and no matter how perfectly you fitted the pieces together again, you'd know that the mending was there. I was such a foolish child that when a thing which was to have been perfect was spoiled the least bit, it was spoiled entirely. If I as much as scratched

the paint on my new wagon I wanted to take the axe and smash the whole thing to bits.

I hated them both then, equally. I'd never speak to them again as long as I lived—I'd run away to town—I'd die. . .

We were all up Monday morning before dawn. But it wasn't like other mornings when we'd eaten in the magic minutes of lamplight, preparing to go somewhere special. That awful speechless synchronization of movement between mother and father still went on. She was taking the strain off the clothesline exactly when he set the milk pails beside the scalded creamer. His blue serge suit was laid out on the bed just before he went up to dress; and just as he was walking back through the hallway to the kitchen again, she was on *her* way through the dining room, to dress, herself.

I hated them separately, then. First one and then the other. When father took every cent of his money from the tureen in the dish closet and then came back and asked me (because mother hadn't offered) to brush off the back of his coat, I hated Mother. "Father, why don't you get someone to *help* you mow that old back meadow next week?" I said, loud, so she could hear. When mother came downstairs and took the precious little bottle of perfume from behind the pendulum of the dining-room clock, her face with the same tight look on it that his had, I hated father. "Let *me* take that creamer down cellar," I said. "It's too heavy for you."

There is something about changing one's clothes and the prospect of movement that stales the validity of an old quarrel. I think either of them might have spoken then. But I suppose that whenever father was tempted to speak the watchful drop of acid would touch a spot where his pride was still raw: "The time I set the boiling kettle on the new oilcloth, I said I was sorry, but she made out I did it on purpose just the same— She says *she* has a hard life." And when mother was tempted to speak, the same whisper would stir up the whole wind of forgotten hurts: "The time I scrubbed till I thought my back would break and then he tracked right through the house with his muddy boots on, just because he couldn't keep Tom *Hannon* waiting a minute for that pair of traces in the attic— He says *he* has a hard life." And when they'd let the minute pass, the silence itself had a kind of unshakable fascination.

We had a sixteen-mile drive before us. It was one of those glorious mornings you get sometimes in late August, with a cleanness about it more of spring than of early fall. Little hair nets of dew clung here and there on the glistening grass. The waking call of the birds sounded sharp and new. It would be hot later, very hot, but now it was cool. Dark shadows of the alders fell across the dusty road, cool as shadows inside a well.

We didn't keep saying what a perfect day it was for the Exhibition, though. No one spoke at all. I didn't ask questions about any of the things that had happened in any of the places we passed, waiting with more, rather than less, excitement, because I already knew the answers from so many stories before. It was all right when the horse was jogging. But when he slowed down to a walk, with the spinning of the wheels a sound of scraping only, as if we were bound to the road, the stretches from turn to turn looked endlessly long. The only way I could sit still at all was to pretend that, with hard enough thinking of the town, some elastic tension would draw us suddenly from here to there.

This was the day that was to have been the most wonderful in my whole life . . .

I suppose the moment when we turned the corner by the old blockhouse and first came in sight of the Exhibition itself was most like the moment when the forces of the ingoing and the outgoing tide balance exactly. I think it was then that the quarrel lost all its *color*, like the flame of a lamp that has burned on into the daylight. There suddenly was the high board fence that encircled the actual wonder and all the throng. We became different people.

We seemed to shrink a little, somehow. Each of us could see, helplessly, as if noticing it was a kind of betrayal, that our clothes were Sunday clothes that had stiffened in the midst of the townspeople who had no idea that they were dressed up.

I think mother must have longed to straighten father's tie, and I couldn't help wishing he would put his coat on again, to cover up the sweat marks that edged the straps of his braces. I wished that mother would take off the sprig of fern she had pinned on her coat lapel, so wilted now that the safety pin showed through. I wiped the dust off the shiny round toes of my brown shoes and for the first time I wished they weren't so patently new. I took off the red-banded straw hat I had spent so long tilting at the right angle, and thrust it beneath the tasseled sewing-machine throw that mother had brought along to protect our good clothes.

Mother and I waited at the gate while father put out the horse. I forgot almost everything else then but the excitement to come. I watched the throng of people going in and the trickle of people coming out. It seemed incredible

that there was no change of any kind in their faces the instant they stepped from the inside to the outside. How *could* they not look back, in soberness, or in satiety, or in longing? How could they *bear* to leave while it was still going on?

When father joined us again, silent still, and with that subtle little flicker of adjustment in mother when she saw his approach, we moved toward the ticket window. Just before we got there, he said to her, "Do you want any money?"

I don't know what there was about that question. It was a curiously hurting thing, to have to ask, and to hear. No matter what had happened, the thought of her maybe having not enough *money*, on a day of pleasure—

"I got money," she said.

At last we were inside. I wish I could say that I stayed close with them all that day. But I deserted them almost at once. They moved through the clotted crowd so slowly. The stream of townspeople kept dividing us, and father would step aside to let them pass. I wished he would walk straight ahead and let them move aside for *him*. I was suddenly angry with them because they didn't talk and laugh together as the others did. I left them, though father had given me a bright fifty-cent piece, so much more wonderful than if it had been in small coins, and mother had given me a quarter though I could see there were no bills in her purse at all. I left them because I thought the only way I could savor the wonder utterly was to know it alone.

It's an odd truth that when a child who has played too much alone pictures himself in the scene of a carnival occasion, he is invariably at the hub of its spirit; but when the time actually comes, he finds himself at the farthest point of its periphery. It was like that then.

Not that some of it could have been more wonderful. The ice cream. The ecstasy of the merry-go-round, heightened by the very dread of the horses beginning to slow down. The songs of the cowboys. It was not they, it was I who was singing. But in between the moments when the movement of the magic swung me irresistibly out of my own body, the sea of strange faces was like a kind of banishment. I stood there among them with such a feeling of nakedness that I wondered why they didn't seem to notice it.

When I came to the howdahlike booth of Madame Zelda, the sense of my fortune being a thing between just the two of us was gone altogether. The others crowded so close, and surely everything she said could be heard. I stood there with my quarter tight and ready on my palm, but no matter how often I struck myself cold inside with the certain resolution to speak to her after she was through with that very next person, when my chance came my heart would beat so hotly that I simply couldn't get a word out. An agony of heat and cold alternated inside me until she put her jeweled hands flat on the counter, leaned out, and called, "Have your future prophe-ciiiiiied-a." It seemed she was staring directly into my face. I made a frantic pretense of looking for something I had lost on the ground and moved quickly away.

I joined mother and father again.

We came to the machine that registers your strength by the height a ball shoots upward at the blow of a hammer.

"Try it," I whispered to father. The man before him, a tall man with thin white town arms, had sent it up two-thirds of the way. I wanted father to show them he could send it right to the top.

Father swung the hammer and the ball shot up almost as far as it had gone before, but not quite, and then fell back. "I guess I need more beans for that," he said, half-addressing the men about us. They glanced at him, without smiling, as if they didn't understand what he meant, or as if his futile little joke was out of place. He stepped back, his own tentative smile twitching and drying up on his face.

And it was just after that that a man and a woman went by on mother's side, and we couldn't help hearing the woman whisper to her husband, "Did you get the perfume? I wonder if she took a bath in it. What is it, Cauliflower Blossom?"

The day was very hot now, and our legs were tired. We walked on past the lunch counter where scraps of bitten food lay on the ground with the dust adhering to them, and past the booth where the sweating men waited for a dead-eyed attendant to set up the Kewpie dolls.

"Are you goin' to take the tablecloth home with you?" father said.

"I might as well," mother said.

Father walked ahead, inside the building, to the central bench where the prize-winning objects were displayed, but it wasn't there. Our hearts skipped in dismay. Had it arrived too late? Had it been lost in the mail?

The tablecloth was there all right, but not on that bench. It was back in one corner, half-concealed by a hooked rug. It hadn't won any prize at all. And now all of us could see why. It was *not* as beautiful as the other things. We couldn't help seeing now that the pattern we

had thought so involved was really plain along-side the peacocks in the prize-winning centre-piece and that the texture of its material lacked altogether the light spiderweb delicacy of the other's crochet.

I couldn't stand the silence then. I slipped away, hardly able to keep running before I got outside.

I ran so fast down the steps when I did get outside that I collided head on with a boy from town. We both tumbled. I picked myself up and half-smiled at him.

"Do you want to fight?" he said, coming close and puffing out his body.

"N-no," I said.

"Well, then, watch where you're going," he said.

When mother and father came out of the building, mother with the tablecloth wrapped up under her arm, I said, "Let's go home."

Mother looked at father. "I'm ready when-ever you're ready," she said.

He said, "I'm ready to go whenever you are."

We must have been halfway to the gate before I remembered Madame Zelda. I *couldn't* leave without that. "You go on—" I said.

I ran back toward Madame Zelda's booth without any explanation. The customers had thinned out now. She was sitting sidewise, with her chin cupped in one hand, talking to the man who ran the merry-go-round. I was so close I could hear what she was saying. She said, "If I have to set here and dish out much more o' this tripe in this bloody heat, I'm gonna murder the next one that comes along." I was so close I could see the green mark that the bright ring she was twirling on one finger had left on her hand beneath.

I turned. I couldn't see father and mother anywhere. And then I started to run again. I think if I hadn't caught up with them before they reached the gate, if they had left me in there alone, I'd have burst out crying.

Now here is where I wish for the subtlety to show you, by the light of some single pene-trating phrase, how it was driving home. But I can only hope that you will know how it was, from some experience of your own that was sometime a little like it.

Do you know how my father felt, remember-ing the woman laughing at the perfume mother had thought such a touch of splendor, and thinking of the time he'd known she wanted to go to the magic lantern show in the school-house because she changed her dress right after supper, in case he should offer to take her, but he'd been angry from chasing cows and said

150

nothing, and she'd taken off her good dress again, saying nothing either, because she knew he was tired? Do you know how he felt, remembering the clothes of the town women that he could never afford to buy her the likes of, and thinking how he'd told her she should have *some* men, they'd show her?

Do you know how my mother felt, remembering his face when the town men had made him appear weak and silly about the strength machine, and thinking of the time she'd gone to the cabbage supper alone, giving him to think he was only pretending to be tired, and coming home to see the single plate and the cup without a saucer where he'd got his own supper on the pantry shelf? Do you know how she felt, remembering him spending all his money on us today as if it were not the price of a bag of flour, and thinking how she'd told him that if he had *some* women they'd put him in his boots?

Do you know how I felt, remembering I had wished that father would put his coat on, and thinking of the Christmas when there was hardly money for bread, but when there had been a sled and crayons for me just the same?

Do you?

Perhaps then you will understand why a different kind of silence had mounted all day, sorer still, after the shifting of the tide. Perhaps you will understand what it was like driving along that night, thinking about the tablecloth, but being able to say nothing more to mother than "Let me take that basket over here, out of your way," or "Are you *sure* you got lots of room?"

And perhaps you will see how a point of fusion might be found after all. In the moment after the cat had brushed our legs in an ecstasy of welcome home, and the faithful fields had been found waiting for us, unaltered . . . after we had changed our clothes, father flipping the straps of his overalls so easily over each shoulder; mother tying behind her, without looking, the strings of the apron that seemed to be the very personification of suppertime; and me feeling the touch of the ground on my feet as immediate as the touch of it on hands, when I took off my stiff shoes and went, in my sneakers, for the kindling. Then it was that mother unwrapped the tablecloth and put it on the dining-room table again.

"It's the prettiest thing I ever seen," father said, "I don't care—"

That was the moment of release. Everything of the quarrel vanished then, magically, instantly, like the stiffness of a sponge dipped suddenly in water.

Because he spoke no less truly than with penitence. The tablecloth *was* more beautiful than anything else now—*here*, where it belonged.

I think I saw then how it was with all of us. Not by understanding, of course, but, as a child does sometimes, with the lustrous information of feeling. My father could lift a bale of hay no man at the Exhibition could budge, but there was a knack in a thing like the strength machine he was helpless against. It hadn't been humbleness that made him step aside for the town men to pass, any more than it had been fear that made me retreat from the town boy who wanted to fight. My mother's hat was as lovely as ever, now it was back in the bag in our closet. This sureness when we were home couldn't be transplanted; but that's why, when we had it all about us and in us, like an invisible armor, it was such a crying thing to hurt each *other*.

Bright pictures of the things I had seen that day still echoed like heat lightning in my mind. But they were two-dimensional. Mother coming to the corner of the shop as if she knew just when our feet were beginning to stumble, and telling father to make that the last furrow, she was having dinner a little early— Father edging the borders of the flower garden so perfectly by just his eye, while mother and I stood by with such strange closeness, because this wasn't *his* work at all— Watching the cows race to the tub after a day on the sun-baked marsh, to fill their long throats ecstatically with the cool well water— These things only were real.

I listened to father and mother talking in the kitchen that night, after I had gone to bed. I listened to them coming up the stairs together. I heard father take the change from his pocket and lay it on the bureau. I heard the murmur of their voices, low in the room, like the soft delicious drum of sleep in my ears. I thought of the quarter that had been so miraculously saved from squandering on my fortune —I could buy father a staple puller and mother a mixing spoon with it, for Christmas. I had never been so consciously happy in my whole life.

But I didn't take any chances this time. I repeated the words from my prayer, quickly. intensely, "If I should die before I wake . . . If I should die before I wake . . ."

I awoke and I heard mother and father talking in the kitchen. I thought, the hay is cut, the hay is cut . . . and this morning we will all walk together through the garden. I could feel already the exaltation when I chose the largest stalk and, as they watched, pulled the first new potatoes from the sweet crumbling earth.

RICHMOND P. HOBSON, JR.

# Nimpo

He is a little black range horse with a noticeably dished face. The irregular splash of white that spreads from his wide nostrils almost to his foretop could possibly be called a blaze. His narrow pinched-up body is just as ugly as his face. A good horseman might notice that his eyes have a strange glint in them, unlike those of other horses, but he would never guess that this nondescript twenty-year-old black cayuse is a famous, almost legendary, figure.

Along the trails and around the campfires of northern British Columbia's last cattle range, wherever ranchers and cowhands meet and the inevitable horse talk begins, someone is sure to tell a new one about Nimpo—the cayuse with the indomitable will and the heart that couldn't be broken, the cayuse whose feats of endurance in the face of great odds have earned for him the title of "The Horse That Wouldn't Die."

In the fierce winter of 1929 most of the wild horses west of the Chilcotin district of British Columbia were wiped out. That was one of those rare winters when deep snows were melted by chinook winds, and in turn frozen by terrific cold. Out on lonely icebound meadows and along glassy slopes of shimmering mountains wild horses made their last desperate attempt to survive. The strongest mares and stallions worked close together in semicircles in front of the bands. They used their front feet like sledge hammers, and cracked at the great ice blocks. When they uncovered a little grass they would nibble a mouthful or two, then carry on with their work, leaving what remained for the colts and the weak and dying horses behind them. The stronger animals, their feet and ankles cut to ribbons by the sharp ice, died first, and it was only a matter of time before the weaker ones followed.

On the lower slopes of a mountain called Sugarloaf, more than 200 bush miles beyond Williams Lake, B.C., Nimpo, then a tiny mouse-colored sucking colt, staggered dejectedly beside the withered body of a black mare. He had survived only because of his mother's rich milk which she had produced for him almost to the moment of her death. He lowered his head and with his ice-caked nostrils touched her frozen body. A few paces away, his little half-brother, a bay yearling with white-stockinged legs, pawed feebly at a patch of frozen ground. Slowly the terrible cold crept into the gaunted bodies of the two colts.

Thomas Squinas, son of the chief of the Anahim Lake Indians, was camped with a group of relations at his trap-line cabin on a wild hay meadow a few miles west of Sugarloaf. He was examining a trap on an open knoll at the base of the main mountain when his well-trained eyes picked up an unnatural blur on the distant snow. Long after dark that night his sleigh pulled into camp with the two little colts.

Squinas was a good horseman. He watched the gradual development of the two colts with unusual interest. He was certain that their sire had been a well-bred Arabian stallion which had broken from a ranch in the Chilcotin district and had run for two years with the Sugarloaf wild band, for each of them was short one vertebra, an Arabian characteristic. The two colts formed a strong attachment for each other as they grew up. Unlike other horses of their age they were businesslike and sober. Even as two-year-olds they did little prancing or playing.

They were turned loose with the Squinas *remuda* when the black was a coming three-year-old, and for two years their whereabouts remained a mystery. Early in the winter of

THE CANADA FOREIGNERS DON'T BELIEVE: SCORCHING SUN ON TORONTO ISLAND PICNICKERS

# THE MANY FACES OF CANADA

THE CANADA OF FOREIGN FACES: A VANCOUVER CHINESE TOTES A LOAD IN COOLIE STYLE

THE CANADA WHERE YANKEES RULE: ON THE PROFESSIONAL GRIDIRON AT VARSITY STADIUM

THE CANADIAN WOMAN: SHE CAN SELL CHIC HATS IN
AN ELEGANT MONTREAL SALON OR GUT A FISH WITH
A SMILE IN A NEWFOUNDLAND PACKING PLANT

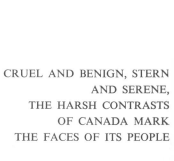

CRUEL AND BENIGN, STERN
AND SERENE,
THE HARSH CONTRASTS
OF CANADA MARK
THE FACES OF ITS PEOPLE

BLUEWATER MEN STRIKE AN ANCIENT POSE AS THEY HAUL NET
ON THE SELDOM-QUIET EASTERN WATERS

INSURANCE SALESMEN SELDOM GET BLISTERS BUT THEY DO
GET ULCERS

IN THE LAND OF CONTRASTS, WORK TAKES A
THOUSAND FORMS—INCLUDING PARKA RANCHING

A NEWFOUNDLAND HOUSEWIFE TAKES UP A SAW
TO MAINTAIN HER VITAL STOCK OF STOVEWOOD

LITHE LUMBERJACKS UNLOCK A JAM AT A MILL
IN BRITISH COLUMBIA. A SLIP MEANS A DUCKING

BEFORE CANADA WAS KNOWN, FISHERMEN TOOK A
LIVING FROM THE TEEMING NEWFOUNDLAND SEAS

EVERY PICTURE TELLS A STORY ON THE BODY
OF THIS SAILOR IN A HALIFAX TATTOO SHOP

GARDENERS PLY THEIR AGE-OLD TRADE AMID THE
RAIN AND SHINE OF VANCOUVER ISLAND

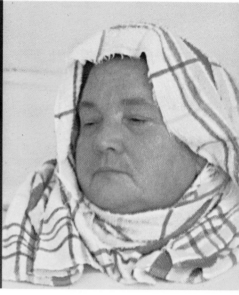

A BALLET DANCER AWAITS HER
CUE ON THE TORONTO STAGE

A WOMAN REDUCING, AGLOW BUT SLEEPY, SHEDS
POUNDS IN AN EDMONTON STEAM-BATH

THE ICE SHOW

MINERS HARVEST THE SALT OF THE EARTH BY
MECHANICAL CUTTERS DEEP IN THE GROUND BENEATH
WINDSOR

A VETERAN COP IN MONTREAL

A VETERAN POSTMAN IN VANCOUVER DECIPHERS
ADDRESSES IN THE CITY'S COLORFUL CHINATOWN

A FISHERMAN OF THE FUTURE, CHUBBY AND CONTENT,
ON THE BARE ROCK OF HIS YARD

A TORONTO WOMAN WAITS ALONE IN THE RAIN AS
INDIFFERENT TRAFFIC HISSES PAST

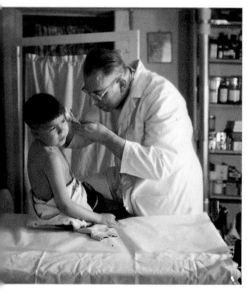

AN INDIAN BOY SUBMITS TO THE CARE OF A DOCTOR
STATIONED ON THE PEACE RIVER

THE PATIENT ART OF THE SCULPTOR BRINGS
LIFE TO A STONE IN A VANCOUVER SETTING

CURTAIN CALL FOR THE PRIMA BALLERINA

LOVE BLOOMS UNDER
THE NORTHERN SUN—A
TEEN-AGE DREAM
AND THE DEEPER WARMTH
OF A FAMILY UNITED

**NIGHT PATROL**

IN HIS PROWL CAR, TENSE AND READY, A VANCOUVER POLICEMAN SIFTS SHADOWS IN THE NIGHT

**DAY PATROL**

WITH CONCERN AND SYMPATHY A MONTREAL POLICEWOMAN CHECKS AN ALLEY ON HER SLUM BEAT

TO THE BOYFRIEND'S CONCERN, THE WOULD-BE STAR EMOTES FROM A PUNT ON STRATFORD'S AVON

A PIG CAN BE A LOVELY THING—TO A HOG FARMER

THE TERROR OF THE RECRUIT—THE BOOMING SERGEANT-MAJOR—STILL THRIVES IN CANADA'S ARMY

SHE'S NOT CHECKING THE QUALITY OF THE FAMILY ROAST, SHE'S A UNION ORGANIZER IN MONTREAL

1934 riders picked up fresh horse tracks near a hidden and seldom-visited lake called Nimpo. Later they found the two horses feeding in the high slough grass along the shore line of the lake. The wary animals were harder to corral than wild horses.

It was in December of that year that I first heard about them. My partner, Panhandle Phillips, and I were up from Wyoming in search of a cattle range, and we had made our headquarters 225 miles beyond the nearest town on an opening known as the Behind Meadows. Sitting before our cook stove, Thomas Squinas described the trouble he and his friends had encountered corralling the two colts. His dark, square-cut face twisted into a crooked grin when he told us about the black. "That cayuse—he don't like any kind of man. Can't get close to him. I feed him lots—but he won't make friends. Now I break him to lead. He fight all the time—won't give in. He got funny look in the eye, not a mean eye—but he look at you hard and cold."

The following day I decided to drop in on the Squinas village and take a look at the black. He was tied by an inch halter rope to a corral post. I could see what Thomas had meant by the horse's cold eyes. They glinted with a strange unfathomable hardness and seemed to say—"I expect no favors from man, and I will give none."

Thomas pointed a finger at the black. "Gonna be lots of work to break that Nimpo Lake cayuse, but I don't think he's gonna buck." I studied the shape of the horse's head, his deep girth, the weird look in his eyes, and knew he had something. I pulled out my pocketbook, stripped off three ten-dollar bills, and showed them to Thomas who quickly relieved me of them. I had the feeling that one of the ten-dollar bills would have swung the deal, and noticed too late that the black had one crooked front foot.

Nimpo was my first British Columbia horse. He was hard to break all right. Each morning I had to throw him down, or squeeze him in between gates to get my saddle on him. The next horse I added to my string was Nimpo's bay half-brother. I called him Stuyve. He bucked a bit at first, but soon settled down to a fast-moving and reliable saddle horse. As the spring of 1935 approached our string of horses grew rapidly. By the first of May, eighteen head of broken and unbroken cayuses bucked and played about our pasture. And Nimpo had taken charge. He was a terrific fighter. No group of horses was too large, and no horse too big for him to handle.

After watching his short but rough encounter with a big, supposedly mean, 1,900-pound half-Clyde stallion, I was convinced that Nimpo was the quickest, shiftiest, and most vicious 1,000 pounds of fighting horse I had ever seen. The clumsy Clyde lasted about ten unhappy seconds.

When hot winds blew in from the west, the frost went out of the ground, and it was time for Pan and me to push our pack train north into the unknown regions beyond the Itcha and Algak Mountains. It was a hard summer on horses. We plunged the pack train through snowdrifts on high mountain passes; pushed them hundreds of miles over rocks and mud and windfalls; mosquitoes, black flies and bulldogs descended on the trail-weary horses in grey buzzing clouds.

Nimpo was our biggest problem. In mosquito country it is cruel to picket or stake horses for they need freedom of movement to roll, twist and wiggle off the insects. Consequently we hobbled them. The average horse is so tired when his pack is removed at night that he is content to feed through the few hours of darkness close to camp. But not Nimpo. No matter how tough the day had been, or how heavy the pack he had toted, Nimpo would hop, jump and lope off down the back trail with his hobbles on. We cursed him, sweated over him, got bitten and mauled in return, and every other day we swore we'd shoot him dead. He didn't give us any rest, and certainly got none himself. Long before the summer was spent he was a rack of shrunken skin and bones.

Squatting in front of the campfire, on lonely rock-bound mountains, with a million glittering stars and a cold white moon pressing down on top of us, I'd listen to the sad tinkle of Nimpo's special horse bell and a twang of sadness would reach through me. "It's not fair," I'd think. "That poor suffering cayuse will keep on fighting until he's dead. We ought to turn him loose."

But then I'd think of the job that lay before us—packing in more than twelve tons of machinery and grub to the new range we had discovered on the headwaters of the Blackwater River. Despite the trouble, worry and loss of sleep that Nimpo caused us, he was a hard and efficient worker. When finally saddled and bridled he put everything he had into the work assigned to him. Nimpo became a good rope horse—nothing on the end of a lariat was too big or fought too hard for him. He was fast on the getaway, learned to turn on a dime, and I could see that some day, if he lived that long, he'd make a top cutting horse.

Once Stuyve and I fell off a beaver dam into a muskeg. Pan and our hand, Tommy Holt, snaked me safely out onto the bank, but Stuyve, with my saddle on his back, sank slowly and agonizingly down into the ooze.

Nimpo whinnied from the bank. His eyes held to the spot where Stuyve's head was slowly disappearing.

"Let's get that pack off Nimpo," Pan yelled, "and throw a saddle on him. If he can't yank Stuyve out there's no other cayuse will."

Pan tied a bowline knot around Stuyve's neck and we shoved small trees and poles down into the mud under him. With the rope stretching from Stuyve's neck to Nimpo's saddle horn Pan spoke in a commanding voice. "Git, Nimpo! Hit her, boy!"

The thin little black leaned hard into the rope. Nothing came—nothing gave an inch. He backed up. The rope slacked. Pan, holding him by the halter shank, said low and harsh. "Ready, Nimpo—now hit her hard, boy."

Nimpo plunged and dug ahead hard against the rope. I saw Stuyve's head come twisting up a foot above the muck. Again Nimpo fell back, this time to his haunches. He was breathing hard. Pan slacked up on the halter shank.

"Too much for any one horse!" Tommy exclaimed. "Much too much. A big team is all that could get that bay out of the suction."

"We can't let Stuyve die that kind of a death," I said.

Nimpo had swung around while we talked. I saw him stare down at his half-brother. And then his eyes changed. He snorted, shook himself, then wheeled suddenly and fiercely into the rope. "Look out!" yelled Pan. "Here he comes."

That blazed-faced, crooked-footed black plunged madly, wildly ahead. A red fiery light flashed out of his eyes. The superstrength that lies dormant in horse as well as in man had come suddenly to life in that little black, and we saw his partner come struggling up out of the depths of the stinking mud and a nightmarish death. We all yelled.

It was late that summer when Pan and Alfred Bryant, a young Anahim rancher, drove the pack train over the Itcha Mountains on a 300-mile round trip to Bella Coola on the coast. There, after the boys had assembled the mountainous pile of machinery into separate pack-horse loads, they were confronted with one awkward and extremely heavy mowing-machine part.

Old-timers said to Pan, "There's only one thing to do. Pick out your toughest, meanest, orneriest cayuse to tote that cast-iron chunk, because you'll have to shoot him when it's over." That load was hoisted onto Nimpo. He made the long terrible journey back all right —150 miles of bush, timber, rock, mud, tortuous passes and mountain summits—with his back-breaking load.

He landed his pack—and then he lay down. We thought he was going to die. He contracted a fever, the flies descended on his emaciated body in swarms. For days only a vague fluttering of his eyelids and the faint pounding of his heart told us that he still lived. We doctored him, fed him horse medicine, tried to tempt him with oats, and close to him kept a smoke smudge burning day and night. He lived, and late in the fall he was fat and just as ornery as ever.

One night, after the first heavy snow of that 1935 winter, we turned Nimpo loose with the other horses who were out rustling. That was the last we saw of him. We knew only too well that he had struck south toward his old home, and as great drifts of snow blocked the high canyons and passes of the Itcha Mountains we concluded that this time Nimpo had gone bull-headedly to his death.

At Anahim Lake the following spring Alfred Bryant and I rode eighty miles through the ghost country of Sugarloaf Mountain on the tracks of a lone wild stallion. He had joined some mares and colts and herded them east across the range. When we finally caught up with the band grazing on an open meadow they threw up their heads and tails and started milling about in a circle. Alfred pulled up his horse alongside of mine and we stared unbelievingly at the "wild stallion." There— gliding stallionlike back and forth around the flanks of the mares and colts, his tail in the air and his coat shining like glass—was a snuffy little black horse with a blazed face and a crooked foot.

We took Nimpo back into our cavy and when in 1937 we drove our first herd of cattle over the Itcha Mountains he was worth two ordinary saddle horses. In November that year he survived a starvation drive when Charlie Forrester and I fought seventy-five head of cattle and eighteen horses through to Batnuni Lake. But his crooked leg went lame the following fall and he was turned loose with some other cayuses on a patch of slough grass near a recently frozen lake.

When Panhandle Phillips rode out to bring in the bunch he found one horse called Big George grazing alone and restless along the shore. A few feet out from its rubbery edge, in a tangled, frozen-in mass, were the bloated bodies of other horses. They had broken through the thin ice while feeding on a watery type of goose grass which grew out of the mud a few feet from shore. Pan assumed Nimpo was among the mass of frost and snow-covered horses protruding above the ice. But acting true to form Nimpo had outwitted both the horse wrangler and the pot-hole lake. At that time he was working south through windfalls and jack pines toward Sugarloaf Mountain.

High in the Itcha Mountains while feeling his way through a blinding snowstorm, Nimpo made a bad mistake. He turned into a dark narrow canyon. It was a blind draw and a trap—cliffs and towering granite walls reached skyward on three sides of him. He turned and at the narrow mouth of the valley he found that his tracks made on entering were smothered beneath an eight-foot snowdrift. He was trapped. Ahead of him stretched three and a half months of high mountain winter in country near the 53rd parallel.

Nimpo stubbornly pitched into the greatest battle of his career. He worked in almost perpetual darkness that 1938 winter on a three-acre patch of grass. The monotonous clacking of his hoofs cracking through the crusted snow rang across the valley floor. January and February passed with shrieking winds and fierce, unrelenting cold. Great drifts of snow shifted and threatened to fill the canyon from wall to wall.

Early in May two Indians rode into the Home Ranch and told Pan about seeing a lone horse in the Itcha peaks. "That cayuse just bone," said one of the Indians, "pretty soon I think he die so I don't bring him in."

Pan backtracked the Indians to the canyon. He was shocked at what he saw. Nimpo's big unblinking eyes stared out of hollow sockets; his hair was long, caked and shaggy. When Pan finally got him home he dosed him with Bell's Medical Wonder and fed him his only sack of oats. And the incredible cayuse recovered.

That fall Nimpo suddenly changed his ways. He had slipped into a muskeg, and as he was too weak to plow his way out of it I had to snake him out with another horse. While I was working at it I noticed him looking strangely at me from the mud. He seemed to be studying me, trying to make up his mind about something. When, dripping with mud, he stood safely on the bank he whinnied softly and touched me with a quivering nostril. Nimpo never again tried to pull out on us, and even a child could handle him after that.

Pan and I sold out to a cattle company, and were made cow bosses of our respective units. We needed lots of horses for our work, and for years Nimpo was one of my top cutting and rope horses.

The year before the company in its turn sold out, Nimpo went permanently lame. He had cut out his last steer. I was instructed to sell him along with the other cripples and old horses to a mink farm for $15 apiece. Something must have happened to Nimpo on the drive to the mink farm. He never got there. That was in 1944.

Strange things still happen up here in the north country. Not so long ago northern British Columbia was under the guns of a northeast blizzard, and things didn't look so good out at my new ranch under the rimrock. I knew that a bunch of cattle were huddled together in a grove of spruce against a drift fence several miles from the barn. If I wanted to save them I had to crack into the storm with a saddle horse and drive them through to the feed yard. I picked the aged but experienced Stuyve for the job, and he got me through to the cattle.

It was while I was riding home behind them that a strange thing happened. Stuyve suddenly threw his head in the air, struggled against his hackamore bit, swung completely around and pranced sideways into the blinding snow and the wind. He plunged and bucked through several drifts, whinnied, then came up sharp against the gate that leads out onto our open range.

Then through the shrieking wind I thought I heard a faint whinny. I tensed in the saddle and tried to see beyond the gate into the swirling greyish-white sheet. A sudden shift in the wind swept a hole in the blowing snow, and for an instant I saw a frosted, emaciated little black horse standing on three legs with his back to the wind and his glazed eyes fastened upon the gate.

Smart old Nimpo, realizing that his blizzard-fighting days were over, had quit the range horses and struggled miles to the only spot that held any chance of getting him through to hay and shelter. His luck had held. No other horse but his lifelong friend Stuyve would have faced into that storm to reach him.

A few days ago a visitor to the ranch asked me why I had built the special horse pasture and fenced off an extra stack of hay for "those two old plugs." Maybe if he reads this story he can figure out the answer.

JOSEPH SCHULL

# William Lawrence and His Wonderful Windjammer

William D. Lawrence had done pretty well in Maitland, Nova Scotia. He was in his middle fifties, he stood six feet three in his boots, and he had lived his life amid the clatter of shipyards. His early years with the broad-axe and the maul had been spent in Dartmouth. Then he had gone south to Boston to learn something of ship design from the famous Donald MacKay, the Shelburne boy who was building clippers for the Americans. After a few years of that he had come north again and settled at Maitland, ready to build his own ships. Somewhere along the road he had learned to play the fiddle.

For his first little ship he had gone into the woods himself, chopped down the trees he wanted and carried out the timber on his shoulders. Soon other men were doing his fetching and carrying. Carpenters' sheds and blacksmith shops and stores of seasoning timber stood beside the Lawrence house along the banks of the Shubenacadie River where it empties into Minas Basin. By 1868 six able vessels had come down his slipways and put to sea.

He was a widower now but his daughter Mary had married Jim Ellis of Shubenacadie, and there were three young grandchildren. It was a fine little family, prosperous and affectionate. The only trouble was that W. D. didn't see much of them. Jim was captain of the Lawrence ship "Pegasus," Mary and the children sailed with him, and Grandfather was left at home. There were the shipyards to occupy him in the daytime, and the fiddle to console him at night, and neither was quite enough.

In the evenings, when W. D. sat alone in his study scraping the bow across the strings, with the housekeeper wincing in the kitchen, he did a lot of thinking. He thought about ships, he thought about the sea, and he thought about Jim and Mary and the children. It occurred to him that he wasn't, perhaps, taking as much advantage as he should of the chances offered to a man by the carrying trade. Most of his ships had been safe but small. It occurred to him that the children were growing up hardly knowing their grandfather. It also occurred to him that he had seen very little of the sea. Six times in his life he had stood by watching a hull he had built move out toward the oceans. And still the far places of the earth were nothing to him but names on bills of lading.

In the summer of 1868 the seagoing Ellises were home for a spell, and Captain Jim found his father-in-law preoccupied. There was no vessel building outside this year, but there were a lot of papers and drawings cluttering up the study. W. D. would shuffle them around and talk a little evasively of the need for bigger ships, ships that would carry twice the cargo of the little ones with the same crew. When he walked with Jim in the woods and talk turned to the next voyage of "Pegasus," he seemed more concerned than usual about the profits that might be made. It wasn't that he was hard up for money, he protested, but money might come in handy in a year or so. His son-in-law looked at the empty yards and thought of the plans in the study. By the time he gathered up Mary and the children and left to join "Pegasus" again, he had a pretty good idea of what was in W. D.'s mind.

"Pegasus" sailed from Saint John in September 1868 with a cargo of timber to Liverpool and went on to Cardiff for coal. For four years and three months she crossed and recrossed the oceans, her hold reeking with guano, black with coal, sweet with sugar.

Ellis had known he would see a ship building when he got back. Bluenose captains had come into Hamburg, Calcutta, San Francisco

156

and Manila with rumors of it. Bluenose ships had hailed him on the high seas to retail the gossip that was running through the Maritime ports and out around the world. But even with all that, he hadn't quite realized what his father-in-law was up to.

The mighty thing towering beside the house had been an unlikely ghost, a wraith in W. D.'s mind four years ago. The bow overshadowed the chimney tops. The hull frame ran like a wall down the length of the lawn to the edge of the Shubenacadie 250 feet away. Seventy-five workmen swarmed about the stocks. The whole neighborhood, from the river bank to the far woods, echoed to the whine of hand-saws, the clink of caulking mallets, and the thud of mauls driving home bolts in timber.

She was going to be the largest wooden sailing ship afloat. Ellis and W. D. passed under the loom of the bows and looked up. Her stem rose forty-seven feet from keel to rail. The two men climbed the brow-stage scaffolding and paced off the 275 feet of her deck length. As Ellis measured her forty-eight-foot beam, his grinning father-in-law supplied some other statistics. The deck timbers were eighteen inches through, and beneath them ran the timbers of two more decks, all as huge, all braced and supported by iron knees. And the ship, as yet, was only half built. There would be two years of work yet, and it would be work by fits and starts as the money came in and ran out. She gulped down the $82,000 earned by "Pegasus," she swallowed most of W. D.'s savings and she put a mortgage on the house. She kept Jim Ellis at home for twenty-four months, hurrying off to Halifax for supplies and gear and tackle, hurrying home to figure out how to pay the bills. And always with the sickening refrain in his ears, humming from the wharves of Halifax to the riverside of Maitland: "She'll never sail," "She'll be too big to handle," "She'll flounder round like a bull playing a fiddle."

W. D. was always around the ship and not concerned, it seemed, either about the bills or the gossip. He had walked one of the noisiest sceptics out of the yards, but the ranting of most drew nothing but a smile and a shrug from him. For the worried Ellis it was a relief sometimes to talk with Isaac Douglas in the smithy where the old man was forging the last of the ship's ironwork. Isaac thought she'd sail. So did Shaw, the wood-carver, tranquilly at work on the bearded, forward-looking gentleman who was to be the figurehead, draped in a flowing cloak and carrying a scroll with the motto, "God Defend the Right."

It began to seem, by the summer of 1874,

that the ship would at least take to the water. The hull was finished. Seams had been caulked, water had been pumped in and out again, and leaks recaulked. Hatch coamings had been fitted, and a village of deck-houses, all as massively built as the ship, stood clustered fore and aft. Topmasts and topgallant masts had grown above the lower masts, and finally it was time for the yards to go up and the riggers to come aboard.

The ninety-five-foot fore and main yards swung up into the blue and settled across the masts with their trusses, lifts and braces anchoring them home. The topsail, topgallant and royal yards climbed above them, and still beyond them went the skysail yards. The forms of the riggers dwindled and their voices grew faint as they rode them up, a hundred feet, a hundred and fifty, two hundred feet above the watchers. The maze of her standing and running gear climbed about the spars. The canvas followed—eight thousand yards of it, all on credit.

The old man had insisted that she have the best of everything. The people who visited her did not exclaim only about her size. Their eyes grew wide as they looked at her seven-ton rudder, at her steam-operated windlass, her patent double-action pumps, and her palatial quarters fore and aft. Nothing that seagoing man had yet thought of was lacking in the big ship, and more than enough of it was still to be paid for.

As the launching day neared, W. D. opened the door and called his son-in-law. He'd made a few decisions, he said, and it was time for Jim to know about them. The vessel was going to be called the "W. D. Lawrence." Jim was going to sail her, of course, and the children would go with them, so that would mean shipping a tutor. Also, he added, clearing his throat slightly, this time Grandfather was going along.

Ellis, weary and harassed by two anxious years ashore, was inclined to explode. Was this what all the fiddling had been about? Every cent they had was sunk in that hull outside, and W.D. was talking about tutors and pleasure trips. What if the ship turned out to be a bad sailer, as everyone expected? And what if they couldn't find the huge cargoes they'd need to make money with her?

W. D. smiled and produced a letter which had come heavily marked with foreign postage a few days before. It was a charter from Dreyfus Frères & Compagnie of France for a cargo of guano. The "Lawrence" would go to Liverpool with timber, and then take on an outward cargo of coal. After delivering the coal she would go to Pabellon de Pica on the west coast of South America and load guano for France. The cargoes would pay the bills, there wasn't any worry about that. This wasn't a pleasure trip, it was a business trip. And business or pleasure, he concluded with that inflexible gleam in his eye, it was a trip around the world and he was going to make it in his own ship.

Tuesday, October 27, 1874, was launching day. For an hour or so in the morning W. D. Lawrence was not among the crowd that filled the yard. In company with the Presbyterian minister and his friend and fellow-giant, Alfred Putnam, he was walking toward the Truro ferry dock with two dejected strangers trundling a large keg of whisky in a wheelbarrow. The strangers with their keg had got off the ferry brisk and beaming, looking forward to a large business in the shipyard. They were now homeward bound with their wares unsold, escorted by three of the most determined teetotalers in Nova Scotia.

The liquor question settled, W. D. returned for the launching. A bottle of innocuous cider smashed against the bow, the keel blocks were split, and at two o'clock in the afternoon the hull began to move down the ways carrying her four hundred tons of stone ballast. The shadow of the bow drew away from the house, the sunny fields and woods that had lain so long out of view on the other side began to reappear, and the ship rode easily out onto the red waters of the Shubenacadie.

Two months later, with her holds full stowed and her deck piled to the rail with timber, she moved out of Saint John harbor for Liverpool. Mary Ellis was below with the children, readying the pine-paneled afterquarters for sea. The big saloon was airy and spacious as her drawing-room at home, with the dining table at one end and the bronze lamp swinging in its gimbals overhead. W. D.'s big cabin and bathroom opened off from one side of the saloon, her own and Jim's from the other, and there was an adjoining cabin for the children. The quarters of Mr. Johnson, the tutor, came next, and beyond them were the cabins of the officers. The cook moved about in his white-tiled galley, and Evans, the steward from "Pegasus," was his old chipper self. The noise overhead told of the usual difficulties with the crew, and a snatch of drunken song floated in through the heavy doors:

*Oh whisky is the life of man,*
*Whisky, Johnnie.*
*It always was since the world began,*
*Whisky for my Johnnie!*

*Oh whisky straight and whisky strong,*
*If you give me some whisky, I'll sing a*
*    song.*

Mary shuddered, and hoped the children wouldn't hear. In the pilot-house on the poop, Jim Ellis stood with W. D. beside the helmsman. The tug had cast off, and they were clearing Partridge Island under lower topsails. Ellis's face began to clear a little as he got the feel of the vessel, and he gave a course to the helmsman that caused W. D. to look at him with surprise. The wider channel lay down the bay off Digby Neck and Brier Island. Ellis was taking her between Grand Manan and the Maine shore. It was a shorter route but a narrower channel, and only a master who was sure of his ship would risk it. W. D. said nothing, but a small complacent gleam came into his eye.

The gleam was a glow by the time they reached Liverpool, and the enthusiasm of the builder was shared by the master. For all her size, the "Lawrence" handled like a yacht. She would never be a fast ship, but she hadn't been designed for speed. She would travel any sea comfortably and surely, and she would probably earn her keep. Her bottom still required copper sheathing for a voyage to southern waters, but the freight on her enormous timber cargo would pay for that.

W. D. left his son-in-law in Liverpool to supervise the sheathing. He was off with Mary and the children to see the wonders of London. He was still away as the ship left drydock and the black torrents of coal came tumbling into her hold. The decks, the sides, the rigging and even the captain himself were covered with greasy soot, but W. D. in immaculate linen and broadcloth was inspecting art galleries and museums and concert halls. Hatch covers had gone on again, holds were sealed, tarpaulins battened down, and the "Lawrence" sluiced up, scrubbed, dusted and painted before he returned.

The ship had her papers for Aden, and everything about her except the monstrous, money-making cargo holds was fresh and sparkling on the night of the farewell party. Twenty Bluenose ships were in harbor in Liverpool, and all the captains and their wives had come on board to say good-by. They had dined regally, sung songs around the piano in the cabin, and W. D. was scraping his fiddle for them when a knock came at the door. An urgent letter had arrived for Lawrence from Dreyfus Frères & Compagnie.

It was necessary, the letter said, to cancel the charter for the cargo of guano. The firm had a surplus on hand, and new synthetic fertilizers had appeared which threatened to destroy the market for guano altogether. Dreyfus Frères regretted the necessity of their action, but Mr. Lawrence would certainly understand.

Lawrence understood. The guano charter was the backbone of his voyage, the only source from which he could pay the debts on his ship. He also understood another thing. The charter had been signed before the "Lawrence" was launched, and a charter is a binding contract. There would be no reply to the letter, said W. D. The ship would sail as planned, and she would return with a cargo of guano.

They moved out of the Mersey next morning, bound for Aden. W. D. had nothing more to say about the charter. He was concerned only with the voyage ahead and with the sailing qualities of his ship. Jim Ellis found it hard to concentrate on either. Charters had been broken before, he knew, and luckless carriers had been left to hold the bag.

Her course lay south through the two Atlantics, around the Cape of Good Hope, and up through the Indian Ocean to blistering Aden near the mouth of the Red Sea. As the links with shore parted, the tangle of debt and worry retreated little by little into the back of the captain's mind. His vessel shouldered cleanly into the long rollers. With thousands of tons of coal settled in her belly, comfortable and secure, she was a giant in her element, a contented ship. The weather held fine. The crew had smartened up quickly under the hands of the mates. The deck watch gathered at the rail now, smirking complacently as passing vessels hailed and admired the mighty product of the Maitland yards. A man forgot about business as he stood on the poop under the sighing cloud of the canvas and read those admiring hoists. He became a seaman again, and a proud one.

W. D. had forgotten about business before they cleared the Mersey, and he was becoming almost too much of a seaman. His pride in the "Lawrence" was open and unblushing now, and day by day his questions and suggestions about the sailing of her came in an unending stream. W. D. was everywhere about his vessel, chatting with the men, absorbing sea lore, returning to the poop with bright ideas. It was amusing and it was delightful to see the old man getting such fun from his ship. But after a while Ellis began to wish he'd spend a little of his time below. The children were struggling with arithmetic there, reluctant prisoners in the hands of Mr. Johnson. W. D.'s authority and his head for figures would be handy in the cabin. On the poop, two captains were one too many.

W. D. was always properly deferential to his son-in-law. Ellis was master of the ship, and Ellis gave the orders. The suggestions from the owner continued, however, and one in particular grew more urgent as they rolled down out of the North Atlantic. It became a constant refrain in the captain's ears, continuing at mealtimes and off-hours in the cabin: "Let's see what she'll do with all her clothes on." It irritated Ellis, partly because he was a sober and responsible master who saw no point in driving the ship to its limit, and more because he wanted to know as badly as W. D. He postponed and evaded as a sop to his conscience, but in his heart he was only waiting for the right day.

When it came it was a day for sou'westers and seaboats and oilskins, a day for a seaman to forget the charters and bills and balance sheets and all the tangle of paper that governed his comings and goings about the world. It was the great boisterous South Atlantic weather that lifted a man's heart. It made him a bit reckless, filled him with exuberant confidence in the mighty teamwork of wind and sea and ship. From early morning, with a guilty throb of excitement under his calm sea mask, Ellis had begun to pile sail on the "Lawrence."

By noon all the kites were set. They climbed to the mastheads, from the huge bellying squares of the courses to the skysails dwindling into foggy shadows amid the low scud at the trucks. The great hull which had seemed so monstrous and unwieldy on the stocks at Maitland lifted cunningly with the crested surges, clove them away in graceful furrows. The white smother at the forefoot was climbing and washing back over the forecastle head. With each lunging roll the lee rail dipped until it was racing almost level with the foaming backwash. The timbers grown beside the Shubenacadie were earning their shillings now, carrying the coal for Aden through the long grey swells at a speed of fourteen knots.

W. D. shouted with excitement as he read off the log. Ellis was grinning in spite of himself. For three hours he held the "Lawrence" to it. Fifteen knots came up on the log count, and he knew it was time to rein in. You could hear the old girl "talking to herself." The high-pitched moan in the rigging told of enormous strain. You could almost see the great fist of the wind driving into that mass of canvas overhead. The mate was eying the captain, and the look in those eyes said, "Shorten down."

Ellis gave the order, and the mate started

for the deck; but W. D. was beyond the proprieties now. He grabbed the mate's arm and turned to the captain, pleading like a boy. Let her run for half an hour—fifteen minutes —she'd go to sixteen, he knew she would. Ellis looked up at the rigging again, shrugged with hypocritical reluctance and told the mate to stand by. He was pretty sure she could make sixteen himself.

She came up to sixteen knots, passed it and began to edge toward seventeen. W. D. was sure she'd reach it, but beads of sweat were standing on the mate's forehead, and Ellis had had enough. He was already turning to call in skysails and royals when there was a warning shout from the deck. The ship had fetched up on the back of a huge surge. It paused for an instant, quivering in every timber at the sudden check. Then the great spars towering to the cloud-rack whipped like match sticks, splintered far above, and the whole head of her upper canvas was sheared away at a stroke. Yards, spars and sails, the three topmasts and the three topgallant masts came thundering down onto the lower shrouds and backstays, bounced off them and plunged over the sides. A vast, fouled-up mess of rope, wire, timber and canvas spread out around the ship, tangling and battering her with the heave of the sea.

It wasn't a disaster. Three days of backbreaking work salvaged most of the gear and sent the "Lawrence" on her way. But she went around the Cape and up through the Indian Ocean a limping jury-rigged cripple, faced with a repair bill that would eat up most of her coal freight. The dreary bunkers of Aden came in sight at last, and the ship dropped anchor in the port on August 1, 1875.

The captain had been aloof and irritable since the accident, and the owner subdued and contrite. W. D. knew that the thing had been a sore blow to a master's pride, and it had been the owner's fault. But he judged that the air was clear enough now to make another suggestion. They were going to need new spars, and they couldn't get them at Aden. Somebody would have to go to Bombay for them, and it might as well be W. D.—with Mary and the children, of course.

Ellis looked at him and laughed, the first good laugh in quite a while. A spot of sea air was turning a sharp old businessman into a boy and a tourist. But it would be good to have Mary and the children away from the heat and coal dust, and it might be nice to ready the ship for her new spars without W. D. forever at his elbow. He forbore from mentioning the cost of repairs and the fact that they had no outward cargo. The family went off

to Bombay, and the captain was left to unload his coal.

The "Lawrence" was a sound ship once more when she put out for Callao, Peru, on September 13. But there had been no cargo to be found in Aden. She was sailing with profitless ballast in her hold, and nothing but a dubious guano charter ahead. W. D. had forgotten about Bombay, but he still wouldn't talk about business. The spell of new lands and waters claimed him as they nosed down through the Indian Ocean and turned into the Timor Sea. It was hard to get him away from the poop for meals. He stood more watches than the captain as they passed along the northern coast of Australia, steered through Torres Strait and the Coral Sea and reached away across the endless breadth of the South Pacific. Callao lifted on the horizon in the first days of December, and as they neared the Peruvian coast W. D. seemed to grow a little more thoughtful. Ellis hoped he was brooding on guano. But when he spoke at last it was of Lima, a lovely city eight miles from Callao. He'd heard of its wonders, and he and Mary and the children ought to see it.

Now at last the captain exploded. They'd come to Callao to get a permit from the Peruvian government to load guano. Had W. D. forgotten about that charter? No, W. D. hadn't forgotten. He'd arrange for the permit all right, but first he'd see Lima.

There was a great festival in Lima, with dancing and bright costumes and lovely women. W. D. came back to Callao enchanted with his visit. He talked about it all the way to the government offices, but his son-in-law was not listening. He had already called at those offices, and he had talked to other masters around the docks. He knew what they would hear. So far as the Peruvian government was concerned, said the officials, it was quite in order for the "W. D. Lawrence" to go down the coast to Pabellon de Pica. She could take guano if she could get it. But twenty ships were already waiting in the roadstead there, and the agents of the guano importers, who held a monopoly, refused to load them. It appeared that there was little market for guano in Europe at the moment. And the thought of paying long ocean freights on an unsalable cargo was most repugnant to such companies as Dreyfus Frères.

As they listened to the polite official, Jim Ellis saw a change come over his father-in-law. All at once the eager tourist was a businessman again. His face wasn't exactly hard, but it wasn't soft either. The official would kindly complete the permit. The "W. D. Lawrence" was sailing for Pabellon de Pica tomorrow.

The "Lawrence" sailed, and at long last the desolate grey-white headland of Pabellon de Pica lifted on the southern horizon. The ship rounded into the open roadstead. Twenty or thirty ships lay anchored in careful order ahead of her. Their barnacled sides and blistered paintwork told of a long stay. The grim faces of the men idly watching from their decks told that it was a hopeless one.

Above the harbor with its rocky, sun-baked shores there were swooping clouds of sea-birds —gulls, pelicans, penguins, gannets, terns and cormorants. In the breathless air stirred only by the wild crying of the birds, the headland stood out waterless, treeless, cheerless. A few miserable shacks clustered on the slopes, and near them were half a dozen tumbledown sheds. Officials of the guano monopoly lived in the shacks, and the large buildings were the bunkhouses of Chinese coolies, brought here to labor till they dropped. Large wooden chutes reached out over the water from the steep brows of the hill. Down these chutes in past years had come a billion dollars' worth of ancient evil-smelling rock and powder. It had circled the world in thousands of ships, and even at this moment it was bringing new life to the hungry soil of Europe. But there was no life here. From the deck you could see a few coolies moving about aimlessly or sprawled in front of the bunkhouses. The chutes were idle.

The bored clerks in the huts ashore had one reply for every captain who came to them. They gave it to Ellis and W. D. There was no guano to load. The grey mountain towering outside their door gave them the lie. Ellis gave them the lie. Weren't they weary of that idiotic story? Very weary, they agreed, but their instructions from France were definite.

A month went by, and the "Lawrence" swung to her anchor with the other ships in the roadstead. A second month passed, and five of the ships gave up and sailed. Four later arrivals looked into the roadstead, sized up the situation, and turned away. Barnacles began to grow on the clean sides of the "Lawrence." Her paint cracked in the heat. The crew leaned on the rails, muttering, as the screaming swarms of the birds crossed and recrossed the grey mountain. A steamer came up the coast bringing fresh provisions, and Ellis eyed his crew dourly. He would have to keep a sharp watch on the men. Some of them were already ripe to jump ship.

He was looking in the wrong direction. The famous port of Mollendo was only a little way up the coast, and from there a railway led into the Andes. Mary and the children were looking a bit pale, and W. D. was of no particular use at the moment in Pabellon. He thought he'd take the trip. Ellis looked at his father-in-law unbelievingly, shrugged and turned away.

The railway led from Mollendo to the city of Arequipa, eight thousand feet above sea level. From there another line climbed seven thousand feet higher to Pizarro's Lake Titicaca. W. D. returned to Pabellon refreshed by mountain air, lyrical over sunsets in the high valleys, and aglow with tales of Pizarro. The tired man waiting on the hot deck in Pabellon found it hard to appreciate them.

His father-in-law seemed to have forgotten, he suggested, that they had come for guano and were not likely to get any. He seemed to have forgotten the bills in Maitland, and the new bills that were growing around the ship every day along with the barnacles. W. D. had not forgotten the bills, he replied mildly, but there was perhaps one thing that the captain had overlooked. A ship kept waiting through no fault of her own was entitled to demurrage charges of $150 a day. Demurrage had now been accruing to the "Lawrence" for about three months. He thought perhaps he'd go fishing with the sailors.

The fourth month went by and the steamer came again. There was a great holiday at hand in Valparaiso—the festival of Chilean independence was to be celebrated. A sight like that shouldn't be missed when a man was so near. W.D. went off for Valparaiso.

By the time he returned the fifth month was wearing away. The sixth, seventh and eighth passed. Twelve of the ships had gone now. The barnacles were a thick crust on the sides and bottom of the "Lawrence," the crew were growling openly. Departing captains had laughed sourly at W. D.'s talk of demurrage charges. A ship that couldn't get a cargo under her charter would certainly not be able to collect demurrage. Ellis believed them. Mary's cheerfulness was failing at last, and the children were dull and listless. In Maitland, half a world away, debts mounted while the ship lay decaying here. The family was already bankrupt and it was time to go home and face the music. Instead there was music to be faced in Pabellon. W. D., immovable as rock, had turned to his fiddle again.

He pointed out that there was a condition attached to the guano monopoly at Pabellon. The company was compelled by the Peruvian government to load at least one ship a year. He would stay that year, if necessary, and he would collect demurrage for the wait.

The ninth, tenth and eleventh months went

by. The crew's sulky fury had begun to change to a kind of dull amusement. They were sorry for Mary and the children and they didn't blame the captain. He was as hopeless as they were, and as bored with the heat and smell and the everlasting clamor of the birds. They'd even stopped blaming the old man. It was interesting in a gruesome sort of way to find out just how stubborn he was.

The ships ahead of the "Lawrence" had given up and departed now, except for one. She was "Antoinette," a ship with a stubborn master too, and a Bluenose. On the night of December 1, 1876, "Antoinette" 's master climbed into a boat and went ashore. It was a night like any other of the 330-odd that had gone before, hot and airless, with the men of the two crews trading bored grumblings across the water. But in the morning there was a change.

Shouts from the deck brought Ellis tumbling out of the cabin. He looked toward the shore, the way the men were pointing. "Antoinette" had moved under the chutes, there were coolies on the hill above, and guano was charging down into her hold.

W. D. took in the scene with a quick glance and ordered out a boat. In half an hour he and Ellis were in the office ashore. The "Antoinette" was being loaded, the clerk agreed, but she would be the only ship. His instructions were definite. W. D.'s reply was equally definite. The operation proceeding outside had demonstrated first that there was guano to be had and, second, that the loading gear was in order. "Lawrence" would be under the chutes within an hour of "Antoinette" 's departure, and she would be loaded—either by the staff at Pabellon or by the "Lawrence" 's crew.

A week later the big ship, deep in the water with all the guano she could carry, was swinging off for the Horn. She rounded it with all sail up, because that was the way W. D. wanted to make the famous journey. With her bottom fouled by a year in tropic waters she made a slow passage through the South Pacific and the two Atlantics, but it was quite fast enough for the unwelcoming Dreyfus Frères in Le Havre. They had canceled the charter, they protested, they did not wish the cargo, and they refused to pay demurrage.

In the law courts of France the suit of W. D. Lawrence versus Dreyfus Frères & Compagnie dragged on interminably, but the time did not drag for W. D. He saw the opera, the circus, the masked balls, Versailles, and the lovely countryside. He stored his memories of France with all the other pictures of the wide world living in his mind, and brought them home at last when the weary mutterings of the lawyers reached their conclusion.

To W. D. Lawrence of Maitland, Nova Scotia, Canada, was awarded the sum of £12,380 sterling in freight, plus demurrage charges in the sum of £10,620 sterling for delay caused his ship through no fault of the operators.

On a memorable day in Maitland the old man stood with Ellis surveying a great pile of golden sovereigns heaped on his study table. Then he swept them all into a huge bandanna handkerchief, and walked down the street in his shirtsleeves to pay the debts on his ship.

GORDON WOODWARD

# Escape to the City

It was almost three o'clock when I arrived in the city that afternoon.

It was that day in late September when I had started out early in the morning while the thick white mist lay close to the ground and I could see the willow bushes down by the river poking up through the filmy blanket beneath the bridge where Clifford and I had always gone fishing; the dew that morning clustered in thick glistening drops on the handlebars of my bike as I wheeled it quietly down from the porch so as not to wake up Jeannie and Father, who would not even know I was gone until they got up and found that note I had left on the kitchen table saying I had gone to the city to visit Clifford.

And I knew Father would be angry, because he hadn't even written to Clifford since that day over two months before when they had argued about Clifford going into the business because he was seventeen and through high school. Clifford had refused; instead he had answered an ad in the newspaper for a position as an apprentice in a chemical firm in the city and then had drawn all of his money out of the local bank (which had been seven dollars and nineteen cents) and had climbed on the bus with no one there to even say good-by to him; and I hadn't seen him since that day.

I was tired. I'd ridden over fifty-three miles since I had turned off by Galloway's Dairy on the outskirts of Abbotsford that morning and then had headed down the highway through the smell of trees and rotting leaves and the sun throwing bright patches of early sunlight across the fields. I pulled over to the curb and took out the letter I had received from Clifford and looked at the house number again; it was in the next block so I rode close to the curb

with my bike wheels crunching over the dried leaves in the gutter until I came to it.

It was one of those big old houses which line the streets in the west end of Vancouver; it was better looked after than most of them and was painted a bright cream-and-brown color. I got off my bike and wheeled it through the gate; then I untied the parcel on the carrier and went up the steps and rang the doorbell.

After a minute a lady came to the door; she was not very old but had grey hair and glasses. "Does Clifford Barton live here, ma'am?" I said.

"Yes, he does," she said. "But he's not in right now."

"Well, I'm his brother," I said.

"Oh, I see." She seemed as though she didn't know what to say.

"I just came in from Abbotsford where we live," I said. I pointed to my blue CCM lying at the bottom of the steps. "I rode in on my bike," I said.

"That's a long way to ride," she said.

"It certainly is," I said. She still didn't move; and I knew she was stalling for some reason. "I haven't seen Clifford for a couple of months," I said.

"That's quite a coincidence, you coming," she said, "because he was telling me just yesterday about all his brothers at home."

"Oh, there must be some mistake, ma'am," I said. "He doesn't have any other brothers except me . . . only a sister." Then all at once I realized that she had been trying to find out if I really was Clifford's brother; and she knew it.

"I'm sorry," she said, and she smiled. "I have to be careful." She opened the door wider. "Would you like to go up to his room? He should be home about six."

I followed her into the hallway and she closed the door and then led me up two flights of winding carpeted stairs to a room on the top floor; she opened the door and let me go in first and then stood in the doorway a moment. "Are you hungry?" she said.

"No thanks," I said. "I had a hamburger and a milk-shake at a place on the highway."

She looked at me for a minute with a kind of warm smile on her face. "You don't look much like Clifford," she said.

"I guess just about everybody tells us that," I said.

"You're the youngest, are you?" she said.

"I'm fifteen," I said. "Just turned fifteen."

"Well, if there's anything you want you just come downstairs," she said. She started to close the door and then she came back again. "The bathroom is right across the hall," she said. She closed the door and I could hear her footsteps going down the stairs.

I sat down on the edge of the bed and looked around at the small room; it was very clean and bright. There was linoleum on the floor and the wallpaper had white flowers all over it. In one corner there was a small cupboard and below it a table covered with oilcloth with a small electric hot plate and a kettle sitting on it; there were also two white wooden chairs. In the opposite corner there was a closet with a door on it; and the bed on which I was sitting was covered with a bright homemade quilt.

I looked at the two windows that opened out above the porch on the front of the house; there were small birds twittering and chirping on the roof outside. The leaves on the maple trees along the sidewalk on the opposite side of the street were yellow and soft brown and yet-bright green, suddenly fluttering one by one to the ground with a frail and brittle scraping sound as though made of balsa wood.

My legs and my backside felt stiff and sore and I lay back on the bed and looked up at the ceiling, just gazing blankly the way I had been lying in my own bed in Abbotsford and looking up at the ceiling that morning Clifford had come into the room all dressed and wearing his pale-blue shirt and the maroon tie I had given him for his birthday, when I hadn't even known he was going anywhere until that moment he said, "I'm going, Pat. Take care of yourself. I'll write," and then was gone.

Not even waiting to say good-by to Father (who wouldn't have answered pleasantly anyway), but just walking out through the door and down to the bus stop and getting on that bus with his battered suitcase in which were all his clothes and that small Wedgwood vase which had belonged to Mother and the sum of seven dollars and nineteen cents in his pocket and heading for the city where he didn't know anyone; so that when I had finally struggled awake that morning and had put on my clothes and jumped on my bike and raced down to the bus stop I had been in time to see the bus pulling away and had pedaled hard to get alongside and catch just one glimpse of his face and have him see me so that he would know that I at least had wanted to say good-by; and yet I hadn't been fast enough. I had been almost two months before that letter had come and I had even known where he was living in the city.

There was a cool breeze coming through the open window and I pulled the corner of the quilt up over me and put my head on the pillow and then I must have fallen sound asleep, because all at once I felt someone shaking me by the shoulder and calling my name. "Pat! Wake up!" Then a slight pause and another shake. "Pat!"

I slowly opened my eyes and saw Clifford standing by the bed grinning at me, the room looking a little darker and shadier than it had been so that I knew I had slept quite a while. "Am I ever surprised to see you!" he said. "You could have knocked me over when the landlady told me you were here!"

I struggled to come fully awake. "Hi, Clifford." I said.

"When did you get here?" he said.

"About three o'clock."

"I was expecting you to write," he said, "but I didn't think you'd be able to come in. How did you ever find the place? Did you come in on the bus?"

"I came on my bike," I said. "Didn't you see my CCM out front?"

"I guess I saw it," he said. "But it never struck me it was yours. Did you ride all the way?"

"Sure," I said. I went to get up and felt the stiffness in my thighs. "But I'm a little stiff now," I said. "I'm not used to riding that far."

"You must be starved," he said. "Wait till I have a wash and we'll go and get something to eat." He took off his jacket and hung it in the closet. "Tell me what's been going on," he said.

"I brought you a fish I caught yesterday by the bridge," I said. "A spring. He put up a good fight." I walked over to the table and started to take it out of the paper bag. "And I swiped a jar of Jeannie's raspberry jam," I said. "Jeannie doesn't make very good jam, anyway." We both laughed.

Clifford took a towel and some soap and went across the hall to the bathroom and I could hear him running water in the basin; then after a few minutes he came back drying his neck with the towel. He had taken his glasses off; he always looked different without his glasses as though his eyes had shrunk. "Holy Moses!" he said. "Was I ever surprised when I came in and found you here!" He put his glasses back on and slipped his tie over his head and tightened it and put his jacket on. Then he went over to the cupboard and took down a small bowl and took some money out of it and then put the bowl back in the cupboard. "Come on, kid," he said. "Let's get some food before you collapse from hunger."

We went downstairs and he knocked on the landlady's door and asked her if it would be all right for me to put my bike in the basement and she said it would so we went around to the side door and put the bike away; then we went down the front sidewalk and out through the gate. The sun was blood-orange and low in the sky and as we walked down the tree-shaded street it threw long shadows down the sidewalk in front of us; our feet crunched on the dried leaves which had fallen on the cement. "How do you like it, Clifford?" I said.

"You mean Vancouver?" he said. "Or my job?"

"Everything," I said. "Being in Vancouver . . . and having your job . . . and living here . . . you know what I mean."

"I like it fine," he said. "I guess I'm pretty lucky." He went along looking at his feet for a minute. "You should see the building I work in, Pat!" he said. "It covers a whole city block."

"I guess it must be a pretty big company," I said.

"Yes," he said. "They're really big . . . they ship all over the world."

"I guess they must have an awful lot of money," I said.

We came to a corner and turned down toward the harbor. There was a sparkling-white freighter heading out toward The Narrows and the deep glow of evening sunlight rolled across the windows in the wheelhouse like bright liquid fire.

"Do they pay you pretty good money?" I said.

He didn't say anything. We turned another corner and went down the street a little way and turned into a café. The place smelled of cigarette smoke and frying food the way Gerry's Hamburger Bar in Abbotsford smelled on Saturday night when all the gang hung around listening to the juke box. There were no vacant booths so we sat down at the counter on the bucket-shaped wooden stool-seats. The waitress came and I ordered some veal cutlets and mashed potatoes and a glass of milk and a piece of cherry pie. Clifford ordered a cup of coffee and some doughnuts. She gave us each a glass of water and went away along the counter.

"Aren't you going to eat?" I said.

"I'm not hungry," he said. "Down at work we're always eating doughtnuts or cookies or candy or some other stuff . . . it ruins a guy's appetite."

"Yes," I said. "I guess it does."

The waitress brought my veal cutlets and I started to eat. I hadn't realized until then just how hungry I really was, and I was enjoying it. Then I happened to look in the big mirror behind the counter and I saw Clifford watching me closely. "Are you *sure* you aren't going to eat something, Clifford?" I said.

"I'm not the least hungry," he said. "Really I'm not. What made you ask that?"

"Nothing," I said.

I finished my dinner and we got up and Clifford took the check and went over to the cashier and put a two-dollar bill on the counter as though he couldn't understand how he happened to have such a small bill in his pocket. She rang up one dollar and ten cents and gave him the ninety cents and we went outside and turned up Granville Street.

"Feel better?" Clifford said.

"Boy, do I ever!" I said. "That was really good!"

It was beginning to get dark; the streetlights were all on and the neon signs flashed red and blue and green and yellow. There were a lot of people crowding up and down the sidewalk and we had to keep dodging first to one side, and then the other. It was hard to think that out in Abbotsford at that moment there would be only a few neon signs shining in the whole town; and the only places which would be even open would be Gerry's Hamburger Bar and Watson's Drug Store. I dodged around a couple of old ladies and came up beside Clifford again. "What do you do at night, Clifford?" I said. "I mean what do you do for fun?"

"Oh, I have lots to do," he said. "I have to study, you know. And every Tuesday night I go to a show."

"Why Tuesday?" I said.

"No reason," he said. "I just started going on Tuesday when I first came here. That's the day I get paid: Tuesday."

"Don't you ever go to parties?" I said. "Or anything like that?"

"I could go to lots if I wanted to," he said, "but I don't usually have time."

"I guess a guy kind of grows out of parties after a while, anyway," I said.

"Yeah," he said. "You get tired of them."

We kept walking down the street. The crowd wasn't quite so thick where we were then and we didn't have to dodge so much. We came to the intersection and had to stop for a traffic light.

"What would you like to do now, Pat?" Clifford said. "Would you like to just walk around or what?" The light changed and we crossed over and when we got to the opposite curb, he said, "If I'd brought more money with me we could have gone to a show. I never carry any more money with me than I need. I keep it all in a bowl on the shelf back at the room."

"Why don't you put it in the bank?" I said.

"I can't be bothered with banks," he said. "Maybe later on when I get better organized."

"Anyway," I said, "this is Friday night, and Tuesday night is when you go to the show."

"That's right," he said. "It is." He didn't say anything for several minutes, and then he said, "Do they still have the shows two nights a week at home?"

"Yes," I said. "But they're talking about making it every night because of all those construction workers coming into town from that camp on the meridian road. It will sure liven the town up," I said.

"It seems like a year since I left," he said. He stopped to look at some cigarette lighters in a window we were passing and I stopped beside him.

"Clifford," I said. "Haven't you got some friend here in Vancouver you go to shows with, or somebody you just chum around with?" He didn't answer; instead he leaned forward a little and looked closer at the lighters. I knew the minute it was out of my mouth that I'd said the wrong thing; because Clifford didn't make very many friends, he was hard to get to know, but when he did make a friend he was really loyal, as though he expected the friendship to go on as long as he was alive. "I guess there are more important things in the world than just having a lot of friends everywhere," I said.

We turned a corner and started along another street. Not far ahead we could see the Court House with its trimming of little white lights; it looked like a fairy palace. After a minute Clifford said, "When do you have to go back, Pat?"

"Tomorrow," I said. "I guess I should head back tomorrow morning."

"It's too bad you couldn't have stayed longer," he said. "If you'd been here Sunday I could have showed you around the city. I don't work Sunday."

"I really think I should go back," I said.

"Yeah," he said. He took out a pack of gum and gave me a stick and then took one himself and put the pack back in his pocket. "Does Father know you came?" he said.

"Yes," I said. " I left before they were up . . . but I left a note and told them."

"He'd be angry when he found out," he said.

"I don't care," I said. "Let him get mad."

We came to another intersection and looking over to our right we could see the harbor and beyond that the mountains on the north shore. The sun had gone down and the whole sky was covered with blood-orange and pink and yellow and purple; it made the mountains look shadowy purple, almost black. There was a dotted line of lights climbing up the side of one of the mountains and I knew it was the mountain chair-lift. "You know what I'd like to do now?" I said.

"What's that, Pat?" he said.

"I'd just like to go back to your place," I said. "Maybe we could look at some magazines or something."

"Okay," he said.

We started walking faster. We passed a little bakery and Clifford went in and I saw the woman take four little chocolate cream things out of the window and put them in a cardboard box and then Clifford paid her and came out carrying the box. "I thought you'd like these," he said. "They're really good . . . I've had them before."

"They looked really good in the window," I said.

We walked back to the house and went upstairs and put on the small drop-cord light. Clifford took the kettle and went in the bathroom and put some water in it and then came back and closed the door. "I'll make some tea," he said. "Would you like some tea?"

"Yes, I would," I said. I sat down on the edge of the bed. My legs really felt stiff and I ran my hands up and down my thighs and watched Clifford. He turned the hot plate on and then got down the teapot and started putting tea bags in it. "How's Father?" he said suddenly. "And Jeannie?"

"They're okay," I said. "I guess."

He didn't say anything else but he seemed to be taking an awful long time to put the tea in the pot, so I said, "Father never mentions you. I guess he's still mad."

"Yeah, I guess so," he said. He walked over to the corner and took down a couple of scribblers from a small shelf. "Like to see some of the stuff I'm studying?" he said.

"Sure," I said.

He opened one of the notebooks and there were some drawings in colored pencil and some handwritten notes and a lot of loose typewritten sheets. "This is what they call biochemistry," he said. "I have to study this before I take my exams."

"When are your exams?" I said.

"Oh, not for a long time yet," he said. "Not until I finish my apprenticeship. But it doesn't hurt to get started ahead of time." He put the book down on the bed and went over to make the tea. I flipped some of the pages. "I guess you get a pretty good salary," I said.

"I don't get very much right now," he said. "You see, I'm only an apprentice and that means they're teaching me. It's like going to school in a way, except that I get paid."

"How much?" I said.

"I get eleven dollars a week right now," he said. "But next year I get fourteen; and I also get a week's holiday with pay next summer."

He poured some boiling water into the teapot and put the lid on it and then turned the hot plate off. I just kept looking around at the room; it was clean and bright and neat, but there wasn't very much homeyness about it. There was a stack of magazines on a chair in the corner and a few pocket novels on the shelf by the bed and a calendar from some produce company on the door of the closet and mother's Wedgwood vase sitting up on top of the cupboard, but there was no radio and there were no lamps or cushions. The window was still open and there was a cool breeze floating in and when I looked out I could see the soft orange squares of lighted windows in the houses across the street.

"A year is a long time," I said.

He brought two cups over and put them on the table and then got a bowl of sugar out of the cupboard and a small can of milk and some teaspoons and put them all on the table. "It's too bad you haven't got a radio, Clifford," I said.

"I've never been much of a guy for listening to the radio anyway," he said. "You know that." He poured out some tea and put the pot back and then opened up the box with the chocolate-cream pastries in it. "Dig in," he said. "They're good. You'll like them."

I picked one up and took a bite out of it; they were really good. I'd never tasted any-thing like that in Abbotsford. Clifford took one and ate it and then started drinking his tea. "Finish them up, Pat," he said.

"You have another one," I said.

"Not for me," he said. "I can't eat much of that stuff. It makes me sick. Besides, I can get them any time I want." He watched me eat them with a little smile on his pale face. "Do you like them?" he said.

"They're super!" I said. "What do they call them?"

"I don't know," he said. "They've probably got some European name." He picked up his cup and took a drink and I noticed that every time he did the steam fogged his glasses and he had to wait a couple of minutes before they cleared again. "What are you going to do now that you're quit school, Pat?" he said.

"I don't know," I said. "I can go to work in Abbotsford. I can even work for Father in the store."

"Is there any kind of work you want to do?" he said. "Anything in particular?"

"No," I said. "I haven't made up my mind yet."

We finished our tea and then Clifford went and washed the cups out and dried them and put them back in the cupboard. We just sat around for a while and then we both decided we were tired so we went to bed and put the light out. I was lying on the outside of the bed. and I could see out of the window without moving.

There were a lot of bright-lighted windows and streetlights and car lights sliding down the street; but they all seemed as though they had nothing at all to do with Clifford and me lying there in the darkened room; then away in the distance against the dark night sky I could see the bright amber-pointed lights of the Lions Gate Bridge curving through the darkness across The Narrows.

I must have been just dozing off when Clifford spoke. "Pat?" he said. "Are you asleep?"

"Not yet," I said.

"Pat, why do you suppose Father got so angry with me?" he said. "I only wanted to live my own life."

I didn't answer for a moment. I wanted to say that it was all because Father was such a bullheaded character; but I knew Clifford wouldn't believe that about anybody, let alone Father. He'd just say there was some reason beneath that. "I don't know, Clifford," I said. "Maybe he just wanted to have his own way."

He didn't say anything for several minutes and I thought he must have gone to sleep; then all of a sudden he said, "So you think he really hates me, Pat?"

"I don't think so, Clifford," I said. "Maybe you just don't see things the same way, that's all. It'll work out okay." I waited for quite a while and there was no sound so I reached over in the darkness and put my hand on his shoulder; he didn't move.

The next morning Clifford woke me up. "Pat! It's half-past seven," he said. "I've got to leave pretty soon. Pat?"

I sat up and opened my eyes; there was bright sunlight pouring through the window and brushing across the cups on the table like liquid amber. Clifford was already dressed and sitting at the table drinking a cup of tea. "I thought I'd let you sleep for a while," he said. "You looked tired."

"I'm okay," I said. I got up and put on my clothes and went across the hall and had a wash and then came back and sat down at the table. "That toast sure does smell good," I said.

"I'm sorry I haven't got more than just toast for your breakfast," he said. "But the fact is that I forgot to get any bacon yesterday."

"That's okay,' I said.

He got up and started to make some toast on the hot plate but I went over and took the bread from him. "I'll do that," I said. "You drink your tea."

He went and sat down again and took a sip of his tea; then he looked out of the window. "You've got a nice day for your trip back," he said.

"Yeah," I said. "It should be okay." I turned the piece of bread over on the wire mesh on top of the electric plate. "What time do you have to leave for work?" I said.

"I usually leave about fifteen to eight," he said. "It takes me about fifteen minutes to walk." He drank the rest of his tea and washed the cup out and then came back and dried it on the dish towel and put it back in the cupboard. "Don't bother with those dishes before you go, Pat," he said. "I'll clean them up when I come home."

"I can do them," I said. I took the toast over to the table and put some butter on it and then poured some tea into a cup. "It won't hurt me to do a few dishes," I said.

"Well, I guess I'd better go," he said. He walked over and opened the door and stood there a minute with his hand on the doorknob. "I guess you'll come in again sometime when you get a chance," he said. "I don't mean right away, but . . ."

"Sure, I'll be in again, Clifford," I said.

He was still standing there with his hand on the doorknob as though he wanted to say something but didn't know just how to say it. "Well, anyway," he said, "watch yourself on the highway. And give my best to Abbotsford when you get back. So long!"

He closed the door and I could hear him going down the stairs; then I got up and went to the window and watched him go out through the gate and start along the street. He was walking very fast and he had his head down; he didn't look back.

I went back to the table and ate the rest of my toast and drank the tea and then I went back to the window. The bright morning sunlight sparkled and shimmered over the harbor and the windows in the buildings on the distant north shore. I kept thinking about Clifford and when he would come home again that night and there would be no one in the room and he would sit down all alone and eat his supper and then wash the plate and the cup and put them back in the cupboard and then maybe go for a walk or else do some of his studying until it was time to go to bed.

I went over to the cupboard and took down the bowl I had seen him taking money from and looked inside. There were some receipts for his room rent every week, each one made out for five dollars and signed by the landlady; and there was one quarter, a nickel, and two pennies. I put the bowl back and sat down on the edge of the bed again. I kept remembering the way he had watched me when I was eating in the café and the way he had put the two-dollar bill on the counter so casually and the chocolate-cream pastries he had bought me on the way home; for a minute I thought I was going to bawl.

After a while I got up and went downstairs and asked the landlady if I could use her phone to call home and told her I would see that she got paid in a few days. Then I called the long distance operator and asked for Abbotsford 723 and waited until the buzzing and clicking stopped and I heard the receiver being lifted on the other end fifty-some miles away.

"Hello?"

"Hello," I said. "Jeannie? This is Pat."

"Patrick Barton!" she said. "Where are you?"

"I'm in Vancouver," I said. "Where did you think I was; Siberia?"

"You don't need to think you're being smart," she said. "You're going to get into plenty of trouble when Father sees you! You'd better get right back here this very minute!"

"I'll just go outside and get in my jet," I

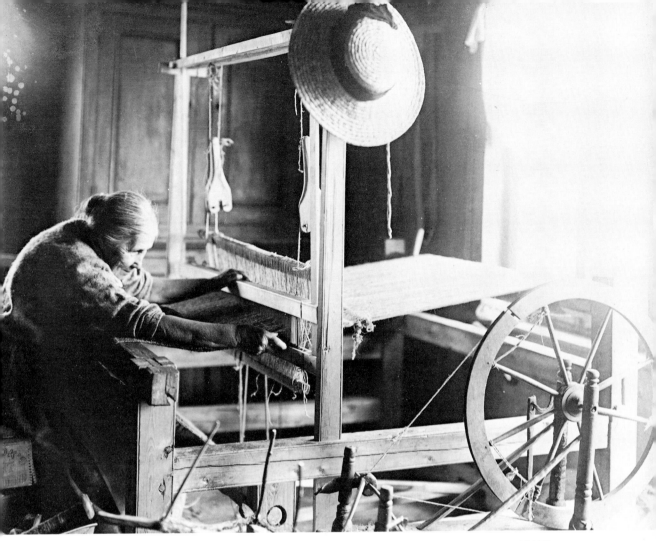

A HABITANT FARMER TILLED HIS FIELDS IN A WARM SHIRT MADE FROM THE ROUGH CLOTH OF THIS LOOM

Montreal's Notman

## THE PRICELESS NOTMAN DISCOVERY

What was Canada really like in the nineteenth century? What did our grandfathers and grandmothers look like when they were young? What did they do for fun? What did *their* grandfathers look like? In the 1950's that question was answered in wonderful detail when Maclean's (in association with the Redpath Museum, Montreal) unearthed, catalogued and presented to the nation the life's work of pioneer photographer, William Notman. Here are eight pages of Notman's camera art, all taken (with bewildering skill) before 1900.

ON A BRITISH COLUMBIA RIVER IN 1864, A CANOE WAS BEACHED

THE VARIETY OF NOTMAN'S SUBJECTS WOULD BEWILDER TODAY'S
PHOTOGRAPHERS. LANDSCAPE, SEASCAPE, PORTRAITS, STILL LIFES,
THEATRICALS—HE'D SET HIS CUMBERSOME CAMERA AT ANYTHING. AND
THE LASTING QUALITY OF HIS NEGATIVES, ALL OF THEM ON GLASS, IS
TYPIFIED BY THE FOLIAGE DETAIL (ABOVE) AND THE CLARITY OF THE
LONG PERSPECTIVE (AT RIGHT). NO KNOWN PHOTOGRAPHER ANY-
WHERE ON THE CONTINENT WAS ACHIEVING BETTER RESULTS; FEW
WERE DEDICATED TO CAPTURING A PERMANENT IMAGE OF THEIR TIMES.

IN "SHOCKING" COSTUME, AN ACTRESS POSED FOR POSTERITY

MAN O' WAR H.M.S. "GARNET" BEFORE STEAM HAD QUITE REPLACED SAIL

POSTAL INSPECTORS? IMMIGRANTS? REPERTORY
HAMS? WE'LL NEVER KNOW, BUT THEIR NAMES
WERE CAREFULLY LISTED: ROP & WAMSLEY

PERHAPS THE MOST BEAUTIFUL WOMAN THAT
EVER WALKED INTO NOTMAN'S MONTREAL
STUDIO. ON THE NEXT PAGE: TWO THESPIANS
—A MONOCLED VILLAIN AND A SWEET MAID

THESE UNKNOWNS—PROBABLY MONTREALERS—
HELD THEIR BREATH WHILE NOTMAN SQUEEZED
THE RUBBER BULB AND COUNTED OFF THE
EXPOSURE SECONDS. TO POSE IN COSTUME WAS
ALL THE FASHION AS THE CENTURY FADED

A MASTER OF MONTAGE, NOTMAN PIECED BOTH
OF THESE SHOTS TOGETHER FROM INDIVIDUAL
PHOTOS OF EACH MAN TAKEN AT SEPARATE
TIMES. ONE OF HIS MAJOR MONTAGES, COLORED
BY HAND, PASSED FOR YEARS AS A PAINTING

said. "I should be there by the time you get out to the back porch." That's the only way I can hold my own with Jeannie.

"I'm not fooling, either," she said.

"Neither am I," I said. "Is Father there?"

"No," she said. "He's gone down to open the store. He's been absolutely *sick* worrying about you!"

"Well, tell him I'm staying here!" I said. "Did you get that? I'm staying here with Clifford!"

"You're what?" she said.

"I'm staying here," I said. "I'm going to get a job here in the city. Don't you understand English?"

"Now look, Mister Man," she said. "Just because Clifford gets too big for his boots is no reason for you to think you can just do what you want! Don't either of you ever think of Father . . ."

"Oh, shut up!" I said. "This call is costing money. Are you going to tell him or not?"

"Of course I'm going to tell him," she said. "And he is going to be as mad as . . ."

"Then he'll just have to be mad!" I said, and hung up.

I went back upstairs and washed the dishes and put them away in the cupboard; then I looked in the want ads in the paper and I saw an ad for a delivery boy so I went downstairs and phoned the number and the man took my name and told me to come Monday morning and I would have first call for the job. Then I got my bike out of the basement and went for a ride down by the docks.

About four o'clock I came back and put the bike away and went down to the shopping district. I still had sixty-five cents I'd been going to use for hamburgers and stuff on the way home, so I bought some butter and some tomatoes and some jam tarts and took them all back to the room. Then I cut some salmon steaks and fried them in butter and put them on a plate and slid it under the hot plate; and after I'd done that I cut up some of the tomatoes and put the kettle on and then set the table.

I kept going over to the window and watching for Clifford; and then all at once I saw him coming down the street. He had a newspaper in one hand and he was walking more slowly than usual and he still had his head down. I waited until I saw him turn in at the gate and then I put everything on the table and poured some boiling water in the teapot and put the lid on it and then I sat down and waited for the sound of his footsteps on the stairs.

ROBERT THOMAS ALLEN

# How to Live with a Teen-Age Daughter

Something that bothers me is the glib way TV and movies create human beings, and one of the most off-handed creations in recent years is the teen-age daughter, who is about as close to anything in real life as Roy Rogers is to a cowboy.

The last TV teen-ager I saw was portrayed by a well-groomed, accomplished young Broadway actress in her midtwenties, who wore blue jeans, a pony tail, said things like "real cool," and evidently figured that was close enough to a teen-ager because she just took off from there. At one point she came on screen smiling and telling her mother to rest while she made supper—a little bit of fantasy that even made my daughters blush. I think it's time we got it straight what a teen-age daughter is really like.

A teen-age daughter is something between a child and a young woman in ten petticoats, bare feet and crooked lipstick. Her main drive in life is to wear spike heels and My Downfall perfume, dress like a $25,000-a-year fashion model out of *Seventeen* magazine, give as much lip as the traffic will bear, stay up till midnight, which she claims every child of normal parents is allowed to do, and to avoid all work, which she claims all normal parents do themselves.

She's never chilly; she's frozen. She's never warm; she's burning. She never dislikes anything; she loathes it—and this sometimes includes her father and mother who, she thinks, won't face the facts of life.

Right now my eldest daughter is learning how to tear an engine apart in one of her courses at school and she believes that anyone —me, for instance—who thinks English, decorum and typing would be more useful, is some weird sort of peasant who is dying out, and none too soon.

"What would you do?" she asked me with scorn, "if your car broke down, say, in the middle of the Sahara desert? Just stand there and look at it, I suppose."

The truth is that's just what I would do. What I can't get across to her is that it's just what she'd do, too, except that she would look at it from inside the car. Already she can stand looking at an unmade bed all Saturday morning without even seeing it.

Those TV conversations between a teenage daughter curled up on the rug and a wise and understanding mother who explains things like how to recognize true love when it comes along I've yet to hear. The conversations in my house are all about hair and clothes and jobs that my daughters are trying not to do.

"Why aren't you at the dishes?"

"I have to do my hair."

"Why didn't you do it this morning?"

"I had to do my homework this morning."

"You had time to do it last night."

"I was looking at Gunsmoke last night."

"You were supposed to be ironing your blouse for the Twirp Dance."

"It doesn't need ironing."

"Which one are you going to wear?"

"The one with the blue trim."

"You'd better press your blue skirt, too."

"I have to do my hair."

"Are you going to let it grow or have it shaped?"

"I'm going to have it the same length all over."

"You should wash it. It's beginning to look dull."

"I have to clean my room."

"You should have thought of that last Friday."

"My hair wasn't dull last Friday."

A teen-ager doesn't care about whether she can recognize real love when it comes along, as long as she's wearing the clothes she wants when it arrives. And she spends about three-quarters of her home life fighting for them with her mother, who just wants her to be clean, dressed so that adults won't laugh, and so that she'll be warm on cold days.

I live near the school-bus stop and can watch the teen-agers gathering in the morning, sneering in the direction of their homes, indignantly showing one another the socks, sweaters, coats, mitts, mufflers their mothers made them wear.

"Look what *my* mother made me wear!" they say, holding things as if they were at a rummage sale. "You'd think I lived at the *North Pole!*" While their mothers, judging by what's going on in my house, have all collapsed in tears over the breakfast table.

Their daughters all come home at three-thirty on the same bus, waving to their mothers, all on the honor roll for citizenship, cooperation and neatness. Then they make cottage-cheese sandwiches, leave the cheese, bread knife and crumbs where they dropped and walk right out of their shoes, sweaters and books and leave them in the middle of the kitchen floor.

Anything a teen-ager discovers for herself, she adopts violently and usually becomes ashamed of her parents for not having discovered it themselves in all these years. The last thing my daughters discovered was religion. They went around praying for me and getting me to drive them to church affairs arranged by some indefatigable woman named Mrs. Henshaw, who evidently lives in church basements and either has the most confused mind in the world, or my daughters get everything she says wrong.

"We're to be at the church tonight at seven-thirty," they say. "You're to bring some nuts."

"What kind of nuts?" This is the first I've heard of it.

"I don't know," they say, from behind a TV guide. "Coconuts, I guess. You're to bring your old glasses too."

"My what?"

"Your glasses. They're for the needy."

"Who needs them?"

"Poor people who aren't as privileged as you. We're to have them there before our rehearsal for The Lonely Tramp. At the church —I think—or somebody's house. Maybe it's Mrs. Henshaw's."

My wife and I spend some weekends snapping out instructions like cab dispatchers. "I'll drive them in as soon as I've had my bath and pick up the halos for them on the way back so they have them for the pageant at three-thirty unless there's a meeting of the Junior Citizenship League," I'll yell, trying to catch up to the schedule of one particularly active minister who keeps telling my daughters to ask me if I've heard God's voice lately.

One time when I was writing to a minister friend of mine in Peterborough, I told him about this and asked for advice on how I could cope with it. He replied that he was glad to hear that my daughters had found a spiritual home, and devoted the rest of the letter to telling me about his new motorboat.

I meet other fathers outside the wrong churches, houses and youth centres, who are as confused as I am. One time a tall, thin father parked outside the Sunday school, wearing a ski cap and dozing. He woke up, leaned out and called, "Is this where I was to bring the bagpipes?"

Another father, backing up slowly and leaning out his door, said, "I thought they said 'gas pipes.'"

One time I arrived with a car full of props and found nobody around but an old gentleman walking on his heels on the church lawn and muttering, "Angels! Angels! Every blessed one of them!" He was evidently referring to my daughters and their friends who were taking part in the last act of a pageant, which I'd thought was going to take place the next night.

Oddly, I knew what he meant. I've sat on hard Sunday school benches, looking at my daughters by candlelight with tears pouring down my cheeks fifteen minutes after I'd been telling them that I'd written for the procedure for getting them into reform school, which I really don't think is the thing to do with teen-age daughters.

There's only one thing to do with them: wait till they're twenty.

ANDREW WALTER ROY

# The Great Cross-Canada Hike

In the cold, high mountain passes and rock cuts of British Columbia five strangely assorted figures—four men and a woman—plodded wearily and determinedly westward on the first days of June 1921. They had come a long way. Their faces were tanned and burned by the sun and wind. They were thin, leg-weary and footsore. Their nerves were worn, and their minds bitter. To people they met in the small mountain railway towns they made angry accusations against the other walkers, calling them cheats and liars.

They were miles apart as they walked—two teams of two and one man by himself. At every whistle stop telegraph keys excitedly chattered the news of their progress. All over Canada thousands of people anxiously called newspaper offices and asked: "Who is ahead now?" . . . "How far to go?"

For this was one of the most memorable treks in Canadian history—an almost incredible hike of 3,645 miles from Halifax to Vancouver, across Canada, in about four and a half months. It was started as a lark by two young men with a feeling of wanderlust and nothing better to do. It ended in a grueling, bizarre and bitter race as five people wore themselves to exhaustion satisfying a clamorous country-wide guessing game as to who could walk farthest and fastest.

From Saint John, N.B., to Vancouver they all followed the same route along the railway tracks of the CPR. They walked through winter blizzards in the Maritimes and Quebec, snow and rainstorms in Ontario and the cold and muddy spring of the prairies. One team got on the wrong track and walked a hundred miles the wrong way. Others were pursued by wolves and fought them off with guns. They slept in Canada's best hotels and in trackside shanties. They were lionized by politicians and by socialites eager to share their limelight. They paid their own way by selling postcards to the thousands who came out to see them in cities and hamlets. They suffered frostbite, blisters, hunger and exhaustion, and in wild stretches of mountain or bush they were sometimes afraid for their lives. In return, they were widely acclaimed.

Their fame and success ended as abruptly as it began—almost the moment they reached Vancouver—after they had walked from January to June. The long hike left none of them rich or famous. Today only a frenzy of old newspaper records commemorates their effort. But they were real Canadian pioneers in the freakish field that later witnessed such sadistic demonstrations as marathon dancing, flagpole sitting, goldfish swallowing and long-distance swims.

The great cross-country hike originated in one man's idle whim. The man was Charles Burkman, born in Port Arthur, Ontario, but who, in the winter of 1920-21, found himself in Halifax and out of work. He had a friend, Sid Carr of Halifax, and one day, footloose and thinking of adventure, Burkman suggested they start walking westward and perhaps find a job.

"How far?" Carr asked.

Burkman hadn't thought about that. "Maybe to Vancouver," he said. And so the idea jelled, and grew stronger.

In early January Burkman and Carr walked into the editorial offices of the Halifax *Herald* and the Halifax *Mail* and announced their plan to walk across the country—on the CNR tracks to Saint John, N.B., and then they would follow the CPR tracks. They had arranged to have postcards printed, showing their picture and telling of their hike, and they intended to sell these to pay their way.

The newspapers seized on the stunt and offered to pay Burkman and Carr for reports on their walks, to be sent by telegraph from railway stations along the route. The *Herald* suggested they carry a letter of greeting from the mayor of Halifax to the mayor of Vancouver.

On Monday, January 17, 1921, Burkman and Carr appeared on the steps of the Halifax city hall to start their trek. In a chill rain and fog several hundred people had gathered.

Hurriedly, Mayor J. S. Parker wished them good luck and handed Burkman a letter to be delivered to the mayor of Vancouver. Then the men set out, many of the crowd on their heels. One admirer, carried away by visions of the adventure, begged them to let him join the trek. Mile by mile, his pleas grew weaker until, after five miles, he sat down on a stone and waved them farewell.

Burkman and Carr planned to walk about fifteen miles a day until the weather improved. Then, in the spring, they intended to step up the pace to thirty miles a day. They had calculated that it would take them seven months to get to Vancouver. If they had any idea that the trip would be a mere stroll for pleasure, it vanished on the third day, when the temperature dropped to ten below zero. Frostbitten but cheerful, they walked all day to reach Truro, Nova Scotia's rail hub, by evening. They had completed sixty-four miles.

The next morning Truro turned out in hundreds to see the two men. They were showered with boots, clothing, food and cigarettes by Truro merchants. The postcards, at ten cents each, sold by the dozens. It was noon before they got away, and more than a hundred people followed them through the railway yards and along the track.

Most of the Maritimes newspapers had taken up the story, and the accounts of how Burkman and Carr were being acclaimed on their route acted as a magnet to other walkers. In Dartmouth an energetic postman named John Behan read them and decided to start out after the Halifax pair. He wrote to the Halifax *Herald* and proposed a father-son walk: Behan, senior, forty-four, and Clifford Behan, twenty-four, would walk to Vancouver in six months—a whole month less than Burkman had estimated. They would pass Burkman and Carr before Montreal, they promised.

The *Herald* agreed to accept stories from the Behans, who fortified themselves with postcards, as Burkman and Carr had done, and started out. Although in middle age, John Behan had been an oarsman and was fit for the walk. Both he and his son had served overseas with the Halifax rifles. Since Dartmouth and Halifax, across the harbor from one another, are constant rivals, the entry of the Behans into the trek gave Dartmouth a chance to crow. The Behans were given a civic send-off in Dartmouth, pocketed a letter from Mayor Simpson to the mayor of Vancouver, crossed the harbor by boat and started walking.

Then, unexpectedly, the casual odyssey became a three-way contest when a well-known Maritimes foot-racer named Frank Dill threw his hat in the ring with that of his wife, Jennie. Dill, from Windsor, N.S., had enjoyed some local prowess as a runner; he worked in a Dartmouth iron foundry. He and his wife were fellow sports; they fished and hiked together. They had decided to head for Vancouver too, they advised the Halifax *Herald*, which by now had found itself a sort of official starter. The *Herald* welcomed the entry, for, in addition to the fact that Dill was a public name, Mrs. Dill had women's interest. Although an angler and hiker, she was by no means mannish, but quite small, dark, feminine and piquant.

Thus, three teams were in the race, and when the fact that it *was* a race became known to Burkman and Carr, the first of a long series of emotional crises appeared. Burkman and Carr, plodding along the right of way, were friendly enough. But when the Behans began to press on their heels, and then the Dills, that was another thing.

"I won't be forced into racing across Canada," Carr insisted. And so, at Petitcodiac, fifteen miles west of Moncton, N.B., he got on a train and went back to Halifax. Burkman went on alone, after a group of Halifax sportsmen, in the throes of civic pride, collected five hundred dollars to spur him on. As January ended, Burkman was at Welsford, N.B., the Behans were at Dorchester, having walked through a blizzard. They had gained a day and a half on Burkman, and were still confident they could pass him before Montreal.

Frank and Jennie Dill appeared on the stage of the old Majestic Theatre in Halifax the last evening in January. They made a big hit, Jennie in particular. The next morning two thousand people met in front of the Halifax *Herald* building to see the couple make their start. Jennie created a sensation dressed in riding breeches, boots with high leather leggings, and a mackinaw jacket and cap. In 1921 it was unheard-of for women to be seen in men's clothing. The iron foundry had given Frank Dill's fellow employees the day off and they turned out with banners and horns.

The popularity of the Dills far exceeded that of the others. At Shubenacadie the Ladies Aid of the Presbyterian Church insisted that they stay at the home of one of its members. In Truro their reception surpassed even the arrival of a circus. They were met by a parade of school children. They sold more than two hundred postcards and left Truro loaded with dimes.

The Behans arrived at Saint John, N.B., on February 4, having walked forty-five miles in one day. They had been royally received everywhere, except at Norton, N.B., where the station agent unexplainedly harangued a crowd to incite violence against the hikers.

By February 6 Burkman was well into Maine—halfway to Montreal. He was traveling on the Maine Central rails, over which the CPR had running rights. He had been caught in a snowstorm and thought he would have to seek shelter, but a snowplow came along and Burkman fell in behind it to cover thirty miles that day. The train crew pleaded with him to get on and ride but he refused. This happened to all the contestants many times.

The night of February 6 the Behans reached Fredericton Junction, N.B., while the Dills made Amherst, N.S., after walking at times up to their knees in slush. All through the next week there were heavy snows in New Brunswick and Maine. The Behans one day made only eleven miles, the Dills ten miles.

By February 15 Burkman had arrived at Sherbrooke, Quebec, having walked 650 miles in twenty-nine days. The Behans were at Longpond, Maine, 531 miles in twenty-one days, while the Dills were at Saint John—275 miles in fourteen days. The Behans announced that they had given up hope of passing Burkman before Montreal, but said they would pass him in northern Ontario.

Walking in wild country, all five contestants often feared they would be attacked by animals, then shrugged it off as unlikely. Suddenly, on February 15, the Behans had a taste of what was ultimately to confront all the walkers. Pacing along a desolate stretch of track, they heard growling in the bushes to the side and three wildcats bounded out. Jack Behan drew a revolver. The wildcats crouched a few yards away, crawling slowly. Then one leaped. Behan fired. The cat, wounded, prepared to leap again. Behan fired twice more and the wildcat fell dead. Its companions vanished like wraiths into the bushes.

No wildcat, but a policeman, stalked the Dills outside Saint John. He took them for tramps and walked up to arrest them for trespassing on railway property.

"This one," he said, placing a firm hand on Jennie Dill's shoulder, "can come along with me."

"Meet the wife," said Frank Dill.

The policeman looked at Jennie and then his face broke out in a grin. "Why, it's Jennie Dill," he said, as he recognized the face from newspaper pictures. He escorted them into Saint John.

Women flocked to see Jennie Dill, and her charm won everyone's heart. Before starting, Jennie had listened to friends plead with her to give up the trip. Some said she would not last to Truro. But here she was, 275 miles later, and feeling better than when she started.

On February 19, crowds lined Montreal streets to see Burkman arrive. He stayed at the Windsor Hotel where kings had stayed before him, and was host to scores of reporters. He had made sixteen changes of boots along the way, but found a broad-toed, heavy pair of shoepacks most comfortable. He had a few blisters—most of his trouble was caused by socks. He said the toughest part of the walk was over, and thus proved himself a poor prophet.

By the time Burkman left Montreal on February 21, the Behans were at Sherbrooke and coming fast. They had covered those 650 miles in twenty-six days—a three-day gain on Burkman. The Dills were at Lambert Lake, Maine, 385 miles from Halifax in nineteen days.

Burkman lost time on the walk from Montreal to Ottawa. The maze of railway tracks put him off, and by mistake he got on the Grand Trunk line instead of the CPR.

On February 25 he finally reached the capital. He was taken in hand by P. F. Martin, MP for Halifax, and was introduced to members, Cabinet ministers, the leader of the Opposition, and to Prime Minister Arthur Meighen. Burkman was a likable young man who made friends easily, and in Ottawa he received hundreds of letters of encouragement from all over Canada.

As February ended, the standing of the contestants was: Burkman at Renfrew, Ontario, 926 miles in 42 days; Behans at Plantagenet, Ontario, 859 miles in 34 days; Dills at Lowelltown, Maine, 577 miles in 27 days.

The Behans arrived in Ottawa on March 1. They had had hard going, especially in Maine, where they had hit the worst of the storms. At one place they had to crawl over a railway trestle on their hands and knees, for fear of being carried away by a gale. The Behans also made the rounds in Ottawa, met the Prime Minister, attended Commons debates. On the road again, they were pursued by animals, this time wolves. They did not have to defend themselves, however, and spent a night sleeping in a barn. They suffered greatly from the cold, and had to get up and walk around to get warm.

The Dills had seen nothing more dangerous than a deer on their travels, but they had one near mishap in Maine. They were walking, one on each rail, with a stick between them for balance. The track was downgrade, with a sharp curve. Suddenly they felt the rails vibrate beneath them. Glancing back they were shocked to see a locomotive bearing down on them. They jumped just in time. The engine had been coasting downhill and the engineer could not see them for the curve.

Back in Halifax, interest in the race was intense. One Halifax man bet a thousand dollars the Behans would catch Burkman by March 12. It had become known that Burkman was having foot trouble. He had reached North Bay by March 8, but his boots were in bad shape and he lost a day getting new boots.

The Behans arrived in North Bay on March 10. Nothing was heard of them for several days and it was believed they were taking a short cut to pass Burkman. But they were merely keeping quiet so as not to inform Burkman how close they were. They failed, however, to overtake him by March 12.

On March 13 Burkman finished a sprint in which he walked seventy miles in two days. He had made himself a roller-skate contrivance which he placed against one rail while he walked on the other. This gadget had a couple of rods with handles, and by leaning against it to maintain balance Burkman could walk along the rail at a steady clip. Necessity was the mother of this invention as the rock ballast on the tracks in Northern Ontario was so coarse that to walk on it was almost impossible.

While the two leaders were neck and neck, the Dills had reached Ottawa. As almost everywhere else, their reception surpassed anything experienced by their rivals. The women of Ottawa flocked to see the little woman who had taken on a man-sized walk.

Then on March 14 the Behans overtook Burkman at Azilda, Ontario. Burkman, passing through Chelmsford, had arranged with the telegraph operator to wire him at Azilda if the Behans, on their arrival at Chelmsford, planned to carry on farther that day. The Behans talked the operator into believing they were staying in Chelmsford for the night. Then they quietly slipped out. Burkman, getting word that the Behans were spending the night at Chelmsford, decided to spend the night at Azilda. The Behans arrived in Azilda late at night and went to the same hotel where Burkman was staying.

About 2 a.m. the hotel proprietor awakened Burkman and told him the Behans were there. Burkman dressed at once and started out. The Behans rose at 4:30 and took after him. They caught up to him at Larchwood, a few miles along the road. The men shook hands, and they walked along together. They covered fifteen miles before stopping for breakfast. For the rest of the day they walked, neither able to pass the other. The railway was double-tracked; each took a track, and they raced abreast.

The middle of March saw the positions as

174

follows: Burkman and the Behans at Pogma, Ontario, Burkman after fifty-seven days on the road, the Behans after forty-nine days; Dills at Ottawa, 871 miles in forty-two days.

The third week of March saw heavy storms in northern Ontario and the hikers had to work for every mile. The Behans and Burkman struggled on together for three days, neither able to gain a lead. On March 18 Burkman finally gave his opponents the slip by getting out ahead at Woman River.

Then followed three days that the Behans were silent. Were they using their strategy of not giving their position away? The truth was that they were lost. They had been told by an Indian guide that a side track, which ran through logging country, joined up again with the CPR and would cut off one hundred miles. Instead, it ended at a camp fifty miles in the bush. The only way to get back on the CPR was to retrace their steps. They walked an extra hundred miles and wasted three days. They loudly blamed Burkman, saying that he had put the Indian up to tricking them to take the short cut.

Meanwhile, mile by mile, the Dills were gaining. They were not without thrills either. On March 22 they were walking along the track near Rutherglen, when a wolf came bounding behind them. Jennie Dill had a revolver in her belt. As the wolf sprang at Frank, she drew the gun and fired. The bullet stopped the wolf. Frank killed it with another shot.

By the time the Behans got back on the main line the Dills were at North Bay. Burkman had kept silent for four days, but on March 26 the Behans again overtook him at White River, 1,497 miles from Halifax. Now, as the Behans and Burkman fought for the lead and the Dills began to press on their heels, an element of intrigue was added to the other fantastic trivia of the cross-country sideshow. Mrs. Dill caused a flurry when she revealed that she had received two letters from Charlie Burkman. She claimed her husband was jealous—he thought Burkman was holding back so the Dills could catch up to him.

At King, Ontario, Burkman again gave the Behans the slip. He moved out in the middle of the night when the Behans were sleeping. The temperature was eleven below zero and he thought this would discourage them from trying to catch him, but when he was ten miles out he was surprised to hear Jack Behan hail him. They walked together the rest of the day and stopped that night at Heron Bay.

The next day the Behans turned the tables and slipped away on Burkman. About one mile out they had their first glimpse of Lake Superior and at Peninsula they were told that the special train of the Duke of Devonshire, Governor-General of Canada, was due in ten minutes. They waited, and when the train stopped they asked to see the duke. They were gruffly refused, but Jack Behan slipped aboard and saw the duke's secretary, who became interested in his tale and arranged for the duke and duchess to receive the two men. The Governor-General autographed their books and they received gifts from the duchess.

The end of March saw the Behans leading at Jackfish, Ontario, 1,596 miles and sixty-five days out of Halifax. Burkman was a short distance behind, and the Dills were at Woman River, 1,310 miles and on the road fifty-eight days.

The first of April brought another intense storm. The station agent at Middleton warned the Behans but they disregarded his advice. They made only sixteen miles that day, and the storm was so bad they again had to crawl over trestles. Burkman was not heard from after this storm and fears were felt for his safety. However, he suddenly walked up and slapped the Behans on the back in the post office at Cavers, Ontario. The Dills were making good time. They did sixty-two miles in two days to reach Woman River and they were doing over thirty miles on most days.

The three men in the lead were walking together on April 4 when they were attacked by wolves. It was near Ruby, Ontario, and they were still going after dark. They heard wolves howling behind them and the men held them off by shining flashlights. Someone had told the Behans there was a shack about four miles along the track and they made for there, the wolves at their heels. At the shack they barred the door. There was little sleep as the wolves howled all night.

This was wild, sparsely settled country, but the Lakehead cities were near. On April 6 the hikers reached Port Arthur. Hundreds were at the station to greet Burkman, while the Behans were met by former Nova Scotians who took them to Fort William. While the leaders were at the Lakehead the Dills reached Franz, Ontario, having struck warm weather. Fair-complexioned Frank Dill was suffering from sunburn.

On April 8 the Behans passed the halfway mark of the journey. This was Savanne, Ontario. Burkman was about eighty miles behind, while the Dills were at Peninsula, after doing forty miles in a rainstorm. They were making better time than any of the others. The Behans now had a two-day lead on Burkman, who nevertheless had a two-day rest and was eager to pass his rivals.

On April 13 the Dills lost time getting boots

repaired. They were entertained at a party given in Cavers. When they left Cavers the wives of the telegraph operators motored to Gurney, eleven miles along the route, cooked dinner in the open, and had it ready when the Dills arrived.

About this time the Behans began to have trouble with blistered feet. On April 14 they walked only seventeen miles. Burkman was not heard from for four days. It was rumored he was injured falling from a precipice on a short cut. He finally turned up at Raith, having been injured when he slipped on a rail and sprained his hip.

On April 20 the Behans reached Winnipeg, eighty-four days after leaving Halifax. The same day, Burkman walked forty-five miles to reach Kenora, while the Dills finished the day at English River.

Past the halfway point in their trek, the walkers began to exert even greater efforts, and the strain told on all of them. On April 28 Burkman walked all night, and covered fifty-five miles before stopping to rest at Portage la Prairie. In Winnipeg two days earlier, he had stopped only long enough to pick up summer underwear. On May 1 the Behans were at Elkhorn and the Dills were in Winnipeg. By May 5 Burkman started traveling at night to avoid walking in the heat of the day. His first night he walked forty-eight miles.

Then, on May 5, a sandstorm caught all the hikers. The Behans, however, made Regina; Burkman was at Virden, forced again to get new boots, and for a few days he was slowed down once more. On May 9 all Canada thrilled to hear that Frank and Jennie Dill had caught up with Burkman at Broadview, Saskatchewan. The Behans were at Ernfold, 161 miles ahead.

The record of the hikers up to this point was: Dills, average 25⅔ miles per day; Behans, average 25½ miles per day; Burkman, average 21⅔ miles per day.

The middle of May saw all contestants driving themselves grimly. The Dills were only a day and a half behind the leaders. Burkman, who was suffering from sore feet, was falling behind. At almost every town the Dills were besieged by photographers and reporters. They put on a sprint to Calgary and walked fifty-two miles at one stretch, which cut the Behans' lead to forty-one miles. However, they now lost a day in Calgary which they greatly regretted later. So many easterners wanted to entertain them that they found it hard to refuse. The Behans thus gained a day's walk.

By the night of May 27 the Behans reached Lake Louise. They had suffered from nosebleeds caused by exertion and the fact that they were unaccustomed to higher altitudes. They slept on the station platform at Lake Louise and this almost cost them the race, for Clifford Behan caught a chill.

The pressure began to tell on the walkers' nerves. When Jack Behan heard that the Dills had walked fifty-two miles in a day he was not only skeptical, but outraged. He claimed it was impossible for a woman to perform such a feat. He said the world's record for walking for a woman was forty-seven miles in one day, held by an American woman. Jennie Dill, however, proved capable of even more.

Behan was beginning to show the results of the long grind. He had lost fourteen pounds and was constantly tired. The Dills now were really driving. They left Morley on a Saturday morning and made Banff by night, having walked forty-two miles. Jennie was so exhausted she couldn't even talk. However, the next morning they left Banff and actually arrived in Field, B.C., a few hours after the Behans had left.

May ended with the race drawing near its end. The Behans were at Glacier, 3,225 miles in 125 days; the Dills were but a few miles behind, being on the road 118 days; Burkman was at Banff. Clifford Behan's back had been bothering him since the cold sleep on the platform at Lake Louise. The pain became so severe he could hardly move. Clifford insisted that his father keep going. He said he would go to Revelstoke by train and seek medical attention.

When Jack Behan arrived in Revelstoke he found his son in bed in the YMCA. A cold had settled in the muscles of his back. But he insisted on getting up, going back by train to where he had abandoned the hike and then walking to Revelstoke to catch up with his father. Thus the Behans pressed on, and by June 4 they were back in their stride. That day they walked fifty miles in fifteen hours to Kamloops. Burkman likewise was now fired with ambition to catch up and he walked a hundred and forty miles in three days.

When the leaders were at Spatsum, the Dills were at Kamloops, forty-seven miles behind. Burkman was at Sicamous, eighty-eight miles behind the Dills. At this point Jennie Dill accused the Behans of cheating. She claimed that, according to the times the Behans reported being in each town, they must on one occasion have walked thirty-three miles in four hours. The Behans made no reply to the charge.

June found the Behans at Haig, with only eighty-nine miles to go. The Dills were at Kanaka, with 149 miles remaining, with Burkman reaching Kamloops on that day. On June 12 the Behans by an all-night hike arrived in Vancouver and nosed out the Dills. They walked sixty-one miles in twenty-two hours and were exhausted to the point of collapse. The Vancouver *Sun* reported that the hike had left its mark and "It was hard to determine who was father and who was son."

The time of the Behans from Halifax to Vancouver was 3,645 miles in 136 days. The Dills arrived on June 14 and were declared the winners. They had gained five full days on the Behans. Burkman was still eighty-one miles out and he arrived in Vancouver on June 16.

Jennie Dill was terribly thin at the end of the hike, and all the hikers were deeply tanned. None had an ounce of surplus weight. This was the end of the great cross-Canada hike, but it wasn't the last heard of the intrepid hikers. Jack Behan took his defeat hard and challenged Dill and Burkman to race from Montreal to Halifax. He claimed that he was the fastest walker, that Dill had been held up by his wife, while he had been held up by his son.

The others took him up, and in Montreal and Halifax interest was intense. Sportsmen in Halifax put up a thousand dollars to be awarded as prizes. The start was set for ten o'clock the morning of July 5, but the previous evening Burkman decided to withdraw. Behan and Dill were still hurling challenges, so it was decided that the two of them would race.

The weather was the hottest Montreal had seen for years. At the start on the morning of July 7, the temperature was over a hundred. The hikers walked along the streets to the tracks of the Grand Trunk Railway. They walked thirty miles to St. Johns, and both men were nearly prostrate with the heat. The next morning they started out, but at Foster, Quebec, Dill collapsed. The temperature was 104 degrees. The doctor refused to let him continue. Behan readily agreed to give up the contest.

What became of the contestants in this grueling test? Frank Dill died in Halifax in 1928. Jennie remarried and died in Halifax in 1941. Burkman had a ticket from Montreal to Halifax, but never used it—he simply dropped from view.

At eighty John Behan still claimed that he and Clifford were the only ones who walked all the way, and he was sorry then that they had. "We came home broke," he said, "our families in debt, and we couldn't get work. We had to move to the U.S. to pay our debts."

Like all the walkers, Behan's fame ended when he stopped walking.

L. JOHANNE STEMO

# The Courting of Jenny

The midsummer's sun set in a billow of flame in the Strait of Georgia. The down of shedding fireweed floated aimlessly on the warm breeze. To Matthew Breckner, making his way home from Hidden Lake, the trail held the quality of all island trails in summer—a dry woodsy aroma spicing the sea breeze, a wink of birds' wings, the call of a distant hooter; while above, the blue dome of the sky ripened into a soft haze.

He was fully clothed again. His faded cotton shirt covered broad shoulders. The stiff canvaslike denims sat easily on him though his knees still held a strange weakness. He was nineteen, balancing on that intangible line from boy to man, the youngest of the Breckner crew.

There were five Breckner boys: Andy, Creit, Bowman, Digby and Matthew. And there was the Old Man. The Breckners lived by a law unto themselves. The Old Man had homesteaded the island in the old days and, one by one, as the boys came, he laid claim to land for each of them: leasing, squatting, warring on all intruders till there were more than six hundred acres under his control.

Matt remembered when they had farmed, grazed sheep, raised a few head of stock. Now all that was changed. The timber off the land had set them free. The Old Man was close to seventy but he still held the deal in all family transactions. Cagily he sold the poorest timber first. The boys took out poles and ties. Now the timber that remained was a stand of pure gold—towering firs, many reaching twelve feet across their butts.

The boys hunted, fished and swam and, when the *manana* atmosphere of the islands palled, the receipts from the timber took care of chartered planes to Vancouver, of careening U-drives and liquor. But so far the Breckner reputation had not touched Matt. Robbery, arson, even murder had at one time or another been linked with the names of the others and rumor had it that the Old Man's coming to the island was the result of a break with the law.

But Matt was different. He even looked different. Where the others were sandy-haired and rawboned he was handsomely dark, with an inner calm that gave an appearance of gentleness. He moved with a catlike grace, without effort. Often in the evenings he could be seen splitting wood, bringing in kindling and water—chores that were considered woman work in the Breckner tribe and beneath a man. And in the dull lustreless eyes of Ma Breckner would come a momentary glint of something akin to hope as she watched her last-born.

Matt topped the rise. To his left the open strait spread below him to dissolve in the distant smoke and mist that shrouded Vancouver and the mainland; through the trees on his right the last rays of the sun gilded the island-dotted channel.

From here the path dipped sharply downward and soon the squat log cabin that he called home came into view. He slowed his steps, not wanting to meet with the others yet; afraid that the turbulence inside himself would communicate itself to them. He spied a log, straddled it and let his mind go back to Jenny and the afternoon.

He had gone down to the far bay to see if the island tug had picked up the two poles he had salvaged a couple of evenings earlier and had come back by the old school trail. A hundred yards off the road he had come upon Jenny filling a pail of blackberries. "How's the picking?" he said.

"Oh—" She was startled. "All right, I guess."

"You come up here often?" He was making conversation, not analysing the reason but wanting to hear her talk, wanting to see the berry-stained lips part in a smile.

"When the blackberries are on." She seemed pleased and surprised that he had stopped to talk.

"Seems forever since we used to come this way to school, doesn't it?"

"Yes," she said, letting her eyes go back. "Two years."

"Three for me," he grinned. "Gosh, them were the days. Ever go up to the lake any more?"

She shook her head. He had a sudden urge. "Let's go up there now. I'll help fill your pail and you can pick it up on your way back."

The sun was high as they turned off the school trail to the overgrown path that skirted Hidden Lake. Once out of the shade of undergrowth the heat rose in waves from the dried marsh grass; sandpipers flitted across the sand dunes; ducks skimmed across the water to settle and feed near the far shore. The sharp blue of dragonflies whirred endlessly.

"Do you hunt up here?" she asked.

"Nah—there's lots of other places to hunt. Wouldn't seem right here."

"No," she agreed, looking at him wonderingly. The escapades of the Breckner tribe were legend on the islands but any scraps of conversation she had overheard involving Matt had given him grudging approval. Her own approval lay open in her face and in the quickening of her pulse beat. "A tiger don't change his spots nor a leopard his stripes," her Gramps had countered but then he was full of quotes and figures of speech that didn't always apply.

"Look," she said. "Look—water-poppies!"

"Sure, acres of them. Want me to get you some?" He dragged off his shoes, turned up his denims and waded knee deep in the water. "Gosh, it's warm."

"Remember when we used to go swimming here?" She kicked off her sandals and paddled in.

"They should have called it Forbidden Lake," he said and laughed out loud. "Gosh, they couldn't have kept us out with a shotgun them days. Wonder if the kids still come up here?"

"I'll bet they do," she said.

"Wonder if the first ones here still get the hole around the bend?"

"And cheat!" She laughed up at him with the shared memory. "When the girls got here first there was always some boy poking his nose through the bushes."

He joined in her laughter. "And what a hornets' nest that started."

They found a partially submerged log running down from the bank and chose a place to sit between its forked branches while their feet still paddled the water. Jenny broke the shimmering that fell between them. "It's like being alone in the world up here."

"When they tell you about Heaven guess there couldn't be a place more beautiful," he said. "Only this is better. There's a place to swim."

Slowly she lifted her eyes to his and the question that was in them was reflected in his own. "We could," he said. "Sure we could. There wouldn't be anything wrong."

He felt the sudden glow that suffused them both and with one accord they rose. "I'll have the far hole," she said and he barely caught the words before she scampered from view around the bend.

For a moment he stood hesitant, his eyes skimming the green duckweed-covered shallows and going on to the crystal clarity of the depths and then he shed the cotton shirt and heavy denims and, stepping down the length of log, clambered out upon a moss-grown deadhead and dived headlong into the pool. Seconds later he heard a splash around the bend.

He swam lazily, effortlessly, feeling the soft flow of the water against his body, swimming frog fashion, crawling, treading, flipping over on his back in a partially submerged arc, arms crossed, staring up at the blue sky, listening . . .

"Matt—" she called.

"Uh-huh."

"It's warm over here."

He turned over and swam again, from the depths of the first pool to the beginning of the bend, splashing and making a great noise. He caught the shimmer of her body through the water. She turned over on her back and her long hair floated in a dark mass on the water. Sunlight caught her face as she laughed over at him.

He slid through the shallows that joined the two pools. They paddled vigorously, splashing, laughing, letting the feel of the slapping water carry the moment; ducking, racing, and, then, breathless, they rested. Her eyes, soft as brown velvet, met his in exciting conspiracy yet so completely innocent that the moment hung suspended like a bubble and neither of them spoke for fear of bursting it.

Finally their glances broke and the water swirled with their bodies. They swam tirelessly, turning, feinting, gliding, or just treading water and then floating for long moments on end. He caught up the dried broken fork of a tree from the bank and they used it to rest their arms. Then they swam again, the sheen of their young bodies glistening through the water; dragonflies whirring over the far green; birds calling; ducks clustering at the far shore, scattering and clustering again as the waters broke in unaccustomed ripples and the quiet of the afternoon echoed and re-echoed with their voices.

It was much later when Matt dived from an outcropping on the far bank and, looking across the water, saw her still clinging to the forked limb. With sudden concern he swam toward her. "Anything wrong?"

She was slowly treading water. He hair hung in long wet strands. Her face looked wan and her eyes dropped from his. "I'm tired."

"Tired?" The word was a stranger to him and then he grasped her meaning. "Tired—oh sure. I'll go." Then, looking up into the sky, he was stunned to find the sun's rays coming low on the horizon. "Gee, I didn't mean . . ."

Crimson suffused their faces and spread. The gossamer web that had clothed the afternoon exploded in their faces and their nakedness was like a pointing finger.

Matt scrambled through the shallows, swam to the first pool, reached the far bank and hurried up. He drew the stiff denims over his still-wet legs and slipped his arms through the sleeves of the old faded shirt. His boots felt hard and uncomfortable on his damp feet.

He went farther up the bank and stood in the dry marsh grass, not wanting to wait but knowing he must, wanting only to hold the past few hours alive in his mind, feeling the soft flow of water around him, seeing the sheen of their bodies, wanting to hold on to all of it because somehow he knew it could never be like this again.

Jenny came up the narrow path and it amazed him that she was still beautiful. He must have been blind all these years. But she was ill at ease now, wanting only to get away.

"Gramps will be looking for me," she said. "I'd better go." She darted ahead of him and soon all he could see was the polka-dotted scarf she had knotted around her head and then she disappeared in a fork of the road.

Matt followed and, when he came to the fork, turned the other way toward home. He'd had nothing but a few berries since breakfast but when he saw the curling smoke from the cabin he stopped in his tracks. He tucked his shirt in under his belt and ran fingers through his hair. It was as though he anticipated a questioning, and yet he couldn't remember that they had ever questioned him.

In his mind's eye he saw Jenny disappearing down the path. Would she have to explain her absence to her grandfather? For the first time he wondered about the strangeness of her life with the hermitlike Gramps who was a fanatic in a sense—living apart from the world and its sins and rearing the granddaughter fate had left him in an atmosphere of Biblical quotes and strict discipline. It could not be much fun for a young girl.

He might have gone on remembering—remembering the flush that had crept up and over her face, the soft eyes, the excitement that had been between them, as crystal clear and shining as the water. But now two mongrel dogs came yapping and racing up the path. He picked up a small stick. "Here, fetch." He tossed the stick far into the underbrush. The dogs leaped forward.

"You think I got nothing to do but serve meals here at all hours?" said Ida, Creit's wife, as Matt stepped into the house. "I got a notion to just sit and twiddle my thumbs an' see how it feels to be a lady."

Creit was cleaning his gun on the front stoop. He ducked his head through the open door. "Long as we're living here you're cooking the grub. Ma washes up. You cook." He paused, then added, "Take more'n twiddling your thumbs to make you a lady." He grinned over at Matt.

Matt sat down to the table and began buttering a slab of bread while waiting for Ida to bring in his dinner. Three of the boys were married, and of the three wives Matt had always liked Ida best.

Bowman's and Digby's women were cringing shapeless creatures with many children. There were times when Matt had felt a stirring of pity for them but there had been contempt too, for their spineless acceptance of everything. In some ways they reminded him of his mother and this filled him with unaccountable anger. There were times when they had the same lustreless eyes with that vague almost vacant expression as though they could close out their surroundings at will and nothing would touch them.

In comparison, Ida was a prancing war horse full of life and vigor. Coarse laughter and violent abuse fell with equal ease from her lips. When Creit returned alone from one of his bouts in town she would make a great show of favoring Matt and asking, "Eggs boiled just right?" and "You'd never let a girl sit home if you was her man."

Creit would wink at Matt and Matt would wink right back and the abuse would fall like a cloudburst. Then the Old Man would rouse from the couch. Like an evil patriarch of bygone days his rheumy eyes would drip fire. His scrawny beard would part and the Breckner tribal laws would be bellowed forth with new ones added as necessary.

Once in a forgotten period of his life the Old Man had attended a camp meeting and, though no noticeable change for the better had come of it, he had nevertheless garnered suitable quotations that, if not entirely accurate, served his purpose. He spouted a few and glared self-righteously.

"Who God hath joined together let them stay put." He cleared his throat and dared anyone to deny the gems that fell from his lips. " . . . The man shall rule over the woman."

"There's other commandments," said Ida. "What about the others?" She plunked the dish she was carrying upon the table.

"Fah," said the Old Man. "I don't know how Creit came to pick you up but you're here an' you'll stay put. I'm still in control an' you don't want to forget it." He settled back on the couch, rolled over and seemingly went to sleep.

Matt's and Creit's glances met, then fell. Andy, the oldest and unmarried, continued reading in his corner. Ma let her knitting drop, eased up from her chair and walked noiselessly out of the room. Ida clattered back to the kitchen and they could hear pots and pans being shoved about, the crash of crockery and the tinkle of glass.

Matt had always had a sort of admiration for the Old Man, a kind of respect as it were for the lion in his den. It came to him now that the others didn't; they hated him. It was the green gold in the hills that tied them to the Old Man's purse strings; that and the freedom that would come with his passing. Matt had never courted a girl. He thought about it now. Tomorrow he would call and make himself known to Gramps. Momentarily he worried about the Breckner reputation, then shrugged. He would go out in the morning and start felling timbers for a log cabin. No one could mistake his intentions then. He'd worry Creit and Andy into helping, and by the end of the month there ought to be a fair house up.

He shoved back from the table and tried to see his surroundings as if he were looking at them for the first time. The grimy oilcloth-covered table, bare in spots, centred the big room. Beneath his feet the floor was worn and slivered. Unnoticed, Ma was back in the rocker, staring into space. Andy hadn't moved. The Old Man breathed with a disconcerting whistle. Ida went tapping about the rooms, restless, challenging, petulant. It was no place to bring Jenny.

"Say, where'd you spend the day, boy? Looks like you got a powerful lot of sunning," Creit shot the charged words at him.

Matt felt his ears burning and cursed inwardly at his lack of control.

"Well, son-of-seacook, if I don't believe the white-haired boy's got himself a female. Ida, come here." Creit gurgled with relish. "What woman you s'pose our boy could have found all by himself this fine and sunny afternoon?"

"Not Matthew!" said Ida. "Not really. Come on, Matt—give. We're going to find out anyway."

"Can't a fellow tie up some salvage without he has to explain every move he makes?"

Creit roared. "Salvage! That's a good one." The laughter petered out; there was a knowing look in his eyes.

Into this Gramps walked with his unwilling granddaughter the next morning. He stomped up to the Old Man and without any preliminaries stated his errand. "I want to know which one o' your boys was up to the lake with Jenny all day yesterday?"

"Tarnation," roared the Old Man, coming upright. "I can't be rightly woke up yet. It sure is news to me." Then seeing the crazy light in Gramps's eyes an appreciative gleam came into his own that ended in a coarse cackle as his beard parted. "If it's true you ought to be stepping on clouds 'stead of pulling that long face."

"I've heard of you Breckners," said Gramps. He pointed his finger right in the Old Man's face.

"Fah," snorted the Old Man.

"You'll not wiggle out from under this. I'll not stand for talk going on about my girl and if she's old enough to go lolly-gagging she's old enough to marry." He looked around the room.

Matt started to say something but Creit cut him off. "You don't have to marry her Matt. He's just an old crackpot."

"Don't you be calling me names." Gramps's voice rose to an unexpected squeak.

Jenny's face was white and drawn. She had been crying and looked as though she might bolt and run at any moment. Matt felt the net close about him, an invisible tenuous thing but a net all the same. His color was up and his breathing labored.

"Well," said Gramps. "You'll marry her?"

The Old Man snorted. "They got nothing on you, boy," said Creit. Ma resumed her rocking and her eyes closed away the room. Ida's fingers drummed on the window sill. Andy sat silent.

Matt looked at Jenny. She seemed to be waiting for him to speak. His eyes turned to Gramps and he disposed of the question with a shrug. "Why not?"

Jenny looked startled, opened her mouth to say something but nothing came out.

"When?" said Gramps.

"I'm ready any time." He might have been discussing the weather for all the emotion his voice registered.

Creit stared as though he couldn't believe his ears. The Old Man laughed. "Well," said Ida. "You're gonna be one of us, honey," and put her arms around Jenny. But Jenny turned her face away. Andy resumed his reading. Unnoticed, Ma left the room.

The wedding was scheduled for the next Saturday. Gramps had wanted a minister but Matt said the local justice of the peace would tie just as good a knot and Gramps, who had not anticipated such an easy victory, did not pursue the argument further.

Andy moved his pillow and blankets from the attic which he had shared with Matt and appropriated the spare couch and a corner of the living room.

"You could fix Matt's room up some," Creit said to Ida.

"If you think I haven't got enough to do without . . ."

"There's no need," said Matt. "Guess she'll have all the time in the world to fix it the way she wants."

Creit looked over at him strangely. The bridal suite was ready.

Matt didn't see Jenny again until Gramps walked her over on Saturday morning. She was arrayed in a new satin dress and she wore a flower in her hair. Her eyes held a pleading puppylike devotion that Matt chose to ignore. They drove the scant four miles to the justice of the peace with Ida and Creit sitting in front with Matt and Gramps and Jenny in the back of the Old Man's Model A. The brief ceremony was over in a matter of minutes.

Matt, Ida and Creit relaxed on the way home, laughing and joshing one another while a pitiful smile grew more and more fixed on Jenny's face.

"Now you're one of us, boy," said Creit.

"I don't feel no different," said Matt.

"You're a card, Matt. Hear that, Creit? He don't feel no different," laughed Ida.

The Old Man was busy pouring drinks when they got home. He passed the bottle around.

Matt felt his mother's eyes upon him and then she called Jenny. They conversed for a moment and then the young girl followed the older woman into the kitchen where Ma had made some cookies while they were gone. Jenny brought out a platterful and passed them.

She's like a child dressed in grown-up clothes, thought Matt as he saw her slimness and the girlish curves that did not fill the fullness of the new dress.

For a brief moment the memory of the day at Hidden Lake came between them. He spurned his own weakness that let emotion rise and dwell unbidden like a flood. He wanted to take her in his arms even though she had dared to bring the foolish Gramps to demand marriage; even though, somehow, she had tricked him with her soft innocence; even though she had thrust herself upon him without a single invitation on his part unless . . . But of course she couldn't read his mind.

His eyes were hard upon her so that she felt his gaze and turned hesitatingly, meeting his look with a questioning awareness. The Breckner blood that was in his veins would not let go of the words that sat on his lips without a struggle. Had they been alone at this moment he might have gone to her, but he couldn't lose face with the family surrounding them.

"Hey, Matt," called Creit. Reluctantly he turned.

"Have another drink. A wedding's no time to stay sober." The bottle changed hands.

Bowman and Digby arrived with various offspring. "We hear you done it," they said and clapped Matt on the shoulder so hard that he spun across the room.

Creit, Digby, Bowman and Andy got into a huddle. Pretty soon they called Matt over. "Hey, got your stake from the Old Man yet?"

"My timber?" said Matt. "He had a lease drawn up the other day. Got to be signed yet."

"What are we waiting for, boy? Call the airlines for a plane. We could do with a couple of Seabees."

"Yeah," said Digby. "The sky's the limit on any lease the Old Man signs these days with the price of timber being what it is. Remember when you got married up with Ida, Creit?"

"Do I?" said Creit.

"Yeah," said Matt. "Yeah. A marriage ought to be celebrated."

"Hear the boy," said Creit.

"Yeah, but this is going to be different," said Matt. "This is going to be a stag." The

boys hooted. "I've always known there'd be a time I'd bust the town wide open and this is it. This is going to be a real humdinger and we don't want no women. This is going to be a stag to top all stags."

"Listen to the boy," said Creit admiringly.

"Hah," laughed the others. "This is sure going to set bad with the islanders. This is going to play plain hell with our reputation. Nobody's ever going to be able to top a stag honeymoon."

"Ssh," said Creit. He looked at the surrounding faces. "I hear a plane."

"Do tell," snorted the Old Man. "They must be mind readers up there." He had his cap in his hand and stomped ahead of them out the door and down the path that led to the bay.

"Can you beat that?" said Matt. "The Old Man must be feeling his oats. He phoned the airlines while we were standing there gassing. Guess his rheumatics must be better. We won't be rid of him for some time."

Ten days later the six of them returned, a little wan in appearance, slightly the worse for wear but much the same. Matt found Jenny staring out the open kitchen window. In the gulf the sun was setting in a billow of flame. The down of shedding fireweed drifted aimlessly. It was close and hot so that the tang of the sea was almost nonexistent. In the distance they heard the call of a hooter.

Jenny looked small and defenseless facing out the window, her shoulders hunched. Matt felt a momentary pang of remorse. "We wouldn't have been gone so long," he said, "only we had to bail the Old Man out of jail." He waited for some recognition of his return. "Well—"

He swung her around, forced her to look at him then dropped her shoulders as though they were hot coals. Her eyes were lustreless and hard. Whatever feeling had been there was screened from his view. She's like those others, he found himself thinking—like Digby's and Bowman's women . . . even Ma. He strode out of the room.

He remembered her as she had come that morning with her fanatic Gramps and scorn filled him. "They trick you into marriage," he said. "And then . . ." He'd heard the words so many times, from Digby and Bowman and Creit. "They trick you into marriage." He said the words over and over and at last he was beginning to believe them. There was no longer room for the doubt that had, from time to time, stirred uneasily within him.

He was a man grown and all Breckner.

BRUCE HUTCHISON

# Southern Ontario Baffles Me

As an exiled native son I always find Ontario baffling. It is the richest, the best known and the most mysterious region in all Canada. Every other region has been typed, if only with a caricature. Ontario has no recognizable image, accurate or inaccurate. In the national gallery its portrait is a composite blur of many faces.

In a stone house beside the St. Lawrence I asked a famous scholar to expound the mystery of Ontario.

"Never talk," said he, "about Ontario. There's no such place as Ontario, and no such thing as an Ontario person. The name is only political; it's not even a geographical expression. Why, I can show you at least half a dozen typical Ontarios and as many typical Ontario breeds. They're just lumped together on the map and they have one government. But they're as different as, say, Nova Scotia is from British Columbia. Ontario is a fiction."

Its name may be a fiction, its face a blur, but Ontario drags us all back to our beginnings. The roots of half the nation west of the Great Lakes are sunk and anchored forever in the old family soil. I began my personal discovery at Prescott where, as I have been reliably informed, I was born about a hundred years ago. Anyway, it seemed that long when I saw what progress had done to a certain house at the corner of Dibble and Edward Streets.

A few years before, I had found the elms of the garden reduced to stumps, the stables gone, the shady porch torn off and everything improved beyond recognition. Now this house, which had seen so many generations of birth in one bedroom, was entertaining another visitor. It had become an undertaking parlor. I turned away. Most Canadian boys must make the same discovery in their birthplace—they can't come home again.

What had happened to Prescott and to every other town along the river? The obese windmill, fortress of the American invaders in 1838, was turned into a lighthouse on the riverbank and snored comfortably in the sun. Fort Wellington looked natural enough within its wall of grass. But everything else had changed.

Where was that dark nest of spicy flavor, the grocery store, and the grocer, Mr. Mayberry, who gave a boy some sticky gumdrops on every errand? Where the tobacco store with the tank of live fish in the window, the rumors of card games and other shocking vices in the back room? Where the jewelry store and another back room in which a boy saw his first motion picture, of flickering cowboys and Indians?

Where all the clamorous family of grandparents, cousins, uncles and those saintly aunts who supported high tariffs and smuggled systematically from Ogdensburg, upholstered with contraband under their ample skirts? All gone.

As I was thus ruminating on a futile question, an aged man shuffled up Dibble Street. "I'll tell you what it is," he said, "the town has growed." Yes, he remembered my people, but it was long ago. "Things," he added, "ain't what they was by a damn sight."

In those few words he had utttered the obituary of an age, of an Ontario beyond resurrection, of a native folk scattered from here to the Pacific coast but still holding a fragment of this place in their hearts.

It was comforting to find that Kingston still stood changeless and serene as the capital of that lost age, and that Kingston's greatest son, John A. Macdonald, faced past and future unshakable in bronze Windsor uniform among the chestnut trees of the park. Town and man shared a hereditary look. Both were fashioned here of hard, grey limestone, were carved with the same wrinkles and wore the same tired smile. The town's pre-Cambrian stuff is so hard that Alexander Mackenzie, an impatient mason, threw down his blunted tools in disgust, went into politics and briefly replaced Macdonald as prime minister.

It will never be easy to change Kingston, even for the better. A new resident recently hired a contractor to build a modern house. These new-fangled plans, the old builder said, were a passing fancy. He and his father before him had built a hundred satisfactory houses here and all of them had been precisely the same "since the war." What war? The American Revolutionary War, of course, the only war worth remembering, the war that brought his Loyalist ancestors to Kingston.

I hasten to add that Kingston still retains a stone-faced humor even in the solemn halls of Queen's University. One of its psychology professors went out to the adjacent penitentiary not long ago and lectured on "Escapism as an Art."

If Kingston is one piece, Brockville is two. Its architecture and split personality deny the flattering myth that the Loyalist migration was composed mostly of aristocrats. The eastern half of Brockville, crammed with some of the finest homes in Canada, was founded by the Jones family. The west side, of business and modest houses, was the work of William Buell, a successful laborer. Both the Joneses and the Buells were determined to affix their names to the whole town and in their long quarrel Brockville became known as Snarlingtown, until General Brock, asked to arbitrate, suggested his own name a few days before he died on Queenston Heights.

I next pursued my study of small-town civilization in Hamilton, one of the largest small towns of the nation and, according to the natives, our third shipping port, a long way from sea. It is also, they complain, Canada's least appreciated community.

The perpetual cloud of factory smoke at the western point of Lake Ontario, the crowded business streets, the handsome residential area and a laboring population two-fifths of foreign extraction represent a miracle of industry. It had a queer origin.

When they were building railways hereabouts, some centuries ago, the steel rails from England buckled in the Canadian frost and were rerolled in Hamilton. Thus began Canada's greatest steel industry and the transformation of fierce old Allan MacNab's Loyalist village of Burlington Heights into a young metropolis.

Nevertheless, it remains a small town. Or so it always appears to me. The natives will reply, quite rightly, that I know nothing about Hamilton and that Canadians always go past it on the train without stopping to discover its peculiar virtues. Hamiltonians, living unknown off the main line, are rather irked by this neglect since their town is obviously the best in the country. A business executive, moved to head office in Toronto, talked to me about his promotion and increased salary like a man who has been sentenced to a concentration camp in Siberia. I agreed with him, expressed a sincere sympathy, dried the tears on my shoulder and set off for Niagara.

My flight through the battlefields of the War of 1812 was as badly organized as the American invasion. Like the invaders, I was soon lost in the maze of the escarpment (Hamilton has elevated it into The Mountain), then in tunnels of spring greenery beside the lake and then in an orchard of red cherries where the Americans were routed at Stoney Creek.

A farmer allowed that some kind of fight had occurred in this vicinity, he wasn't sure how or when, and kindly directed me back to Hamilton. For the second time I ran the gantlet of the town traffic before I rediscovered the broad and brutal Queen Elizabeth Highway. To keep abreast of the natives, I moved toward Niagara at a moderate speed of seventy-five miles an hour.

Now I was in another Ontario, the Ruhr of Canada. A few years before, I had driven exactly the same sort of road, built by Adolf Hitler, through exactly the same combination of factories and smokestacks in the middle of green fields, the same orchards and vineyards, the same process that is turning a peasantry into a proletariat—a common, worldwide process but focused and perfected here as nowhere else in Canada.

I say it is perfected because most of the swelling satellite towns of Toronto are being admirably planned. The factories are as modern, comfortable and sightly as factories can be. The influx of urban workers, many of them recent immigrants, seems to get along well with the farmers who have tilled this land since Loyalist times.

To the old-timer of the Niagara peninsula it is tragic just the same to see the ravenous jaws of industry biting deeper every day into the orchards, the apple trees cut down to make way for a factory, the vineyards overrun by a subdivision of bungalows.

When I came in springtime Niagara was

afoam with apple blossoms and now, on my second visit in the autumn, the trees were heavy with apples, the air with the smoke of leaf fires. On a quiet road I encountered the ancient spirit of Niagara: the man by the wayside was a rosy apple on two legs. His great-grandfather from upper New York, he told me, had brought the adjoining orchard with him in his pocket toward the end of the eighteenth century. In his pocket? "Why sure," the apple man said, "they dried out the seeds down there, they brought 'em up here and they planted 'em yonder."

He pointed to the neat rows of trees around his house. Well, these weren't exactly the trees planted from seed by his great-grandfather, but they came from the same stock. One of them, a gnarled giant, was at least a hundred years old. The present owner had grafted it with scions of Ben Davis just before the last war and it yielded more apples than ever.

"It's the soil," he explained. "There's something in it that you won't find anywheres else. The soil and the moisture and a little frost and the wind off the lake. That makes apples." Being a peaceful man and a cowardly traitor to my own province, I did not dare to admit that I was now a resident and honorary native of British Columbia, home of the world's best apples. The national debate between the eastern and western apple is not a thing to be taken lightly. So I ventured merely that the Okanagan Valley also seemed to produce quite decent fruit. At that the spirit of Niagara exploded.

The apple man's face took on a deeper crimson. He grasped me by the arm, he looked straight into my eyes and pronounced a solemn warning: "Don't let yourself be fooled, son! There's no apples in the Okanagan. Not real apples. Oh yes, they're colored all right but it's just color. Might as well be paint—lipstick, I call it. No flavor. Why? Because they're irrigated, that's why! It's against nature. Look at that"—he pointed to his row of glistening teeth—"I haven't lost a tooth in seventy-eight years. That's from apples. Niagara apples." When I got out of his grip at last, my stomach and car were full of apples much inferior (now I can safely tell the truth from a distance) to the product of my own little Pacific coast orchard.

I was soon lost again in the labyrinth of roads and secret valleys lying hidden behind the escarpment. My objective was the house of John De Cew, to which Laura Secord carried the news of Beaver Dams on June 24, 1813. As my wife is De Cew's great-great-granddaughter and as we had failed to find the house

together in the spring, I had promised to seek it out and bring her back a snapshot. There was little left to photograph—only a square of stone walls two feet thick, a waterfall splashing into a mossy cavern and an abandoned mill house.

Meditating on life's accidents that have spread the offspring of Niagara's first miller across half a continent, I sought my way out of this solitary upland, on to the garden shelf of Lake Ontario. Its almost tropical growth, dense population, clotted traffic and ever-swelling factories amaze and rather terrify the westerner. In this Ontario something more fundamental than economic change is under way.

Here, indeed, the central dilemma of all human kind is being solved. Man is trying to learn how to live with the machine and yet remain a man.

The factory workers in automobiles, crowding the town streets once crowded by farmers in wagons, the emancipated working girls in their invariable uniform of gay bandanna, tight sweater and blue jeans, the dark, potent faces of the immigrants from Europe—these are the shifting atoms in a chemistry more complex and far less calculable than atomic fission. What is coming out of Ontario's gigantic test tube? What kind of city, what kind of society, what kind of human being?

From a hill near Welland one can see both the current symptoms of the revolution and a glimpse of its beginnings, long ago. Farms, towns, factories and smoke roll out to the northern horizon. The towers of the Hydro dance in endless ballet, with outflung arms and pirouette of steel legs. Directly below the hill lies Canada's most revealing monument, the three Welland canals, triple signature of the nation in stone.

The revolution began right here when Canadians undertook their first big construction job and bypassed the continental stepladder of Niagara Falls. First they built a narrow, winding ditch with queer little locks, rising in places by seven separate steps to the mile. Then they built a wider, straighter ditch with larger locks and higher steps. Finally they built the beeline of the present Welland Ship Canal, a broad man-made river carrying an unbroken procession of ships day and night.

Most of the stone walls are still as the masons left them in the old canal and should last as long as Egypt's pyramids. Aeons hence, when visitors from distant planets ask what manner of folk lived in Canada, let them look at these three ditches. They could have been built only by a folk of imagination, courage and faith, hidden under a deceiving look of mere competence and thrift. A barefoot boy was fishing that afternoon from the wall of the oldest canal. The water ran cleanly through the deserted lock and provided good sport. Behind him, in silhouette, a cigar-shaped ship wallowed into the locks of the new canal. The barefoot boy, the narrow ditch, the broad ditch and the big ship—there was Ontario's history.

I never pause long at the Falls, for there is nothing new to say or think about them. The mechanics of the cataract, as Winston Churchill found, have not changed for quite a while. It still revolves like a mangle wringing out a ragged white sheet and soon bores the observer by its monotonous motion. So I drove on to Simcoe, the ideal Ontario town, a relic apparently untouched by the revolution and living spaciously in big brick houses, shady streets and the perfume of blossom.

Such surroundings and a long experience create a definite type of man, one clear portrait in the blurred gallery of the many Ontarios. I found that man in a mellow mansion and listened all evening to his recollections.

His Loyalist grandfather, he said, had come to Canada from New Jersey in 1796. His mother had once ridden back there alone on a sidesaddle of doeskin which he still keeps as a souvenir. Her son remembers her homemade gloves of deer hide, her candles of tallow and, in bad times, her flour ground out of beechnuts. A few miles from Simcoe my friend had traced the rutted remains of the Loyalists' skid roads. On these the first lumberjacks, with eight yoke of oxen, hauled white pine—some of it forty feet long and six feet in diameter—to some local water mill. The descendant of those men watched the retreat of the forest, the advance of the plow and the arrival of industry. All this progress appeared to him a questionable success.

"On the farm now," he said, "we've got water, plumbing, electricity, natural gas and God knows what all, even television. But I doubt we're half as happy as our fathers. And so I've kept my old privy as a kind of reminder. I can see the whole farm from there every morning. It helps me to remember."

"Never underestimate," a historian of this region warned me, "the deep groove of custom in these country people. It's still the largest factor in their society. They take their ideas, or rather their instincts, from their fathers. They're yeomen and they're Tory to the bone, however they vote.

"They really don't think much politically. They only feel. There's no use talking abstract ideas to them. They care nothing for doctrines and theories. That's why the CCF has been a total flop here, even when Ontario votes for socialism on a huge scale in the Hydro and the seaway. Take a good look at this breed. It's being outnumbered and gradually drowned by industry, and in some places by immigration."

I ate my lunch a hundred yards from the road on a beach of sand as lonely as in Loyalist times, with Lake Erie as a blue-green backdrop. A few hours later I beheld the jagged skyline of Detroit, a miniature Manhattan, across the flat garden lands of the Windsor country. Here was another Ontario, much closer, physically and spiritually, to the American metropolis than to Niagara or Toronto.

Watching the unbroken stream of ships on the Detroit River, that narrow trench between two nations, and listening to the grunt of their whistles, I asked a Windsor editor how the boundary had been maintained when the people of Windsor crossed over to Detroit as easily as they crossed their own streets and when the automobile factories on the American side paid substantially higher wages than Canada could afford. The editor, like all Canadians, just didn't know.

"Somehow," he said, "our people like it on this side. Twenty years ago I think a referendum in this town would have given a majority for union with the States. Not now. This is a labor town, a radical town you probably would say, and a quarter of it is of French-Canadian blood, but it's no suburb of Detroit. It's strictly Canadian."

The towers of Detroit soared up before us like a flimsy mirage. That mirage, I thought, had beckoned Canada for nearly two centuries but always faded under our northern sun.

From Windsor I wandered idly up the little Thames on the line of the Canadians' retreat to the battlefield of Moraviantown. The Thames naturally brought me to London, the old farm town now flanked with its "Golden Mile" of industries, and then to Stratford on its imitation Avon, complete with swans. Stratford was in the final desperate throes of preparation for the Shakespearean Festival. Sculptors, painters and costumers worked against time to make a colossal bust of Pompey for *Julius Caesar*, three jewel boxes for *The Merchant of Venice*, some Roman helmets, armor of plastic and enough women's gowns to stock a department store. Caesar, Brutus and Cassius rehearsed under the big circus tent, wearing sweatshirts, slacks and sneakers. Nowhere, not even in the Old Vic itself, had I felt so keenly the magic of the master's lines, bubbling from the lips of these Canadian youngsters.

The proprietor of a delicatessen where I purchased a picnic lunch said it was all very strange and a little crazy. "I can't make head or tail of their lingo," he admitted. "I'd rather see a movie myself. Shakespeare isn't my dish. But they tell me it's quite good for those that like it. Why, when the Festival is on you can't get a room for miles around. I'll say this for Shakespeare—he sure is good for business."

North of Goderich I met on the roadside a jolly old fellow whose white cane indicated his misfortune, but even in his blindness he could still make his way about the paths of his boyhood. His name was John L. Sullivan, his parents having fancifully christened him in honor of the current boxing champion.

Mr. Sullivan thought that a good joke. "I never got into a fight in my life," he chortled. Nor had he strayed far from his birthplace. Why should he? It was the best country he'd ever seen. Then he uttered a profound comment on that loose congeries called Ontario: "Folks go from here to Toronto and they just can't talk to the folks there. And if folks come here from Toronto they just can't talk to us. There's an iron curtain between us. Yes, the city folks are smart all right and make a lot of money. But let the smartest businessman in Toronto try to run a farm. He'd go broke. You've got to be born to it."

They don't all say that much, though. I asked a farmer of Bruce County if it was likely to rain. "It might," he said after reflection, "and then again it mightn't." Was this good farm land? "Some say so, some don't." Who would win the provincial election? "That depends." Was Premier Frost a good man for his job? "Never saw Frost." He asked my business and, learning that I was a reporter, gave me a hard look and added: "Don't you go quotin' my opinions, young fella!"

An editor in the solid brick town of Owen Sound told me he wouldn't take five times his present salary to work in Toronto, and Toronto apparently sees his point. A good part of the city population surges out here in summertime to litter the beaches of Georgian Bay with holiday cottages, to pollute the air with the smell and sputter of speed boats and to create several pretty fair imitations of Coney Island. I fled from this appalling urban annex into the quiet of Huronia, the land of Champlain's vain march to the western sea and the Jesuits' martyrdom.

Barrie was filled that Saturday afternoon with hordes of Toronto refugees moving in solid ranks of cars to the healthful follies of their weekend camps. Orillia was likewise overwhelmed by these brief birds of passage, but I was assured that the old small-town virtue of Orillia still survived. It would break through the crust of the weekend on Monday morning. This is Stephen Leacock's town, the Mariposa of his *Sunshine Sketches*. Leacock's land, and all the many rural Ontarios, remained *terra incognita* to me, and its people strangers, though they were my people by ancestry. I had come far enough now to realize that I would never know them, nor they me.

That will hardly disturb the Ontarios. For all their wealth, culture and industrial revolution they remain, each in its own comfortable compartment, some of the most isolated and provincial areas I had found in Canada. Their people are kindly, intelligent and relatively rich. But they are provincial, conventional and smug to any westerner. You can't go home again.

There was still another Ontario to be faced down the road. So, summoning up my frail reserves of courage, I headed south for that foreign island in the sea of Canada which bears the name of Toronto.

Every Canadian traveler and visiting fireman thinks he knows Toronto and usually dismisses it with a sigh or a sneer. In fact, Toronto has become, like the province around it, a series of diverse elements loosely knitted together by stitches of steel and concrete, articulated by a subway, glued by the adhesive of business but not yet fused like its only rival, Montreal. There's a Toronto of old-timers appalled by the monstrous growth of skyscrapers around their quiet homes, of newcomers dazzled by their first glimpse of Babylon; a Toronto of sober politicians in Queen's Park and brassy tycoons in Bay Street; a Toronto of churchgoers, organized crime and commercialized vice; a Toronto of writers, artists, musicians and scholars tending that tender little plant called Canadian culture; a Toronto of old Loyalist stock, who founded muddy York long ago and retain some of its flavor and all its prejudices; a dozen Torontos of foreign stocks speaking their own languages, eating their own diets and thinking their own thoughts in Canada's central melting pot.

Toronto ravens across yesterday's farmlands. It breeds sub-Torontos wholesale. It proliferates in endless suburban checkerboards where a man can hardly find his own house among ten thousand others of identical design. But it is not yet a city as Montreal is a city. Its body has grown faster than its mind. That body is nourished by the farmstuffs, minerals, timber, oil and water power of half the nation, all sucked into this insatiable maw through the gullet of the lakes and cunningly central-ized here by the national tariff until Toronto must soon become the nation's largest metro-polis. Toronto fattens on mere paper, the sterile certificates of distant ownership, thrives on the labor of unknown men from here to the Rockies, clips every passing coin, wrings out abundant profits and in its own mighty labors ships back the products of its factories and an increasing trickle of thought.

Where is the old Toronto of familiar cari-cature—the spinster lady in Victorian lace who abhorred drink, Sunday sports and the morals of her neighbor downriver? She is gone, or retired into some obscure mansion with blinds tightly drawn. Her voice may grumble some-times in the morning's *Globe and Mail* but is drowned in the afternoon scream of the *Star* and the *Telegram*, the new voice of a Toronto in birth but not quite born, and all the more shrill and positive because it is so uncertain.

Give Toronto time. A city will be born here in due season, a city of prodigious pro-portions and a collective soul. The shiny smug-ness, the well-fed, aldermanic look, the pathetic self-infatuation which so repel the stranger will disappear. A folk who could invent the commonwealth unconsciously at Gallows Hill and Montgomery's Tavern can invent some-thing better than this overgrown country town.

"Toronto," said one of its leading citizens, "will soon be the New York of Canada." He seemed to enjoy that prospect though, God save him, he should have known better, for he had been bred in the Yukon and educated in Vancouver. "Why," he added with the civic patriotism of an immigrant, "hardly anybody in this town seems to have been raised here. We've all come from somewhere else, like a gold rush. That's what makes it so exciting."

I left that man in horror and pity and escap-ed once more into Canada. A forced march took me past the innumerable lakes and week-end sanctuaries of Muskoka, into the safe re-cesses of the Shield.

IAN SCLANDERS

# Lucy of Green Gables

Anne of Green Gables, the best-loved character ever created by a Canadian author, has been tugging at the heartstrings of millions for well over half a century.

She's still a steadily moving item on the booksellers' shelves. Her favorite places, the Lake of Shining Waters, the Dryad's Bubble, the Haunted Wood, the Babbling Brook and Lovers' Lane, are high on the list of Prince Edward Island's tourist attractions and a na-tional park has been built around them. Holly-wood's two versions of her story—one silent, one with sound—were box-office hits.

Yet Anne, with her red hair and big wistful eyes and freckles and her appealing stream of chatter, might easily have been lost to the world. She spent three years in a trunk in the attic of a modest wooden house at Cavendish, a farming and fishing community on Prince Edward Island's surf-beaten northern shore.

Then Lucy Maud Montgomery, a slender attractive young woman who helped her grand-mother run the Cavendish post office, decided to fix up the dress she planned to wear to a pie social. Looking for a piece of ribbon, she opened the trunk in the attic—and found the manuscript of *Anne of Green Gables*. She had written this in 1904, when she was thirty, and after three publishers rejected it she had sighed, shrugged and hidden it away.

188

Now, on a fall day in 1907, she glanced idly at the first few poorly typed sheets. The narrative caught her interest and she read on and on until the sun went down, and then she read by flickering yellow lamplight. The carrot-topped offspring of her imagination moved her to tears and laughter. Anne, she felt, deserved another chance, so she bundled her off to a fourth publisher, L. C. Page and Co. of Boston. The firm, it developed, was willing to buy *Anne of Green Gables* outright, for five hundred dollars.

Lucy Maud was jubilant. By the standards of Cavendish, with a population of two hundred, eleven miles from a railway and twenty-four miles from a town, the amount offered was large. She accepted it in haste. Later, when more than a million copies of her novel had been sold and it had been twice filmed, she probably repented at leisure, knowing that had she struck a better bargain with Page she might have earned a fortune from book royalties and screen rights. As it was, the one payment of five hundred dollars was all she ever got from her first book although its successors were to earn her many times that sum.

*Anne of Green Gables* brought her fame, if not wealth. When the first edition came out in 1908, Mark Twain, who sired those great juveniles, *Tom Sawyer* and *Huckleberry Finn*, pronounced Anne "the sweetest creation of child life yet written." Poet Bliss Carman termed Anne "one of the immortal children of fiction." The book was translated into French, Spanish, Dutch, Swedish, Polish. It was printed in Braille.

Little girls in many lands idolized Anne and tried to act and talk like her. Anne called her friends "kindred spirits." The phrase spread around the world. Anne disliked having red hair and made an unfortunate attempt to dye it. Countless redheads were inspired to do the same thing, with the same unfortunate results.

Fan mail poured to Lucy Maud from the far ends of the earth, not only from youngsters but from missionaries in China, traders in Africa, monks in remote monasteries, soldiers in India, grizzled trappers in the Canadian north. Rudyard Kipling wrote her; so did His Excellency Earl Grey, the Governor-General. In a single week there were seven hundred letters from Australia. Lucy Maud distributed them among Prince Edward Island school children, who answered them, and for years afterward there was a prodigious exchange of correspondence between pen pals of P.E.I. and the antipodes.

Miss Montgomery, now an international celebrity, was swamped with invitations to be the guest of honor of important organizations in important cities, but she politely declined them all. Her sense of duty, her Presbyterian conscience, would not let her leave her widowed grandmother. She stayed on at Cavendish, still helping in the post office, which was a room at the front of the house, and still cooking, washing dishes, scrubbing floors. The fees from the post office were barely enough to support her grandmother and Lucy Maud refused to accept a share of them. Her own income came entirely from her writing, which she sandwiched between more prosaic chores.

Before *Anne of Green Gables* was accepted, she had produced hundreds of verses, articles and short stories for Sunday-school papers and other publications for children. Her output was tremendous but the rewards had been dismally small—rarely as much as ten dollars in a week.

After the success of *Anne of Green Gables*, Lucy Maud concentrated on full-length novels. She wrote a total of twenty-two and Anne was the heroine of half a dozen of them. She also wrote a volume of poetry. All her books, with the exception of the poetry, were popular and met with a ready reception, but *Anne of Green Gables* was her one outstanding triumph, her one best seller.

Lucy Maud's "studio" at Cavendish was a sunny corner in the kitchen, beside a window through which she could gaze out on an apple orchard. When she was writing she perched on a table, her feet against the arm of a sofa, and held her portfolio on her knee.

She would scribble the first draft of a story with a pencil on the backs of official government forms, with which the post office was invariably oversupplied. When she had revised and corrected her work she typed the final draft with two fingers on a battered second-hand machine "that never made capitals plain and wouldn't print m's at all." She forced herself to rise early and once confided to her diary: "I didn't roll out of bed until six thirty this morning. I mustn't be so lazy again."

Avonlea, the village in which she set *Anne of Green Gables* and a number of her other books, was actually Cavendish, and the spots she loved were at her doorstep.

There was a pond, Anne's Lake of Shining Waters: "A bridge spanned it midway and from there to its lower end, where an amber-hued belt of sand hills shut it in from the dark blue gulf beyond, the water was a glory of many shifting hues . . . Here and there a wild plum leaned out from the bank like a white-clad girl tiptoeing to her own reflection. From the marsh at the head . . . came the clear, mournfully sweet chorus of the frogs."

There was a spring. In *Anne of Green Gables*, Anne says: "We've agreed to call the spring down by the log bridge the Dryad's Bubble. Isn't that a perfectly elegant name? I read a story once about a spring called that. A dryad is a sort of grown-up fairy, I think."

There was a spruce grove, Anne's Haunted Wood: "A haunted wood is so very romantic . . . We chose the spruce grove because it's so gloomy. Oh, we have imagined the most harrowing things . . . I wouldn't go through the Haunted Wood after dark now for anything. I'd be sure that white things would reach out from behind the trees and grab me."

There was a tiny stream, Anne's Babbling Brook: "Have you ever noticed what cheerful things brooks are? They're always laughing. Even in winter I've heard them under the ice."

There was a path between tall maples, Anne's Lovers' Lane: "So romantic! Maples are such sociable trees; they're always rustling and whispering to you. I like that lane because you can think out loud there without people calling you crazy."

And there was a fine old farmhouse. It was owned by Lucy Maud's good friends, bearded and bashful David MacNeill, a wise and kindly bachelor, and his spinster sister, Margaret MacNeill, who had a stern face and an austere manner, but a heart of gold. In fiction, this house became Green Gables, Anne's home. Lucy Maud used David and Margaret MacNeill as the models for Anne's unforgettable foster parents, Matthew Cuthbert, bachelor, and Marilla Cuthbert, spinster.

Most of Lucy Maud's characters were, like the Cuthberts, drawn from life. They were her neighbors and schoolmates, disguised and glorified a bit, but still recognizable. Generally, her plots and incidents were suggested by real happenings. She delved into her own memories for ideas and also borrowed and embroidered old tales told by the villagers around their winter fires.

At Cavendish, people say *Anne of Green Gables* "just sort of evolved." They can sketch in the background. When Lucy Maud was an infant, her mother died. Her father later departed for Saskatchewan, where he opened a store at Prince Albert, and she was left behind to be brought up by her maternal grandparents, Alexander MacNeill, a farmer, and his wife, the post-mistress.

She was a bright precocious child. When she was nine she had read Longfellow, Tennyson, Whittier, Scott and Burns, was composing verses herself, and was already determined to be an author. At eleven she had written a boxful of stories. "They were very tragic creations in which almost everybody died," she once recalled. "In those tales, battle, murder and sudden death were the order of the day." At twelve she won a short-story contest for children. When she was fifteen the Charlottetown *Patriot* printed one of many poems which she had submitted, thereby giving her what she described as "the greatest moment of my life."

She attended Cavendish District School (Anne's Avonlea) and Prince of Wales College at Charlottetown (Anne's Queen's). At Prince of Wales she qualified for a teacher's license (like Anne) at the age of seventeen. After that she visited her father in Saskatchewan for a year, spent a year at Dalhousie University in Halifax, then taught at the Prince Edward Island villages of Biddeford and Ellerslie. Meanwhile, Sunday-school papers and juvenile magazines bought some of her stories.

In 1898, when she was twenty-four, her grandfather died. She put a comforting arm around her lonely old grandmother and said, "I'm coming home to stay with you. You'll always have me." She resigned her teaching post and returned to Cavendish, where she wrote for her living. She was happy, in this period, if an editor paid her as much as five dollars for a contribution.

From her tenth birthday on she had been filling scribblers with notes on things which struck her as having story possibilities. When a small niece arrived to stay with David and Margaret MacNeill, Lucy Maud—virtually an orphan herself—had wondered whether the child was an orphan. She had also wondered what the outcome would be if the MacNeills had wanted a boy orphan to help work the farm and had received a girl by mistake. So she jotted down this sentence: "Elderly couple apply to orphan asylum for boy; a girl is sent them."

That single sentence led to *Anne of Green Gables*. At the outset of her novel, Matthew and Marilla Cuthbert apply for an orphan boy. Through an error, they get Anne, an orphan girl. They plan, at first, to send her back to the orphanage, but she is so grateful, so delighted to have a home, that they hesitate. For awhile Anne's fate hangs in the balance, but she so endears herself to the Cuthberts that they keep her. As she grows up, she repays them many times for their kindness.

While the arrival of the niece of David and Margaret MacNeill gave Lucy Maud the idea, Anne is not patterned after the niece, who, as it turned out, was not an orphan, and who became Mrs. Ernest Webb of Cavendish. In Anne, Lucy Maud unconsciously painted a charming self-portrait. Apparently she was about the only person in Cavendish who wasn't aware of Anne's identity, although she sensed that Anne was a real individual and once said, "When I tell people that she is entirely fictitious I have an uncomfortable feeling that I am not telling the truth."

Anne was poor at mathematics; so was Lucy Maud. Anne was a gifted elocutionist: "Her fright and nervousness vanished and she began her recitation, her clear, sweet voice reaching to the farthest corner of the room without a tremor or a break." Lucy Maud was likewise a gifted elocutionist—one of the most popular performers at the fortnightly meetings of the Cavendish Literary Society.

Anne gave up schoolteaching to look after her foster parents when they needed her. Lucy Maud gave up schoolteaching to be with her grandmother. She was so faithful to her pledge, always to look after her grandmother, that although she fell deeply in love she would not marry while the old woman was alive.

The Reverend Ewan Macdonald, with whom she "kept company," was born at Valleyfield, P.E.I., and, like Lucy Maud, he attended Prince of Wales College. He was the Presbyterian minister in the Cavendish district. Lucy Maud was thirty-seven when she and Macdonald were finally wed in 1911, a few months after the grandmother's death. He was forty-one. He had been waiting for her for ten years and rather than leave Cavendish and be separated from her he had turned down several opportunities in bigger places. He and his bride soon moved to Uxbridge, Ontario, but it was too late to repair his career and all his life he remained an underpaid country parson.

His lean income was augmented by his wife's earnings. Up to 1911 four of her books—*Anne of Green Gables, Anne of Avonlea, Kilmeny of the Orchard* and *The Story Girl* —had been published. Between 1911 and 1939, although she had the management of the manse and the upbringing of two sons on her hands, she wrote *Chronicles of Avonlea, The Golden Road, Anne of the Island, Anne's House of Dreams, Rainbow Valley, Further Chronicles of Avonlea, Rilla of Ingleside, Emily of New Moon, Emily Climbs, The Blue Castle, Emily's Quest, Magic for Marigold, A Tangled Web, Pat of Silver Bush, Mistress Pat, Anne of Windy Poplars, Jane of Lantern Hill,* and *Anne of Ingleside.* She also wrote her volume of verse, *The Watchman and Other Poems,* and countless short stories and articles. She once estimated that her writing brought her a total of seventy-five thousand dollars.

Lucy Maud, in middle age, was a handsome and incessantly busy woman. She was active in congregational work, kept her house spotless, and prepared wonderful meals—yet she shut herself up in her bedroom for hours each day to write. She had an enormous collection of books, which she read and reread. They ranged from cheap detective thrillers to metaphysical tomes. A prolific correspondent, she tried to answer all fan mail, and often sent personal friends letters that were twenty or thirty pages long.

Her memory was fantastic and she could recite all of Sir Walter Scott's epic poems. She was fond of cats, would talk to them as though they were human, and always had a grey-striped one named Daffy. There were three Daffys. The youngest died at fifteen, the oldest at twenty-one.

Like Anne, Lucy Maud had a temper. It flamed in 1920 when Page—the publisher who bought *Anne of Green Gables* for five hundred dollars—brought some of her longer short stories out in a book. She sued Page claiming unauthorized publication, and the case was before the courts for nine years. Finally she won a verdict in her favor.

Her temper also flared in 1921 when she saw Hollywood's silent version of *Anne of Green Gables,* starring Mary Miles Minter. Apart from receiving nothing for the film rights, she had no control over the treatment of the story, since she had sold it outright to Page. She considered Mary Miles Minter "too sugary sweet—not a scrap like my gingery Anne." But what burned her most was that the scene of Green Gables had been transferred to the United States and the Stars and Stripes flew over Anne's school.

She forgave Hollywood in 1934 when *Anne of Green Gables* was filmed with sound. Anne's second name was Shirley. The young actress cast in the role adopted Anne Shirley as her screen name and became well-known under it. "The little girl who played the part of Anne is a good Anne," Lucy Maud commented. "There were many moments when she tricked me into feeling that she was Anne . . ." And Canada and Prince Edward Island were given some credit in the story.

"Peace!" Lucy Maud once wrote. "You never know what peace is until you walk on the shores or in the fields or along the winding red roads of Prince Edward Island in a summer twilight when the dew is falling and the old old stars are peeping out and the sea keeps its mighty tryst with the little land it loves. You find your soul then. You realize that youth is not a vanished thing but something that dwells forever in the heart."

She couldn't have written with such feeling about her native province unless she had truly loved it. Prince Edward Islanders loved her, too, and don't believe there will ever again be anybody quite like her. In Cavendish National Park most of the landmarks associated with her childhood—and Anne's—are carefully preserved, although the house in which the author lived with her grandparents has been torn down.

Green Gables, the house in which she placed Anne, has now been taken over by the federal government. On an average summer day, six or seven hundred people go through it—people from all over North America and from other parts of the world. As a rule tourists are fairly noisy: they laugh and shout. At Green Gables they speak in hushed voices, as though at a shrine.

Outside, mothers and grandmothers who were thrilled long ago by the adventures of fiction's immortal redhead wander from the Babbling Brook to Lovers' Lane and watch the sun setting over the Lake of Shining Waters, and suddenly realize, as Lucy Maud did, that youth dwells forever in the heart.

EDNA   STAEBLER

# How to Live Without Wars and Wedding Rings

Not long ago I stayed for a few days with the family of Grossdoddy Martin, in the fieldstone house which his grandfather built in Waterloo County, Ontario, in the days when the Mennonites came up from Pennsylvania to break new ground in Upper Canada. The house and the family are among the oldest in Canada—more than 150 years have passed fruitfully and peacefully, leaving few marks on either.

Grossdoddy Martin and his family belong to the splinter sect of Old Order Mennonites who still live in western Ontario on the farms their families first cleared from the forest. Their ways often seem peculiar to outsiders. They shun everything worldly, everything fashionable, but they don't mind a swig of cider. They use electricity and tractors, but will not buy cars or radios. They won't pose for pictures. They don't have telephones or musical instruments. They refuse old-age pensions and family allowances. They won't go to court or to war and Canadian law has been amended to exempt them permanently. They speak Pennsylvania Dutch. They won't buy insurance or stocks. They don't have wedding rings or jewelry. They look content.

They have changed very little from the ways of their forefathers of 250 years ago who crossed the Atlantic to escape religious persecution. This odyssey took them first to the United States and then, after the revolutionary war, to Canada. Although there are 110,000 Mennonites of various sects all the way from Ontario to British Columbia, there are only two thousand members of the Old Order. They still cling to their ancestors' farms near Waterloo and Kitchener and their five uniform churches are on their own farmlands within a fifteen-mile area.

Like most Old Mennonite farm homes, the Martin house sprawls. The main house is broad with a gabled roof, the plastered wall under the porch is sky-blue. Adjoining is the Doddy House, a small addition to which the generations of old folks retired when their sons took over the farm. Behind the kitchen is the frame summer kitchen, behind it the washhouse, the woodshed and the privy. Prosperity smiles on the home from the great painted barn.

"You don't want to make fun of us?" the Martins were anxious when I asked if I might live with them for a few days to learn and write about them. Though humble and trustful the Martins were always alert. We used our Christian names. They were natural and pleasant, and answered my questions thoughtfully, trustfully, generously, and asked me as many in return—only Grossdoddy, listening with a gentle smile, took no part. I wanted them to speak in their dialect, an unwritten mixture of Swiss-German and English, but they didn't think it would be polite since I couldn't understand all the words. They asked me to correct their English, which was often amusing.

"We're shy to talk English in front of strangers because we don't say our letters always right. Like for Jesus, we say 'Cheesus'; we know it's wrong but we forget. Amongst ourselfs we always talk German—it's easier; and if we don't our own people think we're putting on style."

There was little in the house that was not useful except, in the spare room, two bouquets of paper roses that the parents had given the daughters for Christmas, and calendars that had long outlived their dates. All the walls were whitewashed, the woodwork bright blue. There were seven bedrooms with pumpkin-yellow floors. The tiny parlor had a huge corner cupboard and wooden chairs set side by side against the pictureless walls. The kitchen was the living room, the black stove was always warm, there was comfort in the couch and the rocker in the corner. There were no curtains but tins of geraniums bloomed on the window sills.

"Make the light on," Hannah, the mother, directed after supper on the day I arrived, and the family gathered round the big square kitchen table. David, the father, worked on his income-tax papers; Salema, sixteen, was absorbed by a romantic novel; the twins, Levi and Levina, smiled at me over their schoolbooks; Hannah placidly turned the pages of *The Family Herald*; Grossdoddy sat in the shadows near the passage to the Doddy House.

"I was glad to quit school and earn money when I was eleven but often now I wish I went longer." David frowned at his papers. "If a person went to college his mind would mature in more of a hurry, I guess."

"The teacher wanted Salema to go," Hannah told me. "She finished school already when she was thirteen, but Mannassah Brubacher's wife needed help chust then, so she went there to work. People hate us for our different ways and if she was in town she would have to change her clothes or act like a turtle for shame, then she couldn't belong to us no more."

Salema looked up. "I'd like to learn but I wouldn't want to stay from home," she said. "In the city it seems each day is chust like any other day but in the country every day gives something different."

At 9:30 Hannah led me up an enclosed stair, through a bare corridor to the spare room. I slept on a straw tick and bolster.

Always the first up, Grossdoddy put on his stay-at-home suit over the underwear in which he slept and went into the parlor of the Doddy House where Grossmommy, a black kerchief on her head, lay sleeping on a hospital bed. A young man rose stiffly from a couch. "She made nothing out all night," he said, putting on his hat. "I see you next week again." He was one of the relatives or neighbors who, in the kindly custom of the Old Order, took turns to come every night from nine o'clock till dawn to relieve the Martin family of some of the care of Grossmommy's lingering illness.

There is no fear of insecurity among the Old Mennonites; their sick and aged are always looked after by their next of kin, or someone among them is paid from a church fund to care for them.

"It wouldn't be fair for us to take money from the government, because our boys don't fight in a war," Hannah told me. "Besides, if we did, we might lose our independence."

"What if the country is attacked?" I asked.

"Jesus said we must turn the other cheek— if everyone did that there would be no wars. In the one we chust had, our men helped with the wounded and went in camps and we bought war bonds but didn't take the interest off them."

"But everyone doesn't know about Jesus."

"Then we must be an example," she laughed.

When the morning milking was finished, Salema, singing "Throw out the Lifeline" in her clear young voice, drew the full cans to the cooler in a little cart. Topsy, a collie, followed her. The hens and beeplings fed, Levina pointed out a red patch by the Conestoga River. "Levi went fishing. Can you see him down there by the willow?" At the kitchen sink David pumped rain water to wash. Hannah, by the range, ran plump fingers through the curds that would be made into koch kase (cooked cheese) "when it has that smell that you don't like round the house."

"Make the door shut, Salema, we won't wait for Levi." David was hungry. Hannah tucked a wisp of greying hair under the kerchief that had covered her head during the night. "I'll comb them later," she said. Chairs were drawn up, heads bowed silently over ironstone plates. Grossdoddy reached for coffee cake with his fork. Everyone stabbed a piece and dunked it. Levi came in, pleased with ten pink-headed chub. Porridge was eaten, the remains sopped up with bread so that plates could be filled with fried potatoes, summer sausage and pickled beans. A bowl of boiled dried apples and prunes was passed.

There was talk of the day's work to be done, of things growing; there were questions and answers and there was laughter. -

"Dat, you said slang," young Levi chided.

"Dit I? Now what bad word did I say?" David pretended alarm.

"You said 'swell,'" the little boy was very serious.

"Och, ain't that awful? I must be more careful or my children won't be brought up decent," David declared. "But isn't 'swell' a bad word that could be used good?"

When we rose the plates looked as clean as when we sat down, not a crumb was wasted.

The twins, eager to play with other children, ran across the fields to school though it was only 7:30. David went to plow with the tractor, Grossdoddy sat with Grossmommy, Hannah prepared the invalid's breakfast, I helped Salema with the dishes.

"Isn't that pear tree beautiful?" Salema exclaimed, looking through the window. "I often thought already I'd like to be able to draw it."

"May you draw?" I asked her.

"I may, but I couldn't."

"We chust mayn't make pictures of ourselfs," Hannah explained. "It's in the Ten Commandments, you know, about not having likeness. We have our rules and we got to stick by them. Our retired bishop is real old and his children in Pennsylvania want him in the worst way to spend the rest of his days with them, but he can't because he would have to have his picture taken for a passport and that would set a bad example."

Hannah's hair fell below her waist as she "combed herself" at the little mirror above the kitchen sink. "We never cut them," she said, "and we all do them chust about the same." Parting her hair in the centre, she wet it to smooth out its curl, folded it flat at the sides like the wings of a bird and then wound it into a spiral, pinned firmly on the back of her head. As she tied a dainty white organdie cap with black ribbons under her chin she said, "It's in the Bible that women should keep their heads covered when they pray and we might pray any time of the day or night." Hannah never sounds pious, she accepts her rules as she does the seeding and the harvest.

At dinner, while we ate pork sausage and dandelion salad, I asked if there were any other Old Order Mennonites. "Not in Canada.

There's some in Pennsylvania and Ohio only they're a little different from us, but we visit back and forth and are related with each other. We can marry back and forth too, but it's chenerally only the leftovers that do, most of them get partners at home where their parents can buy them a farm."

David came into the conversation. "We like to stay all together. If a man's barn burns down we build him a new one; if his cattle all die we give him some. We don't have much to worry. "It makes it easier too for us to keep our rules if we aren't mixed up with other people."

"Do you think the rest of us are so bad?" I asked.

"Ach no. We think there's good and bad the same as with us, we chust have different ways."

The talk drifted to other Mennonite sects. "What we call the Newborns broke off from us because they thought we were going too fast and they wanted to be more backward yet," David said. "And the Markham Mennonites wanted cars and telephones and English so they got out, but they still use our churches and paint their cars all black. We don't know nothing about all the others—they have churches in the towns and they don't dress or act like Old Mennonites."

"My cousin in town says we should belong to their Mennonite Central Committee," Hannah said. "They all go together in that and sew and send food and clothes and implements to Mennonites in other parts of the world to give to people that need it, no matter what kind they are. But we don't believe in missions; we chust take care of our own or our neighbors."

The post box had a packet in it for Salema. "It's the books we sent for with the box tops," she smiled. One was a novel, the other a collection of old songs which she leaned over the table to study. If I had told her that her voice was beautiful she would have blushed and had no ambitious thought of the radio or Hollywood though she has eagerness, imagination, wit, a gay red mouth, merry eyes and the roundest of elbows. When a strand or two of her straight brown hair escapes its severity her mother reproves her, but Salema laughingly says, "It looks nicest when it's *shtruvelich*."

"Here comes Uncle Isaiah." Levina had started reading Salema's novel the moment she came home from school but she reported every movement on the road. An old man with a strong stern face came into the kitchen and shook hands all around. "And how is Aunt Lyddie?" Hannah asked him.

"Ach, she ain't goot. She's got the high blood pressure and the doctor says she must lose some fat but she can't—it's natural. Her mother and father together weighed seven hundred pounds." The old man settled to gossip with Grossdoddy.

While we peeled potatoes before supper Hannah said to me, "You haf such a nice apron."

"I'll let you have the pattern for it."

She grinned. "No thanks, we couldn't have one with frills over the shoulder. Our clothes are supposed to be all alike and plain so we won't think about how we look. They protect us from temptation too; we couldn't go to wicked places like picture shows without being noticed."

"Leave me show her how we are in winter." Salema ran upstairs. In a few minutes she was back, shaped like a monstrous black beehive, only her delicate nose and sparkling eyes revealed the lovely girl.

"Salema, I wouldn't know you if we met on the street," I exclaimed.

"You would," she laughed. "I'd yell at you."

A wool crepe veil was folded over her forehead and around the satin bonnet, a thick fringed shawl fastened with a blanket pin covered a loosely fitted coat, a smaller shawl muffled her chin. "It's cold in an open cutter," she explained as she took off the layers of clothes. "See, I fold my shawl straight—if I was married I'd have a point down the back." She handed me her bonnet; it was stiff and heavy as a steel helmet. "That I had since I finished school."

"She'll have to take good care of it till she's twenty-one, then we'll buy her a whole new outfit and have her bonnet made over," Hannah told me while Salema returned her things to the closet.

"Is that when she'll be married?"

"Not necessary, but she might be if she's found a partner she likes. Every Sunday evening the young folks go together to someone's house for a 'singing'; they learn our hymns that way and play games and Salema says some of them dance, but they're not supposed to. If a boy and girl like each other he might drive her home in his buggy."

"Does she go with different ones?"

"Och no, she sticks to the one she chooses at the beginning. She could fire him at the end of a year or two and go with another but never more than two before she gets married or she'd have a bad name and the boys the same. It's not like in the city where young people go with strangers; we know the parents and grandparents of everybody from way back and can tell if a marriage will be all right."

I faltered over the next question: "Do they bundle?"

"Bundle? What's that?" Hannah's innocence was honest.

"Well, they say that when Old Mennonites are courting, they—"

The young girl came back into the room. "Come on, Salema, we got to hurry now with the bean soup," Hannah said.

After supper the children were in a gay mood. They cleaned the fish Levi had caught, they patted the cats, Levina picked violets, Levi and Salema played their mouth organs (the only musical instruments they are allowed), they pranced around the pansy bed, Salema sang a song, Levina held sticks for Topsy to jump at. We smelled the honeysuckle and the daffodils; when darkness came we studied the stars.

"I often wondered already how the colored lights look when they're on in Kitchener," Salema said.

"Do you never go to town?" I questioned.

"Oh yes, to the dentist."

"But we have always to be home in time for the milking," Levina lamented.

Levi was looking at the North Star. "I would like once to see a ship," he declared.

"I, too," said Levina. "I would like to travel round the world."

"I would go with you and if we came to some cannibals they would eat me last because I am the skinniest," said the little boy.

At nine o'clock Hannah called, "Come in now, children, and wash your feet before you go in bed."

On Sunday morning Grossdoddy drove Salema and me to church. Martin's Meeting House on the highway north of Waterloo is more than a hundred years old, its annually painted clapboards gleam white. A wire fence surrounds its yard, kept neat by a munching cow, and the cemetery beside it where rows and rows of plain white slabs mark the grassy, flowerless graves. There are no family plots, here Nathaniel Martin, Josiah Ernst, Susannah Eby, Israel Weber, Veronica Erb and the still-born infants of Noah and Rebecca Shantz lie side by side.

Open buggies, two-seaters and box like *dach wegglis* (top buggies) came in a steady stream as the black-clad people gathered to worship. Horses pranced up to the cement stoop along one side of the hall, women and little girls in shawls and bonnets alighted; grandmothers went through a door near the back, mothers and children near the centre, young girls hurried to the front. Men and boys drove to the hitching chains then entered the church on the farther side. In a crowded cloakroom shawls hung on pegs, black bonnets lay on shelves; on the heads of the chattering girls were caps of white net with colored ribbons tied under their chins—the style of hair and dresses identical.

Light flooded the church from small-paned windows, walls were whitewashed, pine floor and benches unstained and scrubbed smooth. In the centre front was a long lectern; on either side of it were rows of benches facing one another with a space between them in front of the lectern for baptismal and feet-washing ceremonies. Women sat on one side and men on the other, the oldest on the lower benches in front. As a man kissed and shook hands with six men behind the desk before he sat with them Salema whispered, "That's our preacher; he's a farmer too."

Chosen by lot for life from the congregation, the preacher receives no pay, prepares no sermons, his spontaneous word is believed to be inspired. And he has authority. If a church member buys what he is not supposed to, marries outside the Old Order, gets drunk too often or does worldly things, the preacher will speak to him privately. If the vanity or sin is not repented, if it is irremissible, the erring one is denounced publicly. Though cast out of the church he is not treated unkindly and, if contrite, may return.

Salema opened a German hymn book. Led by a man's voice, the congregation sat while it droned each syllable; the bishop preached; we knelt for silent prayer. "To live honestly and at peace with all men," was the text of the long sermon in Pennsylvania Dutch. The older men and women were very still. In the long benches below us there was constant movement of babies and tiny children being hushed or taken by their mothers with bulging black satchels to the anteroom. Two rows of lively little girls, their braids tied up with string or a bit of shoelace, tried not to giggle. The young girls around us turned solemn eyes toward the preacher or stole glances at the young men on the benches beyond them.

During the last hymn the little ones filed into the cloakroom; babies in bright print or lustre dresses, black stockings and colorful bootees, were wrapped up like black or purple bundles. The service over, women and children clustered on the cement stoop to chat till their men picked them up. Salema blushingly told me she was invited out for the day.

"Sunday is our visiting day," Hannah said. "Sometimes we have twenty people drop in."

"And don't you know they're coming?" I asked.

"No, they chust come after church. When Menno Horsts moved to the farm over there behind those maples they had fifty-six the first Sunday."

"How do you feed them?"

"Och, that don't bother us, everybody helps. There's always lots in the cellar or the garden, and every Friday we bake cakes and buns and nine or ten pies. If somebody comes they're all eaten at one time and if not we haf them for the rest of the week."

During the next three days the Martins answered many more questions. "The preachers tell us to vote if we need a new bridge or something, but we don't know enough about politics to vote for the country. Artificial insemination of our cattle gives us better stock. With electricity we can do more work. Salema can run the tractor. Telephones we may have for business—if we sell fresh meat or the like o' that—but not in our houses.

"We wouldn't want our children to know some of the things on the radio. We never heard yet of any of our people stealing and only one married man we know ever went with another woman. If we had musical instruments we mightn't sing so much."

I told them a story about a man who tried to sell a car to an Old Mennonite. The farmer said he couldn't buy it because the devil was in it. "But what about your gasoline motor, it's the same thing—isn't the devil in that too?" the salesman asked.

"Yes, but he's fastened down and I can make him do whatever I want, but in a car he's running around and might get out of control."

The family laughed heartily. "That sounds chust like something Old Daniel Horst would say," David said. "He'd have an answer for anybody that tried to sell him something he shouldn't have. We take a ride in a car sometimes, but it would be a danger for our young people to own one; anyways we love to ride behind our horses—they go fast enough for us.

"Some things we do to stay different and separate, it makes it easier to keep our rules. We don't know why we have some of them; they were handed to us from generation to generation; they're not written down. The bishop, the preachers and the deacons have to change them sometimes and make new ones, but if we don't like what they tell us we can put them out of the church.

"We don't believe in converting people to our ways; we leave them alone and want to be left alone—religion should be quiet and deep in the heart not on the tongue. We're supposed to live simply so we can have more time to think about the Lord; if we got stylish we might get proud. We could never be smart like other people anyway—we're chust farmers, we love to watch things grow; hard work makes us happy and we are boss on our own land."

The last night of my stay in the fieldstone house I said, "I haven't heard a grumbling word since I came here. Don't you ever get mad? Don't your children ever quarrel? Are you never tired of working? Do you never break your rules?"

They looked at each other and laughed.

"We're all extra good just now because you're here," Levina said.

"We're telling you what all we're supposed to do but we don't always do it," Hannah grinned.

"You are so quiet," Salema said to me. "What are you thinking about?"

"I was thinking how peaceful it is here. In the world I'm going back to we are always fighting for peace," I said.

DAVID MacDONALD

# Queen of the Sob Sisters

An American soldier engaged in fighting a war with Spain from the back porch of the Tampa Bay Hotel one day in the summer of 1898 was heard to tell his buddies: "By gosh, for a five-card draw she's hot stuff. There's steam comes out of her boots all the time and the whole Chicago Fire Brigade don't put her out." The warrior was appraising Mrs. Kathleen Blake Watkins, a tall redhead from Canada, who at that time was winning international fame as the world's first woman war correspondent while politely thumbing her nose at her male counterparts. His description might have been equally applicable at any time in the career of this lively Irishwoman who swept onto the Canadian newspaper scene in the Victorian Eighties and remained its most fabulous figure until her sudden death in 1915.

As the social conscience of Ontario she issued dicta on proper manners and morals in the kitchen and on the love seat, and as a news reporter for the Toronto *Mail and Empire* she scored sensational scoops on many of the biggest stories of the day. She was Dorothy Dix, Emily Post, Nellie Bly and Sarah Bernhardt wrapped into one long slim package.

In a pre-Kinsey era she was the champion of virtue who railed at the dangers of kissing.

Thrice married herself, she campaigned to have wife-beaters flogged. For more than twenty years "Kit of the Mail" was read as avidly by Toronto charwomen as she was by Lady Laurier in Ottawa. Society fawned on her but she remained aloof and even refused to receive visitors in her own home.

With her deep auburn hair piled high, flashing eyes the color of sherry, and a queenly manner, she bustled about the streets of Toronto and Hamilton, building up a legend. She was so nearsighted that she wrote in pencil with her nose an inch from the paper; yet she could peer into the human mind and see its secrets. At the time Mrs. Watkins, formerly Mrs. Willis, later Mrs. Coleman, hit the newspaper business, lady wrestlers were held in higher regard than the ladies of the Press. Their survival was easier, too. Newspaper editors grudgingly hired women to write about food and fashions but they maintained that those women who could read were interested in no more than the niceties of preserving kumquats and how to fit a twenty-inch corset around a thirty-inch waist.

E. E. Sheppard, founder of *Saturday Night*, could claim to have "discovered" Kit. He invited her to try her hand at writing. At twenty-five, she had already been twice married and was supporting her two children. She wrote a piece on the Bohemian life of Paris, where she had once gone to school. The article was read by Christopher Bunting, owner of the *Mail*, and he gave her a job in 1889. The first column she brought into the office was pasted up, page after page, to form a twenty-foot strip.

For the next twenty years Kit wrote "Woman's Kingdom" every week. It was a full page of comment and correspondence, illustrated with ornate scrollwork, hearts and flowers. Within a few months she had injected politics, personalities, poetry, satire on society women, books, sports and even sex into her columns. She wrote thousands of words every week, all in rapid mannish scrawl. Her work covered an eight-column page of tiny eye-taxing type. Read today, most of it sounds hopelessly archaic but in her time it was great. She received hundreds of letters every week, most of them asking a question or seeking advice. She didn't bother to print the letters, merely her frank and fulsome replies:

*Fay—It is wrong of you, very wrong . . . Every girl should respect her own body absolutely. She should never permit herself to be kissed and embraced even by a man old enough to be her great-grandfather. Faugh! You hint that a girl should only permit herself to be embraced by the man to whom she is engaged. What of a girl who has been engaged to different men at different times? I knew a girl who was engaged fourteen different times and each time to a different swain. She certainly was adept at kissing when she was at last led to the altar.*

To another who signed herself "Miserable," Kit said:

*How can your husband attend sanely to his business duties if you are always hanging on his shoulder when he comes home, tearful and red-nosed, telling him he doesn't love you any more? I'd like to shake some sense into young married women like you, you are so stupid. Just imagine tearing up a plant every few days to look at its roots to see if it's growing!*

She had an answer for nearly every question and an opinion on most things. She told Young Man that vaseline would be good for his mustache; Mousie that she was suffering from indigestion; Nellie that her sister should see a scalp specialist; and Harold that if he ran off with his boss's wife he would be in danger of losing his job. When Phroso asked her how he could support his family of four on a salary of nine dollars a week, she confessed she didn't know.

Within a short time Kit's column was the most popular feature in the paper. Her salary, which had started at twenty-eight dollars a week, was raised to thirty-five, princely pay for a woman in those days. She never got another raise, but the paper found bigger jobs for her. She went to London in 1892 to write a series of articles on places made famous by Dickens. She spent the entire summer of 1893 at the Chicago World's Fair. Four years later she was back in London again, this time to write about Queen Victoria's Diamond Jubilee.

"The women in the street blaze with diamonds and jewels," she wrote. "These women are largely the American contingent who never, it seems, can be taught the vulgarity of wearing gems on the street."

Sir Wilfrid Laurier, one of the most popular figures at the jubilee celebrations, was also one of Kit's greatest admirers. They had met at a party in Ottawa and corresponded more or less regularly. He invited her to go with him to a garden party at Buckingham Palace. Kit was staying at dingy old rooming house in the East End. When Laurier's carriage from the royal stables pulled up at the door of the rooming house the neighbors hung out their windows and gawked. The door opened and Kit, carrying her parasol like a sceptre, swept out of the house and down the stairs. Lady Laurier sat with her back to the horses and Kit took her place beside the prime minister. She told friends later that on the way to Buckingham Palace she had to restrain herself to keep from nodding graciously to the people on the sidewalks.

Back in Canada she declared war on that deceiving device, the falsie. "Padding in the front of dresses should be avoided," she warned. "The heat of bust pads destroys and wastes the figure." To lend weight to her contention Kit added: "Sarah Bernhardt told me she did not begin to get stout until she laid her corsets aside forever some ten years ago. Now her figure is perfect . . . Ellen Terry never wears the corset, neither does Mary Anderson." With a typical change of pace her next paragraph dealt with theosophy. She could turn easily from a lament on the death of Timothy Eaton to a discussion of the Shah of Persia's kitchen, with its silver stoves.

Kit wrote frequently about her two children by her second marriage, Patsy and Thady. They were mentioned so often in her columns that they eventually became as well known as their mother. When they reached adolescence they took her aside and asked her to stop. Thady, a husky young man who rowed for the Argonaut Rowing Club of Toronto, went to Winnipeg to work in a bank. There he caught tuberculosis and died at twenty-nine. Patsy married a prosperous gentleman farmer.

Kit's first marriage had been arranged for her at sixteen. Her second had been almost as brief and completely unhappy. A third was shaping up in 1898 when she was thirty-four. A young doctor, Theobald Coleman, was paying her court, but his wooing was interrupted by the Spanish-American War. Over her suitor's objections Kit persuaded the *Mail and Empire* to let her cover it. That no woman had ever been accredited as a war correspondent meant nothing to her.

She bustled into Washington and confronted General Russell Alger, the Secretary of War. He laughed at the suggestion. Unabashed, Kit pestered him. A few days later he relented and wrote out credentials for her on a telegraph form. When word got back to Canada that Mrs. Watkins had been accredited, the Eganville (Ontario) *Star* told its readers: "She is the only lady out of one hundred and thirty-five correspondents who will write up the war. But we would rather have Kit's description in preference to the other one hundred and thirty-four combined."

Kit wrote her view of the male correspondents: "No man tells the other that there will be a cavalry drill at six the next morning or that the infantry are going swimming at sundown. These stirring events are locked within each press bosom and every man thinks he's got the scoop."

In one of her first stories she wrote: "There is very little news going, but I am not here to detail the serious events of the war (which have not yet commenced), rather I am here to write that light and airy matter which is ignominiously termed by the trade, guff, but which is not always easy to manufacture." Accordingly, she dug up a story of six desperadoes from Kissimmee Valley who had enlisted because they heard the Spaniards couldn't shoot straight, whereas the sheriff's posse hunting them for rustling were all dead shots. There was also the unlikely account of a recruit from New York who on his first day in camp was bitten by mosquitoes, stung by a tarantula, had a touch of malaria, ran his bayonet into his hand, sat down on an anthill, trod on an alligator, found a snake in his boot and then told her he felt like a dirty deuce in a new deck. "Dis ain't no Klondike, anyhow," he is reported to have observed.

When the American troops moved into Cuba, however, Kit turned serious. She reported that green kids were being shipped over without proper training. The wounded who came back a few weeks later agreed. General William Rufus Shafter, who commanded the army from Tampa, wouldn't let Kit go with the regular correspondents when they sailed for Cuba. She started the wires buzzing to Washington, Ottawa and Toronto. "I'm going through to Cuba," she told her readers, "and not all the old generals in the old army are going to stop me. I beat them in Washington and I'll beat them here." While waiting for help from the north she went on to Key West and got there just as the first wounded were arriving. The other reporters were still cooped up in the Press ship, miles from any action.

A few weeks later she was notified that she could go to Cuba in a Red Cross ship from Key West. But the boat sailed without her, reportedly on the orders of Clara Barton, head of the American Red Cross, who was jealous of her prestige as one of the first women to reach the combat zone. Kit did manage to wangle passage in an old government boat. She was on hand for the battle and surrender of Santiago to Shafter's army. Most of the other correspondents were not.

The *Mail and Empire* played Kit's exploits to the hilt. Black headlines proclaimed: KIT FOLLOWS THE COURSE OF THE ESCAPING SPANIARD. KIT SHOWS REASONS FOR ATTACK FROM LAND SIDE. KIT WRITES OF THE CITY OF STRUCK CAMPS. KIT VISITS THE CAMP OF TEDDY'S TERRORS. KIT TALKS TO THE WOUNDED. HOW KIT, MOUNTED ON A MULE OF HIGH DEGREE, INSPECTED THE TROOPS.

She came back to Florida in the transport "Comal." Moaning wounded lay in rows all over the ship but there were no doctors or medicine. The food was rotten. Kit, the only woman aboard, had a cabin to herself, and one night a drunken steward had DT's outside her door. All the way back Kit tended the wounded herself. She divided her own store of quinine into tiny portions and distributed it among the malaria-ridden soldiers.

Kit was famous. Newspapers in the United States and Britain frequently carried articles and editorials on her activities. So, when she arrived back in the United States, General Alger offered to sponsor her on a speaking tour of the country, to tell the nation's women of the war. She answered him hotly. "Mr. Alger, if I tell the women of the United States what I have seen, you'll have a riot on your hands."

A few months after Kit came back from the wars she married the patient Dr. Coleman. It was a happy union though some years later in a burst of frankness she admitted, not unkindly, that he was "no provider." Coleman was appointed company doctor of the Canadian Copper Company at Copper Cliff, then a bleak mining outpost in northern Ontario. He arrived with his family right in the middle of a smallpox epidemic, and Kit spent weeks working as an emergency nurse. She continued to write her weekly page there for the *Mail and Empire*, frequently referring to the town in unflattering terms. She described it in her column as a Canadian Siberia. For three miles around the town there wasn't a leaf or a blade of grass growing because sulphur smoke had killed all vegetation. After three years the Colemans left for Hamilton, a move which was welcomed by the people of Hamilton and also those of Copper Cliff.

The Toronto police department did a double take the day the *Mail and Empire* published Kit's story on young Josie Kerr. Josie had stolen a baby from a carriage in front of a downtown department store. She kept the child for a few days, then got frightened and drowned the infant. It was several weeks before the mystery was solved and the police caught Josie. Under close guard she was not allowed visitors. The public wondered what had motivated the seemingly pointless kidnaping. The police said nothing. Then Kit's story appeared. It was a long and penetrating character sketch of Josie and an analysis of her motive. The police demanded to know how Kit had reached their prisoner.

In fact, she had gone to the home of one of the jail matrons who attended Josie and announced herself as Kit of the Mail. The Matron, thrilled at such a visitor invited her in for tea. The two women talked about food, fashions and the latest shows, and the matron occasionally made casual remarks about something her celebrated prisoner had said or done. Kit listened politely, filing the scraps of information away. She hurried back to the paper and pieced them together into a revealing picture. She hadn't been within a mile of the girl.

Kit's greatest scoop was an interview with Mrs. Cassie Chadwick, the fabulous fraud from Eastwood, Ontario, who fleeced wealthy Americans and banks of nearly two million dollars shortly after the turn of the century. A dumpy homely woman, her chief weapons were a pair of supposedly hypnotic eyes, consummate brass and several promissory notes for vast sums of money—the largest was for five millions—which bore the poorly forged signature of Andrew Carnegie. She even hinted to several of her victims that she was an illegitimate daughter of the famous multimillionaire. When she was finally sued for nonpayment of loans her fraudulent front began to fall away, revealing an incredible story. People all over the United States and Canada talked about the great hoax.

When Mrs. Chadwick was brought back to face trial in Cleveland where she had lived so lavishly, the *Mail and Empire* sent Kit to get an interview. For days, while Cassie languished in the jail, Kit and a hundred other reporters hung around outside, buttonholing whoever came in contact with the swindler and scheming to see her themselves. Finally the sheriff allowed Kit and a dozen male reporters to troop through the apartmentlike cell where Mrs. Chadwick was kept.

When the first man appeared in the doorway, Mrs. Chadwick threw herself on a couch, buried her face and screamed for them to get out. She didn't see the lone woman with the men. As she was walking away, Kit dropped her gloves on a table. A few minutes later she slipped back to retrieve them. The weeping Mrs. Chadwick was sitting up now and the matron was giving her medicine.

"Are you very ill?" Kit asked her sympathetically.

Mrs. Chadwick went into a spiel about the state of her health. Kit sat down beside her. Later she wrote: "For an hour and a half yesterday I sat beside the low couch on which the cleverest, the sharpest, the boldest financier of the last century, or this, is lying . . . I held the hand of Mrs. Cassie Chadwick, the queen of finance."

That indescribable something that made people unburden themselves to Kit had paid off again. Mrs. Chadwick, unaware that Kit was a reporter, showed her the phony note for five millions. Kit wrote: "So great is the power of seven figures and a certain signature, that crisp, flaunting little note—worthless as the scraps that lie in the waste basket—gives you an awed feeling, a sort of breathlessness not only at its immensity in import, but at its magnificent insolence at being at all. On it was realized so much that brought splendor upon some lives and utmost poverty on others; it is brimful of tragedy, that foolish bit of rustling paper, yet in some extraordinary way it teems with comedy."

Kit, the matronly editor of a proper page for ladies, covered one of the juiciest crime stories American newspapers have ever splashed across their front pages. In 1906 a notorious New York playboy, Harry Thaw, shot and killed Stanford White, the architect of Madison Square Garden. He was avenging the honor of his young wife, Evelyn Nesbitt, who had been seduced by White when she was

200

**THE SPORTING SCENE**

THE PAGES OF MACLEAN'S
OFFER A STIRRING
RECORD OF CANADA'S
GREAT MOMENTS IN SPORT

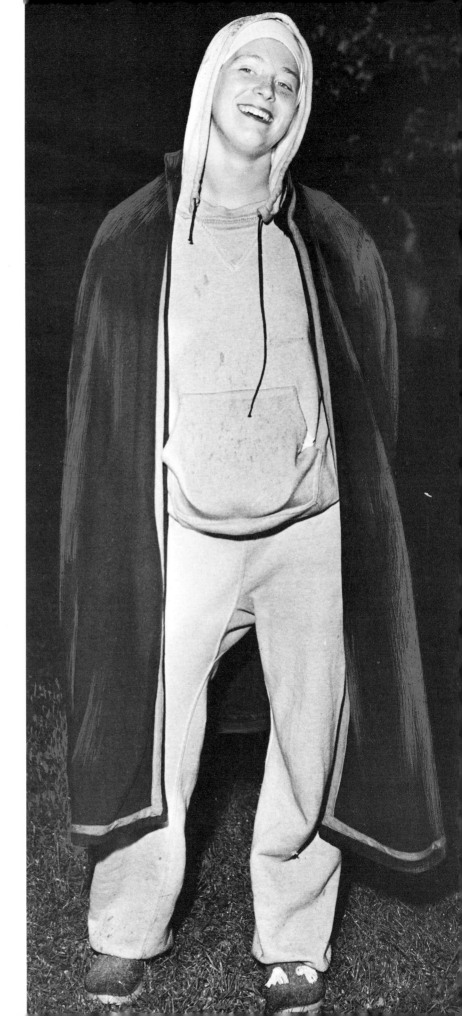

MARILYN BELL SWAM LAKE ONTARIO
AND BECAME A NATION'S DARLING

BARBARA ANN SCOTT LIVED OUT A FAIRY TALE ON SKATES

CALGARY STAMPEDE BRAVELY ASSERTS THAT THE OLD WEST STILL LIVES

THE KID LINE OF THE TORONTO MAPLE LEAFS: CONACHER, PRIMEAU, JACKSON

THE RICHARDS OF THE MONTREAL CANADIENS: MAURICE TAKES A PASS FROM HENRI AT THE TORONTO GOALMOUTH

HOWIE MEEKER,
HOCKEY COACH

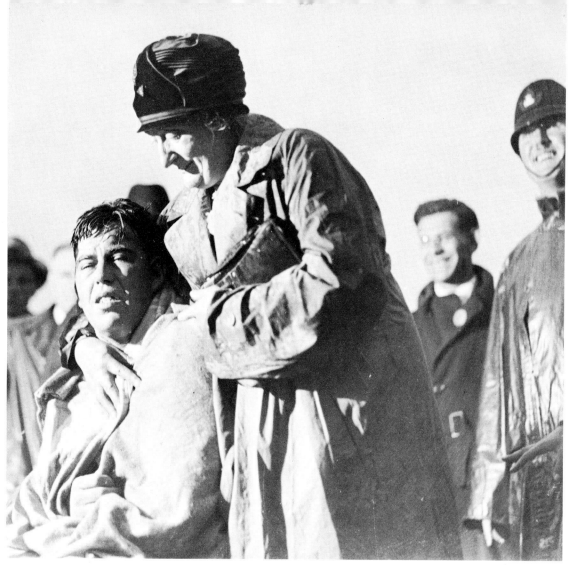

MARATHON SWIMMER GEORGE YOUNG AT THE CANADIAN NATIONAL EXHIBITION

SAM LANGFORD: BOXING BROUGHT HIM FLEETING FAME AND LASTING BLINDNESS

FRANK MERRILL WINS MORE RACES THAN ANY OTHER TRAINER

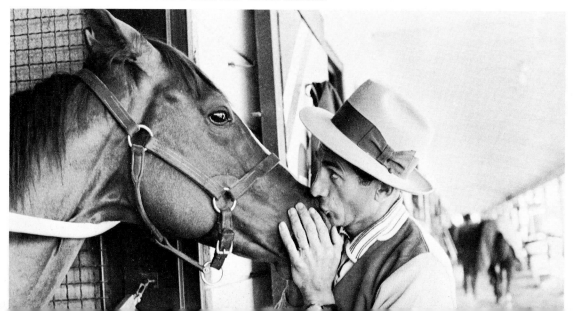

THE ARMORED GIANTS OF THE FALL: ETCHEVERRY CARRIES FOR A GAIN

sixteen. When Thaw went on trial the following year hundreds of newspapermen were on hand to wring every last drop of sensation out of it. Also at the trial were four other women reporters who wrote tear-jerking copy about the "poor young girl." A New York newsman dubbed them the "sob sisters"—a name that has since become the hallmark of girl reporters everywhere.

Kit saw Evelyn Nesbitt differently: "So she went on reciting and reciting, denying, forgetting, sparring, and deeper and deeper sank the impression—a little mercenary, a Broadway waif who would rather do wrong for a few yards of velvet, a handful of lace, a supper at Rector's, than work for a decent living and room in the cold top back room of a New York boardinghouse." The jury disagreed at the first trial. Thaw pleaded insanity at the second and went to a mental hospital, from which he was later released.

Religion popped up frequently in Kit's columns and often provoked bitter controversies. "Is it not rather shocking," she admonished, "to reflect that on no subject—not on politics, finance, public dishonesty or crime—is argument so bitter, so unseemly, so uncharitable, so un-Christlike, as it is when religion is the theme?"

Some took violent exception to her opinions and wrote vitriolic notes to her. She answered:

*Jane Ray—your letter was too impertinent to read further than the first page so I sent it to the devil.*

Kit once jokingly remarked that if she were a man she would never marry because women were a pretty poor lot. A hot and heavy battle of the sexes followed. One argument raged for weeks over whether men or women could keep secrets better. Kit claimed women could stay mum on big matters, "The men that kiss and tell are as numerous as the sands on the seashore, as many a wife and maid can affirm . . . There is only one thing to do—don't kiss."

Her advice to the lovelorn reflected an unwavering regard for the dignity of womankind. "No man has any right to shower a girl employee with gifts of flowers or candy, or ask her to go out to the theatre with him and accept his attentions unless he is prepared to go to the length of asking that girl to be his wife."

Kit had very few close friends and always tried to keep her private life in the background. A member of the Canadian Women's Press Club—of which she was the first president—once had a two-hour stopover in Hamilton on her way back from Buffalo. She telephoned Kit and suggested she might call on her for a few minutes. There was a pause before Kit replied: "Oh no, my dear. That would not be right."

Several famous people were among Kit's few intimates but her favorite was Sarah Bernhardt. They met when Bernhardt was in Toronto and Kit was sent to get an interview. When she stepped into the star's dressing room, Bernhardt stared at her for several seconds, then steered her over to a mirror.

"See!" Bernhardt exclaimed. "We look so much alike." They did, too, except that Kit's hair was naturally red.

Kit was a strange mixture—shy and aggressive, emotional and reserved, sympathetic and moody. She frequently acted on impulse. Once, during her last days with the *Mail and Empire*, a young woman started a correspondence column in another paper, *The News*. Kit wrote her a bitter note, sarcastically accusing her of stealing her ideas. The girl wrote back, said she had always been a great admirer of Kit's. The latter, now in a different mood, sent a sweetness-and-light reply and wished her luck.

Kit was never paid more than thirty-five dollars a week for her women's page, even though she made it the paper's biggest asset. In 1911 the editors asked her to write a brief front-page column every day, in addition to her weekly stint. There was no mention of any more money. She refused. A fight followed and she quit.

Then, falling back on her tremendous popularity all across the country, she wrote Canada's first syndicated column. She sold it to a dozen papers for about five dollars a throw. She didn't even offer it to the *Mail and Empire*.

In May 1915 Kit caught a cold and within two days she was dead at the age of fifty-one.

In 1934 the women of the Press got together and decided to offer a scholarship in memory of Kit of the Mail. She had led the way for Canadian newspaperwomen, they said. But, they admitted, very few—if any—had been able to keep up with her.

FRED BODSWORTH

# How the Prairies Were Made

The event that has done more than anything else to direct and influence the economy, geography and history of western Canada was not the first transcontinental railway, the development of Marquis wheat nor the discovery of oil. It has no official name, but some geologists call it the "big squeeze." The stage for it was set two billion years ago and it has been molding the destiny of western Canada ever since.

It wasn't an economic or political squeeze, although many a westerner will hotly argue that western Canada has been victimized by squeezes of this nature too. The "big squeeze," the two-billion-year-old squeeze, was a gigantic pinching of the earth's crust which has kneaded and molded western Canada into everything it is today. Here's how it came about.

When the earth's crust first cooled, it did so unevenly, leaving thick unyielding islands of rock—the geologists call them "shields"— in some regions, with thinner, weaker zones of the same rock between. As the interior of the earth continued to cool it shrank and the outer crust had to buckle and fold to remain fitted to its interior core, producing earthquakes, mountains, volcanoes and escarpments in the process. The shields have been the earth's unyielding cornerstones and all adjustments to the shrinking interior have had to be made by the regions of thinner, weaker rock between the shields.

The earth's biggest rigid shield is the Pacific Shield which forms the floor of the North Pacific Ocean. The second biggest is the two-million-square-mile Canadian Shield which has its centre under Hudson Bay, covers about half of Canada and gives us most of our mineral wealth. This puts western Canada between the earth's two biggest and toughest crustal zones. And its geologic history is largely a story

of how it has been repeatedly lifted, lowered, wrinkled and tilted by the squeezing of the two great shields that flank it.

In the long, fascinating story of the "big squeeze" lie most of the answers to the questions that puzzled early explorers, to whom the prairies were a perplexity of nature that shouldn't exist. On a continent that had seemed all forest, hills and mountains, the prairies were all wrong. How did they and their westward flanking mountains get that way? Why, in their original state, did the plains grow only grass while practically the whole continent was forest? Why do the prairies possess a thick, rich mantle of soil while only a couple of hundred miles to the north is a barren rockland, many parts of which will hardly grow moss? And why, here so close to the drenching rains of the Pacific coast, is prairie rainfall so scant?

Only now are geologists and geographers getting to the bottom of the "big squeeze" story and beginning to unravel the answers. They still don't all agree but out of the hectic search for oil during the past few years, there has come a new and persuasive theory about the geology of western Canada.

Every day the steel bits of the oil rigs are chewing through strata after strata of bedrock, deep beneath the prairie. They are bringing up in their drill cores the rock samples of a geologic pedigree so ancient that the era of the dinosaurs of a hundred million years ago is, relatively speaking, but yesterday. In its millions of years of growing pains the part of the earth's crust that is now the provinces of Alberta and Saskatchewan has been covered at least a half-dozen times by vast seas. It has seen mountains come and go. It has been steaming tropical swampland and an icecap as cold as the North Pole.

Probably the first essential for an understanding of western geology is a grasp of the tremendous time periods involved in geologic history. If you were to let 13,000-foot Mount Robson, the highest peak in the Canadian Rockies, represent the age of western Canada's oldest bedrock, then a sheet of paper placed on top would represent the time that has elapsed since the arrival there of the first white men. Only some rock formations in East Africa are older.

The story of western Canada can be said to have started 2,300 million years ago. But for almost four-fifths of that prodigious time the west must have remained a stark and barren landscape of rock, pierced by volcanoes belching red-hot lavas, and shuddering frequently with earthquakes. Whatever went on in the Canadian west and elsewhere during that near-eternity of time, there is little record of it left today, for the detailed diary of the rocks doesn't begin until a time geologists believe to be about five hundred million years ago. At this time the long mysterious pre-Cambrian or lifeless era of the earth's history was ending.

Pre-Cambrian North America was considerably larger than today. Hudson Bay was dry land. Greenland and the Arctic islands were all joined in one large land mass to the rest of the continent. On both sides land extended hundreds of miles out into the Atlantic and Pacific. The continent was a low plain which rose little above its surrounding seas. The strip down its centre where the western plains now lie was the lowest area.

Now the "big squeeze" began. The area of the western plains bent slowly downward and the first of many western seas flowed in. This one, the Cambrian Sea, was a long north-south neck of water three or four hundred miles wide that started at the Arctic Ocean and came out to the Pacific again in southern California. It covered what is now the area of the Rockies, most of Alberta but little of Saskatchewan. It made a large island out of Alaska, British Columbia and the Pacific United States.

The Cambrian and succeeding western seas didn't surge in with the violence of floods. Each sea took close to fifty million years to rise and ebb; the same slow changes are being wrought today unseen. The Baltic coast of Sweden, for example, is rising about half an inch a year, a change almost imperceptible in one man's lifetime, but in ten thousand years it will have tilted all the water out of the Baltic Sea and turned it into dry land.

Millions of years of rain eroded the original pre-Cambrian rocks of the Cambrian Sea's shore lines, and rivers carried these sediments into the sea. On the sea bottom the sands and silts were slowly packed and cemented into rock again, so that now a readily recognizable new rock layer lies over the original pre-Cambrian wherever the Cambrian Sea extended. There are spots under the Rockies where the sedimentary rocks built up by this sea remained the longest. As the bottom built up with new rock, the weight bent it lower and the sea therefore never filled up.

By now the Canadian west had its first inhabitants, for the Cambrian Sea teemed with seaweeds and the first simple forms of animal life such as marine worms, sponges, snails, jellyfish and ancient relatives of the squids. But the biggest and most dominant inhabitant was a flattened, many-legged hard-shelled ancestor of our present-day lobster called by scientists the trilobite. Trilobites, though most were four inches or less in length, were the world's most numerous and most highly developed animal. They ruled the seas for a hundred million years—one hundred times as long as man has existed on earth. There were no fish yet. Nor was there anything, plant or animal, yet living on land. Except for thunder and the beating of the sea on the shore, the west had no noise, for there was no animal with a voice, nor were there trees through which the wind could howl.

How do geologists know what creatures lived in the west so long ago? The trilobites and their neighbors died and sank to the ooze of the sea floor. There the soft parts of their bodies decayed but the skeletons or exterior shells remained as fossils and when the ooze altered to rock, the fossils remained like nuts in a cake. In later ages plant leaves and stems were preserved in the same way. Often fossil preservation is so perfect that with a microscope it is possible to count the segments in the feeler of a mosquito dead for two hundred million years.

The contraction of the earth's crust doesn't go on at a uniform rate—geologists don't know why—and eventually a long period came during which the "big squeeze" relaxed. Western North America lifted again and the Cambrian Sea retreated. Now Alberta and Saskatchewan were dry land, but the seas were to come again and again, for this western part of the continent was like a hinge between the two great Pacific and Canadian Shields, and it was constantly being pushed up and down. At a much later age the greatest of all upheavals here produced the Rockies. Today the bowl-like section between the Rockies and the Canadian Shield near Winnipeg is known to oil geologists as the "western Canada sedimentary basin." Actually, only its lowest pre-Cambrian rock layer is bowl-like, for succeeding seas have filled the great hollow with layers of sedimentary rock, forming the level foundation of today's prairies. The basin is deepest at the Alberta end where three miles or more of soil and sea-made rock cover the original pre-Cambrian crust.

For perhaps a 25-million-year interval after the retreat of the Cambrian Sea, Alberta and Saskatchewan remained dry land. Then they sank again, the sea returned, and this one, the Ordovician Sea, covered much of Canada and the United States before its spread was halted by another period of crustal uplift. The third sea to cover western Canada was the Silurian. Apparently it was short-lived, for the sedimentary rock layer it left behind is thin.

Now our time is around three hundred million years ago and the fourth sea slowly covered the west. Geologists know it as the Devonian, and it was a sea destined to leave an important imprint on today's western Canadian economy. Like the Cambrian, it extended down the trough of the western plains from the Arctic to southern California. It covered all of Alberta and Saskatchewan and had a huge arm which reached across southern Manitoba into the present area of the Great Lakes.

The little trilobite was still there but it was no longer ruler of the seas, for now the age of fishes had arrived. Devonian fossils show that fish, the first animal to have a backbone, now dominated the undersea world. Late in this Devonian age strange and very significant fish appeared. They breathed most of the time by gills, but they also had rudimentary lungs by means of which they could survive periods in air when the water in which they were living dried up and left them temporarily stranded. This lung-bearing fish lived in freshwater lakes on the uplands around the Devonian Sea and not in the sea itself. In it nature had met the first requirement for a land-dwelling air-breathing animal.

On the shores of the Devonian Sea there were now forests growing, but no flowering and seed-bearing trees and plants as we have today. Instead the forests consisted of giant, woody-stemmed fernlike plants which sometimes had stumps two feet in diameter. But except for an occasional air-breathing fish that crawled temporarily onto an inland lakeshore, the land still had no animal life as we know it today.

Across vast sections of what is now central Alberta and north into the present region of the Mackenzie Valley, the Devonian Sea for

long periods was shallow and warm. These shallows teemed with minute forms of marine life, just as similar spots in today's seas do, for the fish that eat them prefer deeper water. The shallows were close to shore and sediment from rivers built up rapidly on their bottoms. Often thick layers of the tiny marine animals that had died and dropped to the bottom were covered with silt before they could decay. The silt hardened into impervious shale, cutting off water and air permanently so they could never decay. Ages passed, more and more rock built up above, and slowly under great pressure and heat the hydrocarbons of these undecayed animals changed to oil and natural gas through a chemical reaction that geologists do not yet thoroughly understand. Even then, three hundred million years ago, an important element of western Canada's modern economy was being created by the gigantic forces of the "big squeeze." But one other geologic process was also at work in the Devonian Sea to give twentieth-century Alberta an oil industry.

During this period a much larger part of the world was covered by water than now; ocean currents carried the heat of the tropics throughout the globe, and the whole earth had a warm, humid, maritime climate. Alberta and Saskatchewan were almost tropical, and one of the effects was that corals, which now grow only in the tropics, flourished in the same shallow seas where the minute oil-producing marine animals were being entrapped in mud. Corals are plantlike animals that grow in great colonies and when they die they leave their skeletons behind. These skeletons build up into massive reefs in the sea; then when other rock is formed above them the coral reefs are pressed into layers of porous rock themselves which act as collecting reservoirs for the natural gas and oil.

Geologists know of one vast coral reef within eighty miles of the Arctic Circle in the Mackenzie Valley that is four hundred feet thick and now a third of a mile underground. Farther south in Alberta are several more reefs five hundred feet thick. You will know them too when you hear the names, because their names mark economic milestones for western Canada. They are Norman Wells, Leduc, Woodbend and Redwater. For, although later geologic ages have also produced oil in western Canada, the biggest pools are those that were trapped in the coral reefs of the Devonian Sea when no birds yet flew and the only animal on its shore was a bizarre fish that breathed air.

Tick off another hundred million years. In many parts of the world new seas rose and ebbed and rose again. During this long period the "big squeeze" apparently gave western Canada a rest, and most of Alberta and Saskatchewan remained high and dry. One sea during this time covered a good deal of the United States and sent a shallow brackish arm up into the present foothills territory of southwestern Alberta. It stayed long enough for its microscopic marine animals to produce the gas and oil pools of Turner Valley, Pincher Creek and Jumping Pound. Turner Valley, then, though discovered first and therefore looked upon as the pioneer Alberta oil field, actually belongs to a considerably more recent geologic period than the "new" fields of Leduc and Redwater.

But in other parts of the world this was a highly important geological time for it was the "Carboniferous period"—the age that produced the great coal beds of the Canadian Maritimes, Pennsylvania and England. Alberta's coal formed much later.

On the shores of the sea that produced the oil of Turner Valley there were now air-breathing, land-dwelling animals. It had been only a short evolutionary step from the lung-breathing fish to froglike amphibians which spent the first part of their life breathing by gills in water and their adult life as lung-breathers on land. Up until this time all life had been in the water, but now it was rapidly taking possession of the land, and with it came an important change. Fossil remains show that the first amphibians soon acquired a larynx and voice. Probably it was only a croak, but the land now had animal sounds mingling with the whine of wind and the beat of the seashore waves.

Because Alberta and Saskatchewan had no seas and swamp muds in which to entrap and preserve animal remains during this Carboniferous period, there is little fossil record. From the record elsewhere, though, we know what must have been happening. Slowly, over millions of years, some amphibians developed skins of scales and began laying their eggs on land instead of water. These were the reptiles, the first animals to break completely from the sea and spend their entire lives on land. Around this time, too, the first insects begin to turn up in fossils and for some reason many of them became giants of a size unknown today. There were dragonflies with wings nearly a yard across. But the commonest insect was a cockroach very similar to the one we know today —similar except for size, because they were six inches long. They became so common that sometimes this period is known as the "age of cockroaches" instead of the "age of coal."

The time was now two hundred million years ago. In eastern North America another crustal squeeze wrinkled and upended surface rock layers to produce the Appalachian Mountains of the Atlantic seaboard. They are eroded now until only their roots remain, but for two hundred million years they have served as a supporting ridgepole for the eastern half of the continent, and there have been no extensive oceanic invasions of the east since their appearance. But the west had not yet acquired its Rocky Mountain backbone, the "big squeeze" continued to function there, and western Canada and the United States still had a long turbulent history of ups and downs and inflowing seas ahead of them.

The midwest entered another era of gradual submergence as the Arctic Ocean crept down again and another sea flooded Alberta, southwestern Saskatchewan and many of the western United States. The greenish-grey sandstones that built up on its floor were first identified and dated near Sundance, Wyoming, and it is known as the Sundance Sea. As it receded again, the Sundance Sea left great layers of microscopic marine life buried behind it to produce another oil-bearing stratum at Conrad in Alberta and a number in the Swift Current region of Saskatchewan.

And then, about a hundred million years ago, the last and second-greatest of all western seas began as two broad arms, one creeping down from the Arctic along what is now the Mackenzie Valley, the other reaching up from the Gulf of Mexico. Geologists have named it Cretaceous (chalklike), because this was the geologic period that produced the towering chalk sea cliffs of England. The Cretaceous period was to leave an imperishable imprint on the west, for it gave the west its coal, its dinosaurs and the Rockies, as well as several more oil deposits including the new Pembina field and the fabulous tar sands of the Athabaska River.

At its greatest extent the Cretaceous Sea reached from the Arctic to the Gulf of Mexico and, in Canada, from the Rockies east almost to the Great Lakes. It lasted perhaps forty million years. With so much water covering the land again and moderating the climate, tropical conditions extended far into the Arctic. Fossils of leaves show that palms and figs grew in Alaska, breadfruit and cinnamon trees in Greenland. As the Cretaceous Sea ebbed, it left vast, warm, shallow swamps along its shores in Alberta and southern Saskatchewan. With the hot, humid climate there were dense forests growing in these swamps, making them much like tropical jungles of today. Periodically the sea returned to its coastal swamps, the trees drowned and fell covering the swamp bottoms with tangled mats of vegetation which couldn't decay because water and then inpouring sand cut off the air. By this means the undecaying plant carbons first became peat and then coal just as the animal carbons had become oil and gas during earlier western seas.

Most of the west's Cretaceous coal is in Alberta and the Rockies; the Estevan coal field in Saskatchewan came thirty or forty million years later. Since this western coal is almost two hundred million years younger than the coal of Pennsylvania and the Maritimes, it has been subjected to less kneading and pressure, and is therefore a soft coal of poorer quality than the coals of the east. In the Rockies, though, at Banff, for example, some of this young western coal took such a mauling in the great upheaval that produced the mountains that it is close to anthracite in quality, in spite of its youthful age of one hundred million years. The Estevan coal, a mere twenty-five million years old, is the poorest quality of all.

The same swamps that produced Alberta's coal also provided the two requirements—food and buoyancy—that permitted small lizardlike reptiles to evolve over a period of about a hundred million years into the gigantic, grotesque Frankenstein monsters we call "dinosaurs." The biggest dinosaurs approached ninety feet in length and weighed perhaps twenty tons. To maintain such bulk, a tremendous quantity of food was necessary, and this requirement was admirably met by the Alberta swamps and their tropical climate which permitted rapid year-round growth of plants and trees. But because of their very size they had an enemy that no other animal except the whale has ever had to contend with—that enemy was gravity. Some dinosaurs became so big that their legs could support them for only short periods on land. Just as the whale solved this problem by taking to the sea, the dinosaurs solved it by living in shallow lakes and swamps where they were partially supported by the buoyancy of the water.

Many swampy plains of the world had dinosaurs during the Cretaceus age, but the evidence of the fossils strongly suggests that nowhere were conditions more suitable nor the animals more abundant than in Alberta. One twenty-five-mile stretch of the Red Deer River valley near Brooks has alone produced remains of more than a hundred dinosaurs, thirty-six of them complete or almost-complete skeletons. One square mile near Sand Creek has provided museums with thirteen dinosaur skeletons or partial skeletons. Dinosaur fossils have also been found along the Milk River in southern Alberta and in the Cypress Hills region of southwestern Saskatchewan.

Dinosaurs reached their peak about a hundred million years ago. At that time the Alberta and Saskatchewan swamplands would have been a fearsome and inhospitable place to go strolling or boating. The first of the big dinosaurs were plant-eaters and probably as gentle and peace-loving as cows. But great flesh-eating dinosaurs soon appeared, probably as ferocious as they were big, and it is undoubtedly a blessing of the evolutionary process that there were no men yet on earth to face them.

As the great interior Cretaceous Sea slowly ebbed, there were great forces shaking the land of the west. In previous cycles of uplift, the "big squeeze" had lifted the land sufficiently to spill out the sea, then the uplift had halted. But this time pressure from the west continued for millions of years after the sea had disappeared. The present area of the plains was now reinforced with one to three miles of rock laid down during its many seas, but the British Columbia rock crust was thinner because seas had been less frequent there. As the "big squeeze" continued, something somewhere had to yield. The yielding occurred in the weaker crustal strata of British Columbia, in fact along the Pacific everywhere from Alaska to Central America. The rock layers buckled and shattered, often they were tilted up almost on end. And the first generation of the Rockies was born.

It happened very slowly, so slowly that had man been living there then he would have noted no change in a lifetime. But the Alberta and Saskatchewan area shook frequently with earthquakes. The dinosaurs, if their meagre brains were big enough to know fear, must have listened fearfully to the frequent rumbling of the earth beneath their ponderous feet. And well they might, for it was signaling the end of their hundred-million-year dynasty on earth. Man, before he can boast that he has been master of the earth as long, has another ninety-nine million years to go.

With the rise of the first Rockies, the dinosaurs disappeared. There had been several hundred different species and why they died out so rapidly and so completely without leaving descendants today is a mystery that has the dinosaur experts baffled. One widely held theory is that the Rockies cut off moist winds from the Pacific, the swamps dried up and

206

the climate turned colder and drier. The dinosaurs by now were so closely adjusted, physically and mentally, to their swamp environment that they couldn't adapt to the new conditions. Perhaps they were too big of body anyway to ever live permanently on dry land. When the climate became one of winter and summer, instead of summer the year round, all cold-blooded reptiles had to develop the hibernating habit to survive, and probably the dinosaurs were too big to find hibernating hideaways. Whatever the final cause of their extinction, the fundamental conflict between their weight and the earth's gravity must have entered into it. The fact that nature has never produced animals as big since is taken by some scientists as proof that the dinosaurs simply became too big to survive.

Some scientists see in the disappearance of the dinosaurs a victory of brains over brawn. For at this time small hedgehog-like animals—the first of the mammals—were appearing. They were warm-blooded and better equipped to survive in a climate steadily turning colder. They carried their young within them, instead of laying eggs as the dinosaur did and leaving them at the mercy of any egg-eating animal that came along. And they had a better brain. With plenty of huge dinosaur eggs for food and a brain to keep them out of dangerous situations, the first small mammals prospered at the dinosaurs' expense.

The age of mammals had arrived. The stage was getting set for the arrival of man. The central North American plains had seen their last great sea, although the time is still fifty million years ago. With the Rockies keeping out the moist warm air of the Pacific, the climate of the central plains came under the influence of the Arctic and stayed cool and dry. New plants and trees better fitted for the changed conditions developed in western North America and in several other parts of the world where the climate was similar. They were trees that shed their leaves for the winter, and flowering plants that produced seeds in which life could be suspended during the annual season of cold. It was an important change for with seeds came fruit, nuts and vegetables, the concentrated plant foods that became so important in the diets of later animals. But there were still only a few rudimentary grasses and wild grains. For a long time after the rise of the first Rockies the Canadian west was covered with forest, and the trees were the beeches, birches, maples and oaks familiar today.

Meanwhile the patient, relentless work of rain, streams, frost and glaciers slowly wore down the Rockies until, by twenty-five million years ago, only rows of hills remained. Pacific air could once more circulate freely deep into the continent, the Arctic winters receded northward and a humid, subtropical climate like that of modern Louisiana again claimed the west. Palm trees and alligators came again to southern Saskatchewan. Once more conditions were right for the laying down of coal beds, and the coal mined at Estevan belongs to this fairly recent geologic age.

But the "big squeeze" resumed and a second generation of the Rockies slowly rose—the young, high, craggy and little-eroded Rockies we still have today. During this same period the squeeze was responsible for smaller local uplifts farther east on the plains, producing Cypress Hills, Sweet Grass Hills and Bearpaw Mountains. The climate of the plains turned cool and dry again. The subtropical trees and plants died out. But this time forests didn't return, for a vigorous new branch of the plant world better fitted to take possession of the earth's dried regions had appeared. It was the grasses.

This development and spread of the grasses about fifteen million years ago was one of the great milestones in the history of life on earth. The great grass family, father of all modern grain and forage crops, was destined to become the basic food of man. It spread to many parts of the world where the soil was rich but the climate relatively dry, creating prairies, steppes and velds. One of the first of these grasslands appeared in the lee of the newly risen second generation of the Rockies, and the prairies as we know them today were born.

The western landscape was by then very similar to today's but its animal life was very different. Mammals like the wild horse, camel, rhinoceros and elephant, which today we think of as being exotic Asian and African forms, were then living in western North America; in fact most of them first appeared there. One of the most interesting and most important animals to come out of western North America was the horse. Hundreds of fossil skeletons show how it changed gradually from a small, four-toed mammal the size of a fox terrier to the big single-toed animal we know today.

A long-necked ancestor of the camel which has left its bones in the Cypress Hills of southern Saskatchewan was, judging from the number of fossil remains it has left, one of the commonest animals on the prairies ten million years ago. It migrated to Asia, then died out on the plains where it was born. A camel skull found recently in a Utah cave indicates that camels still lived in the west as recently as twenty-five thousand years ago. The rhinoceros also originated on the North American plains.

Two primitive elephants, the mastodon and mammoth, lived on the prairies, but with them the story is reversed—they migrated here from Asia. The mammoth, a gigantic, shaggy-haired brute ten feet tall with teeth weighing four pounds each, still roamed the west as recently as twenty-five thousand years ago and then it disappeared. The buffalo, also an immigrant from Asia, was a latecomer that arrived within the last fifty thousand years.

Only one large grazing mammal—the buffalo—still survived when white men first saw the plains. For very recently, as geologists measure time, the continent came through a period of violent change and destruction, a time of harsh trial and testing for everything living on it.

It began about one million years ago. Little by little the winds that blew down into Saskatchewan and Alberta from the north grew colder and sharper. In the Northwest Territories west of Hudson Bay more snow fell each winter than the succeeding summer could melt. The snows of innumerable winters slowly piled up and compressed themselves into a steadily thickening icecap. As pressure at the centre increased, the edges flowed outward in an ever widening circle. The great glacier, its fissured front a perpendicular white wall that towered a mile above the prairie, crunched its way south over Saskatchewan and Alberta like a gigantic bulldozer, pushing soil, forests and great rocks before it. For fifty thousand years it advanced until its front was well south of the Canadian-United States border, and the Canadian prairie provinces were almost totally covered. Then the climate turned milder and the ice front slowly melted back until eventually even its far north core had disappeared.

Four times during the past million years this glacier has crept down from the north across the prairies, destroying or driving all life before it. And four times it has melted again and let life return to the plains.

What caused this? The geologists and climatologists have only theories. Some believe that warmth from the sun is periodically reduced by sun-spots. Some suggest that volcanoes filled the atmosphere with fine ash which filtered out the sun's warmth. Others claim that the earth wobbles on its axis and at times tilts away from the sun.

Each glacial period wiped out most of the signs left by previous glaciers, so there is a detailed record only for the last of the four,

the one that sculptured the landscape we see today.

It started its ponderous southward march from west of Hudson Bay about a hundred thousand years ago. (None of them came from the North Pole because cold alone doesn't produce a glacier; there must be heavy snowfall as well.) Arctic animals like polar bears and musk oxen moved south before it. They didn't have to hurry, for the ice moved possibly only fifty feet a year and even snails could keep ahead of it. Thus, no animal needed to be actually engulfed by the ice, yet the glaciers, by drastically reducing habitat and crowding species into the south, must have been a big factor in the extinction of all large prairie mammals except the buffalo.

The fourth and last glacier entered Saskatchewan at its northeast corner. At this time the Canadian Shield, which covers the northern third of Alberta and Saskatchewan, was well covered with soil and its pre-Cambrian rock surface was worn smooth so that it contained few or no lake basins. As the glacier moved south, boulders froze into its surface, turning it into a gigantic sheet of sandpaper. Wherever the Shield was slightly softer it dug into the rock itself, producing thousands of basins which became lakes thousands of years later when the ice receded.

By the time the glacier reached the plains it was shoving mountains of humus, sand and pulverized rock before it, and the Canadian Shield behind in the north was scraped clean. Then it began scraping up vast quantities of new soil-making materials—the clays and limes which had been laid down as limestone and shales by the western seas of ages past. All these materials were kneaded and mixed to produce the rich prairie soils of today. Periodically the glacier rode over the top and left great mounds of these soils behind.

About fifteen thousand years ago, when the ice front was several hundred miles south of the United States border, the last glacier began to recede. As it melted back across the Canadian prairies the towering ice wall cut off normal drainage to Hudson Bay and large lakes of meltwater accumulated. Most of these old glacial drainage systems are now dried up, but remnants of some remain. Last Mountain Lake north of Regina and the valley, now dry, which connects its southern end with the South Saskatchewan River at Elbow, is one. So is the alkaline lake chain, Chaplin Lake to Big Muddy, which runs west and south of Moose Jaw.

Taken as a whole, the rich brown soils of the prairies form Canada's most valuable natural asset. They are the source of more than 10 per cent of the nation's total dollar-value of production, alone contributing more to Canada's economy than all the nation's forests or its minerals. Yet they were born, ironically, out of a grinding devastation of ice that swept all life before it, then left the basis for a richer life in its wake.

What of the future? Will new glaciers and new seas overwhelm the Canadian west in the ages ahead?

Geophysicists say we are still living in the tail end of the last ice age. One-tenth of the earth's surface is still covered by the glaciers that began to recede ten thousand years ago. They are the icecaps of Greenland and Antarctica, both of which are countries where vegetation once thrived. These massive ice sheets will probably continue to melt, pouring their meltwater into the oceans until they are more than a hundred feet deeper than today. New York, London, Halifax, Vancouver and possibly Montreal will be submerged. But this will be a rising of the oceans, not a submergence of the land, and therefore western cities like Regina, Saskatoon, Edmonton and Calgary, whose areas have been drowned by seas so many times before, will this time remain high and dry.

But in the more distant future violent change will come again to the west. According to geophysicists there is every reason to expect that, something like fifty thousand years from now when present icecaps have melted, the glacial cycle will be repeated and another ice mass will begin its sluggish and irresistible flow to add another cataclysmic chapter to the turbulent geologic history of the west.

GABRIELLE ROY

# The Gadabouts

All of a sudden, on Winnipeg's Provencher Bridge, *Maman* told me that she would like to be able to go whenever and wherever she might choose. She told me she still longed to be free; she told me that what died last in the human heart must be the liking for freedom; that even suffering and misfortune did not wear thin within her this inclination toward liberty . . .

But what was it she had so much wanted from life? I had asked her. Was it not a house, her husband, I and the other children?

*Maman* said no; that, at least during her earliest youth, those were not the only things she had wanted; though—she added—her husband, her house, and her children she would not exchange for anything in the world . . .

*Papa* was away. Often he was absent for a whole month or more. *Papa* was a highly considered man, and honored one; yet it could not be denied that the house was much gayer when my father was not there. *Papa* could not endure having the least debt hanging over him; his first concern was to pay debts off, before anything else, and so much so that he rarely had time to be concerned over anything else. He also insisted that we tell him the precise truth, and nothing at times is more misleading than a precise truth; he did not like noise, and he wanted meals served on time, order in the house, the same things—always the same things—at the same hours, day after day.

*Papa* returned this time from Saskatchewan worn out and almost disheartened. His Doukhobors had stripped themselves naked and in that state had wandered all over their village, because the Government wanted to force them to live like everyone else; and the Doukhobors had replied that God created us without a stitch of clothing. My father seemed weary of the human race, and he looked upon us with a trace of envy.

I remember: that day we were all in the large, sunny kitchen, and each of us seemed busy at what pleased her, *Maman* sewing; Alicia embroidering; a saucepan was jiggling slightly on the stove; I was playing with the cat. And *Papa* said, "I don't know if all of you realize how lucky you are! A good roof over your heads; enough to eat; peace and tranquillity. I wonder whether you appreciate your good fortune."

*Maman* looked a bit defiant. "Certainly we appreciate," said she, "what we have; yet all the same, from time to time, it would be nice to get away from the house."

She went on to explain, "There are times, Edouard, when I'd trade my life for yours: to travel, see new things, wander over the country . . ."

As she talked, she became carried away; her eyes began to glow. I saw nothing in this so greatly to annoy *Papa*, but now he began to berate mother as a gadabout, a gypsy, an unstable person.

A little offended, *Maman* replied that it was all very well for a man to talk that way; that a man, because he had the luck to get out of the house, imagined that the house was a sort of paradise . . .

Then *Papa* really lost his temper; he accused all mother's family, saying they were a race of gadabouts. "Truth to tell," he grumbled, "you ought to have been born in a gypsy caravan."

"You know, Edouard, that wouldn't have displeased me a bit!" *Maman* replied. And *Papa* once again departed for Saskatchewan to try to make his Doukhobors see the light.

In order to break away, *Maman* had so many bonds to sever that she became upset over it. I then perceived that freedom, too, grants the human heart small repose. Mother had to part with Gervais, whom she sent to boarding school. At the convent she asked to see Sister Edouard in the parlor. This was our Odette, who then bore a new name. *Maman* asked her to pray for a project about which she could tell her little, but which was close to her heart. A risky project, said she; God would perhaps view it askance. But Odette promised to pray in any case.

Then the middle girls had to be disposed of. We took them to Saint-Anne-des-Chênes; the sisters at this convent had made *Maman* a

very reasonable price for the two of them together—Alicia and Agnes. Both of them had handsome long hair; in those days it took *Maman* a good hour each morning to comb, brush, and braid their tresses. For a woman who valued freedom, what chains she had forged herself! The two middle girls also had dresses covered with flounces, made with small, tight pleats and wide starched collars; to wash and iron those dresses meant a good day's work for *Maman*.

I never saw a sadder house than ours when *Maman* and I got back to it. That it was so large had never struck us before, nor that it echoed the sound of one's voice from room to room. We began walking around on tiptoe. "Noise certainly echoes in this house," said *Maman*; and she sat down to write *Papa* a letter.

"Dear Edouard," she wrote; "I'm leaving with the sewing money I earned, but unfortunately I haven't enough to pay the tradespeople . . ."

Over *Maman*'s shoulder I read a good part of this letter, and I don't like to remember it. This was the first time in my life, I think, when I no longer wanted to be a grown-up; to be a grown-up involved giving too many explanations . . . "You will say, Edouard," *Maman* wrote, "that I ought to have asked your permission. But it's not certain that you would have given it . . . whereas now I can leave with at least the benefit of the doubt . . ."

Afterward we bolted the door of our house; we slipped the key under the mat and we went to the corner to wait for our tram in a cold, thin drizzle. At the station, *Maman* already looked less guilty. For the trip we brought our own food along. If we were silly to go at all, we at least had to be sensible in other matters, especially in our small expenses.

I found Canada immense, and *Maman* likewise seemed proud that Canada should be so large a country. She confided to me that when you came down to it, and had circumstances permitted, she could have spent her life looking at people and cities; that she would have ended up a true nomad, and that that would have been her real misfortune. And I became aware how much travel made mother seem younger; her eyes filled with sparks that glowed at the sight of almost everything we saw. The little evergreens, the water, the rocky ledges along the right of way—*Maman* beheld them all with love. "The world is fascinating," she would say. And I held it a little against *Papa* that he did not more often allow *Maman* to seem youthful. It's really a lovely thing to see an elderly woman take on once again the looks of a young girl. I knew that if I had been a husband, that's what I should best have liked to watch.

Ever since that day I have loved the word *Canada*. Before I had especially liked the Pampas, or Tierra del Fuego. From then on I was just as fond of Canada. You can immediately sense that it is the name of a very large country. And even in those days, I think I should not have wished to live in one of those tiny little countries which are no more than a spot on the map of the world.

We spent yet another night on the train. The next day my mother became a little anxious, and when we entered the Windsor Station, she frankly looked upset. It was because we had no one very close to us in Montreal. *Maman* had often claimed to have a lot of relatives there and, among others, a certain Dr. Nault, her cousin, whose affectionate disposition could not have changed over the years. But in the station *Maman* told me that after all thirty-five years had elapsed since last she had seen this cousin Nault, that he had become wealthy, and that, when they became rich, people found it difficult to recall the things or the faces of other days . . ."

We left our largest bag at the checkroom. "That way," *Maman* explained, "we shall not look like people who have come looking for an invitation to stay. Yet if our cousins insist on keeping us, at least we'll have what we need for the night."

Dr. Nault lived on Rachel Street; we walked along encountering no one save Jews, and then we entered an old-fashioned-looking pharmacy; the counters were full of big glass jars containing dried herbs and powders, on which were inscribed Arsenic, Senna, Belladonna . . . I was in the process of reading all these words when I heard something stir behind a high counter. There stood a slight man, clad in black, with a black beard, very black eyes, and his head covered by a skull cap. *Maman* having asked him, "Are you Dr. Nault?" the old chap replied, "Himself, in person."

"In that case, do you recognize me?" *Maman* asked, planting herself in front of the old fellow, her head cocked to one side and her lovely eyebrows arched, as she did when she looked in a mirror, or wanted to be seen to best advantage.

Without hesitation the old man replied, "Not at all. Am I supposed to know you?"

At that moment a bell jangled on the other side of a partition, not far away. Dr. Nault removed his skull cap and said to us, "Forgive me: a medical customer . . ."

He opened a small door in the wall, which led from the pharmacy into what looked to us like a doctor's office. We saw a woman patient, who was indeed entering this consulting room, but by a door which opened directly on the street.

Ten minutes passed. We saw the patient go out as she entered, holding in her hand a slip of paper on which she seemed to be looking for an address, for she raised her eyes from the paper to the street number on the house. Arriving at the next door, which led into the pharmacy, she walked in. At the same instant Dr. Nault emerged through the small door in the wall; he put his skull cap back on his head. He was at his post as pharmacist when his patient walked up to the counter and he took from her hands the paper he had given her in the consultation room. *Maman* and I, of course, realized that it was his own prescription which Dr. Nault, now the apothecary once more, was about to fill. And indeed he studiously read all that was written there and then proceeded to mix and grind together pinches of powders which he extracted from left and right, from lower and upper shelves, from almost all the glass jars. *Maman* made a gesture to silence my laughter. When his patient had taken her packet and had paid him, Dr. Nault turned to us, eager with curiosity.

"Samuel," *Maman* then asked him, "don't you remember the dozen broken eggs?"

The old fellow looked startled and put on his glasses the better to examine us. "Who are you, anyway? . . ."

"Yes, indeed," said *Maman*, who, it seems to me, did nothing to leave him guessing, "I am your cousin Eveline."

"Oh!" said the old man. "Where on earth have you dropped from?"

"From Manitoba," said *Maman*.

"Yes," he observed, "I did hear you'd gone into exile there. But what are you doing here? Didn't you get married?"

"I certainly am married," *Maman* replied; "this is my little daughter."

The old chap gave me a brief glance and began to ask questions anew: "But what in the world are you two doing hereabouts? Manitoba's not exactly around the corner! . . ."

"It certainly isn't," responded *Maman*, "but with modern means of transport—I mean the railroad—one can move about so quickly nowadays . . . Have you any children, Samuel? . . ."

"Eleven," said he. "But how on earth! . . ."

"I was going through the neighborhood," said *Maman*; "I remembered little Samuel, who was always such a joker . . . do you still play jokes, Samuel? . . . And I thought I'd get some news of how things are going with you, about your family."

"I never thought I'd see you again," said the old fellow.

He made a motion, cast a vague glance at the ceiling. You're not going to leave," said he, "without going upstairs. We live above. Let's go up," he added, without much warmth and scratching his head beneath his skull cap.

On the stairs *Maman* whispered to me not to look so worried; if the Naults did not invite us, she would find other relatives; she had other strings to her bow.

There we were seated on hard sofas facing Madame Nault who was flanked right and left by her daughters; they all had their hands crossed over their skirts in precisely the same fashion, and all these women were clothed in unrelieved black. By way of politeness *Maman* enquired whether the family were in mourning, and Madame Nault dryly replied that her family was practically never out of mourning, some of their people having died almost every year recently.

*Maman* assumed an expression of sorrow and offered her condolence to Madame Nault, who accepted them with a brief nod.

We were at once informed that Madame Nault was both niece and sister to archbishops, that she had been born Delilah Forget, and that young girls of good family did not have the opportunities of former times to marry well; advantageous matches were growing ever scarcer.

*Maman* also took on the airs of a lady of position; she remarked how true this all was, that we should like to prolong our visit with Madame Nault, but that the time had come when we must return to our hotel. Then *Maman* added, as though it were quite incidental, that her husband held a post in the ministry of colonization. She spoke of one thing and another, and found ways to interlard frequent little phrases like, "my husband—in the employ of the Federal Government . . . my husband—a civil servant of the State . . ." and I realized how much better received in society is a woman who boasts of her husband than one who is alone. This seemed to me unjust; I had never noticed that a man needed to talk of his wife in order to appear important.

Each time *Maman* said "my husband, Madame Nault thawed out a little more. And in the end she said that there could be no question of allowing visitors from Manitoba to sleep at a hotel. In the best of them, said she, women alone are exposed to serious dangers,

and it did not take much, she hinted, to lose one's reputation in Montreal.

We spent three days in the apartment above the pharmacy. I do not think it was so much because our visit gave Madame Nault any great pleasure, yet all the same she would not hear of letting us go. "Never shall it be said," she explained, "that I would not receive in my house a cousin from the West . . . Blood is thicker than water; never shall it be said . . ."

When the pharmacy door shut behind us, *Maman* said—I don't know why—"Poor Samuel!"

I no longer remember all the other things we did in Montreal; but it was very tiring. We went to see an illuminated fountain at the other end of the city; then a waxworks museum; but the greater part of our time was spent, as I recall, in talking about the dead, about cousins unknown and of the third and fourth generations.

At Ste. Anne de Beaupré, *Maman* bought one of the biggest candles. Kneeling in front of her statue, she had had a long talk with Saint Anne. I've always thought what *Maman* then asked of her was to cure her forever of the need for freedom—perhaps not too promptly, giving her time for another trip or two . . .

I thought that now all our visits were over and that we should return straight home from the shrine. But no! *Maman* told me, "There is still Odile Constant. How I should love to find Odile Constant just once more!"

I asked her who on earth was Odile Constant.

"Odile," mother replied, "was my dearest childhood friend, when I was a little older than you."

"But where shall we find Odile?"

"That," said *Maman*, "is always possible. If you really make an effort, you can always find an old friend, even if she's at the ends of the earth."

And thus it happened that we went to the village where *Maman* and Odile had been born. First we tried to get information at the priest's house. The pastor had heard that Odile Constant had entered a convent, but he knew not of what order. Then we ventured further, to the home of one of Odile's relatives, and he was able to tell us the name of the order, but not which house of that order; for fifteen years he had not laid eyes on her; she must have been transferred from one place to another; certainly she was still alive.

I was pleased to feel that we were almost

"warm"; it was high time; we had very nearly no money left to continue our search; and besides, *Maman* seemed to set more store by this person than by all our cousins put together.

Once again we encountered the sea gulls as we crossed the river, swimming around tufts of verdure that floated in the water. The Saint Lawrence was very lovely at this spot. We saw a big island; *Maman* told me it was Saint Helen's, which Champlain had given his bride, only twelve years old when he married her, and that there, on the island, he had let her grow up a few years . . . But despite this, it is Odile Constant's name which remains linked in my mind to this landscape.

The longer we searched, the more memories *Maman* recaptured of this little girl of earlier days; she even remembered the color of her eyes—hazelnut. And so, even had we never seen her in the flesh, we should all the same have rediscovered her.

"If God allows me to see Odile once more," said *Maman*, "I can say that I have satisfied my every wish."

I don't know why, but I still had it in my head that it was a little girl we were looking for so desperately.

At last at a convent door *Maman* enquired, "Could you let us see Odile—excuse me, I mean Sister Etienne du Sauveur. I am a very old childhood friend of hers. But don't tell her," *Maman* asked the portress; "I'd like so much to see whether Odile—I mean Sister Etienne du Sauveur—will recognize me."

The portress placed a finger over her lips; her sweet smile told us that the secret would be well kept, and noiselessly she went off to get Sister Etienne du Sauveur.

*Maman* and I were seated on chairs which, at our slightest movement, slipped a little on the gleaming parquet floor. Soon we heard light footsteps coming toward us. Then in the doorway a nun with a pale face and feeble eyes—but grey they were, not hazelnut—was looking at us. *Maman* had urged upon me, "Don't say a word. Don't spoil it. Let me go alone to greet Odile."

The nun gave me a gentle, kindly glance, smiling at me as she did so, then looked at *Maman*. "Odile!" *Maman* called, as though to waken someone asleep.

At hearing this name, the nun trembled. Her two hands rose toward the crucifix hanging from her neck and she clasped it in both of them. Then she moved toward mother; she took her by her arms and led her near a high window at the back of the parlor. She drew aside the curtains, to admit a better light into the room, and began to study *Maman*'s face with a sort of eagerness to recognize her, which was even then utterly charming. Supposedly nuns forswear the affections of this world; ever since I saw Sister Etienne du Sauveur's face, I have believed that they don't always achieve so sad a perfection.

"Do you recognize me, Odile?" asked *Maman* in a thin little voice, which trembled with joyous fear.

Then the expression of the aged nun hurt me, so hard was she trying to look deep into *Maman*'s face. It must have been difficult indeed to discover in an elderly, wrinkled face like *Maman*'s a chubby-cheeked little girl with long braids. The old Sister was making so desperate an effort that her chin, her lips, even her hands were trembling. Finally she narrowed her scrutiny to *Maman*'s very arched eyebrows, and it seemed as though they told her something; little by little there crept into her eyes a glow, at first of disbelief; then Sister Etienne cried out, almost plaintively: "Good Lord! . . . Good Lord! Could it be my little Eveline?"

"Yes, it's I! It's Eveline!" *Maman* exclaimed, and threw herself into the nun's arms.

Then they both began to cry; they embraced, drew apart to stare once again into each other's faces. They kept saying to each other, weeping the while, "I knew you by your eyes . . ." "Oh, but I knew you by the perfect arch of your eyebrows . . . no one but you ever had such beautifully curved eyebrows..."

When they had had a good cry, they sat down facing each other, and Sister Etienne adjusted her headdress a bit, *Maman* having rumpled it somewhat when she held her tight. She said, all impatience, as though out of breath: "And now tell me, Eveline, my dear little Line, tell me about yourself. You must have had many an adventure! You're married! Are you happy? Tell me all about it."

"Yes," said *Maman*, "I married young. You understand, Odile, it was not a passionate love, a foolish love; I was marrying a man much older than I, a responsible man; but one by one I've discovered his fine qualities."

"If your husband has allowed you this fine trip, he's a generous man," Sister Etienne decided.

"Yes, very generous," said *Maman*.

"How happy I am! I'm sure that your husband is a very kindly man; he couldn't be otherwise . . . you have children?"

"I've had nine," *Maman* said. ". . .I've a daughter who is already married . . . Another

is a religious . . . A son long ago gone away
. . . And I lost one child, Odile . . . a lovely
little girl, she died so quickly . . ."

And they began to cry together over my
little sister who had died of meningitis when
she was four.

"But you," said *Maman*, wiping her eyes,
"tell me about yourself . . ."

"I," said Sister Etienne, " I have no history
. . . Tell me more about yourself . . ."

As we were leaving she traced a little cross
on each of our foreheads with her thumb.
After that she gave us medals, scapulars, and
to both of us a picture of her patron saint.

In the entranceway to the convent, they both
began again to embrace each other. "To think
that you have appeared and disappeared, like
a comet!" Sister Etienne complained.

*Maman* begged her, "Pray for me, Odile.
There are times when I sorely tempt Providence."

"Don't say that," the nun replied, as she
studied *Maman* with her tired, kindly eyes.
"I recognize them when I see beings set apart
by Providence . . . set apart to their advantage
. . . and you are such a one . . . such you are,
my little Line. Dear, always trust in Providence . . ."

For a long while, standing in the convent
doorway, she waved her hand after us, just like
a little girl.

On her way back to Winnipeg *Maman* seemed to grow older again. "This northern Ontario
must surely be the most dreary country in the
world," she complained.

She made a little conversation with a lady
who was going as far as Great Slave Lake in
Alberta. "Edouard, my husband, has a delicate
stomach," *Maman* was saying. "He leads an
exhausting life . . . a man of excessive probity;
I'm afraid," said she, "that with me away he'll
have undermined his health even more by
staying up late and eating anything handy."

This lady answered severely, "If you were
fearful of that, you had only not to leave your
husband . . . Why did you leave him?"

*Maman* watched the rain drench over the
window. "Perhaps to become a better wife,"
she replied.

I instantly understood what she meant: it is
when you leave your own that you truly find
them, and you are happy about it, you wish
them well; and you want also to be better yourself. But the lady journeying to Alberta had not
the least idea what *Maman* meant.


TRENT FRAYNE

# The Magnificent Fraud

The morning of April 13, 1938,
broke cold and grey over Prince Albert, a
northern Saskatchewan city struggling to rid
itself of a long and arduous winter; and just
about the time the sharply defined pale-yellow
sun cleared the bleak horizon Grey Owl died
in one of the town's hospitals.

As the newspapers of two continents reminded all that day, he was the half-breed son
of an Apache mother and a Scottish father,
who had saved the Canadian beaver from extinction, who had won an international reputation as an author and lecturer, who had ani-
mated and romanticized the wilderness of
northern Canada for millions of people in
England, the United States and even Canada,
his adopted country.

In the last ten years of his life Grey Owl was
a colorful, romantic, widely publicized figure,
standing six feet two in moccasins, his lean

body and powerful shoulders encased in a fringed buckskin costume. His sculptured face with its strong chin and long sharp narrow nose was set off startlingly by blue eyes and black hair pulled tightly back in two shoulder-length plaits. Matthew Halton, in an interview with him in England in 1936, said he was "one of the most civilized men I ever met; few white Canadians have raised Canada's prestige so high."

Through his books—gripping human-interest stories of the north—and his lectures in which he pleaded for conservation of wild life and an understanding of the Indian, Grey Owl became a sort of symbol of tolerance. "For goodness sake," he said one time, "don't think I'm one of those animal sentimentalists. I am neither a fanatic nor an evangelist. I merely ask for a dignified approach to the animal world."

His success story was recalled in glowing obituaries that April day in 1938 and then, the day after his death, the Toronto *Star* shouted in a three-line heading on its front page that Grey Owl was really an Englishman who had perpetrated the greatest literary hoax of the century. The London papers picked up the story and called Grey Owl a fraud, insisting he had four wives.

A trans-Atlantic newspaper controversy developed, the sensational Press quoting people who claimed to have known Grey Owl when first he came to Canada from England in 1907, the more conservative newspapers equally insistent he was at least part Indian. Grey Owl's publishers, Macmillan's, championed their highly successful writer. They worked for eighteen months trying to find the true story of the man who had written *Pilgrims of the Wild* (which ran through its seventeenth printing), *Tales of an Empty Cabin* (seven printings) and *The Adventures of Sajo and Her Beaver People* (fourteen printings). But from interviews with three of Grey Owl's four wives —or, at least, with three of the women he "married" who were not his legal spouses since he'd never obtained a divorce—from talks with two aunts who had raised him, countless conversations with people who claimed to have known Grey Owl in his early days in Ontario and from documents that included his birth certificate they discovered unalterable evidence that the fabulous benefactor of the Canadian north was, indeed, an Englishman.

Grey Owl played the role of an Indian so long that people who knew him say they believe he convinced himself he was one. And a wild one, at that; a hard-drinking, hot-tempered man in the late stages of his life. One pub-lisher recalled accompanying the spectacularly garbed Grey Owl into the King Edward Hotel in Toronto for a lecture when he was pestered by a drunk. When the man persisted in bothering Grey Owl, the Chief, as they called him, shoved him halfway across the lobby and dived after him, reaching for the hunting knife he carried at his waist. He was intercepted, insisted he merely wanted to flick the buttons from the lout's vest.

Another time Grey Owl, buying a first-class ticket, moved to the observation car of a train out of North Bay. The conductor, apparently touchy about the social standard of his clientele, ordered Grey Owl from the train in curt language. The Chief refused to budge. The conductor walked to the end of the car, opened the door and insisted Grey Owl leave. The latter reached for his knife, zipped it through the air so that it lodged in the woodwork inches from the conductor's head. He did not leave the train.

Grey Owl was Archibald Stansfield Belaney, born September 18, 1888, at 32 St. James's Road, Hastings. He was the first of two sons born to George Furmage Belaney, an Englishman, and Kitty Morris, an American whom Belaney met in Bridgeport, Florida, in 1885. George Belaney, it appears, was shiftless, unreliable, irresponsible; it is recorded he left his wife soon after the second son was born in England and returned to the United States. Archie was placed with two aunts, Ada and Carrie Belaney, in Hastings. They remembered that the boy was fascinated by animals, kept a menagerie and was devoted to cowboys and Indians. He had only one confidante, a little girl named Constance Holmes, who won his confidence because she showed interest in his animals.

In his middle teens Archie told his aunts he wanted to follow his father to America and, though they tried to dissuade him, they eventually yielded and paid his fare to Canada. He worked a year in a dry goods store in Toronto, then was lured north by the silver discoveries at Cobalt.

He was rolled by a knife-wielding prospector as he slept out-of-doors en route, barely escaping with his life. A white man named Jesse Hood, a guide, and two Indians helped him, and Hood got him a job as a canoeman on a hunting expedition. One of the Indians, an Ojibway named Michelle, taught him the rudiments of handling a canoe, took him partridge shooting and taught him how to keep his direction in the woods.

A year in the bush made a marked difference

in Archie's appearance. He was burned brown by the sun and the icy winter winds. His hair hung almost to his shoulders and he kept it tied back with a leather thong as most Indians do. He was tall and lean, walked with a loping stride, and was slightly pigeon-toed. Thus, when he went to Lake Temiskaming where a summer tourist trade flourished he might easily have been mistaken for an Indian guide or canoeman. Bill Guppy, a tourist camp operator, noted his blue eyes and English accent and suspected when Archie asked for a job that he was an Englishman. Archie was noncommittal; he'd been to England, he said, but he'd come recently from Toronto. Guppy liked him and hired him.

Belaney spent three years working for Guppy, learned the woods, moved with him to Temagami where Guppy started a hotel. He preferred the company of Indians. One day when a tourist grinned at him and cackled: "Escape from justice kid?" Belaney replied, half musingly, "No, from injustice."

His winters were spent as mail carrier between Temiskaming and Temagami, a route he traveled by dog team. Frequently he stopped at Bear Island, where a tribe of Ojibways lived, and there he met Angele Uguna who ran away with him and married him his second year in the north. They lived in a cabin a mile from Bear Island.

After some months Archie left Angele and headed into the wilderness to trap, stopping at Biscotasing, a trappers' headquarters, near the Mississauga and Mattagami Rivers. When he walked into Bisco, buckskin and moccasin clad, even more uncommunicative after his lonely winters in the bush, he was taken as an Indian. He gave his name as Archie Belaney and opened an account for supplies and took out a trapper's license. He never returned to the little cabin near Bear Island and Angele, pregnant, returned to her father's house.

Stretching north from Bisco for a hundred miles was the great Mississauga forest reserve and Archie trapped there in complete solitude until the war came in 1914. That summer he had joined the Government Fire Rangers and that fall, with a group of rangers and apparently out of no particular devotion to England, he enlisted. He went overseas with the 40th Battalion and was transferred to the 13th Battalion, Montreal.

In 1917 he was wounded in the foot and was also a victim of mustard gas. His aunts took him from military hospital to Hastings to recuperate. They remember him as a lonely man, filled with deep hatred of war, disliking England and white men, talking constantly of returning to the Canadian northland.

He seemed at ease only with Constance, the little girl who had shared his love for his menagerie. In February 1918 they went through a marriage ceremony and in March his medical board declared him unfit for further active service, said he would be invalided home and granted a pension of seventy-five dollars a month. He eagerly told Constance that now they could go to Canada. But she didn't want to go. Disillusioned and deeply stung, he returned to his northland alone.

At Bisco, where he had avoided white men before the war, he now could hardly bring himself to speak to them. His wounded foot bothered him and his lungs were not recovered from the gas. Had it not been for the Indians he might have died. Ojibway women tended to his wound and fed him. He spent the next four years with them and, except at a trading post in Bisco, he never spoke English. But he learned every watercourse in that north country.

The leader of the Ojibway band was an old man named Neganikabu (meaning Stands First), from whom Belaney learned a lot. Later he was to write of him: "Neganikabu, my mentor, my kindly instructor, my companion in untold hardships and nameless tribulation, has pulled back little by little the magic invisible veil of mystery from across the face of the forest that I might learn its innermost secrets, and has laid open the book of nature for me to read."

Near the end of Archie's fourth year with the Ojibways, Neganikabu adopted him into the tribe in a great firelit ceremony that ended with the chanting chieftain calling him Wa-Sha-Quon-Asin (Shining Beak, the Grey Owl) and, as the tribesmen did their weird dances around the open fire, Archie Belaney became at last an Indian.

And so it was Grey Owl, the half-breed guide, who met an attractive Indian girl aboard the "Temagami Belle" as she plied between Temiskaming and Temagami one morning in May 1925.

"What's your name, lady?" he asked.

"Anahareo. They call me Pony."

"I'm Wa-Sha-Quon-Asin," he said, "Grey Owl. They call me Archie. And with some reason: my father was Scotch."

He was to say this many times in the years that followed; he even declared that his father's name was McNeill. Why he did this he never revealed although one time, many years later when his Toronto publisher was trying through natural curiosity to learn something of Grey Owl's background, he placed his arm across the publisher's shoulder and said, "There is a lot you don't know that you want to know; but you never will know."

Grey Owl saw Anahareo, a full-blooded Iroquois, frequently. He told her once his ambition was the ambition of every trapper: to find new and unspoiled hunting grounds. Encouraged by her enthusiasm he set out that fall, moving on and on, north and east, and when he stopped he was well into Quebec, not far from the tiny village of Doucet. He built a cabin near a lake, and in the fall of 1927 he wrote Anahareo, and she made the long trip by train to join him. He met her at the station and then they tramped, in single file, ten miles into the woods where he had built the cabin.

That winter Grey Owl was engrossed by his work and missed the fact that the sensitive Anahareo was becoming increasingly silent. One day she followed his trap lines. When once or twice a badly wounded animal had to be put to death in a trap, she watched with her hand at her mouth and with frightened eyes as Grey Owl raised his axe to give the death stroke. This day was to be the turning point in his life for he was to become increasingly aware, through Anahareo, of a cruelty that never before had occurred to him as he trapped.

Near spring one of his traps which hung down through a hole in the ice yielded the bodies of three drowned beaver. They were young, barely a year old, and he felt the mother must be close by. He searched fruitlessly for two days. Then toward evening, as he and Anahareo returned in his canoe, he thought he saw a muskrat swimming many yards away. As he later wrote:

> At that distance a man could never miss and my finger was about to press the trigger when the creature gave a low cry and at the same instant I saw, right in my line of fire, another who gave out the same peculiar call. They could both be gotten with the same charge of shot. They gave voice again and this time the sound was unmistakable—they were young beaver.
>
> I lowered my gun and said: "There are your kittens."
>
> The instinct of a woman spoke out at once: "Let us save them," cried Anahareo excitedly, and then in a lower voice: "It is up to us, after what we've done."
>
> And truly what had been done here looked now to be brutal savagery. And with some confused thought of giving back what I had taken, some dim idea of atonement I answered: "Yes, we have to. Let's take them home." It seemed the only fitting thing to do.

They called their beaver McGinnis and Mc-Ginty and grew so to love the little scamps that Grey Owl decided to kill no more beaver, though still regarding himself as a trapper. His philosophy was to be revealed later when an interviewer in England asked him if he would no longer kill a deer or a moose. "Of course I would if I were hungry," he replied. "We have to live and only by death can there be life. Only by killing a tree can a beaver live. If we don't kill the caribou the wolf will. No, we must eat and be clothed. But what makes me sick is the comic sportsman in his trick outfit who invades the woods, kills the giant moose, hangs his stuffed head in a hall to boast about, and leaves the body rotting in the woods."

Just after he acquired McGinty and Mc-Ginnis he met a trapper named Joe Isaac, a Micmac Indian, to whom he related his desire to start a beaver colony in virgin country which also might offer trapping facilities. Isaac, apparently a wildly imaginative man, related wondrous tales of such a hunting ground many miles removed and, even allowing for Isaac's exaggerations, Grey Owl and Anahareo decided it would fill their requirements. They canoed and portaged to Cabano in the Temiscouata district of Quebec, where the country was far less magical than Joe Isaac had painted it, and, though it required some weeks of difficult portaging to reach, Grey Owl and Anahareo and their beaver went on into the wilderness to Birch Lake. By the second week of November they had built a cabin which for the next three years was the House of Mc-Ginnis, their home.

In that first winter of 1928-29 Grey Owl found himself depressed and after Christmas stopped traveling the woods looking for wild life. In the long days and evenings he started to write, with pen and ink, the stories he had told Anahareo, the adventures he had, his observations on their little friends, now hibernating. Particularly, he liked to contrast life as he found it with that portrayed in an English magazine called *Country Life*. After some weeks he decided to piece together many of his stories and in the spring he mailed them, eight thousand words worth, in the form of an article to *Country Life*.

When McGinnis and McGinty came out of hibernation in the spring and entered the beaver colony Grey Owl had constructed, other beaver followed them there. They grew to know no harm would come from the strange twosome who lived in a cabin by the lake, the first time in history beaver had been known to trust man. McGinnis and McGinty showed no fear and would scurry out of the water to the cabin for food. One summer night, however, the two pets swam off into the lake. Grey Owl called to them, cupping his hands to his mouth and wailing something that sounded like "Maw-we-ee-ee" and once, in answer, there came a long clear note followed by another of a different tone. That was the last Grey Owl ever heard of his little friends.

Grey Owl and Anahareo were deeply moved by their loss. Then one night they came upon two baby beaver, a male and a female, and they took them to the cabin in a burlap bag. The male died soon afterward but the female, though she wouldn't eat for days, hung tenaciously to life and eventually began to recover. A certain self-satisfaction that she seemed to ooze gave her the name of Jelly Roll and she turned out to be the most famous of all Grey Owl's so-called Little People. Jelly has been described as determined, wilful, egotistical, cunning and rapturously melting, depending what mood was required to win her way. After she had been with them several weeks Grey Owl went to Cabano for supplies and found a letter from *Country Life* accepting his manuscript and a cheque for about $150. Also there was a letter from the publisher suggesting Grey Owl write a book. He set himself to work that winter on a project in which he wanted to seize the spirit of the wilderness and get it down on paper and, working laboriously with his pen, he produced a book called *The Vanishing Frontier*.

The following summer J. H. Campbell, of the National Parks, visited the cabin to investigate stories he had heard of an Indian who tamed beaver. When he saw Jelly Roll and her antics he was amazed. He explained that a movie of Grey Owl and his beaver could be used by the Canadian government for publicity. Grey Owl told Campbell of his dream of creating a beaver sanctuary, and Campbell said the ideal location would be in one of Canada's national parks.

As Campbell left, Grey Owl went to inspect his traps. One was missing and he located it under a submerged log. In it was an adult beaver, half-drowned, frightened, a piece of his scalp hanging loose and a badly mangled foot. Grey Owl took him to the cabin and nursed him and after a few weeks the loose portion of the scalp had dried and was hanging from the beaver's head like a piece of wrinkled hide. Grey Owl snipped it off and called this new family addition Rawhide.

Jelly Roll was intensely jealous of him but it was Rawhide that gave Grey Owl one of his biggest thrills. He was paddling one day and saw Rawhide swimming many feet away. He called to him and slowly moved the canoe toward him. Rawhide was apprehensive. Then Grey Owl, speaking softly, laid the paddle down to the water so that it made a ramp. He put his hand in the water and slowly Rawhide came to it. The beaver sniffed the hand, then allowed Grey Owl to help him up the ramp into the canoe. Grey Owl was exultant; he had tamed an adult beaver.

In the spring of 1931 a letter arrived from Campbell informing them that Riding Mountain National Park had been selected as the site for the beaver colony and Grey Owl, with Anahareo and Jelly Roll and Rawhide, set off for Manitoba. Cameramen there made a film entitled "The Beaver Family," but Grey Owl was not pleased with the location because it was too dry. He wrote Campbell and the following spring the sanctuary was moved to Prince Albert National Park. There he built a log cabin, and called it Beaver Lodge. At last he had found his perfect location and, too, he had found the perfect confidant in Major J. A. Wood, superintendent of Prince Albert National Park, who joined in his plans with great enthusiasm.

Meanwhile Grey Owl had written another book, *Pilgrims of the Wild*. This one—and the subsequent books, *Tales of an Empty Cabin* and *The Adventures of Sajo and Her Beaver People*, were published by The Macmillan Company. Lovat Dickson of the London firm later wrote his own warm tribute to Grey Owl, entitled *Halfbreed*.

Dickson got the idea of a lecture tour of England by Grey Owl in 1935. The books had been tremendously successful and so was the lecture tour, on which Grey Owl made two hundred speeches in four months. Everywhere he was acclaimed and interviewed and the stories were given front-page attention. He told one interviewer:

*Man, the beaver, the deer, the hawk— each has his own habits. One is no better than the other but they are different and man's difference is that he is blessed—or cursed—with imagination. This makes him dream and build castles and see himself as a conquering hero. It even makes him so stupid as to say: "God made man in his own image," when, actually and quite obviously, men have made a God in their own image. I am a Neolithic man; I am no sophisticate.*

On his return to Prince Albert he was able, through Major Wood, to have his views on beaver conservation heard. In long pleas he pointed out that an unlimited open season was

218

driving the animal toward extinction and, before he died, four provinces—Saskatchewan, Manitoba, Ontario and Quebec—were to have closed seasons for beaver. His efforts are regarded as having saved hundreds of thousands of beaver.

On his return, also, he was to find himself the father of a girl child, Dawn, to whom Anahareo gave birth in Prince Albert. Now the couple discovered their philosophies had changed: because of his traveling he wanted to settle down to rest; she was the opposite. They decided to separate.

Alone again Grey Owl used much of his personal funds to produce a movie of his old haunts on the Mississauga, starting at Bisco and following the trail he had followed years before.

Soon he met a Canadian girl, partly of Indian blood, named Yvonne Perrier; later she took her Indian name, Silver Moon. A month after their first meeting they were "married" and went to Prince Albert together.

In the winter of 1937 he made another successful tour of England, this time appearing before the King and Queen. On neither tour is there any record of the former Archie Belaney visiting his aunts in Hastings. On his return to Canada the fifty-year-old Grey Owl was weary. He spoke to a packed Massey Hall in Toronto where he regained some of his spark but en route west his state of mind was further complicated when Yvonne became ill at Regina and went to hospital for an operation. When she was out of danger Grey Owl continued on to Prince Albert, near mental exhaustion. Two days after he reached Beaver Lodge a ranger received a phone call from him. He was ill. When the ranger arrived Grey Owl was unconscious on the floor. He was taken to hospital in Prince Albert and there he died.

Then, as his friend Major Wood wrote, "Within a day the human pack was on him like nothing so much as the scavengers of the forest rending the dead body of some monarch of the wilderness which they would not have the courage to attack in life. I care not whether he was an Englishman, Irishman, Scotsman or Negro. He was a great man with a great mind . . . He will be remembered for his courageous stand in regard to blood sports . . . He will be remembered for his efforts to rehabilitate the Indian to a point where he would again possess some of his old-time dignity and independence. Any one of these objectives would be a lifetime job for the majority of men. Grey Owl was courageous enough to attack them all."

ROGER LEMELIN

# My Friend Guay, the Murderer

On the afternoon of September 9, 1949, a Canadian Pacific Airlines DC-3 left Quebec City with twenty-three people aboard, heading for Baie Comeau, a lumber town 220 miles to the northeast. Above Sault-au-Cochon, forty-one miles out of Quebec City, the plane exploded like an electric light bulb. All the passengers were killed.

Ten days later a Quebec woman, Marguerite Pitre, who was recovering in hospital after having tried to commit suicide, told police she had put a package aboard the plane on behalf of a young Quebec jeweler, Joseph Albert Guay, whose wife Rita Morel was among the victims. Guay was arrested for the most horrible mass murder in the history of crime in North America.

The details of the murder and the trials

filled the front pages of the nation's newspapers. Albert Guay has been hanged. Marguerite Pitre, who delivered the time bomb which destroyed the plane, and her crippled brother Généreux Ruest, who manufactured it, have died for complicity in the murder. But one question is still being asked: how could a man, no different from any that you might meet on the streets of any town at any time, conceive and carry out such a murder—as useless as it was diabolical?

Of all the journalists who had dealings with him I am the only one who knew Joseph Albert Guay well. He was a neighbor of mine, and a member of our little poker club. I believe that I can lift one corner of the veil which hides this mystery by revealing certain aspects of his character which *did* set him apart from his fellows.

The first thought that came to my mind when I heard the names of the victims over my car radio was: "Why, that's Albert's wife!" And, incredible as it may seem looking back, my second reaction was: "Albert had something to do with that explosion."

The fact that I had instantly and almost instinctively suspected Albert scared me. I started my car but instead of turning in the direction of the Sillery, where I have lived since my marriage, I drove to Lower Town and the St. Sauveur district, where I had lived for the great part of my life and where Albert Guay had lived for eight years. I went into Pat Allen's grocery. Pat came running toward me. His manner was distracted; he pulled me behind some sacks of potatoes and whispered to me, "I think Albert might have blown up that plane." Some of the poker players came in and joined us at the back of the store. The same idea had occurred to all of them—that Albert was responsible for the crash.

How was it that these people could without hesitation believe Guay guilty of so fiendish a murder? These were sensible people; they knew Guay well, knew his charming character, his generosity, his good manners, his childish boasting. Ignorant as they were of even the slightest knowledge of psychology, they were well enough acquainted with this highly strung jeweler, who on the surface appeared not a bad fellow, to believe him quite capable of anything at all. Here then is what all of us, and I in particular, knew of him.

Joseph Albert Guay was the youngest of a family of five. His father died when the boy was still very young. His mother's favorite, he was a thoroughly spoiled child. If he wanted a bicycle he got one. Heaven help the teacher who dared scold him. Madame Guay would

rush to the school and hurl abuse at the unfortunate instructor. Candies and toys seemed to have been invented especially for Albert. He was raised with the idea that nothing could ever be refused him. The most important thing in the world was that his every caprice should be satisfied. By the time he was sixteen he was spoiled beyond redemption. He began to hang out in pool halls and to lead the life of the gay young man-about-town. To keep himself supplied with cash he sold watches and other jewelry on commission. When the war broke out he was taken on at the Canadian Arsenals Limited at St. Malo, where his job consisted of watching a grinding machine. Here he earned forty dollars a week.

In spite of his youthful extravagances, Albert was always neatly dressed, had good manners, and his thin face was that of the successful adolescent. His self-important manner, his air of assurance and the Mercury sedan he drove to work made him popular with the girls who worked in the arsenal and with whom he went out on gay parties in the evenings. Of all these girls Rita Morel was by far the prettiest. With her great dark eyes of Andalusian beauty, a sensual mouth, fine teeth and magnificent black hair, she was far and away the most attractive girl in the factory, though she was slightly plump and rather short. Passionately in love with her, Albert decided she was for no one but him. In Quebec that means marriage. Albert married Rita.

I shall always remember that spring morning when the happy couple, followed by a crowd of singing, laughing wedding guests, appeared suddenly in the Rue Colomb where I then lived to inspect their apartment opposite my house. Joseph Albert was wearing evening dress complete with top hat, a garb rarely seen at a working-class wedding. I was struck by that fact. "There's a bluffer," I thought. On the day of his marriage he resembled nothing quite so much as a boy playing at weddings.

My acquaintance with Guay and his wife dated from that day. One other thing that impressed me was the great show of affection he put on. Each noon Rita would come down the sidewalk with Albert where, in full view of all the neighborhood gossips, he would embrace her passionately at great length in seeming emulation of a Hollywood actor. He would kiss her and call her pet names. His way of embracing his wife before the eyes of the whole parish astonished and shocked the neighbors, who believed that kisses and demonstrations of affection were better indulged in private. At the same time he continued to go out on occasion with girls from the arsenal. Spoiled child as he was and would remain, he could not accept the idea that the possession of one woman robbed him of his right to have affairs with others. Yet Albert was jealous of Rita, who nevertheless was faithful to him. She had a way of looking at men that was at once exciting and inviting. She seemed always on the point of indulging in a flirtation. Some of my friends of that period tried flirting with her, without success.

One evening about five o'clock, when I was driving from work, I met Rita Morel in the Rue St. Joseph and, since we were bound in the same direction, offered to drive her home. In front of her door I stopped to let her out. Albert, in shirt sleeves, was leaning against the house, watching us in a sombre manner. He came up to me. His eyes were cast down; he always looked at the ground and his hands, never still, rattled the coins in his pockets. Guay said, "Roger, I'll give you a word of friendly advice. No more of that. That sort of thing can only end in tragedy." He was given to such grandiloquence and would often engage in solemn conversations on morality and morals. Old women and priests loved to talk to him.

Here is the picture that I have of him at that period. He was a thin young man, nervous, with the features of a tormented youth, often seeming preoccupied when talking as though he had on his mind a problem that it was most important he should solve. From time to time he would emerge suddenly from his abstraction and assume a solemn and authoritative manner. With his toes turned in and his hands in his pockets, he would play the part of Joe Know-it-All among the friends who gathered at the corner grocery or with whom he played poker. He would often take from his pocket a great roll of dollar bills and announce to everyone within earshot that he had a marvelous scheme that would make him very rich, very soon.

He liked to appear more prosperous than his neighbors, and I have often watched him on a Sunday with his wife, both in slacks, leaving our street for a gay outing in the country with a few friends; this in a parish where slacks are not worn and where few of the inhabitants own cars. He made a great impression on the neighbors. Another thing that struck me about him was the fact he always wore black shoes, very narrow and always highly polished. He paid a youngster twenty-five cents a week to shine his shoes every evening.

Guay was always in a hurry. He drove his car through the narrow streets of Lower Town the way a movie cowboy rides his horse. He always leaped out of his car to the sidewalk almost before it had come to a full stop. He was interested in everything, talked of everything, yet knew nothing. He waved his thin hands as he talked to illustrate his conversation. He was completely irresponsible, imaginative yet devoid of any practical sense. He was the kind of man who, if he heard that the Château Frontenac was for sale and that a businessman was interested in buying it, would believe it was quite possible for him to act as an agent and so earn a fat commission without spending a single cent.

Albert Guay, in short, might have sat for the portrait of Monsieur Verdoux as played by Charlie Chaplin. Two men dwelt side by side within his frail body: the ambitious megalomaniac, devoid of any practical gifts to help him achieve his ends, and the sickly passionate lover.

I remember one Saturday afternoon when he decided to check and repair the engine of his car, though he must have known he was completely devoid of any mechanical ability. But the very action of borrowing a few tools and putting on mechanic's overalls seemed to convince him that he was quite capable of tearing down the motor and assembling it again. He poked around all afternoon among the valves and pistons, remaining serious under the jeering sallies of his wife. In the end he abandoned the job to a garage mechanic and went upstairs to supper, announcing that the carburetor needed cleaning.

Guay was afraid of blood. I recall an occasion on which he refused to watch a butcher chopping off a hen's head under the pretense that he "couldn't bear to watch an animal suffer." His great passion was for the dramas of human relationships. Frequently he would intervene in the domestic disputes of his neighbors in an effort to bring about a reconciliation. He was generous, loaned money freely to friends, and did not dun them for the return of loans. His pose always was that some day he would be so rich that small losses of that sort would be unimportant. It was easy for him to do good turns. He often got out of bed in the middle of the night to drive seriously ill neighbors who were too poor to pay for a taxi to the hospital.

A man who is living beyond his means in this manner, who owns a car and is given to generous gestures, obviously cannot live on forty dollars a week. A few months after his marriage every householder in the parish received a business card signed "Joseph Albert Guay, Jeweler." That was the first time any of us had ever heard that he was a jeweler.

He appeared as sure of his ability to repair watches as he had once appeared certain of his skill as a mechanic. Naturally he kept his job in the war factory and he repaired the watches in the evenings at home. At least that is what he said. Actually, he was not at all interested in repairing watches and would send them out to jewelers to be fixed, marking the price up to his advantage. He liked to have his customers believe that a watch in trouble was a mysterious and important thing and that the price could be determined only after the watch had been thoroughly examined and repairs had been completed.

It was in this way that he was later to engage the services of Généreux Ruest. I knew Ruest too. I remember one night, a few months before the crash, when I went to the St. Sauveur district of Lower Town to play poker with some old friends. During the game I noticed my wrist watch was broken, and later I crossed the street to where Albert Guay had opened a small jewelry store in 1945 and asked him to look at it for me. "Let's take it and show it to Généreux," he said and took me into the back shop where he introduced me to the hawk-faced cripple. It was a familiar face to me and I said, "Do you remember me, Généreux?" Ruest nodded and his lips parted in a thin smile.

Fifteen years before, when I was recovering from pleurisy in a public ward in hospital, there was a patient in the bed next to me whom I shall never forget. In the first place he had an odd name—Généreux Ruest. Then, not only did he repair the watches of other patients with remarkable skill, but he displayed an extraordinary aptitude for anything mechanical. He spent the long days constructing various small and ingenious machines of his own invention. For example, wires connected his alarm clock to his radio in such a way that the alarm clock, instead of ringing, turned on the radio at exactly eight o'clock. Finally, Généreux Ruest suffered from an incurable malady. He had tuberculosis in both hips, and he would never walk again.

Guay's specialty was the sale of watches on credit to his fellow workers in the arsenal and his neighbors in the parish. In 1943 I left with him a Roamer watch with the spring broken. Two months later he had not returned it to me. I asked him about it and he told me laughingly, "Your watch had such a complicated movement that I had to send it to New York." Finally he told me the New York experts had telephoned him to say that the watch was useless. In telling me this he had such a serious manner that I could not get annoyed with him.

But from that moment on I realized that he was not honest. Later he gave me ten dollars for the lost watch.

One Saturday evening in July 1944, about midnight, Guay returned home with his wife. A few moments later he came rushing downstairs, waving his arms in the air and yelling, "I've been robbed. Somebody has stolen a thousand dollars' worth of watches from me." The lock of his door had been forced. The thief was never discovered and the insurance company had to pay up. Guay had great faith in insurance companies. In the next two years he was robbed four or five times. People began to look on him with suspicion but Albert continued to hold his head high.

On Sunday mornings, arm in arm with his wife, a great prayer book under his left arm, he would make his pious way to high mass. He neither drank nor swore and was on good terms with the parish priest. Moreover, he often spoke sadly to us of the thefts of which he had been a victim. "I was born under an unlucky star," he would say. "Fortunately I was insured."

In 1945 the arsenal closed. Albert Guay opened his jewelry store just opposite the parish church. His business went well enough in 1946 and 1947. It should be noted that on two occasions his store was damaged by fire. Again the insurance companies paid up. Then quarrels broke out between Guay and his wife. Rita had learned of her husband's little adventures and to make him jealous had engaged in a few mild flirtations. Neighbors have told me that in their quarrels the Guays would throw bottles and yell insults at one another. The day after an argument of this kind Albert frequently bought his wife a present.

About this time I used to see Albert in Pat Allen's grocery store. He seemed more pensive than ever. All his features seemed pinched in, as though concentrating on a single fixed idea. Life was not bestowing its rich gifts on the spoiled child. He had not become rich; on the contrary, he was running into debt. Yet for eight years he had been telling everybody that one of these days he was going to be a rich man. What would people think of him? Certainly he had done everything in his power to achieve his end. He had become a third-degree Knight of Columbus and was taking steps to obtain the coveted fourth degree. Several priests were recommending him for that honor. He had a current account with the bank, a lawyer to collect his bad debts, and he even sponsored a short radio program to advertise his jewelry business. He had several agents who journeyed through the villages of Quebec selling his watches on the installment plan. It was Guay who had planned all of this not inconsiderable business. But since he was without practical qualities he could not prevent his agents from pocketing the money paid by their customers; and he was too timid to demand his money from them. When he believed that he was to be invested with the honors of a fourth-degree Knight of Columbus he had a magnificent suit of clothes made. When the time of the initiation was approaching he was informed that he had been rejected on account of his debts. It was one of the greatest disappointments of his life. That evening, soon after Albert returned home, Rita went to the grocery. She told Pat Allen, "Poor Albert! He's crying like a child. They've turned him down. He wanted to become rich too quickly."

It was at this time that he met Marie-Ange Robitaille. I have said that there dwelt two men in Albert Guay: the ambitious man and the sensualist. Now his ambitions were bankrupt. To forget, he threw himself passionately into a love affair. As his sentimental life too was to founder, these two failures, coming in contact with one another, closed the fatal circuit.

He met Marie-Ange in the restaurant Chez Gérard, where she was a waitress. She was still almost a child, only seventeen years of age, and looked like a timid girl fresh from a convent. Under an assumed name he began to call on her three nights a week like a young suitor with serious intentions. Marie-Ange's parents saw a good match for their daughter in this distinguished young man who occupied the big armchair in their living room and paid conventional suit to their daughter. When he visited Marie-Ange at her home he took the name of Roger Angers. He hated the name Albert and once told me I had a nice Christian name.

Guay possessed to a high degree the gift of creating for himself a world of illusion and of believing firmly in the world of his own creation. Calling on Marie-Ange gave him the illusion that he was once more a boy with a successful future. He was no longer the thirty-year-old man who had failed to become rich; he was the ambitious youngster. The little game lasted several months. He even bought an engagement ring for Marie-Ange. Then one night Rita Morel burst into the Robitaille living room and the game was up.

Rita Morel had signed her own death warrant.

The spoiled child wanted the moon and he would spare no effort to get it. Marguerite Pitre, the sister of Généreux Ruest, who repaired watches, began to feature in the affairs of the couple. It was she who gave shelter to Marie-Ange when she left home at Guay's urging. Guay had an extraordinary mastery over the minds of people of little importance. He dominated Marie-Ange and Généreux Ruest, the first by the intensity of his passion, the other by the scope and brilliance of his plans for the future.

Guay took Marie-Ange to Sept-Iles, where they lived together for some time as husband and wife. She left him, then returned to him. Finally Marie-Ange realized there was no future in this affair and that she was wasting her time. She left Albert, telling him that since he was married there was little object in continuing the liaison. In despair the spoiled child took stock of his situation. His home life was destroyed, his ambitions ruined; and now his mistress was abandoning him. That couldn't happen to him, not to Albert Guay who expected everything from life and to whom life owed everything.

Without being conscious of it, Guay had probably been giving thought to the problem of getting rid of his wife ever since she had made her sensational entrance into the Robitaille living room. For was she not the great obstacle between him and Marie-Ange, between him and the moon? But how was it to be done, he must have asked himself. He was afraid of blood. He might shoot her, of course, but he lacked the courage for that. Besides, he could not look at a dead person. It would be best, he apparently decided, if his wife were to disappear in some sort of an accident. That was it—an accident!

By the time the plan had fully formed in his mind it is quite plausible to believe that Guay had ceased to think of himself as a murderer at all. It is possible that the idea of a bomb dwelt in his subconscious as a result of his experience in the arsenal. It probably swam into his conscious thoughts during an air journey from Sept-Iles to Quebec. The mechanics of the murder took shape in his mind and began to haunt him. Since the bomb was to have a time device, the plane would fall apart over water. There would be only bits of unrecognizable bodies if, indeed, anything was recovered; so there would be no corpse to identify. He would erase the presence of Rita as he might rub out a drawing from a book. Finally, everyone would be so convinced the explosion was an accident that he himself would come to believe it.

Perhaps, too, the great explosion would succeed in shattering the ill fortune that had dogged his steps and he could begin life all over again with Marie-Ange, a life full of hope and love. This time he would not fail. He would become rich, for with the insurance money he would receive on his wife's death he would pay off his debts. Guay had $5,000 on his wife's life, to which he added another $10,000 at the airport before she took off on the fatal flight. Above everything else he hated owing money.

And what of the other passengers in the plane? His mind refused to dwell on that problem. How could he, Albert Guay, prevent accidents from happening? Consider now this aspect of his character. He was capable of conceiving this grandiose scheme of murder down to the last detail; and yet with a curious lack of caution he shared his secret with Ruest, who made the bomb for him.

By the time of the crash Guay had succeeded completely, it seems, in convincing himself that it was all an accident. On receipt of the news he burst into tears of unfeigned grief. Astonishing as it may seem, there were signs that Guay loved his wife dearly.

Two months before the tragedy he and Rita, with a couple of friends, had made a tour of the Gaspé. These friends have since told me that Rita and Albert, riding in the back seat, acted like a young honeymoon couple. There was a succession of kisses and caresses, and he kept using sentences like, "There, little darling, there isn't anyone like you, not anyone in the whole world." Two weeks before the crash he bought his wife flowers, as he had so often done since their marriage. Before they hanged him for his crime he requested that he should be buried beside her.

For the funeral of his dead wife he ordered a magnificently bedecked mortuary chamber. He had a floral cross made, five feet high, bearing the inscription, "From Your Beloved Albert." He thought of everything. He had mourning cards printed by his friend Victor Tardif, urging him to take special pains to see that Rita's photograph came out well on the cards. In spite of his grief, his drawn features and his weariness, he remained at the funeral parlor from morning till night.

All those who had suspected him regretted their shocking first thought. It was inconceivable that one of our group could have killed twenty-three people. I believe that I was the only person to persist in my doubts. I wanted to keep close to him and, as a reporter, to interview him. But frankly, after having seen that mortuary chamber, I had not the courage to do so, and I began to think that I was a little crazy to be imagining such things.

Dressed in black, thin and pale, he shook hands with those who called to pay their respects. When I offered him my condolences he said, "You know how much I loved her. But the important thing is that she didn't suffer. You don't think she suffered, do you?" Then he stifled a sob which was not feigned. He appeared to completely lack realization of the nature of what he had done. While I was at the funeral parlor a priest entered. Guay asked him to recite the rosary. Everyone kneeled. As other priests came in he would ask each to recite the rosary. After one such occasion I heard a man sobbing in the room above us. It was the husband of Madame Romeo Chapados who, with her three children, had died in the crash. Guay made his excuses, quickly went upstairs and began to console Chapados. He said: "He brave, M. Chapados. Do as I do: put your trust in God. I have lost my young wife." Several times he went upstairs to console him.

Albert came back to me and I told him that some of the newspapers were talking of an explosion of dynamite as the cause of the crash. He shrugged his shoulders. "I can't believe it," he said. "In my opinion it was a faulty feed line. There's nobody monstrous enough to blow up a plane." Then, with his hands in his pockets, he looked down at his feet, with his toes slightly turned in, as if hypnotized by the gleam of his highly polished shoes.

He believed in the accident now, as he had believed in thieves when he himself was organizing the robberies of his jewelry store to collect the insurance. At the funeral he was proud of the great crowd which followed the hearse and he said to Victor Tardif, "See how well known I am and how much everyone loved Rita." At the cemetery, as the coffin was lowered into the grave, he said to his little daughter, "Look, dear! Mama is leaving us forever." Then he burst into real sobs. He cried so hard and became so weak that he had to be helped into the taxi.

Two days later I met him again. Under his eyes were dark shadows and his face was white. He said to me, "Do you realize that Pat Allen didn't come to the funeral? I shall never forget that." He appeared deeply injured. Allen, who had communicated his suspicions about Guay to several people immediately after the crash, now went in fear of Albert, believing that if he really was a criminal Guay might murder him in revenge. But it wasn't at all that way. Guay was hurt that Pat, who had been his grocer for eight years, had not come to the funeral.

After his arrest, indeed up to the time that Marie-Ange Robitaille began her evidence, Guay conducted himself with all the offhandedness of a man who has been arrested by mistake. In prison he hummed little French songs. He played endless games of rummy with his guards, whom he consistently beat to his great satisfaction. Shortly before his trial he said to one of the guards, "I've been held here three months now. Think of all the money this nonsense is making me lose. When I get out of here I'm going to sue the government."

I covered the trial and I saw Guay remain impassive as witness after witness gave evidence. Then Marie-Ange was called, the woman for whom he had killed his wife and twenty-two other people. I shall never forget the brief glance between them. It cannot be described. The eighteen-year-old girl was well dressed and her auburn hair hung down to her shoulders. She spoke in a weak but clear voice, her eyes full of tears, of her liaison with Albert Guay. She wove a rope for her lover's neck without once looking at him and, when she concluded with the words, "I don't love him any more," Guay's face turned ashen grey, his lips took on a bluish tinge. He looked like a man whose body was beginning to decay while he still lived. Then he closed his eyes. He made no motion, said nothing.

The sentence of death he received almost absent-mindedly, his eyes on his polished shoes. He was asked if he wanted to enter an appeal. "Why? For whom?" he said to his lawyer. "I've no more interest in living."

In the condemned man's cell another interesting aspect of his personality revealed itself. He wanted to sell the story of his life to a magazine to earn a little money for his daughter, to obtain the widest possible publicity and to teach a moral lesson to his readers. To the Crown attorneys he made a confession that filled a hundred pages. It ended with words like this: "And now I hope that this story will serve as a terrible lesson to those who, like me, have been blinded by passion and ambition."

The newspapers reported that he faced his death with arrogance, saying, "I die famous." That is not true. For a week before his execution he was unable to eat. During all the last day he kept asking the prison doctor, "Will it hurt? Will I still be conscious when my neck breaks? You do die instantaneously, don't you?" He was a pitiful remnant of a human being as he walked to the scaffold. Two guards had to support him.

JAMES BANNERMAN

# The Biggest Spender We Ever Had

In the summer of 1918, just before the end of the First World War, a Chicago sporting newspaper named *The Eye* told in front-page headlines about a naval engagement that had nothing to do with the waning war at sea. Even without the sound and flash of dreadnoughts' guns, however, it was arresting enough: NAVY OFFICER IN GIGANTIC COUP WINS FORTUNE AT SPA. The Spa referred to was Saratoga Springs, a race track and resort town in upstate New York, where the navy

officer was "credited with engineering the most stupendous coup of the present racing year, making the previous splurges of other high flyers look like the veriest piking efforts."

The officer wore the uniform of the Canadian Navy, the paper said, without identifying him further. It reported, however, that he had wagered $25,000 at the race track on a horse named Canso, and another $25,000 at booking establishments all over the continent. And Canso won the race. But that wasn't all: Canso was only part of a parlay on which the navy officer cleaned up a million dollars. The New York Jockey Club had felt obliged to tell him to ease up because he was spoiling the sport for more moderate bettors.

The officer—a handsome six-footer—was living the kind of life most men can only dream about, and for a decade he was Canada's most flamboyant and glamorous figure. His name was J. K. L. Ross.

Two years before he brought off his big coup at Saratoga, Ross inherited sixteen million dollars from his father. He had a forty-room house on Montreal's Peel Street, high above the city on the slopes of Mount Royal, with thirty servants. At one time or another he owned seven yachts, not counting two he bought simply to give away. He kept two racing stables, each with its string of thoroughbreds, and his black-and-orange colors were famous and familiar at every big track from Montreal to Mexico. He once admitted betting fifty thousand dollars on a single race. The money he gave to hospitals and schools and for charity ran into millions.

In 1928, twelve years after he got his inheritance, he was declared bankrupt, but he even went broke in the grand manner. He still had an income of at least fifty thousand a year his creditors couldn't touch, and until he died in 1951 it supported him in sunny elegance on an estate in Jamaica, in a house that was one of the show places of the island.

In Ross's heyday, from the end of the First World War to the beginning of the boom that burst when the stock market crashed in 1929, he stood out as Canada's supreme example of the millionaire sportsman—our solitary counterpart to the Whitneys and Vanderbilts of the United States. Other wealthy Canadians of that golden age, like Sir John Eaton, the Toronto department-store owner, and financier Sir James Dunn, had both princely tastes and the means to gratify them. But none had quite the glamour and gusto of Ross, and none had quite his magnificent way with money.

When he invited a party of friends to the races, he took them there from Windsor Station in downtown Montreal in a private railway car he had specially built for him. It was longer and heavier than a standard Pullman and, in addition to half a dozen staterooms with proper beds instead of mere berths, it had a dining room, a living room, and a bathroom with a huge tub and gold-plated taps. And on the way to the track, as the veteran Montreal sports columnist Elmer Ferguson once wrote, Ross provided his guests with "a chef, a wonderful meal, and champagne flowing like oil in Texas." Ferguson also wrote of a day at the Blue Bonnets race track when he parked his modest automobile alongside one of Ross's six or seven Rolls-Royces—a sleek red roadster that couldn't have cost less than twelve thousand. While he was admiring it Ross came up, and asked him if he liked it. When Ferguson assured him he did, Ross said, "Then take it, with my compliments. It's a nice little car, and I'd like it to be owned by someone who appreciates it." Ferguson didn't feel he could accept, but the offer didn't surprise him. As he said, "Ross was that kind of a guy."

Once, after Ross had a slight argument with his wife, he decided to give her a necklace. He told David Hogg, his confidential business agent, to go to New York and buy one. When Hogg asked how much he wanted to spend, Ross said he didn't think anything very grand was indicated, and that $125,000 would be about right. When Hogg got back to Montreal and showed his employer the glittering treasure he'd bought, Ross barely glanced at it and dropped it into his pocket as casually as if it had been a penny matchbox.

His lavishness was not merely a matter of prodigious spending. There was an exuberance about him that made whatever he did seem a little larger than life-sized, and gave it the bright implausible color of a travel poster. He went in for yacht racing with a flourish that has seldom been equaled. His seventy-five-foot "Gloria" was in the same exalted class as George V's famous "Britannia," and he raced her as a fellow member of the King's own club —the super-exclusive Royal Yacht Squadron at Cowes.

When he took to tuna fishing for sport, off the Nova Scotia coast in the summer of 1908, he made his arrangements on the scale of a maharajah setting out on a tiger hunt. Although he fished from a small rowboat he kept a motor cruiser standing by, and a launch shuttled between boat and cruiser to bring him refreshments. For the first three seasons his bad luck was characteristically spectacular. All the fifty-odd tuna he hooked got away, after fights that lasted up to nineteen hours. When the run of bad luck ended toward the close of his fourth season, the change was even more spectacular. The tuna he finally landed weighed 680 pounds—the biggest caught until then with hook and line.

Ross, good-natured and unaffected with everybody from princes to taxi-drivers, was the son of a man of monumental shrewdness. James Ross, a Scottish-born civil engineer, came to Canada in the 1870's by way of the

United States, where he had been in charge of construction and maintenance on a couple of old Commodore Vanderbilt's early railways. When his son was born, at Lindsay, Ontario, in 1876, James was manager and chief engineer of a small local road; but in 1883 he got the contract to build the whole of the Canadian Pacific's main line from Winnipeg west over the Rockies. Soon after that he gave up engineering and concentrated on making money, with such relentless determination and in such enormous amounts that by the first years of this century a newspaper felt free to describe him as a flint-hearted financier.

James Ross gave his son three names— James Kenneth Levenson. When J. K. L. was ten he was sent to Bishop's College School at Lennoxville, Quebec, an English-type private school for the well-to-do. Though his career at Bishop's was undistinguished, both in the classroom and on the playing field, he blossomed out when he entered McGill University in 1893. There he stood near the top of his classes and shone as a star lineman on McGill's 1896 champion football team. Meanwhile his father had bought into the street railways of Toronto, Montreal and Winnipeg, owned a large part of the tramway system of Birmingham in England, and controlled the vast Dominion Coal Company, which operated most of the mines of Nova Scotia. When young Ross graduated in 1897 with the degree of Bachelor of Science, the old man began grooming him to be his heir, and put him to work in Montreal as a kind of apprentice manager in several of his businesses.

In 1898 Ross was shipped off to England for two years of similar apprenticeship there. As a boy he had been shy and diffident, and even at the beginning of the English phase of his training he still hadn't developed much ease of manner. This bothered his father, who thought up a wildly original plan to correct it. Old James had a theory that few men have more unshakable self-control than a conjurer. He ordered Ross to get in touch with what he called "a prominent magician" before he left England and to take lessons. Ross did as he was told, discovered he had a natural gift for sleight of hand, and for the rest of his life liked to startle a new acquaintance by suddenly producing an ace of spades from his left ear, or astonish his guests with an after-dinner display of card tricks.

When he returned to Canada in 1901 J. K. L. brought back with him a Napier, one of the first motor cars on Montreal's streets. Not content to confine his driving to city streets, he made the ten-mile trip to Dorval over atrocious dirt roads. There he was greeted by reporters sent out on the off-chance that he would arrive. A year later he married Ethel Matthews, daughter of the Toronto financier W. D. Matthews, and his father made him assistant to the general manager of the Dominion Coal Company. The mines were near Sydney, N.S., where Ross lived when his not-too-demanding duties didn't require him to be at the head offices in Montreal, or he wasn't at his summer place on St. Ann's Bay on the northeast coast of Cape Breton, or out fishing for tuna, or in England sailing "Gloria" in the races of the Royal Yacht Squadron, where he enjoyed himself hugely but never won any important trophies.

In 1913, when Ross was thirty-seven, old James died and left him virtually the whole of his fortune. Ross wasn't to get the full estate until his fortieth birthday, but in the meantime he was to have an allowance of $75,000 a year. He also got an immediate legacy of $50,000, and a clause in the will directed the executors to pay him any sum up to one million dollars at any time after his father's death, if he should want it to go into business or buy property.

Since he could get the money simply by asking for it, Ross was now in effect a millionaire and could live an even more ample life. He began doing it by ordering a 106-foot motor yacht, the "Albacore." She was designed with six staterooms for the owner and his guests, a dining saloon paneled in maple, and accommodations for two officers and a crew of four. Ross looked forward to long cruises in her, but soon after "Albacore" was launched the First World War broke out, and he changed his plans.

Canada's three-year-old Navy consisted largely of one ancient cruiser taken over from the English. Ross had been an ardent supporter of Sir Robert Borden's proposal in 1913 that Canada should spend $35 millions to build three battleships for the British Navy. The so-called "Dreadnought Bill" passed the Commons but was defeated in the Senate. Ross thought there ought to be a public subscription to raise the money and made it known he was willing to start one with a gift of half a million. When war broke out before the project got really under way, he gave the half million to the government instead, to use for any war purpose it saw fit. He also loaned his new yacht to the Canadian Navy for service as a patrol vessel, and decided to do still more.

Ross bought a big U.S. steam yacht, the "Tarantula," from W. K. Vanderbilt, and turned her over to the Navy as an outright gift. To get her out of the still-neutral United

States he had to pretend he had bought her for pleasure, but as he'd had her painted battleship grey this wasn't entirely believed. To make it more credible he brought his eleven-year-old son along when he took delivery of "Tarantula" at a shipyard near Boston and sailed, flying the peaceful flag of the New York Yacht Club, with the boy ostentatiously in view on deck.

That was less than two weeks after the outbreak of war. Within a month Ross had bought another steam yacht, the "Winchester," from a wealthy Englishman, and given her also to the Navy. The Navy renamed her "Grilse," commissioned Ross a reserve lieutenant, and put him in command. He was at sea in the "Grilse" for two years, on patrol between Halifax and Bermuda. He never had her in action, but got two mentions in dispatches for the seamanlike way he handled her in Atlantic winter storms and a hurricane off Bermuda.

On the last day of March 1916, Ross had his fortieth birthday—the fateful day on which he inherited the sixteen-million-dollar balance of his father's fortune. That spring he went off active duty at sea. In the fall, still in the Navy, he was loaned to the government to be chairman of the newly formed Dominion Board of Pension Commissioners. At the same time he set about the happy task of living up to his immense new wealth.

He promptly gave almost a million to the Royal Victoria Hospital for a building in memory of his father, and another million to his old school, Bishop's College. He invested a million and a quarter in a trust fund for his wife. In 1914 he'd bought a couple of race horses and had got a taste for racing which now grew to a passion. The year of his inheritance he spent a million or so to start a breeding farm at Verchères on the St. Lawrence—a site he picked chiefly because the grass and water were good and it was near enough to a railway station to be convenient for shipping horses, but also because he could get there from Montreal by yacht. He had all the stables and barns painted the black and orange of his racing colors, and before long he'd got together a string of forty-seven horses.

In 1917 the Navy promoted him commander, skipping the intervening rank of lieutenant-commander as a special honor to the man who had given it two ships and loaned it a third. That year Ross had his private railway car built, in which he sometimes took friends to the track where his horses happened to be running. Perhaps because of his public service there was no public criticism of him for buying such a luxury at the height of the war in France.

Although his entertaining was as wholeheartedly lavish as everything else he did, Ross himself ate and drank moderately. But he liked to see less abstemious people having fun, and gave parties wherever he went. He gave a particularly cheerful party at the Casino in Saratoga Springs to celebrate his reported coup there in 1918, and his betting activities became the talk of race tracks all over the continent. Public guessing on his wagering barely managed to keep up with the truth and—amazingly, in view of the large amounts he bet—when people guessed he was losing fortunes they were all wrong. According to the records Ross kept, he was one player who actually beat the races. His son James later made a tabulation of Ross's betting books for 1918 to 1924, noting that bets before and after that were "negligible." In 1918, when Ross was supposed to have made a fortune at Saratoga, the books show he did indeed make one, and cleared $98,000 altogether. In 1920 and 1924 Ross went down a total of $60,000 but those were his only losing years. In 1919, his best year, he won $189,000. His biggest single bet that year was $50,000, which he won, bringing him a $50,000 profit. Some of the ninety-two other bets he made in 1919 were in the low hundreds, but fifty-one were for $1,000 or more, including twenty-three for $5,000. His books show that in 1924, when he stopped betting heavily, he made $18,000, and that his five winning years so far offset his two losing ones that he ended up $315,000 ahead of the game.

In the year 1919 his horse Sir Barton won the Kentucky Derby at Churchill Downs— the first time a Canadian owner had ever taken that famous race. Another of his horses, Billy Kelly, coupled with Sir Barton in the betting, finished second. Ross had gone to the Downs a day or two earlier with a party of friends, but the night before the race he got word that his father-in-law, W. D. Matthews, was dying in Toronto. He left at once, and so became one of the few winning owners in the long history of the Kentucky Derby who didn't see his triumph.

Long afterward, at the time of Ross's death, sportswriter Jim Coleman told how Ross had wired Abe Orpen in Toronto and Con Enright in New York, saying to each, "Bet twenty thousand my entry SP." They knew it referred to his Derby entry, but weren't sure what he meant by the letters "SP" at the end. In those days there were private bookmakers who took bets at agreed odds before the race, as well as some who paid off on the pari-mutuel odds at the time it started. After consulting by phone Orpen and Enright decided Ross wanted them each to bet $20,000 straight and $20,000 place at starting odds, and made arrangements accordingly.

Sir Barton won by five lengths, with Billy Kelly second, and the entry paid $7.20 to win and $6.70 to place. As Orpen and Enright had understood the wire, this meant they owed Ross $99,000 apiece. He wouldn't accept it. He said he'd intended the letters "SP" as the English racing abbreviation for "starting price," that he'd bet only on a straight win, and that consequently they just owed him $52,000 apiece. That was all he would take, and he insisted they were to keep the difference. It came to $47,000 each. When the story got out it wasn't generally realized that Ross had refused the money because he didn't want to profit by a misunderstanding. He already had such a reputation for magnificence that in spite of the fact that both Orpen and Enright were wealthy men themselves, there was a widespread belief that Ross had handed them an enormous and lordly tip.

In 1918 all horse racing had been stopped in Canada for two years, except for the annual running of the famous King's Plate in Toronto and the less well-known Quebec King's Plate in Montreal. Ross had bought a second big breeding farm, at the race-track town of Laurel in Maryland, and sent most of his horses there to continue racing in the United States. They did so well that in 1918 he headed the list of winning owners and won $99,179 in purses. He was at the head of the list again in 1919, with $209,303. In 1920 when he was second to H. P. Whitney, the purses he won amounted to $250,586—his biggest take in any one year and a great sum for those days. But in spite of the purse money his horses brought him, it was costing close to a hundred thousand a year to keep the two stables going.

The most spectacular reward he got for this outlay came when Sir Barton won not only the Kentucky Derby, but the Belmont Stakes and the Preakness. No other owner in racing history had ever won all three classics in a single year. More newsworthy even than the first winning of the triple crown was the match race arranged in October 1920 between Sir Barton and Man o' War. Out of ten starts in 1919, Man o' War had won nine, having been beaten for the only time in his career by a horse appropriately named Upset. Of ten starts in 1920 he had won all and went to the post against Sir Barton at Kenilworth Park in Windsor an odds-on favorite. Sir Barton lost by seven lengths. The defeat was particularly crushing because it was obvious Man o' War wasn't going to full out. From that day on

both Man o' War and Sir Barton were retired to stud, never to race again.

The next five years were the last of Ross's fame. He entertained on such a scale that it was quite usual for twenty people to sit down to dinner in the vast mahogany-paneled dining room of his Peel Street house in Montreal. After these dinners there was often music, of a serious sort which Ross himself didn't care for, but which his wife loved. It was provided by concert violinists and pianists and singers, in Montreal on tour, whom she'd engaged to come to the house so the dinner guests could hear them in luxurious privacy.

In 1923 Ross spent a quarter of a million dollars to remodel the Peel Street house and make it even larger, adding such luxuries as a darkroom to develop photographs. By way of a housewarming, he invited fifty for dinner and a hundred and twenty-five for dancing afterward to meet the Duke of Windsor, then Prince of Wales and traveling incognito as Lord Renfrew. The royal guest couldn't get enough of the party, and stayed on and on. "In consequence," a Montreal paper said in a discreet story, "Lord Renfrew did not arise very early yesterday."

Although 1923 was apparently a brilliant year for Ross, it was clouded by worry of a kind he'd never felt before. His yachts, the private railway car, seven or eight Rolls-Royces, thirty or forty servants, houses in Montreal and at Laurel, and above all the expenses of racing and keeping up the two breeding farms, were beginning to be a noticeable drain on his resources. That fall he met a man named W. A. Read, a promoter and financier who was interested in racing and knew a lot of Ross's friends in upper-class English sporting circles. Read suggested that if the Maryland farm were incorporated as a company for breeding, selling and importing blood horses, it might become profitable instead of costly.

Ross agreed, and in October 1923 the farm went into business as the Laurel Park Stud Company. But the hoped-for profits didn't materialize, and the farm continued draining money. About a year later Read made another suggestion. He had certain properties in the oil well regions of the United States, more especially in Oklahoma, which needed development. If Ross bought into those, together with one or two of Read's English associates, the money from oil might carry the cost of the stables at Laurel. It seemed like a good idea to Ross, and he took a quarter of a million shares of a company called Caltex Oil.

It was the first of a series of what he later

called "unwise investments." The phrase was a monumental understatement. The Caltex development didn't pay off. Ross, who had spent money in the grand manner, now proceeded to go broke in the grand manner. When Caltex was expanded to take in other oil properties—also backed by Ross—it turned out to be equally disappointing. Until 1927 he was able to go on racing, but by the spring of that year his losses in oil had reached the point where he was in desperate need of money. In May, at Toronto's Thorncliffe Park, he sold what remained of his stable—fourteen horses and a lead pony. A few days later he made a general assignment to his creditors. He was three million dollars in the hole.

His principal creditor was the Baltimore Trust Company, which held drafts for almost half a million that Ross had endorsed and guaranteed. In November 1928 the company forced him into bankruptcy. The Montreal *Star*, owned by Ross's friend Lord Atholstan, tactfully headlined its story MOST REGRETTABLE LOCAL INSOLVENCY and went on to speak feelingly of the bankrupt, who, it said, "through kindheartedness allowed himself to be victimized by designing people whom he had befriended." After listing his philanthropies, the *Star* said: "The adversity which through cunning overcomes such a generous citizen constitutes a public calamity."

The bankruptcy proceedings showed that Ross's approach to business had been rather remarkably confiding. When he was questioned about a trip to the Oklahoma oil fields he'd taken in 1926 with Read and a Sir Hector MacNeill, one of the lawyers asked if the object of the trip hadn't been to examine oil properties and discuss plans to expand their operations. Ross said he was chiefly interested in just looking around. "I had never seen an oil field in my life. I don't pretend to know anything about oil or oil wells." And when the lawyer asked if there had been any question of the cost of buying new properties, Ross said: "Mr. Read talked so many figures that I left it entirely to him."

It also appeared from the proceedings that Ross had been in the habit of signing batches of promissory notes in blank from time to time, and that these had been sent from Montreal to the farm at Laurel to meet current expenses—often several thousand dollars at a time. When the astonished examiners wanted to know how many of these blank notes he'd signed, Ross said he hadn't the slightest idea but that he supposed there might have been three hundred. But in the whole of the evidence there wasn't a word of complaint. He was bankrupt, and that was that.

A codicil to his father's will had set up a trust fund of a million dollars, the income from which was to be paid to Ross during his lifetime and afterward to his two children, James and Hylda. Since the fund had been well managed by the trustees for the fifteen years since the old man's death, it had grown considerably. Furthermore it couldn't be attached by Ross's creditors, because it wasn't part of his estate. Hence he could still count on at least $50,000 a year on which to begin a new life. His creditors got fifty cents on the dollar.

JACK SCOTT

# Ricky Will Never Grow Up

Life had never looked better to Richard McCallum than it did one bright July morning when he stepped into an elevator in Vancouver's Medical-Dental Building.

A tall, fair, quiet-mannered man of thirty, Dick McCallum dressed and looked the part of a successful young executive. In three years of civilian life after his wartime hitch in the Air Force he had become purchasing agent of a large Vancouver electrical firm. He and his high-school sweetheart, Lorraine, had been married for five years. They were happy together and popular in their set. A few weeks before this July day they had moved into their new six-room ranch-style bungalow among the evergreens in Capilano Highlands, and the new lawn was coming up nicely.

But McCallum was happy for a better reason. It was just four days since his wife had given birth to a boy, their first child, and while they'd assured each other it wouldn't matter, it was a boy each secretly wanted. They had decided to call him Richard, too. The baby was born six weeks prematurely and weighed only five pounds, one ounce. He was not feeding properly and McCallum presumed that Lorraine's obstetrician had called him to his office now to explain why this was so.

The doctor offered McCallum a cigarette and said, "You'd better sit down for this one, Dick. I have to tell you that your baby is not right."

McCallum sat down.

The doctor began, "Ricky is what we call a Mongolian Idiot . . ."

"The bottom of the world fell out," McCallum told a friend some time later, "but I didn't know how to feel about it. If the doctor had said, 'Your baby is blind,' or 'Your baby has a club foot' or something like that I'd have known what it meant. I might have rationalized things. But this was beyond my grasp. I could only think, 'God, why did it have to happen to us?' "

The realization that he would have to be the one to tell Lorraine helped McCallum weather the shock. He remembered then that Lorraine had been worried about the baby. The nurses in the maternity ward had suspected little Ricky was an "ill-finished child." Because there was still an element of doubt they had kept their secret. But Lorraine seemed to have sensed something was wrong. Twice when the baby was brought to her she had taken him from his swaddling clothes to look at him. He was small and weak but he seemed perfectly formed.

"The doctor's phrase, the medical term for it, made me imagine a little monster," McCallum recalled, "but I knew better. Ricky looked good to me. He was what everybody calls a cute baby. We were worried about him, of course, because of the premature birth and because he wouldn't take the breast, but we were crazy about him."

That was the beginning for the McCallums of an excursion into one of the most bizarre and tragic regions of medical science. When Dick went to the hospital two days later to tell Lorraine, he had already found the answers to her first flood of questions. He knew that Mongoloid birth is far from rare and that Lorraine and he were not to be alone in their unhappiness.

In every thousand births two babies will be marked for an existence in which they'll lag far behind in physique, intellect and emotions with no chance whatever to know a normal life. At the very best such children develop at only 30 per cent of normal, the darkness of their lives lit only by the fact that mentally they live their lives with the innocence of children. Because so many of these children are concealed behind closed doors in homes or institutions, there is no general awareness of the frequency of such births. "When we came to know more about it," McCallum says now, "we were amazed and shocked to find it so common."

Dick had discovered, too, that these births have nothing whatever to do with heredity. Mongolism may strike in any family, rich or poor, educated or illiterate, young or old, black or white. It may be the first child or the last or in the middle. In the majority of cases, however, the Mongoloid child is the last born of a long family of normal healthy children and to a mother over the average age. One United States study of 2,800 cases showed more than half the mothers were over thirty-five. Another survey indicated that mothers between forty-five and forty-seven produced twelve Mongoloids in one hundred births.

While the authorities all recognize this factor of an advanced maternal age, there is disagreement about the cause of Mongolism. It is generally thought to be the result of some ovarian disorder which slows the growth of the baby before birth. A recent theory holds there is some shock to the fetus—perhaps through a shortage of oxygen—about the eighth week of pregnancy.

From the moment Lorraine McCallum heard her husband's grave account of Ricky's fate she was determined her own sorrow and nameless dread of the future would never come between her and her love for her baby. It was a decision that probably saved her from disaster. Later they were to learn that many parents crack up physically and mentally when faced with such a sudden change in their lives. Many more become bitter and develop a psychopathic hatred toward the child.

Lorraine is a year younger than her husband. She is an attractive and vivacious woman who speaks now in an almost clinical manner about Ricky's deficiency. "Getting emotional about it was just a luxury," she says. "It wasn't a case of enduring a situation but of accepting it. I determined to bring up Ricky in as normal a way as I could. We knew from the beginning that there was no hope of a cure. We never let ourselves chase rainbows. If I cried about it, I cried alone."

From the beginning both Dick and his wife accepted this realistic approach that denies them the hope of a cure. Experimental remedial work in the field of mental deficiency has been largely confined to the field of cerebral palsy where the decreased blood supply to the brain is the apparent cause of the deficiency. In these cases—unlike the Mongoloid—the child possesses a normal mind and only his physical handicap denies him its use.

When Lorraine went home to their new bungalow, Ricky remained behind in the hospital. He was there nearly four months, being fed intravenously at first, then put on a special diet to build up his strength. In their regular visits the McCallums looked anxiously for signs of deformities. They could find none.

"The day I brought him home I felt happier than I'd ever felt before," Lorraine says. The next year was one the McCallums now regret. They decided to keep their problem a secret from their relatives and friends. It was a decision based on the knowledge that Ricky had a slim chance of survival. The majority of Mongoloid children die before their first birthday, perhaps mercifully. They are rarely strong enough organically to survive. Most die of heart defects. Others succumb to a variety of infectious diseases. They are particularly susceptible to respiratory diseases and 75 per cent of those who reach the age of ten will die of tuberculosis. Mongoloid children seldom live beyond the age of fifteen and the age of forty is extremely rare. Those who do survive undergo a change that is swift and shocking. After a prolonged babyhood and infancy these "unfinished children," at an average age of twenty, almost overnight become old people with all the symptoms of senility—baldness, wrinkles, hardening of the arteries and the rest.

"We would not admit to a feeling of shame or that we had anything to hide," McCallum recalled, "but if Ricky was to be with us for only a short time it seemed unfair to our relatives and friends to ask them to share our problem."

Only the baby's grandparents were to know, and Lorraine and Dick thought a good deal about how to break the news to them. One day, browsing in the public library, Dick came upon an article by Pearl Buck, in the *Ladies Home Journal*, that seemed to answer their problem. It was about the author's daughter and it was called "The Child Who Never Grew." "The minds of retarded children are sane minds, normal except that, being arrested, the processes are slowed." Pearl Buck had written. "When your little child is born to you not whole and sound as you had hoped, but warped and defective in mind or body or perhaps both, remember this is still your child. Remember, too, that the child has his right to life, whatever that life may be, and he has the right to happiness, which you must find for him. Be proud of your child, accept him as he is and do not heed the words and stares of those who know no better."

It seemed to the McCallums that these words expressed perfectly the viewpoint they were striving for. That night they invited the grandparents to their home. After dinner Dick read the article to them. When he had put it down he said simply, "That's the story of Ricky."

That evening was important to the McCallums because they realized for the first time that it was right for them to be candid. The sympathy and understanding of these older people were their first real therapy since Ricky was born.

"We knew then that people would be tolerant and kind when they knew what it was all about," Dick recalls. "All we had to fear was ignorance. We'd know, ourselves, what that could mean. Why, the medical terms themselves—Mongoloid, cretin, moron, imbecile, idiot—they all sound frightening and strange. We knew that our only course was to try to make people understand."

After Ricky's first birthday he began slowly to assume an appearance that is classic in such cases, yet the change was so subtle that his parents, with him from day to day, were almost unaware of it. Most Mongoloid children look enough alike to be sisters or brothers. "There is a little face that belongs to them all," Lorraine puts it. They are stunted in growth, rarely reaching more than five feet in height, even in adulthood. The children have long bodies with dwarfish legs and arms. Their hands and feet are small and broad with short fingers and toes. The skull is joined imperfectly at the top of the head. In facial appearance they are strangely Oriental, an effect resulting from the broad flat passive features. The nose is spread out because the bridge of bone is not developed. The cheekbones are high and conspicuous. The eyes are small and almond-shaped. It was this appearance that inspired the word "Mongoloid," although many doctors now refer to such cases as "ill-finished" or "unfinished."

Yet as Ricky grew into this tragic mold he was developing a personality that endeared him to his parents. Most Mongoloid children have a gift of mimicry that is highly developed, and Ricky's tricks of imitating his parents delighted them. They had read that such children occasionally have a destructive make-up and may become unmanageable, but from the beginning Ricky seemed to have a feeling for others that was touching.

"His affectionate nature won over even those of our friends who might have been uncomfortable with him," Lorraine says. "There was a streak of stubbornness in him. Once he'd started something he was determined to finish it. But two-thirds of the battle, as I sometimes thought of it, were happiness and affection.

"It's been Ricky's loving nature, more than anything, that has turned us against the idea of institutions. We know how much love he has to give and how much he needs. Almost every doctor and pediatrician believes the child is better off in an institution, that there's just no place for him in a normal home. We may have to think that way, too, when the time comes. But now he needs us."

The question of institutions arises in every home darkened by Mongolism. It is not always possible in Canada to find such refuge. Both public and private institutions have long waiting lists, and it is rare for a backward child to be admitted before the age of six. The doctors recommend institutions for a number of reasons. They say the child may grow physically to a semblance of adulthood with the mind of a small child and that he will be left alone and helpless should the parents die. They believe, too, that the emotional strain on normal families may cause illness or a mental breakdown. This has been the case in many such families, particularly with the mothers who must bear most of the load. Some parents, the doctors point out, have been known to sacrifice the whole family for the sake of the unfortunate child, neglecting the healthy children who, in their opinion, don't need so much care.

The most important reason of all for "institutionalizing," however, is one the McCallums faced on August 12, 1950. That was the date their second son, Eric, was born. Here, too, the McCallums were following the considered advice of authorities. Most doctors believe the parents of retarded youngsters should have more children. Dick and Lorraine had read the typical advice of one medical man to the mother of an idiot boy: "Have five more children. You cannot save this one, but a few more will save the parents."

Like his brother, little Eric is blond and blue-eyed, but he is a normal bright boy in every way. "Having Eric wasn't an easy decision to make," Lorraine recalls. "We spent many and many a night talking about it until the dawn. The doctors said I had no reason to worry about the second child. It was perhaps a cold-blooded way to look at it, but they said it was just a matter of odds, and the odds are overwhelming against a second case of Mongolism. Of course, I *did* worry, as any woman would."

The addition of Eric to the family presented a whole new outlook, and in many respects the McCallums had to start from the beginning in their adjustment. "We knew we had to think of Eric, now, just as much as we thought of Ricky," Dick explained. "We asked ourselves how we were ever going to make Eric understand. We dreaded the day it would be necessary. Would he be ashamed of his brother? Would he be reluctant to bring his friends home, knowing they might jeer at Ricky? We thought of the inevitable things that would happen later on. We thought of Eric becoming engaged. Supposing he brought his fiancée home. Would *she* understand when she knew about Ricky or would she have the same ignorant fears we'd known, particularly about heredity? We knew this would be as close to Eric as it is to us and that it would surely affect his life and his chance for happiness."

An ever deeper conflict is involved in trying to decide how much Ricky may be exposed to society. "We're trying to be frank about it with everyone," Dick confesses, "but I can still break into tears when I think of the future. How is he going to get along with other youngsters? We mustn't coddle him too much, I know, but he could never protect himself in the pack. If he plays with the neighbors' children, what happens when there's a birthday party and he's not invited? Should we keep him here in our own backyard? And if we do that, aren't people going to look at that high fence and say to themselves, 'There's a strange little boy who's not right'? Will that be fair either to Ricky or to our second boy? And we know, too, that if we hide Ricky we must to some extent hide ourselves as well."

The McCallums tried to solve this by taking Ricky out. These trips were bitterly disappointing. "A friend volunteered to drive us to the beach and I thought, 'Now is as good a chance as any to see what happens.' When our friend called for us she said she knew just the place to go. It was an out-of-the-way spot, she said, and there'd be almost nobody there. I knew she meant to be kind. It hurt, just the same, to feel that we must be kept away from people.

"Still, as it turned out perhaps she was right. It was an awful afternoon. Ricky loved it and played in the sand, but he moves awkwardly, and suddenly I knew the other people on the beach were watching him closely. I saw some children stop and nudge each other. A couple nearby pointed and whispered. My heart was breaking. I wanted to grab Ricky and run from there."

Soon after this, Lorraine tried again. "Dick had the car and so I took Ricky into town on the bus. It was his first time in the bus. It was crowded and he was a little frightened. He climbed up into my lap. I suppose that attracted people's attention because he's so big. I felt everyone's eyes on us, not merely curious, but staring openly. I tried to remind myself that only three years ago I might have been guilty of this myself, without thinking. I knew that each of these people would be understanding if Ricky's condition were familiar to them, that they'd accept it and look away as people look away from a crippled boy. But then I just felt angry, I wanted to stand up and shout, 'Don't stare at us!'"

Whenever Dick or Lorraine recall such experiences they invariably make an attempt to look on the optimistic side. One day recently Dick was describing to a friend how Lorraine had taken Ricky to buy new shoes. Looking up, she had seen a couple stop to watch them. He cut off the story abruptly. "I shouldn't be dwelling on that kind of thing," he said, reproaching himself. "When I see other families who have this problem I know we're lucky. Lorraine and I sleep at night. There are many who don't. To us Ricky is still an attractive child. In so many cases the children are grotesque and deformed.

"Ricky hasn't needed any special care and economically we're on sound ground. Many families with children like Ricky aren't so well off and often have heavy bills for doctors and hospitals. We have a home of our own, but we know of families who have searched for months to rent a house because landlords won't accept them with such a child.

"Most of all, we're lucky that we've been able to work out a kind of philosophy about this. In a great many cases this sort of thing has brought a feeling of guilt and recrimination and been a kind of death sentence for the family."

In their own home the McCallums take a pride in showing the progress Ricky is making against fearful odds. Recently they entertained an old Air Force friend of Dick's from Montreal who hadn't known of the McCallum's problem. The two children were having their afternoon nap when he arrived. On learning about Ricky the friend expressed an interest in his daily life.

Lorraine said proudly that Ricky was coming along well. He plays with his younger brother, but mostly he amuses himself with his toys. He was ungainly because of his short legs and his weight, but he had learned to walk at a year and a half, which is unusual, and at three he was able to navigate the stairs. He understands his mother and with his gift of mimicry he is able to make her understand him. She had been able to teach him to nod his head for "yes," but he could not learn to nod his head for "no."

Lorraine explained to me that she had subscribed to a series of home-training lessons, and that in these she could not be guided by Ricky's real age, but by his mental age. She had taken him to the provincial Child Guidance Clinic and there, through a series of simple tests, they had decided Ricky had a mental age of eighteen months at the age of three. In the unhappy lexicon of the mentally deficient this ratio between Ricky's real and mental age was described as "a very low moron," but in the circumstances it was remarkably high. Both "imbecile" and "idiot" are categories below that of "moron."

"That must have been encouraging," I said.

"It's odd, but it wasn't, and for two reasons," Lorraine replied. "We know that if Ricky continues according to type he will never in all his life have a mental age above ten years. And so it's only fooling ourselves to hope for too much." She explained that the mental age of the average adult victim of Mongolism is between two and five and that few, if any, develop beyond a mental age of ten in their lifetime. Most of these children take ten years to accomplish what the normal child may accomplish in two years. The maximum of ability is reached at twenty, but even then a vocabulary of fifty words is the highest ever known and that only after extensive training. By these standards Ricky was doing extremely well. It was precisely this that worried Lorraine.

"It is something that only people who have gone through this would understand," Lorraine told me, "but the curious thing is that we don't want him to do *too* well. Ricky will be better off as a lower type. Then he is less liable to be hurt by the reaction he causes or by the ridicule he's bound to encounter. He won't know he's different, you see. He'll know only his own kind of happiness in his own kind of world."

At this point Ricky entered the room with his grandmother. He was dressed in a plaid playsuit and, prepared for the worst, I was agreeably surprised. The little boy hesitated and looked dully about the room. Then, seeing his mother, his face lit with happiness. He walked across to her and put his arms about her.

"We have a visitor, Ricky," his mother said.

The little boy looked up at me, then walked across the room and put his arms out to me. I hugged him and then looked across to Dick and Lorraine who were smiling.

"I guess this is the only way to really understand what it means," I said.

ERIC HUTTON

# He Started the Stork Derby

October 31, 1926, was a Sunday and the elevators were not running in the Crown Life building on Yonge Street, Toronto. So Charles Millar, an impatient man when anyone disputed his recollection of a point of law, ran up the three flights of stairs to his office. George Anderson, a post-office official, and Charles Kemp, Millar's law partner, followed at a more leisurely pace.

When they entered his office Millar already had a law book open on his desk and his pink, totally bald head was bent over it. His long expressive face, which could change so quickly from sardonic to humorous, was tightened in concentration as he searched for the technicality over which the three men had disagreed, amiably but emphatically, during an expansive luncheon in the nearby King Edward Hotel. With a grunt of satisfaction Millar jabbed his forefinger at the page, turned to speak to Anderson and Kemp and suddenly slumped in his chair.

The events of the next three days followed the usual pattern of mourning for a substantial citizen. Obituaries in the four Toronto papers were long and laudatory. (The *Telegram*'s heading, though, seems rather archaic for even a quarter-century ago: "Lawyer, Sportsman, Business Man Expires Without a Moment's Warning in His Law Office.") Millar, a prominent lawyer and financier, left an estate which was eventually worth close to a million dollars.

He was buried at Aylmer, Ontario, near the farm on which he had been born seventy-three years before. The funeral in Toronto can only be described as distinguished. Judges, government officials, lawyers, company executives, hotel magnates, stockbrokers and an aggregation described somewhat vaguely as "the sporting fraternity" crowded by the hundreds into Millar's big frame house at 75 Scarboro Road to hear the Reverend T. H. Cotton deliver a eulogy on his life and deeds. Four second cousins were among those present.

That was the last time a clergyman was to say a good word about Millar; the last time the great majority of his friends, relatives and acquaintances were to speak of him with respect; certainly the last time any newspaper was to print a dignified item concerning him. Overnight Charles Vance Millar underwent a posthumous change from a rich respectable stuffed shirt into a fabulous character who was to receive more conversational and news-page space than practically any other subject between World Wars I and II.

The reason why Millar's fame was greater during the decade after his death than in the seventy-three years before it, was that he left a will the like of which had never been seen before and probably never will be seen again. The very phrase "Millar Will" has become part of Ontario's folklore. To most people, however, that term recalls only the final clause of the will, in which a reticent and rather stiff-necked bachelor bequeathed the bulk of his fortune to the woman who, in the ten years following his death, happened to give birth in Toronto to the largest number of children. Most of the long-term deploring and viewing-

with-alarm in high places centred around this "stork derby" clause. But when the terms of the will were first made public to start a career as a ten-year wonder, Clauses Five, Six and Seven were considered equally combustible. In the years to come distant relatives and some people whose only connection was the name "Millar" fought vainly to have the controversial will disallowed.

Clause Five bequeathed "to Hon. W. E. Raney, A. M. Orpen and Rev. Samuel D. Chown each one share in the Ontario Jockey Club, provided that three years from my death each of them becomes enrolled as a shareholder." But Millar directed that if any one of the three declined membership in the racing organization, all the shares, which had a value of $1,500 each, were to revert to the estate.

The plot of Clause Five's little drama was that Judge Raney, former attorney-general of Ontario, and Dr. Chown, former head of the Methodist Church in Canada, were sworn enemies of horse racing in general and betting in particular. Raney, as attorney-general, had been Millar's personal opponent at committee hearings on a private bill which sought to expand racing in Ontario. Abe Orpen, on the other hand, was the colorful personality who operated Dufferin Race Track in competition with the Jockey Club's Woodbine Park. Millar sought, via the inducement of $1,500 each, to make these three men partners.

Clause Six gave one share in the Kenilworth Jockey Club, Windsor, "to each duly ordained minister of a Christian church (except one Spracklin, who shot a hotelkeeper) resident at my death in the towns of Walkerville, Sandwich and the city of Windsor, and earning an annual salary expounding the Scripture to the sinners there." There are two or three extraordinary features in this clause. The obvious one was Millar's perversity in willing race-track stock to ministers, the natural enemies of betting; but Millar added insult to injury—his Kenilworth stock was worth exactly half a cent per share. His specific exclusion of "one Spracklin, who shot a hotelkeeper," was a clue to one facet of his personality, which will be discussed later.

In Clause Seven of his will Millar left one share of O'Keefe Brewing Co. stock "to each Protestant minister exercising his clerical function at an annual salary and resident in Toronto at the time of my death, and to each Orange Lodge in Toronto." (The O'Keefe company had been founded by Roman Catholics.")

Actually, even the seemingly innocent

clauses of Millar's famous will contained hidden implications. The very preamble warned that what was to follow was no conventional testament: "This will is necessarily uncommon and capricious because I have no dependents or near relatives and no duty rests on me to leave any property at my death, and what I do leave is proof of my folly in gathering and retaining more than I required during my lifetime."

He started the disposal of his fortune by getting something off his conscience: "To A. L. Gourlay of the J. J. McLaughlin Co., Toronto, I give ten thousand dollars as he lost approximately that sum in a business transaction with me." That would appear to be the only one of his multitudinous deals in which he felt he had a moral, if not a legal, obligation to a man he had bested. Certainly others did not share that feeling. One man declared ruefully, a few weeks after Millar's death, that the latter had "taken me for at least a hundred thousand dollars." Another man sued the Millar estate for $25,000 over an unusual deal. Millar, he claimed, had sold him some underwater lots in the Detroit River, promising that earth dug to make the Windsor-Detroit tunnel, for which Millar was drawing up incorporation papers, would be supplied to bring the lot's surface above water and convert them into tremendously valuable real estate. After Millar died no signed agreement to supply the fill could be produced, and the man was stuck with some acres of water.

It was not like Millar to fail to keep a verbal contract. Abe Orpen once said that he had had "hundreds of deals with Charlie Millar, with never a word in writing." But, Orpen added, that was because he knew that Millar would not break his word, yet very likely he would have tried to break a written contract if he could find a weak spot in it.

Millar was an expert at spotting loopholes in contracts or agreements. One of Toronto's most prominent lawyers later admitted: "Most of my success is due to a few words of advice Millar once gave me: 'Always let the other fellow write the contract. Then you can see where he leaves you an opening, and when you act he hasn't a leg to stand on because he wrote it.' "

The only "straight" bequests in Millar's will were $500 to his housekeeper, a Mrs. Wilson, and $1,000 to C. H. Kemp, who shared his law office and his home. But even these comparatively niggardly bequests had deeper implications.

When Colonel John Bruce, a court registrar who helped draw up the will and who wit-

nessed it, asked Millar why he left money to people he did not know but passed up persons who had worked for him long and faithfully (his secretary for twenty years received nothing) Millar replied blandly: "If I left them money they would be glad when I died. I don't want anybody to look forward to my death."

Thus Millar's gift of his summer home near Kingston, Jamaica, was not meant to bring joy to the recipients, T. P. Galt, K.C., J. D. Montgomery and James Haverson, K.C. Millar believed these three legal lights were not friendly with each other and he apparently hoped that joint ownership of the property would lead to open dissension.

It does not require a psychiatrist to discern that there were a number of motivations influencing Millar when he drew up his will. As a matter of fact, a couple of psychiatrists were asked by a newspaper to analyse the probable workings of Millar's mind. They took a look at the evidence and begged off. Certainly Millar believed that every man had his price. He often used that scornful phrase in conversation and claimed to have ample evidence of its truth. For example, there was one prominent man on whom a client of Millar's wanted to serve a summons. But the man proved very elusive. After several weeks of failure Millar took charge: "The summons will be in our man's hands tomorrow, and he'll sign the receipt."

Millar placed the summons in a neat box and sent it to the man with all express charges paid. The value of the contents was marked as $25 on the label. The recipient not only accepted the package but signed a receipt for it. Millar would chuckle when he told the story: "No man can resist accepting a prepaid package valued at twenty-five dollars. A lesser value might not tempt him, a larger one might make him suspicious. A twenty-five-dollar something-for-nothing is just about right for most men."

One of Millar's favorite pastimes was to sit on the veranda of the old Queen's Hotel and watch the reaction of men, women and children, rich and poor, old and young, to the sight of a dollar bill lying on the sidewalk. Millar would drop the bill on the ground when no one was in sight, then sit in an inconspicuous corner, partially hidden by a newspaper, to study the facial expressions of passers-by when they first spotted the bill, then underwent brief conflict deciding whether to pick it up or ignore it. "It was an education in human nature by itself," Millar told friends.

Millar probably regarded those dollar bills

as an investment in learning—he was not given to tossing away money for nothing. One Toronto lawyer recalls dining with Millar in the Old Russell House in Ottawa about ten years before Millar died. After dinner Millar suggested that they toss to decide who should pay for both meals.

"Charlie," asked the other lawyer drily, "how much are you worth?"

Millar missed the irony of the question and took it literally. He scribbled figures on the tablecloth for several minutes then answered: "Just $487,000."

A week later the other lawyer went to see Millar. He was soliciting donations for a home for underprivileged children and asked Millar for a hundred dollars. The latter threw up his hands in horror. "No, no, I can't do it," he said.

"But a few days ago you told me you were worth nearly half a million."

Millar was adamant. "I can't do it. I won't do it. I . . . I'm supporting my poor old mother."

Millar's streak of thrift probably dated back to his early years as a lawyer. Although he was a brilliant student and won several prizes, after he was called to the bar he was paid only three dollars a week by the law firm he joined. That was not enough to live on, even in those days. The manager of the Queen's Hotel, a man named McGaw, came to Miller's rescue by giving him a room and meals on credit. McGaw did more than that. He threw Millar the hotel's legal business and referred to him guests who needed legal advice.

With this help Millar was soon out of the financial woods, but he never forgot his debt of gratitude to McGaw. For twenty-three years he lived in a single room at the Queen's, long after he had entered the big-income bracket as a corporation lawyer and landlord of a dozen Toronto houses. His gratitude even showed, quixotically, in his will when he excluded the Reverend Mr. Spracklin from inheriting even a half-cent share of stock because he had shot a hotelkeeper. Hotelkeepers were automatically Good Guys in his complex assessment of the human race.

Millar did not buy a home of his own until his father died and he had to "support his poor old mother." It was then that he built the big home on Scarboro Road and installed his mother there. She died, at a great age, only three years before Millar. Millar's home life was exemplary, if dull. During the days of his poverty, he confided to a few close friends, he had fallen in love with a beautiful young girl, member of a socially prominent Toronto family. His story was that the girl loved him but that a three-dollar-a-week lawyer, son of a farmer, did not suit her parents. Whatever the facts, nothing came of the romance. Millar never went courting again. "I would not say that he became a woman-hater," a friend said after his death, "but he incorporated women into his belief that everyone had a price—and he never cared to spend much money."

Six nights a week Millar would have one drink before dinner and be in bed at 9:30. One night a week he had a few friends in for poker at low stakes and then he might have two drinks after dinner. But even on these gala nights he insisted on breaking up the party by 10:30.

Millar owned a successful racing stable, but his real hobby was rowing. For years he and Chief Justice Armour, of the Ontario Supreme Court, owned a houseboat which they moored at the foot of York Street, and three or four afternoons a week in summer they were to be seen rowing lustily about the bay.

Millar came to be regarded as a man with the Midas touch. But the fact is that he made so many bad investments that his whole plan to create a bombshell of a will nearly fizzled for lack of big money. At his death his only large asset was a block of O'Keefe shares worth $104,000. On the other hand his portfolio of stocks included more than a million shares, in eight companies, with a total value of sixteen dollars. But for a stroke of posthumous luck Millar's estate, after all other obligations and taxes had been deducted, would have amounted to a few thousand dollars, which would scarcely have made the stork derby front-page news in every North American newspaper. The stroke of luck was possession of one hundred thousand shares in the Windsor-Detroit Tunnel Co.

When Millar died he did not even have those shares listed among his holdings. The tunnel, as someone put it, was still "only a gleam in some promoters' eyes," and the shares had no market value. But the tunnel went through, the shares soared in value, and when Millar's executors finally cashed them in to pay off the stork-derby winners they realized nearly three-quarters of a million dollars. This was the residue of the estate after the other provisions had been met.

In his earlier years Millar had no time for leisure. In the early Eighties he accumulated a holding of a dozen houses in lower-middle-class districts of Toronto. When depression struck a few years later he managed to hang on to his properties only by sheer hard physical work. The houses either could not be rented at all, or could bring a return not sufficient to keep them in repair. So Millar, after a full day at law, would don overalls and make the rounds of his houses, doing his own repairing and maintenance work to save money.

Millar personally was a strange mixture of painful shyness and irascibility. He was impatient of the fixed opinions of others. Once he listened to Abe Orpen and a group of professional horsemen talking about the technicalities of the racing game, and the great skill, knowledge and judgment required for success. "Nonsense!" Millar declared. "I know nothing, absolutely nothing, about horses. But I'll bet you I could succeed at it as well as the next man. I could win next year's King's Plate if I set my mind on it."

The bet was covered by the sceptical horsemen. Millar promptly hired a trainer, commissioned him to buy the two best horses available in Ontario. The trainer bought Tartarean and another horse from the Livingstone stable. Tartarean and his stablemate ran first and second in the 1915 King's Plate. But Millar was so shy that he stayed away from the Woodbine that day. He twice declined being made a king's counsel because the honor would focus some public attention on him.

Although Millar's law office was in the Crown Life building he carried no personal insurance and kept up a feud with insurance companies. In fact, he once forgot his shyness long enough to issue a public challenge to supporters of insurance to prove that it wasn't "gambling pure and simple." The circumstances were that Millar owned a horse, Lee Rose, which was entered in the Toronto Cup at Woodbine. Lee Rose was insured for $15,000. A month before the race the horse was accidentally killed. Millar wrote the Toronto papers pointing out that the $15,000 he had collected was a bet—"the insurance company bet me this large sum against a small sum that my horse would not die before a given date. I challenge all casuists and ethical authorities to show any difference between the insurance transaction and a bet that my horse would not run in the cup race. To anyone who can do this I will pay the fifteen thousand." There were no applicants.

On another occasion a 75-year-old acquaintance came to Millar with his life savings, $10,000. "I'll give you this money if you let me live in your house and be taken care of until I die," he said.

"In other words," said Millar, "you want to bet me that you will die before I spend the ten thousand on you. No, I know someone who will give you better odds than that."

He took the old man to an insurance company, where he was offered a life income of $2,400 a year in exchange for his ten thousand in cash. It remained a source of satisfaction to Millar that ten years later the old man was still alive and had, as he put it, "been paid off at odds of nearly two and a half to one, with the odds getting juicier every year."

Just what Millar expected his will to accomplish cannot, of course, be stated with any certainty. Colonel Bruce, to whom Millar confided more than to any other associate and who helped draw up the will, maintained that the stork-derby clause and the gifts of brewery and race-track shares to ministers and public men were meant by Millar to be "a great lesson against the 'holier than thou' attitude," a protest against the teaching that certain things are unqualifiedly bad and other things flatly good. "Millar believed that a lot of human misery and poverty resulted from uncontrolled childbearing, which in turn he blamed on the ban against birth-control information then in force in Ontario. Charlie's hope was that, by turning the spotlight on unbridled breeding and making us a laughing stock before the world, he could shame the government into legalizing birth control."

On the other hand, there is evidence that Millar drew up that will solely because Sir Robert Falconer, President of the University of Toronto, failed to keep an appointment with him. It was the lawyer's intention to discuss with Sir Robert the best procedure for leaving the bulk of his money to the university. He had told friends that his happiest years had been spent at the university and he intended it to have his money.

If the will was made in a mood of resentment it was a mood that was to endure for five years. It has been suggested that the will was no whim, since it was drawn up with such legal care that it survived ten years of attacks in courts and an attempt by the Ontario government to break it (on the grounds that it was "against public policy"). But James Haverson, K.C., who knew Millar well and was one of his "beneficiaries," discounted that. "It was," he declared, "impossible for Charlie Millar to draw up a bad legal document."

Certainly none of Millar's circle took the will seriously at first. Charles Kemp refused to discuss it at first. "I found some writing in a form that resembles a will," he put it. "But it is not a will. It is a joke. We are searching for the actual will now and undoubtedly it will turn up."

But no "real will" turned up. The "joke" was the last testament of Charles Millar. And a few months later Kemp, as chief counsel for the estate, found himself defending the strange document against attack from a dozen quarters—and defending it successfully. For the next ten years there was no time when the will was not before one or another court as Exhibit A in a lawsuit or application for an injunction. The favorite basis for taking the will to court was that the stork-derby clause encouraged immorality and was against public policy. Mr. Justice Middleton finally settled that point nearly eleven years after Millar's death with this simple memorable ruling: "I cannot find that reproduction of the human race is contrary to morals."

The narrowest squeak the will had was late in the stork derby when a plump young redhead named Mae Clark turned up as a contestant. Mae was the mother of ten children, five by her husband and five by a later attachment. Millar's will had made no mention of legitimate children but simply said that his accumulated residue was to be given after ten years to "the mother who has since my death given birth in Toronto to the greatest number of children as shown under the Vital Statistics Act."

Millar's second cousins saw their final and best chance of breaking the will. Their counsel, I. F. Hellmuth, K.C., declared in court: "No one who knew Charlie Millar doubts that he intended to include the mothers of illegitimate children." If the court found that to be true the will might indeed be deemed to outrage public policy by encouraging the production of illegitimate children. But the court gave Millar's intentions the benefit of the doubt. Millar did not intend, the judge ruled, to include illegitimate children.

If the intention of the will was to create high public feeling, to lay bare the spectacle of thousands of clergymen torn between avarice and piety, to start an orgy of reproduction, then the shade of Charles Millar, looking on what he had wrought, can only conclude that the project was a flop. There was a spate of words, but the indignation was largely synthetic and newspaper-created. One small group of clergymen, for example, dreamed up the idea of using their O'Keefe stock to vote the brewery out of existence until they found that their potential combined holding was a pitifully small minority. The Roman Catholic church probably handled the Millar will with greatest dignity and dispatch. Under its terms, priests in the Border Cities were entitled to a share of Kenilworth stock. The Catholic hierarchy announced briefly and with great finality that no priest wanted anything to do with it.

There was another Catholic involvement in the will which the church rejected so emphatically that the clause was never even published as part of the will. This clause left $500 to the church for Masses for the soul of Major Joseph Kilgour, a Protestant.

Of 303 Protestant clergymen in Toronto, ninety-nine applied for their O'Keefe shares. The Orange Lodges were less squeamish and 103 of 114 lodges accepted the stock. Most ministers were not reluctant to state the uses to which the proceeds were put. The Reverend J. O. Johnston, for instance, wrote the trustees that he was using the money to help the wives and children of men jailed for drunkenness.

Millar apparently had miscalculated on several points. If it was true that every man had his price, that price was not likely to be $58.20, the value of one O'Keefe share. Again, Millar did not realize that the most strait-laced man can broaden his conscience a little in the name of charity. Certainly Judge Raney and the Reverend Dr. Chown showed no embarrassment in handling their Jockey Club stock. On August 27, 1927, they became members of the Ontario Jockey Club for five minutes. This formality was necessary under O. J. C. regulations providing that shares can only be disposed of by members. Another member of the club paid more than $3,000 for the two shares, which was promptly endorsed to the Poppy Fund. Abe Orpen remained a member.

Looking back on the stork derby launched by the Millar will, which caused sustained interest and excitement for ten years, it becomes a dreary affair. Newspapermen who worked on the story seldom discuss it nowadays. One explained: "The things I remember most are the smell of many children in bad houses; the unnatural talk about big money by tired women living on relief; the resigned resentment of husbands whose procreative powers had suddenly become world news." In fact, everyone heaved a collective sigh of relief when it was over. No monstrous childbearing resulted. The four winners were tied with nine children each, while elsewhere in the world women with no fortune at stake were recorded as bearing twelve and even fifteen children during the same ten-year period.

Mrs. Dionne would have been an easy winner had she lived in Toronto.

# RALPH ALLEN

# The Land of Eternal Change

Spring came this year to the provinces of Saskatchewan and Alberta as spring always comes there—full of new hopes and old anxieties; aglow with a thousand shades and forms of beauty of which only a few can be detected by a stranger; bursting with variety and surprise. The dominant qualities are variety and surprise.

To anyone whose notions of it have been acquired through movies or train windows, a close inspection of the west in spring would bring mixed feelings of recognition and disbelief. At the equinox, the southern wheatlands dig themselves out of ten-foot snowdrifts. As April turns the corner into May, both provinces slosh through blizzards, sometimes followed by floods of disaster size. When the gleaming prairie sun comes out, apparently to stay, those magnificent clichés, the meadow lark and the crocus, again offer their yearly paean of melody and fragrance.

Although it is true that the melody now competes with the angry clatter of drill rigs and the fragrance is sometimes engulfed in the reek of petroleum fumes, there are other things that still have at least the appearance of timelessness. When the moon is out coyotes call longingly, as they did a thousand years ago, from the silver clumps of wolf willow on the hillsides. On the golden faces of the Rockies mountain sheep and goats march primly up past timber line, as they did centuries before the first explorers. Other native creatures have seen fit, like the men and women who grew up there, to modify the interests and habitations of their ancestors. Magpies dart out of the chokecherry bushes and poplar bluffs to snoop about the Christmas trees and pumps of thousands of producing oil wells, and great stark ravens croak in the morning sunlight above the uranium mines north of Lake Athabaska.

For humans there have been large changes too. Their standard living-unit is still a four-, five- or six-room farmhouse which may or may not have paint, may or may not have plumbing and may or may not have electricity. But the other pole of domestic architecture—the California suburb—has now planted itself in all the major cities. The chief characteristic of this newest of all the west's new phenomena is the residents' apparent determination to be themselves and to let the neighbors be the same. The result, which reaches its climax in an Edmonton housing development called Glenora, is a wildly unfettered mixture of shapes and colors: scale-model castles-in-Spain cheek to jowl with plywood living machines; plaster against clapboard, stucco against brick, aquamarine blue against coral pink, alligator green against daffodil yellow, midget minarets beside open-deck verandas.

It is not only the dwellings that change. Strawstacks no longer burn on the prairie summer fallow. This year it is giant torches of gas that hiss and flame and break the black silence of the night sky. On the rims of the cities, where the last lonely streetlamps used to mark the beginning of the open plain, the refineries with the marching lights of their cracking towers now stand guard like fairy battleships.

The belief that the west goes on repeating itself, mile after mile and year after year and generation after generation, has never stood up under close scrutiny. Neither has the belief that it is almost wholly populated by the same kind of people doing the same kind of thing for the same kind of reason. If you exclude the Indians, who were there at least three thousand years ago, the first substantial influx of permanent settlers began in 1870. It was led across what is now the Manitoba-Saskatchewan border by métis hunters, just defeated in the first Riel Rebellion and now seeking space, buffalo and freedom from the white man's red tape. Almost at once a great pincers movement began to envelop the half-breed hunters: missionaries pursuing them from the east to save their souls, whisky traders riding in from the south to swindle them out of their buffalo hides.

The next and largest wave of settlers—the English, the Irish and the Scots, the Americans and eastern Canadians, the Ukrainians and Germans, the Scandinavians, the Hungarians and Rumanians and Russians and Poles—had even more diverse origins and equally diverse reasons for coming. Some were drawn by fear, some by faith, some by ambition, some by greed, some by gullibility. The one statement that can be applied to all of them and all of their descendants is that they've seen a very great amount of history in a very short time. Men who trembled or rejoiced at the hanging of Louis Riel will still be alive in Saskatchewan this summer to tremble or rejoice at the opening of a fabulously rich uranium mine. Homesteaders whose first salable crop was whitened buffalo bones are now living in retirement on their oil royalties. Taxpayers who a half-century ago had no real voice in their own government have lived to shake the country's whole political structure by electing the CCF in Saskatchewan and Social Credit in Alberta. Half-broke dirt farmers who once had no choice but to sell their wheat for as little as the grain dealers cared to offer and to buy their groceries and fuel for as much as the retailers cared to ask are today the owners of a huge co-operative empire of elevators, stores, factories and even oil wells and a refinery.

From the start, the story of the two provinces that were carved out of the Northwest Territories in 1905 has been a story of the unexpected and the unknown. It must remain so for many years. For Saskatchewan and Alberta represent a union whose fruit is unpredictable—the union of a very old land with a very young people. Some of the land, the northern rocks of the Canadian Shield, is as old as any land in the world. The prairies are older than the Nile, older than the hills of Jerusalem, older than Galilee and the valley of the Jordan. And the people are just as spectacularly young.

It took the old land many millions of years to hew out its rocks and mountains, to bury its twenty-ton lizards and flying dragons, to sift and grind its soil, to hide its lakes of inflammable ooze and its underground hills of coal and metal. It took the young people who came there a maximum of decades and a mini-

mum of weeks to size up the land and guess how best to live with it. In reality they knew very little of what to expect from the climate, or what the soil would stand, or what lay secreted beneath the soil.

It was no accident that they were naïve and ill informed. As the transcontinental railway pushed through the plains in the early 1880's it pushed through empty country. The whole prairie from Winnipeg west had only sixty thousand white inhabitants when the decade began. Halfway through the Eighties the Dominion government had had fewer than twenty thousand takers for the free homesteads it had begun offering more than ten years earlier, and more than half of these had already abandoned their farms and gone back to Ontario or the United States. The CPR had no traffic for its railway and no buyers for its twenty-five million acres of land along the right of way. By the mid-Nineties the expected wave of settlement still had shown no sign of coming. Clearly, unless something quick and drastic were done the rails would turn to rust and with them the dream of a Canadian nation stretching from coast to coast.

The needed and drastic thing was done, by a quick and drastic man named Clifford Sifton. Sifton was federal Minister of the Interior. His was the chief responsibility for trying to fill a void a third as large as Europe. During the years between 1896 and 1905 Sifton and the CPR, with some help from the Hudson's Bay Company, the Grand Trunk Pacific and a few private colonization companies, staged the largest, noisiest and most successful medicine show in history. It covered two continents and was conducted in a dozen languages. Its message was simple and direct: whatever ails you, come to western Canada! In his role as chief barker, Sifton published millions of pamphlets extolling the free land of the Northwest Territories, and offering it gratis to anyone who would come and get it.

For every worthy human aspiration, and for some that weren't so worthy, the new paradise offered the virtual certainty of fulfillment. Poor? Where else could you acquire 160 acres of land for a ten-dollar registration fee? Where else would a railroad take you halfway across a continent for six dollars? Opposed by conscience to military service? What other nation would offer conscientious objectors a guarantee against conscription? In a hurry? This from a pamphlet that bore Sifton's name: "The shrewd and sturdy settler who plants a little capital and cultivates it can, with due diligence, in a few years, produce a competency." Lazy? J. Obed Smith, one of Sifton's departmental

242

assistants, assured the prospective immigrant: "He can make his crop in less than four months."

The cold prairie winters and the hot dry prairie summers were never a serious embarrassment to Sifton, who contented himself with calling them "splendid." To have said anything less would have been, according to the relaxed idiom of the times, to have tampered with the truth.

The siren song was heard halfway around the world. Those earthy mystics, the Doukhobors, heard it in Russia and in a single month seven thousand of them streamed off the gangplanks at Saint John and boarded the colonist cars for Winnipeg and the central plains of Saskatchewan. Heartsick Ukrainians, without land and without a country, heard it under the flag of Austria, under the flag of the Imperial Czar, even under the flag of Brazil. They were soon to be western Canada's second largest racial group, second only to the Anglo-Saxons. Cockneys heard it in the crowded mews of Hackney. Members of the minor gentry heard it on the minor estates of Surrey and invited their younger sons into the study for a serious talk about the future. Ontario farm boys heard it as their time grew near for leaving home. So did ranchers from Texas, Oklahoma and Montana, cramped by fences.

Once the people started coming, Sifton did his best to retrieve his promises. At the railway terminals and along the staging routes, the Dominion government opened ninety immigration halls and staging camps, where bunks, cookstoves, surveyors' maps, advice and interpreters were available free of charge. By 1901 Saskatchewan's population was more than ninety thousand and Alberta's more than seventy thousand and in the next ten years these figures were quintupled. The dream of a nation had been redeemed.

The cost of its redemption and its reaffirmation in the half-century since 1905 bore no relation to the estimates on the immigration folders. The ancient land proved alternately hospitable and cranky, kind and savage, benign and spiteful. Thousands of the settlers were wholly ignorant of agriculture. Even the relatively experienced Europeans knew little about farming large acreages; to them the basic tools were the grub hoe, the scythe, the hand flail and winnow and the wooden plow. Erosion and soil drifting were as foreign to the settlers' thoughts as nuclear energy. Drought, hail and autumn frost were unheard of—at least in the sunny folklore of the Department of the Interior. Grasshoppers, rust and weeds did not begin to appear north of the border until well after the turn of the century.

Thus the pioneers were ripe for ambush. Their mistakes were frequent, and ranged from the tragic to the bizarre. So did the vindictiveness of nature and the land. Of the first four white people to die in Saskatoon, two froze to death in blizzards, one drowned in the Saskatchewan River and the other died of exhaustion after fighting a prairie fire. In Alberta in 1906-7 the Chinook failed. The owners of the big ranches had no hay for their herds, for they had come to depend on the soft winter wind to uncover the uncut grass. Cattle and horses starved or froze by the tens of thousands. The Bar-U Ranch alone lost twelve thousand head. A physician attached to the famous Barr colony, a mass pilgrimage of English families to Saskatchewan in 1903, complained that he spent most of his time patching up self-inflicted axe wounds.

The individual settlers' ideas of how to equip themselves for life on the frontier were often imaginative but odd. Not long ago Ray Coates, who arrived from England in 1903, recalled with amusement that he had come armed with dumbbells, boxing gloves and other muscle-building devices. Georgina Binnie-Clark, a spinster lady of quality, arrived in the Qu'Appelle Valley in 1905 with an expensive and ornate bathtub. She discovered that to fill it she would have to haul water three hundred yards, a pail at a time, from a well barely capable of supplying enough drinking water. So she sold the tub to another English lady, who discovered that she would have to haul water two miles to fill it. It ended up as a storage bin for seed. Mrs. Robert Wilson, of Bienfait, Saskatchewan, recently recalled a disaster that may have been unique: a horse once fell through the roof of her family home, a sod hut which her father had built on a hillside.

Their loyal children and their sentimental grandchildren have tried to enforce the tradition that the pioneers endured their troubles, large and small, with unfailing cheerfulness and courage. The theory is only partly supported by the written history of the period and by a cross-check with almost any of the thousands of men and women who lived through it and are still here to tell about it. In the last few years the provincial archives office of Saskatchewan has been asking original settlers to put their experiences on paper. To the question, "How did you learn farming?", Frank Baines, of Saltcoats, replied succinctly: "By trial and error, with large portions of the latter." R. E. Ludlow recalled: "Nobody had nothing, and we all used it." Mrs. May Davis, who came to Canada from England in 1883, drew a haunting picture of the finality with which so many people committed all their earthly hopes into what for many of them was a literal void. "I can most particularly remember one poor sick-looking woman who was coming to Canada to join her husband, who had left England some months before. She had seven little boys with her, the youngest a baby at her breast. At our last sight of her she was on the wharf at Halifax, seated on a box of her 'effects,' waiting for her husband to come and claim them all. Did he come, I wonder—oh, but surely!—and where did they go and what became of them all? Perhaps by now one of those poor shabby little fellows has his name on the roster of Canada's famous men. Who can say? This is a land of opportunity and it is all a long, long time ago."

The society that took shape was one of the most heterogeneous in human history. Its axis of advance was along the main line of the CPR, and later along the CPR's branch lines and on the lines of its competitors. But the land immediately adjoining the right of way soon ran out or priced most buyers out of the market. As they fanned out from steel, by Red River cart, bull train or covered wagon and sometimes on foot, the Europeans tended to move north, where there were wood and water, no less important than soil and equally hard to come by in most of their native lands. The Americans, eastern Canadians and English, Irish and Scots concentrated on the open prairie, where the treeless ground was ready for the plow.

In the first generation they set up islands bounded by language. Sometimes some special objective or special philosophy strengthened the ties of race. Saskatoon was founded as a temperance colony by a group of Toronto Methodists and as late as 1890 a man who wanted to buy a lot there had to agree not to "manufacture, buy, store, sell, barter, exchange, receive or give away or in any way deal in or use, possess or have intoxicating liquors or stimulants."

In the Eighties, before Sifton's time, a group of French aristocrats settled near Whitewood, in what is now southern Saskatchewan. Their purposes were to lead a civilized life and to make expenses by engaging in forms of trade that would not have been considered appropriate to men of their class in France. From Paris they imported paté, truffles and fine wines for their tables; servants for their kitchens and drawing rooms; hunting dogs for their kennels;

fashionable hats and gowns for their ladies; white gloves and top hats for themselves. It was one of the memorable experiences of a memorable era to see the Marquis de Roffignac, M. le Comte Soras, M. le Comte Beaudrap and M. le Baron van Brabant sweeping across the still almost virgin plain in their shining imported phaetons drawn by their blooded horses, their liveried footmen sitting stiffly in attendance, their wives and daughters beside them smiling demurely beneath silk parasols. Unfortunately, the counts had not reckoned with a fact that later residents of Saskatchewan have found painfully obvious: as a home of industry, even of small industry, the thinly settled base of the Palliser Triangle just doesn't make sense. The counts tried manufacturing brushes, sugar and Gruyère cheese. One of them attempted to raise and tin chicory, although the nearest sizable market for chicory was back in France. One by one they lost their ruffed satin shirts and went home, disenchanted but uncomplaining. Many of the domestic servants they had brought out from France stayed behind; their descendants are still there, most of them, prospering modestly on their farms.

The outlines of the first conglomerate pattern of settlement are still clearly visible. There is scarcely a man or woman living anywhere in Europe or North America who could not, somewhere in Saskatchewan or Alberta, find a sizable community that speaks his language, sings his songs, and worships his gods. But he would still be first of all among Canadians. The fusion and assimilation of the west's unwieldy mixture of racial, religious, social and economic groups has been almost unbelievably rapid. With one notable exception it was accomplished without serious shock. Some eighteen hundred members of the Yorkton Doukhobor colony threw the whole country into confusion and dismay when, in 1902, they abandoned their community farms, turned their cattle loose and began marching the three hundred miles to Winnipeg, chanting prayers and hymns. Their exact reason was never fully established, for few of their leaders spoke English and those who did spoke in the mysterious symbols of the obsessed. Probably they had at least three main reasons: an intuitive belief that their messiah, Peter Verigin, who was then in Russia, would meet them somewhere on the way; a recent letter from Verigin condemning the cultivation of land and the ownership of cows and horses; a determination to seek out a climate warm enough to allow them to respect Verigin's injunction against the use of clothing. The Mounted Police turned back the women and children at once. The men and boys, many of them barefoot, reached Minnedosa, 150 miles from their starting point, before they too were rounded up by the police and returned to their homes by special train. For many more years the Doukhobors, with their constant revolts against sending their children to school, taking the oath of allegiance, or registering births, marriages and deaths, showed few signs of reaching a bare working agreement, much less a state of understanding, with their neighbors. Oddly enough they became easier to get along with after Verigin himself appeared on the scene. He ordered a relaxation of the more uncompromising articles of faith. This alienated the most fanatical of his followers, the barn-burning, disrobing Sons of Freedom, who left and thus transferred the "Doukhobor problem" from the prairies to British Columbia.

As the young people of the west have grown in understanding of each other, they have continued to grow in understanding of the old land. For from the first day of the first white man, the land has turned a different face to everyone. Three pioneer wheat growers recently recalled what they remembered best about the first trek into their homesteads. Fred Martin wrote about walking into the Qu'Appelle Valley when the rosebushes and morningglory vines were higher than his head. Cecil Angell told of his memories of driving an ox team to his homestead near Saskatooon; the land had just been burnt over and was "rough, hummocky and black as ink." Oscar Anderson, who packed into La Glace in the Peace River country, told of seeing dead horses standing upright in the muskeg of the Edson Trail.

The land, nature, the machine age and the law of supply and demand have among them confounded prophets from the beginning. In the 1880's it would have seemed impossible that the patient, essential ox could become obsolete or, in 1915, that the day would come when farmers would be selling good horses for meat. In 1925 the disappearance of the threshing gang would have seemed not much more likely than the disappearance of wheat. In 1935, when the drought was into the seventh of its nine years, it would have been a feeble and tasteless joke to suggest that the farmers of Saskatchewan alone would lose nearly four hundred million dollars worth of grain because of too much rain in 1954 and that floods would threaten damage on an equal scale in 1955. Ten years ago, when rust was all but licked by new crossbreeds of wheat, only a writer of science fiction would have

imagined that the rust fungus might counterattack by inventing its own crossbreed and thus make 1954 the worst rust year in history. Texas talk, oil still hasn't begun to make the Yet all these things happened. And for all the west independent of agriculture. Oil companies are spending a million dollars a day in the two provinces and still aren't taking nearly that amount out. This has provided tens of thousands of jobs, given business a general lift and, in Alberta, made provincial financing a simple problem in arithmetic. But the big fluctuations in income and well-being still follow wheat.

The most maddening and intriguing riddle of all is the Athabasca Tar Sands, one of the greatest treasure stores ever beheld by man, worth far more than all of South Africa's diamonds and India's rubies and Canada's gold put together—and less than worthless until someone finds a way to mine them. The tar sands lie deep in northeastern Alberta. They are a 30,000-square-mile deposit of individual drops of oil wrapped around individual grains of sand. In some places they are hidden by a thin overburden of rock, soil and scrub. In others they lie uncovered on the ground like vast black slabs of molasses candy. The most conservative estimate is that they contain a hundred billion barrels of crude—thirty-five times Canada's known reserves from other sources. Other estimates go as high as three hundred billion barrels, twice as much as the whole world's liquid reserves. Private companies and government experts were experimenting with the Athabaska field fifty years before Leduc and Redwater came in. They proved long ago that the oil and sand can be separated, but no one has ever proved the job can be done at a practical cost.

The enigma of the tar sands is in the soundest, most enigmatic western tradition: anyone who thinks he knows what to expect next from that part of the world is an optimist. Not an optimist about the west itself—for there is a great deal of ground for optimism there—but an optimist about his own powers of divination.

If a westerner today were to try to forecast what the old land of the west holds for his children, he would have to depend as much on individual intuition and individual experience as on the collected weight of history. A shepherd in the Cotswolds makes a reasonable deduction when he decides his son will probably be a shepherd in the Cotswolds too. That is what his great-grandfather was and his great-grandfather's great-grandfather before that. And so it is with a rice farmer in Japan or a weaver in India or to a somewhat lesser extent with a dairy farmer in Ontario or Quebec or a rancher in Texas. They and their ancestors have had time to learn about the land they live on, what it demands, what it will tolerate, what it conceals, what it will support. Barely a tenth of the mineral-rich land of Saskatchewan and Alberta has been drilled, even on a modest scale, for minerals. Working with the law of averages and the still meagre figures on the rates of return, geologists of large experience and only moderate optimism can almost prove the two provinces will ultimately produce more oil than Oklahoma and California and as much uranium as the rest of the world put together. Conversely, hardly anyone is brave enough to try proving a thing about the future of wheat, except that, as always, it is reasonably hopeful and unreasonably unsure.

Perhaps my boyhood friend Bob Pegg, who once quit the prairie in despair and returned to it with confidence, is as good a witness on these matters as anyone. Driving out of Oxbow we turned left at the river to pick up his three children, who had been visiting their grandparents. The river was still and white under a foot of snow. I said I hoped that in the summers Bob's children would have as much fun beside the river as he and I and our brothers and sisters once used to have there.

"Oh, they'll like this country," Bob said. "They like it already." After a moment he added: "I wonder if they'll ever really get to know it."

# A NOTE ON THE AUTHORS

RALPH ALLEN (p. 235), distinguished sportswriter, war correspondent and novelist, was editor of *Maclean's* from 1951 to 1960; ROBERT THOMAS ALLEN (pp. 70, 169) has become one of Canada's best-known humorous writers; JAMES BANNERMAN (p. 225) is a free-lance writer and regular contributor to the CBC; PIERRE BERTON (pp. 132), *Maclean's* managing editor until 1958, now a columnist and TV panelist, is one of Canada's most controversial personalities; FRED BODSWORTH (p. 202), once a *Maclean's* staff writer, is now a novelist of international repute; ERNEST BUCKLER'S (p. 146) sensitive novels and stories have given a literary lustre to tiny Bridgeport, N.S.; MORLEY CALLAGHAN (p. 52) holds a unique place as a loving interpreter and biting critic of the Canadian way of life; JUNE CALLWOOD (p. 110) finds time to remain one of Canada's busiest writers while being wife to writer Trent Frayne and mother of their three children; MARJORIE WILKINS CAMPBELL (p. 17) is a Governor-General's Award winner for her lively historical works; THOMAS B. COSTAIN (p. 32) at one time chief editor of *Maclean's*, is now one of the world's most widely known historical novelists; MAZO DE LA ROCHE (p. 21) is the beloved creator of the Whiteoaks of Jalna; DORIS DICKSON (p. 99) writes for many Canadian periodicals; GEORGE A. DREW (p. 119) has kept an interest in writing while Premier of Ontario, Leader of the Opposition in the federal government, and High Commissioner in London; ROBERT FONTAINE (p. 117) parlayed the reminiscences of his French-Canadian boyhood into the hit play, *The Happy Time*; BLAIR FRASER (p. 8), currently the editor of *Maclean's*, was for sixteen years a well-known commentator on federal political affairs; TRENT FRAYNE (p. 214), sportswriter and commentator, was once a *Maclean's* staff writer; RAY GARDNER (p. 196) is the West Coast resident editor of *Maclean's*; FRANK HAMILTON (p. 106), for years a successful free-lance writer, is now in the federal civil service; JOHN NORMAN HARRIS (p. 89), several times a prizewinner in fiction contests, is public relations officer for the Canadian Bank of Commerce; RICHMOND P. HOBSON (p. 152), an American convert to B.C.'s northland, has published two books about his ranching experiences; HAROLD HORWOOD (p. 137) is a bearded Newfoundlander who specializes in the history and folklore of his province; BRUCE HUTCHISON (pp. 13, 183), editor of the *Victoria Times*, is equally famed as a political and economic analyst and as a historian; ERIC HUTTON (pp. 1, 58, 235), formerly a newspaperman and free-lance writer, is now articles editor of *Maclean's*; STEPHEN LEACOCK (p. 94), Canada's most famous humorist, was at one time associated with *Maclean's*; ROGER LEMELIN (p. 219) is perhaps best-known for his creation, *The Plouffe Family*; W. O. MITCHELL (p. 42) continues his folksy and famous *Jake and the Kid* stories from High River, Alberta; FARLEY MOWAT (p. 26), when not sampling igloo life on the Barrens, lives in Palgrave, Ontario; DAVID MACDONALD (p. 197), articles editor of the *Star Weekly*, has written many articles for both Canadian and American periodicals; COLIN MCDOUGALL (p. 72) built the prize-winning short story published here into a prize-winning novel; HUGH MACLENNAN (p. 56) is distinguished as a novelist, essayist and teacher; DUNCAN MCLEOD (p. 141) is a free-lance writer living in Niagara Falls; PHYLLIS LEE PETERSON (p. 46), of Montreal, is equally at home in fiction and non-fiction; MCKENZIE PORTER (p. 84), a graduate from Fleet Street to *Maclean's* editorial staff, recently completed a work of Canadian historical value; THOMAS H. RADDALL (p. 80), veteran novelist, has a special interest in Maritimes history; ANDREW WALTER ROY (p. 171), of the Maritimes, was a free-lance writer in several media until his death early in 1960; GABRIELLE ROY (p. 209) is internationally renowned for her sensitive portrayals of French-Canadian life; FRANKLIN RUSSELL (p. 38) is a New Zealand-born free-lance writer, dividing his time between books and magazines; JOSEPH SCHULL (p. 156) is as at home in radio and TV as he is in books and magazines; IAN SCLANDERS (p. 188) is now *Maclean's* resident editor in the United States; JACK SCOTT (p. 231) is one of British Columbia's best-known newspapermen; EDNA STAEBLER (p. 192) has made Canada's ethnic groups her special interest; L. JOHANNE STEMO (p. 177) doubles as a busy housewife in British Columbia; GORDON WOODWARD (p. 163) is represented in several important fiction anthologies.

## A Note on the Editor

LESLIE HANNON has been in journalism for twenty-three years, beginning in New Zealand at the age of seventeen. Formerly managing editor of *Maclean's*, he is now chief of the magazine's European Bureau.

## A Note on the Designer

EUGENE ALIMAN was born in London, England, and has been art director of *Maclean's* for ten years. His work has been awarded many prizes in Canada and abroad.

# ACKNOWLEDGMENTS

We wish to thank the authors of the stories and articles that appear in this book for their kindness in permitting us to reprint their material here. It all appeared originally in *Maclean's Magazine*, and copyright in each case is registered in the name of the author. The following additional sources should be specifically noted:

A WRITER'S MEMORIES: from *Ringing the Changes* by Mazo de la Roche, by permission of the author and the Macmillan Company of Canada, Limited; MY OLD MCGILL: courtesy of Phyllis Lee Peterson; HOW THE KLONDIKE RUSH BEGAN: from *Klondike: the Life and Death of the Last Great Gold Rush*, by Pierre Berton, McClelland and Stewart, Limited, 1958; THE FIRING SQUAD: copyright 1959 by Colin McDougall; HOW GEORGE WASHINGTON LOST CANADA: Doubleday, Canada, Limited; WILLIAM LAWRENCE AND HIS WONDERFUL WINDJAMMER: from *The Salt Water Men* by Joseph Schull, by permission of the author and the Macmillan Company of Canada Limited; THE GREAT CROSS-CANADA HIKE: by permission of Gwendolyn M. Roy; THE GADABOUTS: from *Street of Riches* by Gabrielle Roy, McClelland and Stewart Limited, translated from the French, *Rue Deschambault*.

We wish to thank the following sources for permission to reproduce the paintings which have appeared in these pages:

THE SLEIGH RACE by Cornelius Krieghoff: courtesy of the Sigmund Samuel collection, Canadiana Gallery, Royal Ontario Museum; THE JACK PINE by Tom Thomson, ALGOMA, NOVEMBER by A. Y. Jackson, and NORTH SHORE by Lawren Harris: The National Gallery of Canada; PRESENCES IN A THICKET by Jack Shadbolt and CENTENNIAL REGATTA by B. C. Binning: The University of British Columbia; GABRIOLA ISLAND by Ed Hughes: the Dominion Gallery, Montreal; LAURENTIAN HEAVE by Jacques de Tonnancour: the Maclean-Hunter Publishing Company; AUTUMN by Ghitta Caiserman: Dorothy Sangster and Sidney Katz; DREAM AT A WHITE VILLAGE by Alfred Pellan: the artist; FARMER'S DAUGHTER by John Lyman: the artist; TANGLED LANDSCAPE by Gordon Smith: the artist; RECLINING NUDE by Frederick H. Varley: C. S. Band.

We wish to thank the photographers for the use of the following photographs:

Album 1—THE PROVINCES OF CANADA: DAMP MOMENT, Jack Long; A SAW WHINES and A FOOTHILLS CATTLE RANCH, Peter Croydon; CALGARY STENOGRAPHERS, Harry Rowed; AN OLD BUGGY and A SCHOOLHOUSE, Peter Croydon; A COMPLEXITY OF SIGNS and THE GRAIN EXCHANGE, Paul Rockett; A FARMHOUSE, Peter Croydon; NEW BLOOD, NEW FACES, Walter Curtin; BEYOND FRONTENAC'S SPIRES, Ronny Jaques; MONTREAL'S SHERBROOKE STREET, Peter Croydon; THE GARDEN OF THE GULF and THE CHURCH, THE STORE, Ronny Jaques; SAILORS and SAINT JOHN'S KING STREET, Horst Ehricht; OLDEST COLONY, Ronny Jaques.

Album 2—A GALLERY OF FAMOUS CANADIANS: J. A. D. MCCURDY, Norman James; STEPHEN LEACOCK, Yousuf Karsh; TOBY ROBINS, Bob Ragsdale; WILLIAM SHATNER, Nolan D. Patterson; GLENN GOULD, Paul Rockett; MELISSA HAYDEN, Ronny Jaques; THE CABINET, Yousuf Karsh; A. R. M. LOWER, Walter Curtin; JOHN DIEFENBAKER, Rosemary Gilliat; ACADEMIC KNIGHTS, Ken Bell Photography Ltd.; LOIS SMITH AND DAVID ADAMS, John de Visser; JOHNNY LONGDEN, Don Ollis; WAYNE AND SHUSTER, Steve Oroz Associates; MAZO DE LA ROCHE, Paul Rockett; DORA MAVOR MOORE, Walter Curtin; CHRISTOPHER PLUMMER, Werner Wolff; VINCENT MASSEY'S GIFT, Ken Bell; SAMUEL BRONFMAN, Ronny Jaques; LOUIS ARCHAMBAULT, Sam Tata; ALFRED PELLAN, Gaby of Montreal; ROBERTSON DAVIES, Desmond Russell; OSCAR PETERSON, Peter Croydon; STEPHEN BASUSTOW, Nolan D. Patterson; CARDINAL LEGER, Desmond Russell; ALAN JARVIS and LESTER B. PEARSON, Jack Olsen; MSGR. RÉNÉ LUSSIER, Gaby; WILDER PENFIELD, Bazil Zarov; JOSEPH SMALLWOOD, Yousuf Karsh; GARFIELD WESTON, John Steele.

Album 3—THE PAINTER'S CANADA: A. Y. JACKSON, Walter Curtin.

Album 4—THE MANY FACES OF CANADA: THE CANADA FOREIGNERS DON'T BELIEVE, John de Visser; THE CANADA OF FOREIGN FACES, Jack Long; THE CANADA WHERE YANKEES RULE, John de Visser; THE CANADIAN WOMAN—SHE CAN SELL CHIC HATS, Peter Croydon; OR GUT A FISH, Ronny Jaques; BLUEWATER MEN, Ronny Jaques; INSURANCE SALESMEN, Paul Rockett; IN THE LAND OF CONTRASTS, Peter Croydon; A NEWFOUNDLAND HOUSEWIFE, Ronny Jaques; LITHE LUMBERJACKS, Peter Croydon; BEFORE CANADA WAS KNOWN, Ronny Jaques; EVERY PICTURE, Horst Ehricht; GARDENERS PLY THEIR AGE-OLD TRADE, Jack Long; A BALLET DANCER, John de Visser; A WOMAN REDUCING, Bruce Moss; THE ICE SHOW, John de Visser; MINERS, John Sebert; A VETERAN COP, Peter Croydon; A VETERAN POSTMAN, Jack Long; A FISHERMAN OF THE FUTURE, Ronny Jaques; A TORONTO WOMAN, John de Visser; AN INDIAN BOY, Peter Croydon; THE PATIENT ART, Jack Long; CURTAIN CALL, John de Visser; LOVE BLOOMS UNDER THE NORTHERN SUN—opposite page, John de Visser; centre left, Peter Croydon; upper right, Paul Rockett; centre right, Peter Croydon; lower right, Horst Ehricht; NIGHT PATROL, Jack Long; DAY PATROL, David Bier; TO THE BOYFRIEND'S CONCERN, Paul Rockett; A PIG CAN BE A LOVELY THING, Walter Curtin; THE TERROR OF THE RECRUIT, Ken Bell; SHE'S NOT CHECKING, Bazil Zarov; ESKIMO FISHING, Richard Harrington.

Album 5—THE PRICELESS NOTMAN DISCOVERY: The photographs in this album are from the Notman Photographic Collection by courtesy of McGill University Museums.

Album 6—THE SPORTING SCENE: BARBARA ANN SCOTT and CALGARY STAMPEDE, Yousuf Karsh; THE KID LINE, Turofsky Brothers; THE RICHARDS, Michael Burns; HOWIE MEEKER, Walter Curtin; GEORGE YOUNG, Turofsky Brothers; FRANK MERRILL, Paul Rockett; SAM LANGFORD, Werner Wolff; THE ARMORED GIANTS, Ken Bell.